ADVANCED MATHEMATICS

Pure Mathematics 1

Rosemary Emanuel

John Wood, General Editor

Acknowledgements

The author would like to thank:
Philip Cooper and Dr Ben Yudkin who have contributed exercises and made many useful suggestions.
George Ross, Frankie Elston, Michael Ross, Sheila Hill and John Emanuel for their help and Barbara Morris who has checked the manuscript and remained unfailingly supportive.

We are indebted to the following examining bodies for permission to reproduce various questions from past 'A level Mathematics' and 'Pure Mathematics' examination papers:

Assessment and Qualifications Alliance (AQA) for Associated Examining Board (AEB) and Southern Examining Group (SEG); OCR for University of Cambridge Local Examinations Syndicate (UCLES); University of London Examinations Board (London/Edexcel), and Welsh Joint Education Committee (WJEC).

The author and publishers are most grateful to John Backhouse, Peter Houldsworth and Peter Horril for permission to incorporate various questions from *Pure Mathematics 1* and *Essential Pure Mathematics* in this book.

Pearson Education Limited
Edinburgh Gate
Harlow
Essex CM20 2JE
England

© Pearson Education Limited 2001

The right of Rosemary Emanuel to be identified as the author of this Work has been asserted by her in accordance with the Copyright, Designs and Patents Act, 1988.

All rights reserved. No part of this publication may be reproduced, stored in a retrieval system, or transmitted in any form or by any means, electronic, mechanical, photocopying, recording, or otherwise without the prior written permission of the Publishers or a licence permitting restricted copying in the United Kingdom issued by the Copyright Licensing Agency Ltd., 90 Tottenham Court Road, London, W1P 9HE.

First published 2001

ISBN 0 582 40550 5

Editorial by First Class Publishing Ltd., Knaphill, Surrey
Typeset by Tech-Set Limited, Gateshead, Tyne and Wear
Printed in Italy by G.Canale & C.S.p.A Borgano T.se – Turin

The Publishers' policy is to use paper manufactured from sustainable forests.

CONTENTS

Preface

ure Mathematics 1 and *Pure Mathematics 2* have been written for the pure mathematics requirements of the ew AS and A level Mathematics specifications. *Pure Mathematics 1* consolidates the work of GCSE and overs topics in the AS level modules. *Pure Mathematics 2* completes the coverage for A2 level modules and ncludes extension material to assist preparation for Advanced Extension Awards.

his book is designed for use as a class text and for self-help by students. The use of graphic calculators or omputer packages and spreadsheets are strongly recommended but not absolutely essential. All topics are noroughly covered, with clear explanations of terms and techniques.

he order of teaching topics can be varied.

Chapters 1–6 provide basic tools, particularly in algebra.
Chapters 7–13 and 15–17 apply the tools to a variety of topics.
Chapter 14 covers problem solving using geometry, trigometry and algebra. This provides useful revision or coverage for those who did not study these topics at GCSE.
Chapter 18 is useful for a better understanding of limits.
Chapter 19 discusses proofs.

he chapters include:

Worked examples with comments on the steps in the solutions
Exercises to practise techniques including *extension questions* of a more challenging nature – *extension questions* and questions which require techniques covered later in the book indicated by a tinted question number
Extension exercises providing harder questions on the work of the chapter
Miscellaneous exercises consisting of practice questions covering the work of the whole chapter
Test Yourself exercises consisting of multiple choice questions for revision
Key Points summarising the important results in the chapter.

here are separate sections of *Revision Exercises* and *Examination Questions* at intervals throughout the ook. These cover topics from all chapters in the preceding section.

owards the end of the *Pure Mathematics 1* is a *Spot The Error* exercise. This gives opportunity to identify, nd hence avoid, common mistakes. Towards the end of *Pure Mathematics 2* is a *Challenge* exercise which resents a miscellany of puzzles that can be solved using mathematics, and an *Extension Examination Questions Exercise*, which gives opportunity to practise harder questions in preparation for Advanced Extension Awards.

nswers are given either exactly or, if approximately, the usual approximation is to three significant figures r to one decimal place (e.g. for angles measured in degrees).

he books should be used in conjunction with the specification being followed.

grid matching the contents to each current A level specification can be found on the companion website www.longman.co.uk/advancedmathematics. Key Points from *Pure Mathematics 1* are also available on the website; these can be downloaded if required for use with *Pure Mathematics 2.*

Both books include a glossary of mathematical terms and a list of notation for reference.

1 Sets of Numbers, Surds and Indices

1.1 Sets of numbers

The most fundamental building blocks in mathematics are **numbers** and the **operations**, such as adding and multiplying, which can be performed on them.

*Primitive man needed no more than the numbers 1, 2, 3, ... (the **natural numbers** or **counting numbers**) to be able to count his animals and his children. Later, to be able to divide three loaves equally between seven people, for example, the need for fractions (the **rational numbers**) arose.*

*The Greeks thought that all numbers could be expressed as fractions until they tried to find a fraction which when multiplied by itself would be equal to 2. Unable to find it, they eventually realised such a fraction did not exist. Thus **irrational numbers** were discovered (or should it be 'invented'?).*

*In the sixteenth century, mathematicians were frustrated by not being able to solve quadratic equations such as $x^2 + 1 = 0$. By inventing (or discovering!) the imaginary number $\sqrt{-1}$, called i, the problem was solved and all quadratic equations had solutions. So the set of **complex numbers** (numbers with an imaginary part) was added to previously defined sets.*

Consider these sets of numbers:

The set of **natural** (or **counting**) **numbers** $\mathbb{N}$ is the set of numbers $\{1, 2, 3, 4, 5, \ldots\}$.

The set of **integers** $\mathbb{Z}$ is the set of whole numbers $\{\ldots -3, -2, -1, 0, +1, +2, +3, \ldots\}$.

The set of positive (+ve) integers $\mathbb{Z}^+$ is the set $\{+1, +2, +3, \ldots\}$.

The set of negative (−ve) integers $\mathbb{Z}^-$ is the set $\{-1, -2, -3, \ldots\}$.

The set of **real numbers** $\mathbb{R}$ is the set of numbers that correspond to points on the number line.

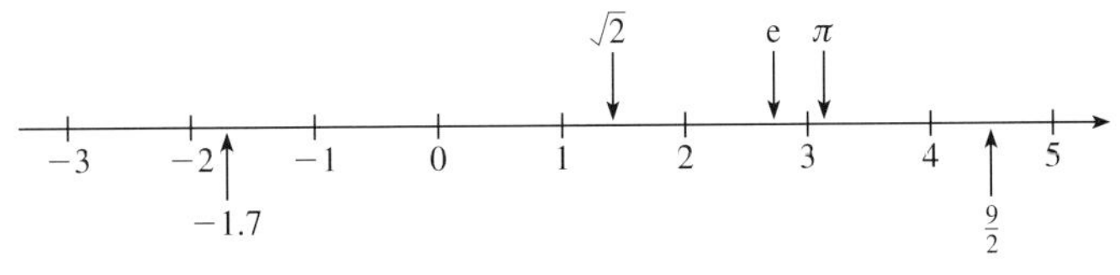

The set of real numbers can be separated into two distinct subsets: the **rational numbers** $\mathbb{Q}$ and the **irrational numbers** (no letter is given to this set).

The **rational numbers** are those that can be expressed as p/q, where p and $q \in \mathbb{Z}$, the set of integers, and $q \neq 0$.

Examples of rational numbers are

$\frac{4}{7}, \frac{9}{5}, 6 = \frac{6}{1}, 3.7 = \frac{37}{10}, 0.\dot{3} = \frac{1}{3}$.

A fraction $\frac{p}{q}$ is normally written in **lowest terms**, i.e. numerator p and denominator q share no common factor.

The set of rational numbers includes

- all decimals which terminate or recur (these can be written as $\frac{p}{q}$, see page 3)
- the integers, since an integer n can be written as $\frac{n}{1}$.

The set of **irrational numbers** is the set of real numbers which are not rational. Examples of these are $\sqrt{2}$, $\sqrt{7}$, π and e.

The set of ***complex numbers*** $\mathbb{C}$ *is the set of numbers which have an* ***imaginary part****. For example, the number* $3 + 2i$*, where* $i = \sqrt{-1}$*, is a complex number. The real part of the number is 3; 2i is the imaginary part.*
(Complex numbers are mentioned here for completeness.)

Some equations have solutions in some of the sets of numbers, but not in others.

Example 1

a $x + 3 = 7$
$\Rightarrow\ x = 4$

4 is a natural number
$4 \in \mathbb{N}$

b $x + 7 = 3$
$\Rightarrow\ x = -4$

-4 is *not* a natural number.
It does, however, belong to the set $\mathbb{Z}$ of integers.
$-4 \notin \mathbb{N},\ -4 \in \mathbb{Z}$

c $3x = 7$
$\Rightarrow\ x = \frac{7}{3}$

$\frac{7}{3}$ is *not* an integer.
It does, however, belong to the set $\mathbb{Q}$ of rational numbers.
$\frac{7}{3} \notin \mathbb{Z},\ \frac{7}{3} \in \mathbb{Q}$

d $x^2 = 2$
$\Rightarrow\ x = \pm\sqrt{2}$

$\pm\sqrt{2}$ are *not* rational numbers.
They do, however, belong to the set of irrational numbers and, therefore, to the set of real numbers.
$\pm\sqrt{2} \notin \mathbb{Q},\ \pm\sqrt{2} \in \mathbb{R}$

e $x^2 = -1$
$\Rightarrow\ x = \pm\sqrt{-1}$
$= \pm i$

$\pm\sqrt{-1}$ are *not* real numbers.
They do, however, belong to the set $\mathbb{C}$ of complex numbers.
$\pm\sqrt{-1} \notin \mathbb{R},\ \pm\sqrt{-1} \in \mathbb{C}$

Division by zero and the concept of infinity

One interpretation of $\frac{12}{2}$ is how many times can 2, the denominator, be subtracted from 12, the numerator, until nothing is left. The answer is 6.

Apply this to $\frac{12}{0}$. How many times can 0 be subtracted from 12 until nothing is left? The process can continue indefinitely; 0 can be subtracted an infinite number of times and 12 still remains.

The idea of infinity (symbol ∞) is not easy to grasp. It should *not* be thought of as a number, or as having a position on the number line. It can be thought of as the process of counting without end ($+\infty$ in the positive direction on the number line, $-\infty$ in the negative direction).

Since there is no numerical answer to a division by zero such a division is not allowed. For example, $\frac{12}{0}$ is not defined and, when $x = 1$, neither is

$$\frac{3}{x - 1}$$

Rational numbers and their decimal representation

All rational numbers can be expressed as either

- decimals which terminate, such as 0.72, or
- recurring decimals, such as 0.102 432 432 43 . . .

0.102 432 43 . . . can be written as $0.10\dot{2}4\dot{3}$. The dots indicate the set of digits which recur.

Conversely, all decimals that terminate or recur represent rational numbers. A method for converting a terminating decimal into a fraction is shown in Example 2a.

Irrational numbers cannot be expressed as terminating or recurring decimals. Conversely an infinite decimal that never recurs cannot be expressed as a rational number. For example, in 0.101 001 0001 . . . the number of zeros increases by one before each digit 1, so the decimal never recurs and it cannot be expressed as a ratio of two integers.

To sum up: Rational numbers can be represented by terminating or recurring decimals and *vice versa*. Irrational numbers are non-terminating, non-recurring decimals and *vice versa*.

Example 2 Express decimals as fractions in their lowest terms.

a $43.72 = \dfrac{4372}{100}$

43.72 is 4372 hundredths.

10	1	$\frac{1}{10}$	$\frac{1}{100}$
4	3	7	2

Divide numerator and denominator by 4.

$= \dfrac{1093}{25}$

The fraction cannot be cancelled further. It is in its lowest terms.

b $0.\dot{7}$

Let $x = 0.77\dot{7}$ ①

Then $10x = 7.77\dot{7}$ ②

Multiply both sides by 10. Since one digit recurs, this lines up the recurring digits.

$9x = 7$

Subtract line ① from line ②.

$x = \dfrac{7}{9}$

Divide both sides by 9.

c $0.\dot{2}\dot{4}$

Let $x = 0.\dot{2}\dot{4}$ ①

Then $100x = 24.\dot{2}\dot{4}$ ②

Multiply both sides by 100. Since two digits recur, this lines up the recurring digits.

$99x = 24$

Subtract line ① from line ②.

$x = \dfrac{24}{99}$

Divide both sides by 99.

$x = \dfrac{8}{33}$

Cancel to lowest terms.

For an alternative method for converting recurring decimals to fractions, see Example 34 in Chapter 12, page 289.

Example 3 Express fractions as decimals.

a $\dfrac{3}{25} = \dfrac{12}{100} = 0.12$

By multiplying numerator and denominator by 4, the denominator can be made into a power of 10 (i.e. 10, 100, 1000, etc. . . .). The conversion to decimal form is then simple.

b $\dfrac{6}{7}$

When the denominator cannot be made into a power of 10, the numerator must be divided by the denominator.

Divide 6 by 7

$$7 \overline{\smash{)}6.0^{4}0^{5}0^{1}0^{3}0^{2}0^{6}0\ldots} \quad \text{quotient } 0.8\,5\,7\,1\,4\,2\,8\ldots$$

The group of six digits will recur.

$$\frac{6}{7} = 0.\dot{8}57\,14\dot{2}$$

✓ *Note* Division of the numerator by the denominator can always be used to convert a fraction to a decimal.

Use of calculators

Many calculators have a fraction button and, with practice, all fractions and their equivalent decimal form can be found using a calculator.

The serious student must aim, however, to be fluent with numerical work and this means acquiring the ability to calculate speedily and accurately with and *without* a calculator. Being skilful with numbers is satisfying as well as an important basis for further mathematical development.

Exercise 1a should be completed *without* a calculator. A calculator can be used to check that an answer is correct or, at least, to provide supporting evidence. For example, in section 1.2, it will be shown that

$$\frac{\sqrt{2}}{3\sqrt{2}-1} = \frac{6+\sqrt{2}}{17}$$

Evaluating both these expressions on the calculator gives 0.4361 correct to 4 d.p. This does not *prove* that the expressions are equivalent but it does provide some support and reassurance!

EXERCISE 1a

1 Express each of these decimals as a fraction in its lowest terms.

a $0.\dot{6}$ **b** $0.\dot{4}$ **c** $0.\dot{1}\dot{2}$ **d** $0.30\dot{5}$

e $0.1\dot{2}$ **f** $3.4\dot{0}\dot{7}$ **g** $0.\dot{4}\dot{8}$ **h** $4.\dot{2}$

2 Express each of these fractions in decimal form.

a $\frac{7}{50}$ **b** $\frac{2}{125}$ **c** $\frac{5}{9}$ **d** $\frac{4}{11}$

e $\frac{44}{7}$ **f** $\frac{1}{6}$ **g** $\frac{3}{8}$ **h** $\frac{5}{7}$

3 Explore the decimal representation of all proper fractions (< 1) with these denominators.

a 7 **b** 9 **c** 11 **d** 13 **e** 19

4 What must be true of the integers a, and/or b, if $\frac{a}{b}$ terminates when expressed in decimal form (assume that $\frac{a}{b}$ is in its lowest terms)?

To prove that $\sqrt{2}$ is irrational

The ancient Greeks, who were among the most accomplished mathematicians of antiquity, believed that any number could be written as a fraction. They were troubled by the number representing the length of the diagonal of a unit square. Using Pythagoras' theorem, they knew that this number was $\sqrt{2}$. After trying in vain to find a fraction that, when squared, gave 2, the Greeks finally realised – and managed to prove – that it was impossible. This breakthrough was celebrated by sacrificing 100 oxen.

Proving any proposition requires an argument, a series of steps, which will convince a reader of the truth of the proposition.

There are various methods of proof. The proof given here uses a method called *reductio ad absurdum* (reduction to the absurd). In this method of proof, the proposition to be proved true is assumed to be false. Logical steps are then deduced leading to a contradiction. The assumption that the proposition was false has led logically to a contradiction. Therefore that assumption must have been incorrect and the proposition must be true.

Proof

Assume that the proposition is not true, i.e. that $\sqrt{2}$ is rational.

Then $\sqrt{2}$ can be expressed as $\frac{p}{q}$ where p and q are integers.

Assume that $\frac{p}{q}$ is in its lowest terms.

Let $\frac{p}{q} = \sqrt{2}$

A fraction can always be reduced to its lowest terms.

Squaring $\frac{p^2}{q^2} = 2$

So $p^2 = 2q^2$ ①

and hence p^2 is even.

Even × Even = Even
Odd × Odd = Odd

Since p^2 is even, p must also be even, so one can write

$p = 2m$ where m is an integer

Substituting in ① $4m^2 = 2q^2$

Dividing both sides by 2 $2m^2 = q^2$

So q^2 is even and therefore q is even. But if both p and q are even then $\frac{p}{q}$ is not in its lowest terms.

Since there is a contradiction, the original assumption must be false. That is, $\sqrt{2}$ cannot be rational.

$\therefore$ $\sqrt{2}$ is irrational.

It is extraordinary that $\sqrt{2}$, with just two symbols, expresses a number that can otherwise only be expressed in decimal form and, however many decimal places are given, will only be an approximation!

Precision

Pure mathematics poses questions for which *exact* answers are sought.
The calculator provides approximations which are valuable in certain situations.
For example, in measuring a distance, 3.73 m is a more useful answer than $(2 + \sqrt{3})$ m.
The number 3.73 is correct to 3 significant figures.

Unless a problem asks for an answer to a certain degree of accuracy, always give an **exact answer**, such as those given in the table.

Exact value	*Approximate answer*	*Degree of accuracy*
$\frac{1}{6}$	0.1667	4 d.p.
$\frac{1}{3}$	0.3	1 d.p.
$0.\dot{6}$	0.67	2 d.p.
$\sqrt{2}$	1.414	4 sig. figs
π	3.141593	7 sig. figs

Use fractions, in pure mathematics, in preference to decimals.

1.2 Surds

Consider these three roots. All three can be expressed as rational numbers.

$$\sqrt{4} = 2 \qquad \sqrt{\tfrac{9}{25}} = \tfrac{3}{5} \qquad \sqrt[3]{27} = 3$$

Roots that cannot be expressed as rational numbers are called **surds**. So surds are irrational; they cannot be expressed either as fractions or as terminating or recurring decimals. $\sqrt{2}$, $\sqrt{7}$ and $\sqrt[3]{11}$ are examples of surds.

On a calculator, an *approximate* value of any root can be found. For example,

$\sqrt{2} \approx 1.414\,213\,562$

This gives $\sqrt{2}$ correct to 9 decimal places.

Surds are required to give exact results. They are not in the least unusual. Consider, for example, $\sqrt{n}$ where $1 \leqslant n \leqslant 1000$. Only 31 out of the 1000 possible square roots are rational; 969 (or 96.9%) are surds.

Manipulation of surds

It is often necessary to be able to manipulate expressions with surds.

These two useful results can be illustrated by substituting values for a and b.

$\sqrt{a} \times \sqrt{b} = \sqrt{ab}$ $\qquad \sqrt{4} \times \sqrt{9} = 2 \times 3 = 6$ $\qquad \sqrt{4 \times 9} = \sqrt{36} = 6$

$\dfrac{\sqrt{a}}{\sqrt{b}} = \sqrt{\dfrac{a}{b}}$ $\qquad \dfrac{\sqrt{64}}{\sqrt{16}} = \dfrac{8}{4} = 2$ $\qquad \sqrt{\dfrac{64}{16}} = \sqrt{4} = 2$

$\sqrt{a} \times \sqrt{b} = \sqrt{ab}$

$$\frac{\sqrt{a}}{\sqrt{b}} = \sqrt{\frac{a}{b}}$$

Note the special case: $\sqrt{a} \times \sqrt{a} = \sqrt{a^2} = a$

Example 4 Simplify surds.

a $\sqrt{2} \times \sqrt{18} = \sqrt{2 \times 18} = \sqrt{36} = 6$

b $\dfrac{\sqrt{50}}{\sqrt{2}} = \sqrt{\dfrac{50}{2}} = \sqrt{25} = 5$

Example 5 Square surds.

a $(\sqrt{7})^2 = \sqrt{7} \times \sqrt{7} = 7$

b $(4\sqrt{3})^2 = 4\sqrt{3} \times 4\sqrt{3} = 4 \times 4 \times \sqrt{3} \times \sqrt{3} = 16 \times 3 = 48$

c $\left(\dfrac{\sqrt{2x}}{3\sqrt{5y}}\right)^2 = \dfrac{\sqrt{2x}}{3\sqrt{5y}} \times \dfrac{\sqrt{2x}}{3\sqrt{5y}} = \dfrac{2x}{9 \times 5y^2} = \dfrac{2x}{45y^2}$

$\sqrt{a} \times \sqrt{b} = \sqrt{ab}$ can be used to simplify expressions containing square roots of composite numbers.

It is sometimes possible to factorise a number so that one factor is a perfect square. The root of this factor can then be taken outside the surd.

To express in terms of the *simplest* possible surd, no perfect square factor should remain under the root sign.

Example 6 Express surds in simplest possible terms.

a $\sqrt{18}$

It is easy to see that 9 is the largest perfect square factor of 18.

$\sqrt{18} = \sqrt{9} \times \sqrt{2} = 3\sqrt{2}$

Using $\sqrt{ab} = \sqrt{a} \times \sqrt{b}$

b $\sqrt{600}$

100 is the largest perfect square factor of 600.

$\sqrt{600} = \sqrt{100} \times \sqrt{6} = 10\sqrt{6}$

c $\sqrt{968}$

It is hard to spot the largest perfect square factor of 968. There are two ways round this problem: find any perfect square factor of 968 to start with (e.g. 4) or express 968 as a product of prime factors.

Using any perfect square factor

$\sqrt{968} = \sqrt{4} \times \sqrt{242}$

$= 2\sqrt{242}$

To factorise 242, notice that 121 is a factor and is a perfect square.

$= 2\sqrt{121}\sqrt{2}$

$= 2 \times 11\sqrt{2}$

$= 22\sqrt{2}$

Factorising completely

$\sqrt{968} = \sqrt{(2^3 \times 11^2)}$

Once 968 has been completely factorised, it is possible to see that the largest square factor must be $2^2 \times 11^2$.

$= \sqrt{(2^2 \times 11^2)} \times \sqrt{2}$

$= 2 \times 11\sqrt{2}$

$= 22\sqrt{2}$

Example 7

The method illustrated in Example 6 may be used in reverse, as in this example.

Express a surd as the square root of a rational number.

a $2\sqrt{6} = \sqrt{(2^2 \times 6)} = \sqrt{24}$

To put 2 under the square root sign, it must be squared.

b $\dfrac{4}{3\sqrt{5}} = \sqrt{\dfrac{4^2}{3^2 \times 5}} = \sqrt{\dfrac{16}{45}}$

Note: 4 and 3 are squared under the root sign.

Rationalising the denominator

The process of removing surds from the denominator of an expression is called rationalising the denominator. An answer to a question should usually be given with the denominator rationalised.

Differing reasons are given for rationalising the denominator.
One belongs to the days before calculators, when, for example, $\sqrt{3}/3$ could be easily evaluated by looking up $\sqrt{3}$ in tables, whereas $1/\sqrt{3}$ was difficult to calculate. Rationalising the denominator is now the accepted convention and is considered more elegant.

The denominator of an expression is rationalised by multiplying both numerator and denominator by the same number. The choice of number depends on the type of expression in the denominator.

In Example 8, simply multiplying the numerator and denominator by a surd rationalises the denominator.

In more complicated examples, like Example 9, a number has to be chosen that makes use of the 'difference of squares' to give a rational denominator.

➤ **Difference of squares**

$$(x - y)(x + y) = x^2 - y^2$$

Hence

$$(\sqrt{a} - \sqrt{b})(\sqrt{a} + \sqrt{b}) = a - b$$

Example 8

Rationalise the denominators of these expressions.

a $\dfrac{1}{\sqrt{3}} = \dfrac{1}{\sqrt{3}} \times \dfrac{\sqrt{3}}{\sqrt{3}} = \dfrac{\sqrt{3}}{3}$

Multiplying numerator and denominator by $\sqrt{3}$ makes the denominator rational.

b $\dfrac{1}{2\sqrt{5}} = \dfrac{1}{2\sqrt{5}} \times \dfrac{\sqrt{5}}{\sqrt{5}} = \dfrac{\sqrt{5}}{10}$

Multiplying numerator and denominator by $\sqrt{5}$ makes the denominator rational. There is no need to multiply by the 2 in the denominator, which is rational already.

Example 9 Use the difference of squares to rationalise the denominators of expressions involving surds.

a $$\frac{1}{\sqrt{5}-\sqrt{2}} = \frac{1}{\sqrt{5}-\sqrt{2}} \times \frac{\sqrt{5}+\sqrt{2}}{\sqrt{5}+\sqrt{2}}$$

Multiplying by $\sqrt{5}+\sqrt{2}$ makes use of the 'difference of squares'.

$$= \frac{\sqrt{5}+\sqrt{2}}{5-2}$$

$$= \frac{\sqrt{5}+\sqrt{2}}{3}$$

Alternatively, write $\frac{1}{3}(\sqrt{5}+\sqrt{2})$.

b $$\frac{\sqrt{2}}{3\sqrt{2}-1} = \frac{\sqrt{2}}{3\sqrt{2}-1} \times \frac{3\sqrt{2}+1}{3\sqrt{2}+1}$$

$3\sqrt{2}+1$ is chosen to make use of the difference of squares.

$$= \frac{6+\sqrt{2}}{9\times 2-1}$$

Note the simplification of the numerator.

$$= \frac{6+\sqrt{2}}{17}$$

All these alternative versions are correct.

$$\frac{6}{17}+\frac{\sqrt{2}}{17} \qquad \frac{1}{17}(6+\sqrt{2}) \qquad \frac{6+\sqrt{2}}{17}.$$

Any of these versions is acceptable as an answer to an examination question unless the examiner specifies a particular version by stating 'show that ...'.

✓ *Note* A calculator can be used to check answers. Evaluating both

$$\frac{\sqrt{2}}{3\sqrt{2}-1} \quad \text{and} \quad \frac{6+\sqrt{2}}{17}$$

will give 0.4631 correct to 4 d.p. This is no proof that the expressions are equivalent but it provides evidence and reassurance.

c $$\frac{1+\sqrt{2}}{3-\sqrt{2}} = \frac{1+\sqrt{2}}{3-\sqrt{2}} \times \frac{3+\sqrt{2}}{3+\sqrt{2}}$$

$3+\sqrt{2}$ is chosen to make use of the difference of squares.

$$= \frac{3+\sqrt{2}+3\sqrt{2}+2}{9-2}$$

Simplify the numerator.

$$= \frac{5+4\sqrt{2}}{7}$$

Example 10 Simplify expressions, each involving two different surds, so that only one surd remains in each expression:

a $$\sqrt{24}+7\sqrt{54} = \sqrt{4}\times\sqrt{6}+7\sqrt{9}\times\sqrt{6}$$
$$= 2\sqrt{6}+7\times 3\times\sqrt{6}$$
$$= 2\sqrt{6}+21\sqrt{6}$$
$$= 23\sqrt{6}$$

Expressions like this addition can be simplified only if the terms can be expressed as multiples of the same surd. In this case, both are multiples of $\sqrt{6}$.

b $$\sqrt{12}\times\sqrt{15} = \sqrt{4}\times\sqrt{3}\times\sqrt{3}\times\sqrt{5}$$
$$= 2\sqrt{3}\times\sqrt{3}\times\sqrt{5}$$
$$= 2\times 3\sqrt{5}$$
$$= 6\sqrt{5}$$

Noticing that the numbers under the root signs have a common factor of 3, makes it possible to simplify the expression without multiplying 12 by 15.

Example 11 Express $(\sqrt{5}+1)^2$ in the form $A+B\sqrt{C}$ where A, B and C are rational numbers.

$$\begin{aligned}(\sqrt{5}+1)^2 &= (\sqrt{5}+1)(\sqrt{5}+1)\\ &= 5+2\sqrt{5}+1\\ &= 6+2\sqrt{5}\end{aligned}$$

So $A=6$, $B=2$, $C=5$.

Example 12 Find A, B and C such that

$$\frac{3}{\sqrt{5}-1} = A+B\sqrt{C}$$

$$\frac{3}{\sqrt{5}-1} = \frac{3}{\sqrt{5}-1} \times \frac{\sqrt{5}+1}{\sqrt{5}+1}$$

Choose $\sqrt{5}+1$ to rationalise the denominator.

$$= \frac{3\sqrt{5}+3}{5-1}$$

$$= \frac{3\sqrt{5}+3}{4}$$

$$= \frac{3}{4} + \frac{3}{4}\sqrt{5}$$

Compare this expression with $A+B\sqrt{C}$.

So $A=\frac{3}{4}$, $B=\frac{3}{4}$, $C=5$.

EXERCISE 1b

This exercise may be done orally. Do not use a calculator.

1 Square

a $\sqrt{5}$ **b** $\sqrt{\frac{1}{2}}$ **c** $4\sqrt{3}$ **d** $\frac{1}{2}\sqrt{2}$ **e** $\sqrt{\frac{a}{b}}$

f $\sqrt{3}\times\sqrt{5}$ **g** $\sqrt{3}\times\sqrt{7}$ **h** $\frac{\sqrt{p}}{\sqrt{q}}$ **i** $\frac{1}{2\sqrt{p}}$ **j** $\frac{3\sqrt{a}}{\sqrt{2b}}$

2 Express these in terms of the simplest possible surds.

a $\sqrt{8}$ **b** $\sqrt{12}$ **c** $\sqrt{27}$ **d** $\sqrt{50}$ **e** $\sqrt{45}$

f $\sqrt{1210}$ **g** $\sqrt{75}$ **h** $\sqrt{32}$ **i** $\sqrt{72}$ **j** $\sqrt{98}$

3 Express these as square roots of integers.

a $3\sqrt{2}$ **b** $2\sqrt{3}$ **c** $4\sqrt{5}$ **d** $2\sqrt{6}$ **e** $3\sqrt{8}$

f $6\sqrt{6}$ **g** $8\sqrt{2}$ **h** $10\sqrt{10}$ **i** $5\sqrt{7}$ **j** $14\sqrt{2}$

4 Rationalise the denominators of these fractions.

a $\frac{1}{\sqrt{5}}$ **b** $\frac{1}{\sqrt{7}}$ **c** $-\frac{1}{\sqrt{2}}$ **d** $\frac{2}{\sqrt{3}}$ **e** $\frac{3}{\sqrt{6}}$

f $\frac{1}{2\sqrt{2}}$ **g** $-\frac{3}{2\sqrt{3}}$ **h** $\frac{9}{4\sqrt{6}}$ **i** $\frac{1}{\sqrt{2}+1}$ **j** $\frac{1}{2-\sqrt{3}}$

EXERCISE 1c

Calculators should not be used for this exercise.

1 Simplify

a $\sqrt{8}+\sqrt{18}-2\sqrt{2}$ **b** $\sqrt{75}+2\sqrt{12}-\sqrt{27}$

c $\sqrt{28}+\sqrt{175}-\sqrt{63}$ **d** $\sqrt{1000}-\sqrt{40}-\sqrt{90}$

e $\sqrt{512}+\sqrt{128}+\sqrt{32}$ **f** $\sqrt{24}-3\sqrt{6}-\sqrt{216}+\sqrt{294}$

2 Express these in the form $A+B\sqrt{C}$, where A, B and C are rational numbers.

a $\dfrac{2}{3-\sqrt{2}}$ **b** $(\sqrt{5}+2)^2$ **c** $(1+\sqrt{2})(3-2\sqrt{2})$

d $(\sqrt{3}-1)^2$ **e** $(1-\sqrt{2})(3+2\sqrt{2})$ **f** $\sqrt{\tfrac{1}{2}}+\sqrt{\tfrac{1}{4}}+\sqrt{\tfrac{1}{8}}$

3 Rationalise the denominators of these fractions.

a $\dfrac{\sqrt{3}+\sqrt{2}}{\sqrt{3}-\sqrt{2}}$ **b** $\dfrac{\sqrt{5}+1}{\sqrt{5}-\sqrt{3}}$ **c** $\dfrac{2\sqrt{2}-\sqrt{3}}{\sqrt{2}+\sqrt{3}}$

d $\dfrac{\sqrt{2}+2\sqrt{5}}{\sqrt{5}-\sqrt{2}}$ **e** $\dfrac{\sqrt{6}+\sqrt{3}}{\sqrt{6}-\sqrt{3}}$ **f** $\dfrac{\sqrt{10}+2\sqrt{5}}{\sqrt{10}+\sqrt{5}}$

4 Simplify these as far as possible, given that $x=\sqrt{3}$, $y=\sqrt{12}$.

a y^2 **b** x^3 **c** xy **d** $\dfrac{y}{x}$ **e** $x+y$ **f** $y-x$

g $\dfrac{12}{x}$ **h** $\dfrac{1}{y}$ **i** $\sqrt{75}y$ **j** $\dfrac{\sqrt{48}}{x}$ **k** $\dfrac{x^5}{3}$ **l** $5x+3y$

5 Simplify these expressions.

a $\sqrt{15}\times\sqrt{24}$ **b** $\sqrt{18}\times\sqrt{32}$ **c** $\sqrt{3}\times\sqrt{6}\times\sqrt{12}$

d $\sqrt{5}-\dfrac{1}{\sqrt{5}}-\dfrac{1}{\sqrt{125}}$ **e** $\dfrac{4}{\sqrt{8}}+\dfrac{6}{\sqrt{2}}$ **f** $\dfrac{\sqrt{8}\times\sqrt{10}\times\sqrt{12}}{\sqrt{2}\times\sqrt{20}\times\sqrt{24}}$

EXERCISE 1d

Calculators should not be used for this exercise.

1 Express these in the form $a\sqrt{b}$, where b has no perfect square factors.

a $\sqrt{192}$ **b** $\sqrt{1452}$ **c** $\sqrt{77760}$

2 Express these in the form $A+B\sqrt{C}$, where A, B and C are rational.

a $\dfrac{1}{\sqrt{6}}+\dfrac{1}{\sqrt{216}}$ **b** $\dfrac{\sqrt{8}+3}{\sqrt{18}+2}$ **c** $\sqrt{3}+2+\dfrac{1}{\sqrt{3}-2}$

3 Rationalise the denominators of these fractions.

a $\dfrac{2\sqrt{5}+1}{2\sqrt{5}-1}$ **b** $\dfrac{3+\sqrt{2}}{\sqrt{3}+\sqrt{2}}$ **c** $\dfrac{1}{1+\sqrt{2}+\sqrt{3}}$

d $\dfrac{\sqrt{x}+\sqrt{y}}{\sqrt{x}-\sqrt{y}}$ **e** $\dfrac{1}{a\sqrt{b}+\sqrt{c}}$ **f** $\dfrac{\sqrt{x+1}-\sqrt{x-1}}{\sqrt{x+1}+\sqrt{x-1}}$

4 Prove that $\sqrt{3}$ is irrational (see proof for $\sqrt{2}$ on page 5).

EXERCISE 1d *(continued)*

5 Find a, b such that $14 - 4\sqrt{6} = (\sqrt{a} - 2\sqrt{b})^2$.

6 Simplify

a $\sqrt[3]{54}$ b $\sqrt[6]{192}$ c $\sqrt[4]{1280}$

7 Express these in surd form and rationalise the denominators.

a $\dfrac{1}{1 + \cos 45°}$ b $\dfrac{2}{1 - \cos 30°}$ c $\dfrac{1 + \tan 60°}{1 - \tan 60°}$

d $\dfrac{1 + \tan 30°}{1 - \tan 30°}$ e $\dfrac{1 + \sin 45°}{1 - \sin 45°}$ f $\dfrac{1}{(1 - \sin 45°)^2}$

8 What percentage of $\sqrt{n}$, where $n \in \mathbb{Z}$, are rational, where

a $1 \leqslant n \leqslant 2000$? b $1 \leqslant n \leqslant 10000$?

1.3 Indices

x^n means x multiplied by itself n times.

$x^n = \underbrace{x \times x \times x \times x \times x \times \cdots \times x}_{n \text{ of these}}$

So $5^2 = 5 \times 5$ Say: 5 squared.

$2^3 = 2 \times 2 \times 2 = 8$ Say: 2 cubed.

$a^4 = a \times a \times a \times a$ Say: a to the power 4 (or: a to the fourth).

In the expression x^n, x is called the **base** and n is the **power** or **index** or **exponent**.

Rules for indices

Where numbers are expressed as powers of the *same* base the following rules can be used to multiply and divide the numbers.

➤ *Multiplication*: $a^m \times a^n = a^{m+n}$

To *multiply* the numbers *add* the indices.

$$2^3 \times 2^4 = (2 \times 2 \times 2) \times (2 \times 2 \times 2 \times 2) = 2^{3+4} = 2^7$$

➤ *Division*: $\dfrac{a^m}{a^n} = a^{m-n}$

To *divide* the numbers *subtract* the indices.

$$\frac{6^5}{6^3} = \frac{\cancel{6}^1 \times \cancel{6}^1 \times \cancel{6}^1 \times 6 \times 6}{{}_1\cancel{6} \times {}_1\cancel{6} \times {}_1\cancel{6}} = 6^{5-3} = 6^2$$

Indices can be *negative*.

$$\frac{6^3}{6^5} = \frac{\cancel{6}^1 \times \cancel{6}^1 \times \cancel{6}^1}{{}_1\cancel{6} \times {}_1\cancel{6} \times {}_1\cancel{6} \times 6 \times 6} = \frac{1}{6^2}$$

Subtracting the indices gives

$$\frac{6^3}{6^5} = 6^{3-5} = 6^{-2}$$

Comparing these two expressions, $6^{-2} = \dfrac{1}{6^2}$

➤ *Negative indices*

$a^{-n} = \frac{1}{a^n}$ or more generally, $\left(\frac{a}{b}\right)^{-n} = \left(\frac{b}{a}\right)^n$

A number raised to a *negative* power is the **reciprocal** of the number raised to the positive power.

Meaning can be given to a *zero power* by putting $m = n$ in

$$\frac{a^m}{a^n} = a^{m-n}$$

$$\frac{a^n}{a^n} = a^{n-n} = a^0$$

But for $a \neq 0$

$$\frac{a^n}{a^n} = 1$$

So $a^0 = 1$, e.g. $4^0 = 1$.

➤ *Raising an expression to the power zero*: $a^0 = 1 \quad (a \neq 0)$

Any number (other than zero) to the power of *zero* equals one.

Powers of powers

$$\begin{aligned}(5^2)^3 &= 5^2 \times 5^2 \times 5^2\\ &= 5^{3\times 2}\\ &= 5^6\end{aligned}$$

➤ *Raising a power to a power*: $(a^m)^n = a^{mn}$

To *raise* to a power, *multiply* the indices.

Fractional indices

$$2^{\frac{1}{2}} \times 2^{\frac{1}{2}} = 2^{\frac{1}{2}+\frac{1}{2}} = 2^1 = 2$$

and $\sqrt{2} \times \sqrt{2} = 2$

so $2^{\frac{1}{2}} = \sqrt{2}$

Similarly $8^{\frac{1}{3}} \times 8^{\frac{1}{3}} \times 8^{\frac{1}{3}} = 8^{\frac{1}{3}+\frac{1}{3}+\frac{1}{3}} = 8^1 = 8$

and $\sqrt[3]{8} \times \sqrt[3]{8} \times \sqrt[3]{8} = 8$

so $8^{\frac{1}{3}} = \sqrt[3]{8}$

➤ *Fractional indices*: $a^{\frac{1}{n}} = \sqrt[n]{a}$

Fractional indices correspond to **roots**.

In general, taking the product of n factors $a^{\frac{1}{n}}$

$$a^{\frac{1}{n}} \times a^{\frac{1}{n}} \times a^{\frac{1}{n}} \times \cdots \times a^{\frac{1}{n}} = a^{\frac{1}{n}+\frac{1}{n}+\frac{1}{n}+\cdots+\frac{1}{n}} = a^1 = a$$

So $$a^{\frac{1}{n}} = \sqrt[n]{a}$$

$a^{\frac{m}{n}} = \left(a^{\frac{1}{n}}\right)^m$	For $a^{\frac{m}{n}}$ *either*
$= (\sqrt[n]{a})^m$	take the nth root and then raise to the power m
or	*or*
$a^{\frac{m}{n}} = (a^m)^{\frac{1}{n}}$	raise to the power m and then take the nth root.
$= \sqrt[n]{a^m}$	

Example 13

Find the value of expressions involving indices.

a $4^{-2} = \dfrac{1}{4^2} = \dfrac{1}{16}$

b $\left(\frac{2}{3}\right)^{-3} = \left(\frac{3}{2}\right)^3 = \frac{27}{8} = 3\frac{3}{8}$

Invert the fraction and reverse the sign of the power.

c $16^{\frac{1}{4}} = \sqrt[4]{16} = 2$

d $16^{\frac{3}{4}} = (\sqrt[4]{16})^3 = 2^3 = 8$

or

$16^{\frac{3}{4}} = (16^3)^{\frac{1}{4}} = \sqrt[4]{4096} = 8$

e $4^{-\frac{3}{2}} = \dfrac{1}{4^{\frac{3}{2}}} = \dfrac{1}{(\sqrt{4})^3} = \dfrac{1}{2^3} = \dfrac{1}{8}$

or

$4^{-\frac{3}{2}} = \dfrac{1}{\sqrt{4^3}} = \dfrac{1}{(\sqrt{64})} = \dfrac{1}{8}$

Note When applying rules of indices the bases must be the same.

$2^3 \times 2^5 = 2^8$ (same base) $\qquad 2^3 \times 3^5$ cannot be simplified (different base)

$2^3 + 2^5$ cannot be expressed as an integer power of 2.

If, in a product or quotient, the powers are the same, but the bases are different, then some simplification is possible.

$a^m \times b^m = (ab)^m$ and $\dfrac{a^m}{b^m} = \left(\dfrac{a}{b}\right)^m$

$2^5 \times 3^5 = (2 \times 3)^5 \qquad \dfrac{2^5}{3^5} = \left(\dfrac{2}{3}\right)^5$

Evaluating expressions containing indices

There are a number of ways of using a calculator to evaluate, for example $\left(\frac{16}{9}\right)^{-\frac{3}{2}}$. Examples in this chapter, however, should be worked out *without* a calculator. The calculator can be used for checking and reassurance but will not help in understanding and working with indices.

EXERCISE 1e

This exercise may be done orally. Do not use a calculator.

1 Find the values of

a $25^{\frac{1}{2}}$ **b** $27^{\frac{1}{3}}$ **c** $64^{\frac{1}{6}}$ **d** $49^{\frac{1}{2}}$ **e** $\left(\frac{1}{4}\right)^{\frac{1}{2}}$ **f** $1^{\frac{1}{4}}$

g $(-8)^{\frac{1}{3}}$ **h** $(-1)^{\frac{1}{5}}$ **i** $8^{\frac{4}{3}}$ **j** $27^{\frac{2}{3}}$ **k** $25^{\frac{3}{2}}$ **l** $49^{\frac{3}{2}}$

m $\left(\frac{1}{4}\right)^{\frac{3}{2}}$ **n** $\left(\frac{4}{9}\right)^{\frac{1}{2}}$ **o** $\left(\frac{27}{8}\right)^{\frac{1}{3}}$ **p** $\left(\frac{16}{81}\right)^{\frac{1}{4}}$

2 Find the values of

a 7^0 **b** 3^{-1} **c** 5^0 **d** 4^{-1} **e** 2^{-3} **f** $\left(\frac{1}{2}\right)^{-1}$

g $\left(\frac{1}{3}\right)^{-2}$ **h** $\left(\frac{4}{9}\right)^{0}$ **i** 3^{-3} **j** $(-6)^{-1}$ **k** $\left(-\frac{1}{6}\right)^{0}$ **l** $\left(\frac{2}{3}\right)^{-2}$

m $\left(-\frac{1}{2}\right)^{-2}$ **n** $\dfrac{1}{3^{-1}}$ **o** $\dfrac{2^{-1}}{3^{-2}}$ **p** $\dfrac{2^0 \times 3^{-2}}{5^{-1}}$

3 Find the values of

a $8^{-\frac{1}{3}}$ **b** $8^{-\frac{2}{3}}$ **c** $4^{-\frac{1}{2}}$ **d** $4^{-\frac{3}{2}}$ **e** $27^{-\frac{2}{3}}$ **f** $\left(\frac{1}{4}\right)^{-\frac{1}{2}}$

g $\left(\frac{1}{8}\right)^{-\frac{1}{3}}$ **h** $\left(\frac{1}{27}\right)^{-\frac{2}{3}}$ **i** $\left(\frac{4}{9}\right)^{-\frac{1}{2}}$ **j** $\left(\frac{8}{27}\right)^{-\frac{1}{3}}$ **k** $\left(\frac{16}{81}\right)^{-\frac{1}{4}}$ **l** $\left(\frac{27}{8}\right)^{-\frac{4}{3}}$

4 Find the values of

a $0.16^{0.5}$ **b** $\left(\frac{4}{9}\right)^{1\frac{1}{2}}$ **c** $\left(2\frac{1}{4}\right)^{1\frac{1}{2}}$ **d** $(0.\dot{4})^{\frac{1}{2}}$

Algebra with indices

It is useful, and will be particularly so in Chapter 9 on differentiation, to be able to convert expressions with indices to the form kx^n.

Example 14

Convert expressions to the form kx^n.

a $\dfrac{1}{x^3} = x^{-3}$ $\quad k = 1, n = -3$

Using $a^{-n} = \dfrac{1}{a^n}$

b $\dfrac{3\sqrt{x}}{2} = \dfrac{3}{2}x^{\frac{1}{2}}$ $\quad k = \frac{3}{2}, n = \frac{1}{2}$

Using $\sqrt{a} = a^{\frac{1}{2}}$

c $\dfrac{2}{5\sqrt[4]{x}} = \dfrac{2}{5x^{\frac{1}{4}}} = \dfrac{2}{5}x^{-\frac{1}{4}}$ $\quad k = \frac{2}{5}, n = -\frac{1}{4}$

Using $\sqrt[n]{a} = a^{\frac{1}{n}}$ and $a^{-n} = \dfrac{1}{a^n}$

EXERCISE 1f

This exercise may be done orally.

1 Convert these to the form x^n.

a $\frac{1}{x}$ **b** $\frac{1}{x^2}$ **c** $\sqrt{x}$ **d** $\sqrt[3]{x}$ **e** $\frac{1}{x^4}$ **f** $\frac{1}{x^{-4}}$

g $\frac{1}{\sqrt{x}}$ **h** $\frac{1}{x^{-7}}$ **i** $\frac{1}{\sqrt[3]{x}}$ **j** $\sqrt[3]{x^2}$ **k** $\frac{1}{\sqrt[4]{x^3}}$ **l** $\frac{1}{\sqrt{x^5}}$

2 Convert these to the form kx^n.

a $\frac{3}{x}$ **b** $\frac{4}{3x}$ **c** $6\sqrt{x}$ **d** $\frac{5}{x^3}$ **e** $\frac{1}{4x^4}$ **f** $\frac{\sqrt{x}}{3}$

g $\frac{1}{5\sqrt{x}}$ **h** $\frac{6}{x^{-7}}$ **i** $\frac{4}{5\sqrt[3]{x}}$ **j** $7\sqrt[3]{x^2}$ **k** $\frac{2}{\sqrt[4]{x^3}}$ **l** $\frac{8}{3\sqrt{x}}$

Example 15

In this example, to simplify algebraic products, the coefficients are multiplied and any powers of the same letter are combined using $a^m \times a^n = a^{m+n}$.

a $5a^2 \times 7a^{-3} \times a^5 = 5 \times 7 \times a^2 \times a^{-3} \times a^5$
$= 35a^{2-3+5}$
$= 35a^4$

b $8a^2bx^4 \times 5a^3b^2 = 8 \times 5 \times a^{2+3} \times b^{1+2} \times x^4$
$= 40a^5b^3x^4$

Put the letters in alphabetical order.

Example 16

This example uses $(a^m)^n = a^{mn}$ to simplify algebraic products.

a $(x^x)^2 = x^{2x}$

b $(x^x)^x = x^{(x^2)}$

Example 17

In this example, the coefficients are divided and any powers of the same letter are combined using

$$\frac{a^m}{a^n} = a^{m-n}$$

a $\frac{27x^5}{9x^3} = \frac{\overset{3}{\cancel{27}} \times x^5}{\underset{1}{\cancel{9}} \times x^3} = 3x^{5-3} = 3x^2$

b $35a^3b^2c^3 \div -7ab^4c = \frac{\overset{5}{\cancel{35}} \times a^3b^2c^3}{-\underset{1}{\cancel{7}} \times ab^4c}$

$= -\frac{5a^2c^2}{b^2}$

Alternatively, write $-5a^2b^{-2}c^2$.

Example 18

This example uses $(a^m)^n = a^{mn}$.

$$(10c^{-3})^2 \div (5c^{-1})^3 = \frac{(10c^{-3})^2}{(5c^{-1})^3}$$

$$= \frac{\overset{4}{\cancel{100}}c^{-6}}{\underset{5}{\cancel{125}}c^{-3}}$$

$$= \frac{4}{5c^3}$$

$(10c^{-3})^2 = 10^2(c^{-3})^2 = 100c^{-6}$

$\frac{c^{-6}}{c^{-3}} = c^{-6-(-3)} = c^{-6+3} = c^{-3}$

Alternatively, write $\frac{4}{5}c^{-3}$.

Example 19

This example uses $\sqrt[n]{a^m} = a^{\frac{m}{n}}$.

a $\sqrt{4b^6} = \sqrt{4} \times \sqrt{b^6} = 2 \times b^{\frac{6}{2}} = 2b^3$

The *square* root of the coefficient 4 is found and the power of b is divided by 2.

b $\sqrt[3]{27b^{12}c^3} = \sqrt[3]{27} \times \sqrt[3]{b^{12}} \times \sqrt[3]{c^3}$

$= 3 \times b^{\frac{12}{3}} \times c^{\frac{3}{3}}$

$= 3b^4c$

The *cube* root of the coefficient 27 is found and the powers are divided by 3.

c $(16b^{12})^{\frac{1}{4}} = 16^{\frac{1}{4}} \times b^{\frac{12}{4}} = \sqrt[4]{16} \times b^3 = 2b^3$

Example 20

Solve equations involving indices.

a $x^{\frac{1}{2}} = 7$

$x = 7^2 = 49$

Squaring both sides will give x. $x^{\frac{1}{2}} \times x^{\frac{1}{2}} = x$

b $3x^3 = -81$

Divide both sides by 3.

$x^3 = -27$

Taking cube root of both sides gives x.

$x = \sqrt[3]{-27} = -3$

$x = \sqrt[3]{-27}$ or $x = (-27)^{\frac{1}{3}}$

c $2(\sqrt{x})^3 = 250$

$(\sqrt{x})^3 = 125$

$\sqrt{x} = (125)^{\frac{1}{3}} = 5$

$x = 5^2 = 25$

Alternatively use $(\sqrt{x})^3 = x^{\frac{3}{2}}$

$x^{\frac{3}{2}} = 125$

$x^3 = 125^2 = 15\,625$

$x = 25$

EXERCISE 1g

1 Simplify

a $a \times a \times a$ **b** $4 \times b \times b$ **c** $x^3 \times x^5$ **d** $y^2 \times y^2 \times y^7$

e $3b^3 \times 2b^2$ **f** $2a \times 3a^2 \times 4a^3$ **g** $3x^2y \times 5x^3y^2$ **h** $a^{1+n} \times a^{1-n}$

i $x^4 \div x^2$ **j** $\frac{y^7}{y^3}$ **k** $(4a^2)^3$ **l** $4(a^2)^3$

m $(a^{m+1})^m$ **n** $(a^{m+1})^2$ **o** $\frac{4y^2z}{2xyz}$ **p** $(u^{-2})^{-3}$

q $(v^x)^2$ **r** $(v^x)^3$ **s** $(v^{2x})^3$ **t** $(v^{2x})^x$

u $x^{\frac{1}{2}} \times x^{-\frac{1}{2}}$ **v** $x^{\frac{1}{2}} \times x^{-\frac{1}{3}}$ **w** $a^x \times a^{-y} \times a^z$ **x** $\frac{3y^{19}}{y^{11}}$

y $p^{-1} \times p^{-4}$ **z** $q^2 \times q^{-2}$

2 Simplify these, giving each answer in two forms x^{-n} and $\frac{1}{x^n}$.

a $\frac{s^2}{s^4}$ **b** $\frac{y^3}{y^8}$ **c** $\frac{t^a}{t^{a+b}}$ **d** $\frac{x^p}{x^q}$

EXERCISE 1g *(continued)*

3 Square

a $4\pi r$ b $2a^3$ c b^2c^3 d $\frac{2a}{b}$

e $3y^3$ f $\frac{10^2a^3}{b^2}$ g $2a^{\frac{1}{2}}$ h $\frac{3}{4}a^{\frac{1}{4}}$

4 Simplify

a $\sqrt{x^8}$ b $\sqrt{4y^2}$ c $\sqrt{25a^2b^4}$ d $(36x^6)^{\frac{1}{2}}$

e $\sqrt[4]{a^{-8}b^{12}}$ f $\sqrt[3]{-8a^3}$ g $\sqrt[3]{27x^3y^9}$ h $\sqrt{\frac{100}{81x^{10}y^8}}$

5 Simplify

a $\frac{12x^2y}{3x^4y}$ b $\frac{6abc^2}{18a^2bc^2}$ c $\frac{(2st)^2}{3s^3}$

d $\frac{pq^2 \times p}{(pq)^2}$ e $(2a)^3 \div (4a)^2$ f $(4b)^{-1} \times (6b)^2$

g $3x^{\frac{1}{3}} \times 4x^{\frac{2}{3}}$ h $3x^2y \times 4xy^2 \times 5x$ i $8a^3 \times \frac{1}{2a} \times a^2$

j $\frac{ab^2 \times 2ab^3}{4a^2b}$ k $\frac{20x^3y^5}{5x^{-3}y^{-5}}$ l $\frac{9x^9}{3x \times x^2 \times 3x^6}$

m $\frac{8b^3c^5}{-4b}$ n $\frac{-32l^5m}{8l^3}$ o $\frac{-4x^6y^3}{2x^5y}$

p $(d^2e^3)^5$ q $-3a^2 \times 4ab^3 \times -5$ r $m^3n^5 \times (mn)^{-4}$

s $(-m)^5$ t $(-n)^6$ u $6h^2 \div 3h^{-3}$

v $(4p^{-2})^3$ w $(9a^{-3})^2 \div 6a^{-1}$

6 Solve these for x.

a $x^{\frac{1}{2}} = 5$ b $2x^3 - 128 = 0$ c $x^{-\frac{2}{3}} = \frac{1}{100}$ d $2x^{\frac{1}{4}} = \frac{64}{x}$

e $32x^{-3} = \frac{\sqrt{x}}{4}$ f $\sqrt[3]{x} = 8$ g $\sqrt[3]{2x} = 2$ h $27x^{-\frac{3}{2}} = 1$

EXERCISE 1h (Extension)

1 Given $3^x = 2$ and $3^y = 125$, calculate

a 3^{x+y} b 3^{2x} c 3^{y+1} d 3^{-x}

e 3^{-y} as a decimal f 3^{y-x} g $3^{y/3}$ h 9^{x+1}

2 Find these roots by expressing each number in prime factors.

a $\sqrt{9801}$ b $\sqrt[3]{2744}$ c $\sqrt[5]{7776}$ d $\sqrt[4]{20736}$

e $\sqrt{7744}$ f $\sqrt[3]{421875}$

3 Simplify

a $\left(\left(x^{\frac{1}{2}}\right)^{\frac{1}{2}}\right)^{\frac{1}{2}}$ b $\left(\left(x^{\frac{1}{3}}\right)^{\frac{2}{5}}\right)^{-30}$

4 If $x^y = y^x$ prove that $\left(\frac{x}{y}\right)^{\frac{x}{y}} = x^{\frac{x}{y}-1}$.

EXERCISE 1h *(continued)*

5 Find the value of

a $\dfrac{16^{\frac{1}{3}} \times 4^{\frac{1}{3}}}{8}$ b $\dfrac{27^{\frac{1}{2}} \times 243^{\frac{1}{2}}}{243^{\frac{4}{5}}}$ c $\dfrac{12^{\frac{1}{3}} \times 6^{\frac{1}{3}}}{81^{\frac{1}{6}}}$ d $\dfrac{32^{\frac{3}{4}} \times 16^{0} \times 8^{\frac{5}{4}}}{128^{\frac{3}{2}}}$

6 Simplify

a $\dfrac{8^{n} \times 2^{2n}}{4^{3n}}$ b $\dfrac{3^{n+1} \times 9^{n}}{27^{2n/3}}$ c $\dfrac{x^{-\frac{2}{3}} \times x^{\frac{1}{4}}}{x^{\frac{1}{6}}}$ d $\dfrac{x^{2n+1} \times x^{\frac{1}{2}}}{\sqrt{x^{3n}}}$

7 Prove that $3^{\frac{1}{3}} > 2^{\frac{1}{2}}$.

8 Insert brackets to make this a true statement: $\sqrt{2}^{\sqrt{2}^{\sqrt{2}^{\sqrt{2}}}} = \sqrt{2}^{\sqrt{2}^{\sqrt{2}}}$

EXERCISE 1i (Miscellaneous)

1 Simplify as far as possible, given that $x = \sqrt{5}$, $y = \sqrt{20}$

a x^2 b y^2 c $x + y$ d $2x - 3y$

e $\dfrac{y}{x}$ f x^3 g $\sqrt{xy}$

2 Express these in terms of the simplest possible surds.

a $\sqrt{80}$ b $\sqrt{32}$ c $\sqrt{72}$ d $\sqrt{180} + \sqrt{125}$

3 Rationalise the denominator of these fractions.

a $\dfrac{1}{\sqrt{3}}$ b $\dfrac{1}{\sqrt{2}}$ c $\dfrac{4}{\sqrt{7}}$ d $\dfrac{1}{4 - \sqrt{10}}$

e $\dfrac{2}{\sqrt{6} + 2}$ f $\dfrac{3}{2\sqrt{6}}$ g $\dfrac{3}{\sqrt{6} - \sqrt{5}}$

4 A square has area $6\,\text{cm}^2$.
Find its perimeter.

5 A rectangle has sides $(4 - \sqrt{7})$ cm and $(3 + 2\sqrt{7})$ cm.
Find its perimeter and its area.

6 A rectangle has area $(6 - \sqrt{3})\,\text{cm}^2$ and the length of one of its sides is $(2 + \sqrt{3})$ cm.
Find the length of the other side.

7 The sides of a rectangle are in the ratio 2:3. The diagonal is of length 26 cm.
Find the perimeter.

8 A cube has volume $10\,\text{cm}^3$.
Find the sum of the lengths of the sides, and the total surface area.

9 Given that $72 = 2^x \times 3^y$, find x and y, given that $x, y \in \mathbb{Z}$.

10 Simplify

a $3^{\frac{1}{4}} \times 3^{\frac{3}{4}}$ b $\sqrt{64} \times \sqrt[3]{64} \times \sqrt[6]{64}$ c $7^{\frac{1}{2}} \times 7^{\frac{1}{3}} \times 7^{\frac{1}{6}}$

d $(0.2)^4 \times 5^4$ e $(2.5)^3 \times 4^3$ f $\dfrac{6^{\frac{1}{4}} \times 36^{\frac{1}{8}}}{\sqrt{6}}$

EXERCISE 1i
(continued)

11 Work out these values, giving each answer in index form where possible.

a $7^3 \times 7^2 \times 7^4$ **b** $3^4 \times 3^5 \times 3^2$ **c** $4^3 + 4^2$

d $5^2 \times 5^4 \times 5$ **e** $2^{10} - 2^5$ **f** $\frac{2^{10}}{2^5}$

g $\frac{8^3}{8}$ **h** $6^3 + 6$ **i** $\frac{7^6}{7^3}$

j $(7^2)^2$ **k** $(5^3)^3$

12 Simplify these, where possible.

a $a^4 \times a^3 \times a$ **b** $b^5 + b^3$ **c** $2c^3 + 3c^3$

d $d^3 \times d^4 \times d^2$ **e** $e^2 + e^3$ **f** $3f^2 \times 2f^3$

g $4g^3 \times 5g^2$ **h** $(h^4)^3$ **i** $(i^3)^4$

j $(3j)^2$ **k** $(2k^3)^2$ **l** $(7l^6)^2$

m $(m^2n)^3$ **n** $(p^2q^4)^3$ **o** $(3rs)^2$

p $v^2w \times vw^2$ **q** $\frac{x^4}{x^3}$ **r** $\frac{y^6}{y^2}$

s $\frac{z^6}{z}$

13 Simplify these, where possible.

a $a^4 - a^3$ **b** $3b^6 - 3b^3$ **c** $7c^5 - 7c^3$

d $\frac{3d^6}{3d^2}$ **e** $\frac{10e^3}{2e^2}$ **f** $\frac{49f^4}{7f^2}$

g $\sqrt{g^6}$ **h** $\sqrt[3]{h^{12}}$ **i** $\sqrt{25i^4}$

j $9j^5 - 8j^5$ **k** $3k^3 + 4k^4$ **l** $\sqrt[4]{l^8m^{20}}$

m $\sqrt{4n^2p^2}$ **n** $\sqrt{q^4}$ **o** $r^7 + r^7$

p $3s^4 + 4s^4$ **q** $15t^9 - 15t^9$ **r** $u^2 - u$

Test yourself

1 $(3\sqrt{5})^2$ is equal to

A 45 **B** 15 **C** $9\sqrt{5}$ **D** $\sqrt{\sqrt{45}}$ **E** $6\sqrt{5}$

2 $(a^6)^{-2}$ is equivalent to

A a^4 **B** $\dfrac{1}{a^{12}}$ **C** a^3 **D** $\dfrac{1}{a^3}$ **E** $-\sqrt{a^6}$

3 The expression $4\sqrt{63} - 5\sqrt{28}$ is equal to

A $-\sqrt{35}$ **B** $2\sqrt{7}$ **C** $16\sqrt{7}$

D $\sqrt{308}$ **E** none of these

4 $7 \times 10^{100} + 8 \times 10^{102}$ is equal to

A 1.5×10^{102} **B** 5.6×10^{101} **C** 7.08×10^{100}

D 8.07×10^{102} **E** 1.5×10^{203}

5 $\dfrac{(2a^2b)^3}{(ab)^5}$ is equivalent to

A $\dfrac{6}{a^3b^4}$ **B** $\dfrac{8a}{b^2}$ **C** $\dfrac{8}{b^2}$ **D** $(2a)^{\frac{3}{5}}$ **E** $8a^{-9}b^{-12}$

6 $\sqrt{12}\sqrt{15}\sqrt{20}$ is equal to

A 60 **B** $60\sqrt{15}$ **C** $30\sqrt{2}$ **D** $60\sqrt{12}$ **E** $\sqrt{\sqrt{60}}$

7 $\left(\frac{8}{27}\right)^{\frac{2}{3}}$ is equal to

A $\frac{64}{19683}$ **B** $\frac{64}{729}$ **C** $21\frac{1}{3}$ **D** $\frac{4}{9}$ **E** $\dfrac{2\sqrt{2}}{3}$

8 When two surds are multiplied, the result is

A always a surd

B never a perfect square

C never rational

D sometimes rational

E either irrational or prime

9 $\dfrac{\sqrt{6}}{2 + \sqrt{3}}$ is equal to

A $\sqrt{2} + \dfrac{\sqrt{6}}{2}$ **B** $2\sqrt{6} - 3\sqrt{2}$ **C** $\dfrac{12 + 3\sqrt{2}}{7}$ **D** $3\sqrt{2} - 2\sqrt{6}$ **E** $\sqrt{12} - \sqrt{6}$

10 $\left(\dfrac{a^4b}{c^2}\right)^{-\frac{1}{2}}$ is equivalent to

A $-\dfrac{a^2\sqrt{b}}{c}$ **B** $\dfrac{a^{\frac{7}{2}}b^{-\frac{1}{2}}}{c^{\frac{3}{2}}}$ **C** $\dfrac{c}{a^4b}$ **D** $\dfrac{c\sqrt{b}}{a^2b}$

E none of these

Key points

Sets of numbers

$\mathbb{N}$ the natural (or counting) numbers $\{1, 2, 3, \ldots\}$

$\mathbb{Z}$ the integers $\{\ldots, -2, -1, 0, 1, 2, \ldots\}$

$\mathbb{Q}$ the rational numbers $\left(\text{e.g. } -\frac{2}{3}, 4, \frac{5}{6}, \frac{78}{9}\right)$

$\mathbb{R}$ the real numbers $\left(\text{e.g. } -\frac{2}{3}, \pi, -\sqrt{5}, 67\right)$

$\mathbb{C}$ the complex numbers $\left(\text{e.g. } 2 + \text{i}, 3 - 4\text{i}, \text{ where i} = \sqrt{-1}\right)$

Surds

$\sqrt{a} \times \sqrt{b} = \sqrt{ab}$ Special case: $\sqrt{a} \times \sqrt{a} = a$

$$\frac{\sqrt{a}}{\sqrt{b}} = \sqrt{\frac{a}{b}}$$

To **rationalise the denominator**

$\dfrac{a}{b\sqrt{c}}$ Multiply numerator and denominator by $\sqrt{c}$.

$\dfrac{a}{b\sqrt{c} \pm d\sqrt{e}}$ Multiply numerator and denominator by $b\sqrt{c} \mp d\sqrt{e}$.

Indices

Multiplication

$a^m \times a^n = a^{m+n}$ To multiply, add the indices.

Division

$a^m \div a^n = \dfrac{a^m}{a^n} = a^{m-n}$ To divide, subtract the indices.

Negative indices

$$a^{-n} = \frac{1}{a^n} \qquad \left(\frac{a}{b}\right)^{-n} = \left(\frac{b}{a}\right)^n$$

Raising to the power zero $(a \neq 0)$

$a^0 = 1$

Raising a power to a power

$(a^m)^n = a^{mn}$

Fractional indices correspond to roots

$$a^{\frac{1}{n}} = \sqrt[n]{a} \qquad a^{\frac{m}{n}} = (\sqrt[n]{a})^m = \sqrt[n]{a^m}$$

2 Algebraic Expressions

Before starting this chapter you will need to know

- how to work with indices.

2.1 Algebraic expressions

Algebraic expressions can be of many forms, for example

$$3x^2 - 2x - 1 \qquad 3x^2 + 2x + \frac{1}{x} \qquad -6x^2y - 2 \qquad \frac{3x^2 + 2x}{x^2 - 3}$$

A **term** consists of products of numbers and letters, so $3x^2$, $-6x^2y$ are terms.

The number multiplying the letters is the **coefficient** of the term.

$3x^2$	$-2x$	-1
x^2 term Coefficient is 3	x term Coefficient is -2	Constant term is -1

2.2 Function notation

Many relationships are studied in mathematics, for example, $y = 3x^2 - x$, $y = 2^x$ and $y = \sin x$. All such relationships can be written using function notation. One commonly used notation is

$$f(x) = 3x^2 - x$$

Read this as: f of x equals $3x^2 - x$.

Functions are dealt with more fully in Chapter 10. It is useful, however, to be familiar with the notation at an early stage.

Example 1

Evaluate $f(x) = 3x^2 - x$ for given values of x.

a $x = 4$

$f(4) = 3 \times 4^2 - 4 = 44$

f(4) means evaluate the function with $x = 4$.

b $x = -\frac{1}{2}$

$$f(-\tfrac{1}{2}) = 3 \times (-\tfrac{1}{2})^2 - (-\tfrac{1}{2})$$
$$= \tfrac{3}{4} + \tfrac{1}{2}$$
$$= \tfrac{5}{4}$$

Replace x by $-\frac{1}{2}$.

c $x = a$

$f(a) = 3a^2 - a$

Replace x by a.

d $x = a + h$

$$f(a + h) = 3(a + h)^2 - (a + h)$$

Replace x by $a + h$ and simplify.

$$= 3(a^2 + 2ah + h^2) - a - h$$

$$= 3a^2 + 6ah + 3h^2 - a - h$$

EXERCISE 2a

1 Given that $f(x) = x^2 - 2x$, find the values of

a $f(9)$ **b** $f(-4)$ **c** $f(\frac{1}{2})$ **d** $f(n)$ **e** $f(3k)$ **f** $f(a + 1)$

2 Given that $g(x) = x^3 + 1$, find the values of

a $g(0)$ **b** $g(5)$ **c** $g(\frac{3}{4})$ **d** $g(-2)$

e $g(1)$ **f** $g(-1)$ **g** $g(a)$ **h** $g(3k)$

3 Given that $f(x) = x^2$, express as simply as possible

a $f(5 + h)$ **b** $\frac{f(5 + h) - f(5)}{h}$ $(h \neq 0)$ **c** $\frac{f(a + h) - f(a)}{h}$ $(h \neq 0)$

2.3 Polynomials

A polynomial in x has the form

$$a_n x^n + a_{n-1} x^{n-1} + a_{n-2} x^{n-2} + \cdots + a_2 x^2 + a_1 x + a_0$$

where all the coefficients, $a_0, a_1, a_2, \ldots a_{n-1}, a_n$, are constants (not all of them zero) and n is a positive integer (i.e. $n \in \mathbb{Z}^+$).

The **degree** of the polynomial is the highest power of x.

✓ ***Note*** If $a_n \neq 0$ in the polynomial above, the polynomial is of degree n.

A polynomial of degree 1 is called **linear**
degree 2 is called **quadratic**
degree 3 is called **cubic**
degree 4 is called **quartic**.

For example, $4x^7 + 3x^2 - 2x + 1$ is a polynomial in x of degree 7. The polynomial has four terms. It is expressed in *descending* powers of x (highest power of x first). In *ascending* powers of x, it would be written as $1 - 2x + 3x^2 + 4x^7$. The x^2 term is $3x^2$; the coefficient of the x^2 term is 3.

Adding and subtracting polynomials

Only like terms (those with identical letters and powers) can be added or subtracted. So

- $3x^2y - 7x^2y = -4x^2y$
- $3x^2 - 7x$ cannot be expressed as a single term, and
- $3a^2b - b^2 - 2ab + 2b^2 + 5a^2b + 7b = 8a^2b + b^2 - 2ab + 7b$

Multiplication of polynomials

When expressions in two brackets are multiplied, *each* term in the first bracket must multiply *each* term in the second bracket.

So $(a+b+c)(d+e) = a(d+e) + b(d+e) + c(d+e)$
$= ad + ae + bd + be + cd + ce$

Example 2 Expand the brackets (two terms in each bracket)

> Be methodical: multiply
> - **f**irst term in each bracket
> - **o**uter pair
> - **i**nner pair
> - **l**ast pair term in each bracket.
>
> ***Remember*** **FOIL**

a $(3x-1)(4x+3) = 12x^2 + 9x - 4x - 3$
$= 12x^2 + 5x - 3$

b $(x+y)(3x-y) = 3x^2 - xy + 3xy - y^2$
$= 3x^2 + 2xy - y^2$

c $(x+4)(x-4) = x^2 - 4x + 4x - 16$
$= x^2 - 16$

> The first line of working can be omitted, if the two middle terms can be combined mentally.

Expressions like $x^2 - 16$ are called **difference of squares**: $x^2 - y^2 = (x+y)(x-y)$.

Example 3 Expand the brackets in $(x+1)(2x-1)(x+5)$.

> With three brackets, multiply any two first and then multiply their product by the third bracket.

$(x+1)(2x-1)(x+5)$
$= (x+1)(2x^2 + 9x - 5)$
$= x(2x^2 + 9x - 5) + (2x^2 + 9x - 5)$
$= 2x^3 + 9x^2 - 5x + 2x^2 + 9x - 5$
$= 2x^3 + 11x^2 + 4x - 5$

> Collect like terms.

Example 4 If $\mathrm{f}(x) = 3 - x + 2x^3$ and $\mathrm{g}(x) = 7 - x^2 + 5x^3$, find

a $-2x\,\mathrm{f}(x)$ **b** $\mathrm{f}(x) + \mathrm{g}(x)$ **c** $\mathrm{f}(x) - \mathrm{g}(x)$
d $\mathrm{f}(x)\mathrm{g}(x)$ **e** $4x - (x-2)\mathrm{g}(x)$.

Solution

a $-2x\,\mathrm{f}(x) = -2x(3 - x + 2x^3)$
$= -6x + 2x^2 - 4x^4$

> Each term in the bracket is multiplied by $-2x$.

b $\mathrm{f}(x) + \mathrm{g}(x) = (3 - x + 2x^3) + (7 - x^2 + 5x^3)$
$= 3 - x + 2x^3 + 7 - x^2 + 5x^3$
$= 10 - x - x^2 + 7x^3$

> Brackets not necessary here; they show, however, the two expressions being added.

c $\mathrm{f}(x) - \mathrm{g}(x) = (3 - x + 2x^3) - (7 - x^2 + 5x^3)$
$= 3 - x + 2x^3 - 7 + x^2 - 5x^3$
$= -4 - x + x^2 - 3x^3$

> Brackets are needed here for $\mathrm{g}(x)$ because of the preceding − sign. Remove brackets. Each term in the second bracket is multiplied by −1.

d $\mathrm{f}(x)\mathrm{g}(x) = (3 - x + 2x^3)(7 - x^2 + 5x^3)$
$= 3(7 - x^2 + 5x^3) - x(7 - x^2 + 5x^3) + 2x^3(7 - x^2 + 5x^3)$
$= 21 - 3x^2 + 15x^3 - 7x + x^3 - 5x^4 + 14x^3 - 2x^5 + 10x^6$
$= 21 - 7x - 3x^2 + 30x^3 - 5x^4 - 2x^5 + 10x^6$

✓ ***Note*** Substituting a value for x such as $x = 1$ in the first and the last line of Example 4d will give some indication of whether the answer is correct.

e $4x - (x-2)g(x)$

$= 4x - (x-2)(7 - x^2 + 5x^3)$

$= 4x - [x(7 - x^2 + 5x^3) - 2(7 - x^2 + 5x^3)]$

$= 4x - (7x - x^3 + 5x^4 - 14 + 2x^2 - 10x^3)$

$= 4x - (7x - 11x^3 + 5x^4 - 14 + 2x^2)$

$= 4x - 7x + 11x^3 - 5x^4 + 14 - 2x^2$

$= -5x^4 + 11x^3 - 2x^2 - 3x + 14$

All of $(x-2)(7 - x^2 + 5x^3)$ is being subtracted so it must be evaluated within a bracket.

Example 5 Find the coefficient of x^3 in the expansion of $(x^2 + 3x + 4)(3x^2 - 2x - 7)$.

$(x^2 + 3x + 4)(3x^2 - 2x - 7)$

x^3 term $= x^2 \times (-2x) + 3x \times 3x^2$

$= -2x^3 + 9x^3$

$= 7x^3$

So the coefficient of the x^3 term is 7.

The term in x^3 will come from two products

$x^2 \times -2x$ and $3x \times 3x^2$

from 1st bracket, from 2nd bracket, from 1st bracket, from 2nd bracket

The other terms in the multiplication can be ignored in this case.

➤ **Useful products and factorisations**

$a(b+c) = ab + ac$

$(a+b)(c+d) = ac + ad + bc + bd$ $\quad (x+a)(x+b) = x^2 + (a+b)x + ab$

$(a+b)(a-b) = a^2 - b^2$

$(a+b)^2 = a^2 + 2ab + b^2$ $\quad (a+b)^3 = a^3 + 3a^2b + 3ab^2 + b^3$

$(a-b)^2 = a^2 - 2ab + b^2$ $\quad (a-b)^3 = a^3 - 3a^2b + 3ab^2 - b^3$

$a^3 - b^3 = (a-b)(a^2 + ab + b^2)$

$a^3 + b^3 = (a+b)(a^2 - ab + b^2)$

Note: $a^2 + b^2$ *cannot* be factorised.

$a^2 - b^2$ is the **difference of squares**.

Example 6 Expand brackets for squares and the difference of squares.

a $(x+2)^2 = x^2 + 4x + 4$

Parts **a**, **b** and **c** use $(a \pm b)^2 = a^2 \pm 2ab + b^2$.

b $(2x+3)^2 = (2x)^2 + 2 \times 2x \times 3 + 3^2$

$= 4x^2 + 12x + 9$

c $(5x-3)^2 = (5x)^2 + 2 \times 5x \times (-3) + (-3)^2$

$= 25x^2 - 30x + 9$

d $(2x-3)(2x+3) = (2x)^2 - 3^2$

$= 4x^2 - 9$

Part **d** uses the difference of squares.

EXERCISE 2b

1 Express these polynomials in descending powers of x and state their degree.

a $2x^3 - x + x^4 - 5$ **b** $1 + 3x^3 - x^5$ **c** $6x^4 - 2x^2 - x^3$ **d** -10

2 For the polynomials in Question 1 state the coefficient of the x^3 term and the constant term.

3 Simplify, by collecting like terms

a $7x + 3y^3 - 2xy + 2xy - 5x - 6y^3$

b $2x^2 - 4xy + 3y^2 - (8x^2 - 2xy + 6y^2)$

c $(2x^3 + 5x) - (3x^2 + 2x) + (x^3 - 6x) - (x + 4x^2)$

d $5ab + 6a^2b - 7ab^2 + 2a^2b - 3ab$

4 Expand and simplify

a $(x + 1)^2$ **b** $(x + 2)^2$ **c** $(2x + 1)^2$

d $(x - 5)^2$ **e** $(x + 1)(x + 2)$ **f** $(x + 3)(x + 4)$

g $(x + 3)(x - 4)$ **h** $(x - 2)(x + 1)$ **i** $(2x + 1)(x + 1)$

j $(x - 4)(3x - 2)$ **k** $(4x - 3)(4x + 3)$ **l** $(x - 2)(x + 2)$

5 Expand and simplify

a $(2a + 1)(a - 3)$ **b** $(4d + 3e)(d + 2e)$ **c** $(2 - x)(3 - 4x)$

d $(8 - 7w)(8w - 7)$ **e** $(3l - 5)(3l + 5)$ **f** $(3x + 4)^2$

g $(2h + 5)(2h - 7)$ **h** $(5x + 7)(2x - 3)$ **i** $(2x + 1)(3x + 4)$

j $(2 - 7x)(2 + 7x)$ **k** $(2y - 3)^2$ **l** $(b^2 + 4)(4 - b^2)$

m $(x - 1)^3$ **n** $\left(a^{\frac{1}{2}} - b^{\frac{1}{2}}\right)\left(a^{\frac{1}{2}} + b^{\frac{1}{2}}\right)$

6 Expand and simplify

a $(k + 7)(2k + 3) + (2k + 1)(k - 1)$ **b** $(m + 2)(3m - 1) - (m + 3)(m - 4)$

c $(s + 4)(3s - 2) + (2s - 1)^2$ **d** $(v - 3)^2 + (v + 3)^2$

e $4(y - 1)^2 - 2(y + 3)^2 - (2y + 1)^2$

7 Given that, $f(x) = x^2 + 3x - 1$, and $g(x) = x^3 - 2x^2 + 5$, find

a $f(x) + g(x)$ **b** $f(x) - g(x)$ **c** $f(x)g(x)$

d $(x + 1)f(x)$ **e** $(f(x))^2$ **f** $3x f(x) - 2g(x)$

8 If $f(x)$ and $g(x)$ are polynomials of degree 7 and 8 respectively, state the degree of

a $f(x) + g(x)$ **b** $(f(x))^2$ **c** $f(x)g(x)$

9 Find the coefficient of the x^2 term in these expansions. (Do not work out all the terms.)

a $(x^2 + 2x - 1)(x^2 + 3x + 4)$ **b** $(2x^2 - x + 4)(x^2 + x + 3)$

c $(x^3 - 2x + 2)(4x^2 + 3x - 1)$ **d** $(4 - x - x^2)(2 + x - x^2)$

10 Given that $f(x) = 3x^2 - x + 2$, and $g(x) = 7x^4 - 2x^3 + x^2 + 1$, find

a $f(x) + g(x)$ **b** $f(x) - 2g(x)$ **c** $f(x)g(x)$ **d** $x^3f(x) + x\,g(x)$

11 Find the coefficient of the x^3 term in these expansions.

a $(x^4 + 3x^2 - 2x + 1)(x^3 - 2x^2 + x - 7)$

b $(2x^3 - x^2 + 5x - 4)(-x^3 + 4x^2 + 2x + 1)$

12 Expand and simplify

a $(7x^2 + 5x - 1)(6x^3 - 3x^2 + 2x + 4)$ **b** $(x^2 + 2xy + y^2)(x^2 - 2xy + y^2)$

c $(y^3 + 3y^2 - 2y - 2)(4y^4 - 2y + 7)$ **d** $(u^3 + v^2 - 2w)^2$

e $(3xy + 1)(2x^2 - 3y)$ **f** $(2x + 1)(3x - 1)(2x + 7)$

2.4 Factors, including highest common factors

A **factor** divides exactly into an integer or algebraic expression.

When a factor divides into two or more integers or algebraic expressions it is called a **common factor**.

So 5 is a common factor of 10, 15, 20
a^2b is a common factor of a^2b^2, a^3bc

The **highest common factor (HCF)** of two (or more) integers or algebraic expressions is the largest factor common to both (or all).

The common factors of 12, 42, and 54 are 1, 2, 3 and 6.

So the HCF is 6.

6 is the largest of all the common factors.

The common factors of a^2bc and a^2b^3 are 1, a, ab, a^2b.

So the HCF is a^2b.

The HCF is the expression with the highest powers of a and b.

Example 7 Find the HCF of numbers.

a 14 and 24

$14 = 2 \times 7$

$24 = 2 \times 12$

The HCF of 14 and 24 is 2.

The only common factor is 2.
This can be seen by inspection.
7 and 12 share no common factor.

b 9 and 25

The HCF of 9 and 25 is 1, because 9 and 25 have no common factor other than 1.

✓ *Note* Any numbers whose HCF is 1 are called **co-prime**.

c 56, 168 and 140

To find the HCF of 56, 168 and 140, first express each integer as the product of prime numbers.

$56 = 8 \times 7$

$= 2^3 \times 7$

$168 = 7 \times 24$

$= 7 \times 8 \times 3$

$= 2^3 \times 3 \times 7$

$140 = 10 \times 14$

$= 2^2 \times 5 \times 7$

$56 = 2^3 \times 7$
$168 = 2^3 \times 3 \times 7$
$140 = 2^2 \times 5 \times 7$

$\text{HCF} = 2^2 \times 7$

$= 28$

The highest power of 2 which appears in every number is 2^2.
The other factor which appears in every number is 7.
So $2^2 \times 7$ is the HCF (the product of the highest powers).

The HCF of 56, 168 and 140 is 28.

✓ *Note* Expressing integers as the product of prime factors is helped by using divisibility tests (see Glossary, page 477).

Example 8 Find the HCF of algebraic expressions.

a $21a^4x^2$, $35a^2x^4$ and $28a^3x$

The HCF of 21, 35 and 28 is 7. — First look at the coefficients.

The highest power of a which divides into a^4, a^2 and a^3 is a^2. — Then a.

The highest power of x which divides into x^2, x^4 and x is x. — Then x.

So HCF is $7a^2x$.

b $12(x^2 - 4)$, $6x - 12$ and $18x - 24 - 3x^2$ — The expressions must first be factorised.

$$12(x^2 - 4) = 12(x - 2)(x + 2)$$

$$6x - 12 = 6(x - 2)$$

$$18x - 24 - 3x^2 = 3(6x - 8 - x^2)$$

$$= 3(2 - x)(x - 4)$$

$$= 3(x - 2)(4 - x)$$

Multiplying both brackets by -1 does not alter the value of the expression.

So the HCF is $3(x - 2)$.

The HCF of 12, 6 and 3 is 3. $(x - 2)$ is a factor of each expression.

2.5 Multiples, including lowest common multiples

An integer or algebraic expression divides into its **multiples** exactly.

A **common multiple** of two (or more) numbers or algebraic expressions is one into which both (or all) divide exactly. So

- common multiples of 4 and 6 are 12, 24, 36, ...
- common multiples of a^2 and ab^2 are a^2b^2, a^3b^2, a^3b^3, $6a^2b^2$, ...

The **lowest (or least) common multiple (LCM)** of two (or more) integers or algebraic expressions is the lowest multiple common to both (or all).

- The LCM of 4 and 6 is 12, since 12 is the lowest of the common multiples.
- The LCM of a^2 and ab^2 is a^2b^2. This is the expression with the lowest powers of a and b into which a^2 and, separately, ab^2 can be divided.

Example 9 Find the LCM of numbers.

21, 35 and 28

$21 = 3 \times 7$ — To be a multiple of 21, the LCM must contain the factors 3 and 7.

$35 = 5 \times 7$ — To be a multiple of 35, the LCM must contain 5 and 7.

$28 = 2^2 \times 7$ — To be a multiple of 28, the LCM must contain 2^2 and 7.

$\text{LCM} = 2^2 \times 3 \times 5 \times 7 = 420$ — The least set of factors required for a multiple of 21, 35 and 28 is $2^2 \times 3 \times 5 \times 7$.

Example 10 Find the LCM of algebraic expressions.

$21a^4x^2y$, $35a^2x^4y$ and $28a^3x^3y^3$

The LCM of 21, 35, 28 is 420 (see Example 9).

The lowest power of a divisible by a^4, a^2 and a^3 is a^4.

The lowest power of x divisible by x^2, x^4 and x^3 is x^4.

The lowest power of y divisible by y, y and y^3 is y^3.

So the LCM is $420a^4x^4y^3$.

Some uses of HCFs and LCMs

- HCFs are used when cancelling fractions, and in factorising.
- LCMs are used when adding and subtracting fractions.

EXERCISE 2c

1 Find the HCF and LCM of

a 12, 15 **b** 7, 8 **c** 30, 36, 40

d 10, 12, 14 **e** 21, 30, 35 **f** 9, 14, 25

2 Find the HCF and LCM of

a $a(a+b)$, $b(a+b)$ **b** xy, x^3y^2

c $2x^3$, $4x^2y$ **d** $3ab^3$, $2a^2b$

e cd^5, $4c^3d$ **f** $2cd$, $4c^2$, $6abc$

g $12ab^2c$, $8a^2b^4$, $4a^3bc^2$ **h** $51p^4q^2r^3$, $34p^2r^5$, $17p^3r^4$

i $(3x+1)(2x-1)$, $x^2(3x+1)$ **j** $2x(x+1)(x-1)$, $x^2(x-1)$

k $ab^2(b+c)$, $a^2b(b+c)^2$ **l** $4(a+b)(c+d)$, $12(c+d)$

Cancelling fractions

To reduce a fraction to its **lowest terms**, divide the numerator and denominator by their HCF.

Example 11

a $\frac{16}{24} = \frac{2}{3}$

The HCF of 16 and 24 is 8. Divide numerator and denominator by 8.

b $\frac{6a^2b}{9ab^2} = \frac{2a}{3b}$

The HCF of $6a^2b$ and $9ab^2$ is $3ab$. Divide numerator and denominator by $3ab$.

c $\frac{x^2+xy}{xy+y^2} = \frac{x(x+y)}{y(x+y)} = \frac{x}{y}$

Numerator and denominator must be factorised first. Divide both by their HCF, $(x+y)$.

d $\frac{a-b}{b-a} = \frac{-(b-a)}{b-a} = -1$

Note: $a-b = -(b-a)$
Cancel $b-a$.

2.6 Factorising

In algebra, factorising is the reverse process of multiplying out brackets, i.e. putting into brackets. If there is a factor, common to all terms (the HCF of all the terms), it can be taken outside a bracket.

Example 12

a $x^2 + 2x = x(x + 2)$

b $3x^2 - 12x^2y + 9xz$

$= 3x(x - 4xy + 3z)$

$3x$ is the HCF of the terms $3x^2$, $12x^2y$ and $9xz$.

c $\frac{1}{4}\pi r^2 + \frac{1}{3}\pi rh$

$= \frac{1}{12}\pi r(3r + 4h)$

When the coefficients contain fractions the factor taken outside the bracket should be chosen so that there will be no fractions inside the bracket. (The denominator, 12, is the LCM of 4 and 3.)

d $(3m - 2n)^2 - 5n(3m - 2n)$

$= (3m - 2n)(3m - 2n - 5n)$

$= (3m - 2n)(3m - 7n)$

The two parts have a common factor $(3m - 2n)$.

Example 13

This example shows how looking for common factors can make calculations easier.

$16 \times 14 + 19 \times 14 - 15 \times 14 = 14(16 + 19 - 15)$

$= 14 \times 20 = 280$

14 is the HCF of the three terms.

EXERCISE 2d

1 Cancel to lowest terms (*without* using a calculator)

a $\frac{8}{24}$ **b** $\frac{17}{51}$ **c** $\frac{30}{81}$ **d** $\frac{14}{91}$ **e** $\frac{105}{147}$ **f** $\frac{99}{264}$ **g** $\frac{345}{405}$ **h** $\frac{252}{1728}$

2 Cancel to lowest terms

a $\dfrac{10x^2}{5x}$ **b** $\dfrac{2ab}{4a}$ **c** $\dfrac{6a^2b}{3a \times 2b}$ **d** $\dfrac{6x^2}{3xy}$

e $\dfrac{abc^2}{a^2bc}$ **f** $\dfrac{18p^4q^2}{27q^2}$ **g** $\dfrac{12a^2b^3c^2}{8ab^2c}$ **h** $\dfrac{x^2yz^3}{x^3y^2z}$

i $\dfrac{(3x + 1)(x - 2)}{(x - 2)(x + 1)}$ **j** $\dfrac{x - 4}{4 - x}$ **k** $\dfrac{2x^2(x + y)}{(x + y)(x - y)}$ **l** $\dfrac{16x(x + 1)}{24x^2(x + 1)}$

3 Factorise, where possible, by taking out the HCF.

a $b^2 - b^3$ **b** $a^2 + ab$ **c** $5a^2 - 10a$

d $y^5 - y^4$ **e** $18c^3 - 9cd^2$ **f** $4a^2 - 16a^2b$

g $81x - 54$ **h** $3x^3 - 6x^2 + 9x$ **i** $4x^3 + x^2 - x$

j $2a^3 - 4a^2 - 2a$ **k** $7a^2 - 7a^2b + 14ab^3$ **l** $3x^4y - 6x^3y^2 + 9x^2y^3$

4 Factorise, where possible, by taking out the HCF.

a $\frac{1}{2}g^2h + \frac{1}{2}ghj$ **b** $\frac{1}{2}ah + \frac{1}{2}bh$

c $\frac{1}{3}l^2m - \frac{2}{3}lm^2$ **d** $\frac{4}{3}\pi r^3 + \frac{1}{2}\pi r^2h$

5 Without a calculator, use factors to find

a $34 \times 48 + 34 \times 52$ **b** $61 \times 87 - 61 \times 85$

c $29 \times 31 + 29 \times 104 - 29 \times 35$ **d** $16.14 \times 19 - 16.14 \times 9$

e $3.5^2 - 3.5 \times 0.5$ **f** $158 \times 7 + 158 \times 3$

g $\frac{3}{4} \times 134 - \frac{3}{4} \times 94$ **h** $27 \times 354 + 27 \times 646$

Factorising by grouping

Some expressions can be factorised by grouping the terms in pairs.

Example 14 Factorise $2ac + ad - 2bc - bd$.

There are two ways of grouping the terms: $(2ac + ad) - (2bc + bd)$ or $(2ac - 2bc) + (ad - bd)$

$2ac + ad - 2bc - bd$ — Each pair has a common factor. Take the common factor out.

$= a(2c + d) - b(2c + d)$ — Take care with the signs. The same bracket, $(2c + d)$, appears.

$= (2c + d)(a - b)$ — $(2c + d)$ is a common factor so it can be taken outside a bracket.

Alternatively

$2ac - 2bc + ad - bd$ — Here the terms are grouped in different pairs.

$= 2c(a - b) + d(a - b)$ — Take the common factor out of each pair.

$= (a - b)(2c + d)$ — $(a - b)$ is a common factor and can be taken outside a bracket.

✓ ***Note*** Not all expressions with four terms can be factorised by grouping.
The method will work if, and only if, after grouping and taking out the common factors, the same bracket appears, as it does in Example 14.

Factorising a quadratic expression of the form $ax^2 + bx + c$

The technique of factorising a quadratic expression (i.e. putting it into brackets using integers) requires plenty of practice, good facility with number and some trial and error but is a skill worth acquiring.

The methods given here are a *suggested* approach to factorising. Once the skill has been acquired, many factorisable quadratic expressions can be factorised without consciously applying a method. Aids and short cuts are available: the quadratic equation formula can be used (see pages 62 and 70) as can calculators and computer software.

✓ ***Note*** Most quadratic expressions cannot be factorised with integers.
Check that the expression is either in ascending or descending powers of x, and rearrange if necessary.
Always check that the factorisation is correct by multiplying out the brackets.

Before considering all the possible cases of factorising quadratic expressions, here are some observations on the signs and the numbers.

Numbers

$x^2 + (p + q)x + pq = (x + p)(x + q)$

The **coefficient** of the x term, $(p + q)$, is the *sum* of the constant terms in the brackets.

The **constant term**, pq, is the *product* of the constant terms in the brackets.

Signs

When the second sign of the quadratic is +, both brackets will contain the *same* sign:

- both + if the first sign is +
- both − if the first sign is −

The middle number, 5, is the *sum* of 2 and 3; and 6 is the *product* of 2 and 3.

$x^2 + 5x + 6 = (x + 2)(x + 3)$

$x^2 - 5x + 6 = (x - 2)(x - 3)$

$6 + 5x + x^2 = (2 + x)(3 + x)$

$6 - 5x + x^2 = (2 - x)(3 - x)$

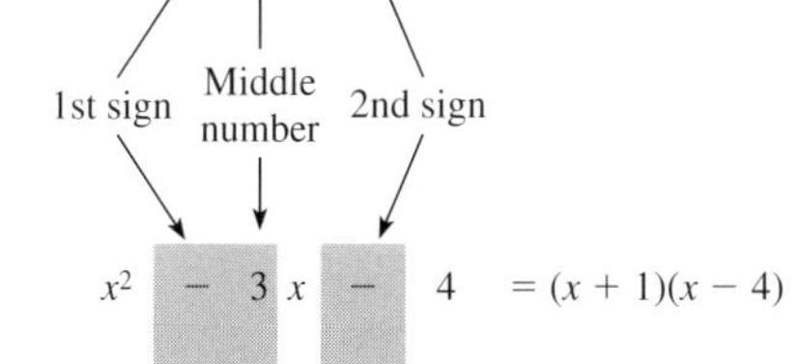

When the second sign is −, the brackets will contain *different* signs, one +, one −.

The middle number, 3, is the *difference* between 1 and 4, and 4 is the *product* of 1 and 4.

$x^2 - 3x - 4 = (x + 1)(x - 4)$

$x^2 + 3x - 4 = (x - 1)(x + 4)$

$4 + 3x - x^2 = (1 + x)(4 - x)$

$4 - 3x - x^2 = (1 - x)(4 + x)$

In factorising $ax^2 + bx + c$ different techniques are required depending on the values of a, b and c. These are illustrated in Examples 15 to 20.

Example 15

$c = 0$.

No constant term. Take the common factor outside the bracket.

$3x^2 - 12x = 3x(x - 4)$

$3x$ is the common factor and is put outside the bracket.

✓ ***Remember*** This type of expression occurs frequently: be on the lookout for it.

Example 16

$b = 0$.

No x term. This type can only be factorised if of the form $a^2 - b^2$ (difference of squares). $a^2 + b^2$ cannot be factorised.

a $x^2 - 16 = x^2 - 4^2$

$= (x - 4)(x + 4)$

Difference of squares: $a^2 - b^2 = (a - b)(a + b)$

b $25x^2 - 9y^2 = (5x)^2 - (3y)^2$

$= (5x + 3y)(5x - 3y)$

Difference of squares: $a^2 - b^2 = (a - b)(a + b)$

c $3x^2 - 12 = 3(x^2 - 4)$

Take out the common factor, 3.

$= 3(x - 2)(x + 2)$

Then use difference of squares.

d $x^2 + 16$

Cannot be factorised (using real numbers).

Example 17

$a = \pm 1$.

Factorising $x^2 + bx + c$ depends on the signs of b and c.

a $x^2 - 7x + 6$

The thought process is shown below.

1st sign (−), 2nd sign (+)

The brackets will start with x. $(x \quad)(x \quad)$

Second sign is +ve, so both signs in brackets are the *same*.

First sign is −ve, so both signs in brackets −ve. $(x - \quad)(x - \quad)$

Second sign is +ve, so *sum* is needed.
Find two numbers whose product is 6 and whose sum is 7.
Numbers are 1 and 6. $(x-1)(x-6)$

So $x^2 - 7x + 6 = (x-1)(x-6)$

Check by expanding the brackets.

b $x^2 + 5x - 6$

The brackets will start with x. $(x \quad)(x \quad)$

Second sign is −ve, so the signs in the brackets are *different*.
Don't put the signs in yet!

Second sign is −ve, so the *difference* is needed.
Find two numbers whose product is 6 and whose difference is 5.
Numbers are 1 and 6.
Place signs by trial and error. $(x-1)(x+6)$

So $x^2 + 5x - 6 = (x-1)(x+6)$.

Check by expanding the brackets.

c $12 + 4x - x^2$

The brackets will end with x. $(\quad x)(\quad x)$

Second sign is −ve, so the signs in the brackets are *different*.
Don't put signs in yet!

Second sign is −ve, so the *difference* is needed.
Find two numbers whose product is 12 and whose difference is 4.
Numbers are 2 and 6.
Place signs by trial and error. $(6-x)(2+x)$

So $12 + 4x - x^2 = (6-x)(2+x)$.

Check by expanding the brackets.

Example 18

$a \neq \pm 1$ and a is a prime number.

$3x^2 - 11x - 4$

The coefficient of x^2 is 3. Since 3 is prime its only factors are 3 and 1. So the brackets will start with $3x$ and x. $(3x \quad)(x \quad)$

Second sign is −ve, so the signs in the brackets are *different*.
Don't put signs in yet!

The numbers at the ends of the brackets have a product of 4.
They could be 1 and 4, 4 and 1, or 2 and 2.
Try out the possibilities until the correct pair is found. $(3x+1)(x-4)$

So $3x^2 - 11x - 4 = (3x+1)(x-4)$.

Check by expanding the brackets.

Example 19 $a \neq \pm 1$ and c is a prime number, e.g. $6x^2 + 13x - 5 = (2x + 5)(3x - 1)$.

The numbers at the ends of the brackets have a product of 5.
Since 5 is prime, its only factors are 5 and 1.
So the brackets must end with 5 and 1.

Since the second sign is −ve, the brackets will contain different signs.
The numbers at the start of the brackets will have a product of 6.
They could be 1 and 6 or 6 and 1 or 2 and 3 or 3 and 2.

Try out the possibilities until the correct pair is found.

Example 20

This example illustrates the 'worst' case: neither a nor c prime. There are various methods for factorising expressions like this. The one suggested can also be applied to polynomials of the type in Examples 18 and 19.

Neither a nor c prime, e.g. $15x^2 + x - 6$.

Multiply the coefficient of the x^2 term by the constant term. $15 \times -6 = -90$. Find two numbers whose product is -90 and whose sum is $+1$ (the coefficient of the x term). The numbers are $+10$ and -9.

$15x^2 + x - 6$ — Rewrite the x term as $+10x - 9x$.

$= 15x^2 + 10x - 9x - 6$ — Factorise by grouping.

$= 5x(3x + 2) - 3(3x + 2)$ — $(3x + 2)$ is a common factor. Take this outside the bracket.

$= (3x + 2)(5x - 3)$

Note When factorisation is difficult, the formula for solving a quadratic equation can be used. See pages 62 and 70.

Example 21

This example could be done by multiplying out the brackets. A neater method, using difference of squares, is given.

Factorise $(2x + 3)^2 - (2x - 7)^2$.

$(2x + 3)^2 - (2x - 7)^2$ — Using $a^2 - b^2 = (a + b)(a - b)$.

$= (2x + 3 + 2x - 7)(2x + 3 - (2x - 7))$

$= (4x - 4)(2x + 3 - 2x + 7)$

Note the effect of the minus sign outside the bracket when the bracket is removed. $-(2x - 7) = -2x + 7$

$= (4x - 4) \times 10$

$= 4(x - 1) \times 10$

$= 40(x - 1)$

Example 22 Find, *without* using a calculator, $8.91^2 - 1.09^2$.

$8.91^2 - 1.09^2 = (8.91 - 1.09)(8.91 + 1.09)$ — Using $a^2 - b^2 = (a - b)(a + b)$.

$= 7.82 \times 10$

$= 78.2$

Example 23 Factorising polynomials.

a $5x^2 + 56xy + 11y^2$
$= (5x + y)(x + 11y)$

Both brackets will contain a + sign. 5 and 11 are both prime so there are only a few possibilities to try.

b $4x^3 - 6x + 10x^2$
$= 4x^3 + 10x^2 - 6x$
$= 2x(2x^2 + 5x - 3)$
$= 2x(2x - 1)(x + 3)$

Arrange in descending powers of x. Then, take the common factor, $2x$, outside a bracket.

EXERCISE 2e

1 Factorise

a $x^2 - 36x$ **b** $6x^2 - 36x$ **c** $2x^2 - 4x$
d $5x^2 - 2x$ **e** $x^2 + 3x$ **f** $4x^2 + 4x$

2 Factorise, where possible

a $x^2 + 3x + 2$ **b** $x^2 + 8x + 7$ **c** $x^2 + 6x + 8$
d $x^2 + 9x + 8$ **e** $x^2 - 4x + 3$ **f** $x^2 - 8x + 15$
g $x^2 - 12x + 20$ **h** $x^2 - 3x - 4$ **i** $x^2 - 6x - 8$
j $x^2 + 7x - 8$ **k** $x^2 + 3x - 4$ **l** $x^2 - x - 90$
m $x^2 - 3x - 180$ **n** $x^2 + 4x + 5$ **o** $x^2 - 9x - 10$

3 Factorise, where possible

a $3x^2 + 14x + 11$ **b** $3x^2 + 22x + 7$ **c** $2x^2 + 10x + 5$
d $2x^2 + 5x + 2$ **e** $4x^2 + 6x + 2$ **f** $3x^2 + 6x + 3$
g $7x^2 + 47x + 7$ **h** $3x^2 + 7xy + 3y^2$ **i** $5x^2 + 11xy + 2y^2$
j $8p^2 - 14pq + 5q^2$ **k** $6x^2 - 25x + 4$ **l** $48 + 6q^2 - 44q$
m $9 + 10y^2 - 21y$ **n** $6a^2 - 13a + 6$ **o** $5c^2 - 15c + 10$
p $10p^2 - 13p + 5$ **q** $9z^2 - 12z + 4$ **r** $12x^2 - 35x + 3$
s $3x^2 - 3x - 36$ **t** $2 + 25x^2 - 15x$

4 Factorise, where possible

a $a^2 - 5a - 14$ **b** $b^2 + 4b - 21$ **c** $c^2 + 2c - 8$
d $d^2 + 5d - 6$ **e** $e^2 - 5e - 6$ **f** $2f^2 - f - 1$
g $2g^2 + g - 1$ **h** $2h^2 - 2h - 1$ **i** $x^2 + 4xy - 21y^2$
j $3j^2 - 4j + 1$ **k** $2k^2 - 5k - 3$ **l** $15 - 2l - l^2$
m $1 - 2m - 8m^2$ **n** $n^2 + 2np - 8p^2$

5 Factorise, using difference of squares

a $a^2 - 4$ **b** $b^2 - 144$ **c** $c^2 - 9d^2$
d $25e^2 - 16f^2$ **e** $36g^2 - 1$ **f** $49h^2 - 64j^2$
g $16k^2 - 100$ **h** $25l^2 - 225$ **i** $3l^2 - 12$
j $2m^2 - 50n^2$ **k** $9z^4 - a^2$ **l** $e^2f^4g^6 - 121$
m $81h^4 - 16$ **n** $l^8 - 256$ **o** $169 - m^2$

6 Factorise

a $2 + 9z - 5z^2$ **b** $2 - 7y + 5y^2$ **c** $2 - 5w - 3w^2$
d $3 + 5y - 2y^2$ **e** $3 + 2t - 5t^2$ **f** $1 - j - 2j^2$
g $6 + x^2 - 7x$ **h** $2 - x - x^2$ **i** $18 + 3x - x^2$

7 Factorise, where possible

a $f^2 - 4f + 4$ **b** $x^2 + 3x + 2$ **c** $2k^2 - 32$
d $1 + v - 20v^2$ **e** $7x^2 - 7x - 14$ **f** $7 - 28c^2$
g $4h^2 - 24h + 9$ **h** $6 - 7j + 3j^2$ **i** $1 - 9u + 20u^2$
j $ax^2 - 3ax - 4a$ **k** $19s^2 - 27s + 8$ **l** $2l^2 - 12l$
m $10g^2 + 13g + 4$ **n** $6a^2 + 19a - 25$

8 Factorise by grouping

a $my + ny + mz + nz$ **b** $cx + dx - cy - dy$ **c** $5x - 5y - nx + ny$
d $a^2 - ac + ab - bc$ **e** $5a + ab + 5b + b^2$ **f** $6ac - 2cy - 3a + y$
g $x^4 + x^3 + 2x + 2$ **h** $y^3 - y^2 + y - 1$ **i** $ab + b - a - 1$

9 Find, *without* a calculator, the value of

a $36^2 - 34^2$ **b** $102^2 - 98^2$ **c** $42.5^2 - 57.5^2$
d $0.7^2 - 0.3^2$ **e** $48^2 - 52^2$ **f** $1007^2 - 1000^2$

10 Factorise, where possible

a $t^2 - t - 6$ **b** $6t^2 + 11t - 10$ **c** $7 + 40t - 12t^2$
d $6t^2 - 7rt + 2r^2$ **e** $12t^2 - 25t + 12$ **f** $t^2 + 6 - t$
g $6t^2 + tu - 15u^2$ **h** $12t^2 - 12t - 24$ **i** $24t^2 - 2t - 15$
j $24t^2 + 23t - 12$ **k** $5x - 6x^2 + 1$ **l** $6t^2 - 17t + 12$
m $8 - 15t^2 + 14t$ **n** $7 - 28c^2$ **o** $12t^2 - 52t - 8$
p $12t^2 - 23t - 9$ **q** $4t^2 - 23t - 6$ **r** $4t^2 - 12t + 9$
s $4t^2 - 17t + 15$ **t** $4t^2 - 59t - 15$ **u** $100t^2 - 4$

11 Factorise, where possible

a $n^4 - 9n^2$ **b** $\pi R^2 - \pi r^2$ **c** $ax^2 + bx^2 + 2a + 2b$
d $e^4 + 4e^2 + 3$ **e** $6 - d - d^2$ **f** $2x^4 - x^3 + 4x - 2$
g $c^2 - 4d^2$ **h** $4t^2 - 5t - 1$ **i** $2ax + ay + 2bx + by$
j $12t^2 - 18t - 9$ **k** $4t^2 - 8t + 4$ **l** $2 - s + 4s^2$
m $l - 2l^2 - 3l^3$ **n** $x^2 - x - 56$ **o** $12 - 6x^2 - 6x$

EXERCISE 2e *(continued)*

12 Find the HCF and LCM.

a $2a, \quad 3a$

b $ac, \quad bc$

c $2x^2y, \quad 5xy^2$

d $2a+6, \quad 3a+9$

e $3b-3, \quad 4b-4$

f $4a-8d, \quad 6a-12d$

g $a^2-ab, \quad b^2-ab$

h $2abc, \quad 6a^2b, \quad 10bc^2$

i $6ab, \quad 5cd$

j $x^2-3x-10, \quad x^2-6x+5$

k $x^2-5x+6, \quad x^2-x-6$

l $2a-6b, \quad a^2-9b^2$

m $2pq^2, \quad 8p^4q^3$

n $2x^3, \quad 4x^2y$

o $2cd, \quad 4c^2, \quad 6abc$

13 Find the HCF and LCM.

a $c^2-c, \quad (c-1)^2, \quad c^3-1$

b $d+2, \quad d^2-4, \quad d^3+8$

c $15a^2+8a+1, \quad 12a^2+a-1$

d $a^2-ab-2b^2, \quad a^2+3ab+2b^2$

e $x^4-27x, \quad x^4+2x^3-15x^2$

f $x^3-x, \quad 2x^4-3x^3+x^2$

14 Factorise, as fully as possible

a $(x+2)(x-1)-(x+2)^2$

b $x(x+3)-(x+1)(x+3)$

c $(x+1)^2-(x-1)^2$

d $x(x+1)(2x+7)+6(x+1)(x+3)$

e $N^2(N+1)^2+4(N+1)^3$

f $(a+b)^3-3ab(a+b)$

g $x(x+7)^2(3x-1)-x^2(x+7)$

h $(3x+7)^2-(3x+5)^2$

i $(3x+7)^2-(2x+5)^2$

j $(3x+7)^2-(2x+7)^2$

2.7 Fractions

Algebraic fractions can be added, subtracted, multiplied and divided, just like numerical fractions.

Adding and subtracting fractions

Fractions like $\frac{1}{3}$ and $\frac{1}{2}$ can be added only if they are written with the same denominator. Quarters can be added to quarters, thirds to thirds, etc., but before quarters can be added to thirds, the fractions must be expressed with equal denominators.
The same principle applies to algebraic fractions.

$$\frac{a}{b}+\frac{c}{d}=\frac{ad+bc}{bd}$$

Example 24

Add and subtract numerical fractions, using LCMs.

a $\frac{2}{15}+\frac{7}{10}=\frac{2\times 2}{15\times 2}+\frac{7\times 3}{10\times 3}$ — Common denominator is 30, the LCM of 15 and 10.

$=\frac{4}{30}+\frac{21}{30}$ — In all there are 25 thirtieths.

$=\frac{25}{30} \quad =\frac{5}{6}$ — Cancel to lowest terms.

b $173\frac{5}{12} - 108\frac{3}{4} = 64\frac{2}{3}$

Deal with whole numbers separately.

$173 - 108 = 65$

$\frac{5}{12} - \frac{3}{4} = \frac{5-9}{12} = \frac{-4}{12} = -\frac{1}{3}$

Then the fractions.

$65 - \frac{1}{3} = 64\frac{2}{3}$

Example 25

Add and subtract algebraic fractions, using LCMs.

a $\frac{x}{6} + \frac{5x}{21} = \frac{7 \times x}{42} + \frac{2 \times 5x}{42}$

Create equivalent fractions using 42, the LCM of 6 and 21, as the denominator.

$= \frac{7x + 10x}{42}$

$= \frac{17x}{42}$

b $\frac{a}{3x} + \frac{b}{2x} = \frac{2a}{6x} + \frac{3b}{6x} = \frac{2a + 3b}{6x}$

$6x$ is the LCM of $3x$ and $2x$.

c $\frac{3a}{bc} + \frac{2b}{ac} = \frac{3a \times a + 2b \times b}{abc} = \frac{3a^2 + 2b^2}{abc}$

abc is the LCM of bc and ac.

d $\frac{2}{x+1} - \frac{3}{2x+1}$

Common denominator is $(x+1)(2x+1)$.

$= \frac{2(2x+1) - 3(x+1)}{(x+1)(2x+1)}$

Take care of signs when removing brackets.

$= \frac{4x + 2 - 3x - 3}{(x+1)(2x+1)}$

Leave denominator in factors.

$= \frac{x - 1}{(x+1)(2x+1)}$

e $5 - \frac{4}{x+3} + \frac{10}{x^2 - 9}$

$x^2 - 9 = (x+3)(x-3)$.
So LCM of $x + 3$ and $x^2 - 9$ is $x^2 - 9$.

$= \frac{5(x^2 - 9) - 4(x - 3) + 10}{x^2 - 9}$

Take care of signs when removing brackets.

$= \frac{5x^2 - 45 - 4x + 12 + 10}{x^2 - 9}$

$= \frac{5x^2 - 4x - 23}{x^2 - 9}$

The numerator cannot be factorised so no further simplification is possible.

f $5 - \frac{x-2}{3} - \frac{1}{4}(2x+1) - x$

12 is the LCM of 3 and 4.

$= \frac{5 \times 12 - 4(x - 2) - 3(2x + 1) - 12x}{12}$

Take care of signs when removing brackets.

$= \frac{60 - 4x + 8 - 6x - 3 - 12x}{12}$

Collect like terms in the numerator.

$= \frac{65 - 22x}{12}$

Multiplying fractions

The product of two fractions is a fraction whose numerator is the product of the numerators and whose denominator is the product of the denominators.

➤ $$\frac{a}{b} \times \frac{c}{d} = \frac{ac}{bd}$$

Before multiplying, cancel any factor which appears in both the numerator and denominator.

Never cancel part of a bracket, only the whole bracket.

Example 26 Multiply fractions.

a $5\frac{1}{3} \times \frac{3}{8} = \frac{\overset{2}{\cancel{16}}}{\underset{1}{\cancel{3}}} \times \frac{\overset{1}{\cancel{3}}}{\underset{1}{\cancel{8}}} = 2$

Before multiplying, $5\frac{1}{3}$ must be expressed as an improper fraction. 3 and 8 can be cancelled.

b $6 \times \frac{2}{5} = \frac{12}{5} = 2\frac{2}{5}$

Think: 6 lots of two fifths is twelve fifths. $\frac{6}{1} \times \frac{2}{5} = \frac{12}{5}$.
Note: The integer $6 = \frac{6}{1}$, so when multiplying an integer by a fraction only the numerator of the fraction changes.

c $60 \times \frac{3}{4} = \overset{15}{\cancel{60}} \times \frac{3}{\underset{1}{\cancel{4}}} = 45$

4 can be cancelled.

Example 27 Multiply algebraic fractions.

a $\frac{3x}{2y^2} \times \frac{6y}{x^2}$

Numerator and denominator can be divided by x, y and 2.

$$\frac{3\cancel{x}}{{}_1\cancel{2}y^{\cancel{2}}} \times \frac{{}^3\cancel{6}\cancel{y}}{x^{\cancel{2}}} = \frac{9}{xy}$$

b $\frac{x^2 - 4}{xy^2} \times \frac{2xy}{x^2 - 4x + 4}$

Factorise where possible. Cancel x, y, $(x - 2)$.

$$= \frac{(x+2)\cancel{(x-2)}}{\cancel{x}y^{\cancel{2}}} \times \frac{2\cancel{x}\cancel{y}}{(x-2)^{\cancel{2}}} = \frac{2(x+2)}{y(x-2)}$$

Dividing fractions

Dividing by a fraction is equivalent to multiplying by its reciprocal.

- Dividing by 2 is equivalent to multiplying by $\frac{1}{2}$. $6 \div 2 = 6 \times \frac{1}{2} = 3$
- Dividing by $\frac{1}{3}$ is equivalent to multiplying by 3. $6 \div \frac{1}{3} = 6 \times \frac{3}{1} = 18$
- Dividing by $\frac{2}{7}$ is equivalent to multiplying by $\frac{7}{2}$. $8 \div \frac{2}{7} = 8 \times \frac{7}{2} = 28$

Dividing by $\frac{a}{b}$ is equivalent to multiplying by $\frac{b}{a}$.

➤ 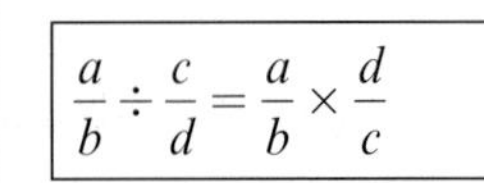

$$\frac{a}{b} \div \frac{c}{d} = \frac{a}{b} \times \frac{d}{c}$$

When dividing fractions, one of two methods is used:

Either numerator and denominator are multiplied by the same number or expression – this does not change the value of the fraction.

Or division by a fraction is replaced by multiplication by its reciprocal.

Example 28

This example shows how fractions can be simplified where numbers are divided.

a $\dfrac{15}{2\frac{1}{2}} = \dfrac{30}{5} = 6$

Numerator and denominator are both multiplied by 2.

b $4\frac{2}{3} \div 3\frac{1}{2} = \dfrac{14}{3} \div \dfrac{7}{2}$

Before dividing, express $4\frac{2}{3}$ and $3\frac{1}{2}$ as improper fractions.

$= \dfrac{^{2}\cancel{14}}{3} \times \dfrac{2}{\cancel{7}_{1}} = \dfrac{4}{3}$

Division by $\frac{7}{2}$ is equivalent to multiplication by $\frac{2}{7}$.

Example 29

This example shows how fractions can be simplified where expressions are divided.

a $\dfrac{a}{\frac{b}{c}} = \dfrac{ac}{b}$

Numerator and denominator are both multiplied by c.

b $\dfrac{\frac{a}{b}}{\frac{c}{d}} = \dfrac{a}{b} \times \dfrac{d}{c} = \dfrac{ad}{bc}$

Division by $\dfrac{c}{d}$ is equivalent to multiplication by $\dfrac{d}{c}$.

c $\dfrac{1}{\frac{x}{y}} = 1 \times \dfrac{y}{x} = \dfrac{y}{x}$

Division by $\dfrac{x}{y}$ is equivalent to multiplication by $\dfrac{y}{x}$.

d $(3x + 2) \div \frac{1}{2} = (3x + 2) \times 2$

$= 2(3x + 2)$

Division by $\frac{1}{2}$ is equivalent to multiplication by 2.

e $\dfrac{7x - 1}{\frac{2}{5}} = \dfrac{5}{2}(7x - 1)$

Division by $\frac{2}{5}$ is equivalent to multiplication by $\frac{5}{2}$.

f $\dfrac{c^2 - 16}{c^2 - 8c + 16} \div \dfrac{2c + 8}{3c - 9}$

Division by $\dfrac{2c + 8}{3c - 9}$ is equivalent to multiplication by $\dfrac{3c - 9}{2c + 8}$.

$= \dfrac{\cancel{(c - 4)}\cancel{(c + 4)}}{\cancel{(c - 4)}(c - 4)} \times \dfrac{3(c - 3)}{2\cancel{(c + 4)}} = \dfrac{3(c - 3)}{2(c - 4)}$

Expressions must be factorised before cancelling.

Example 30

These examples could have been simplified by expressing both numerator and denominator as fractions, and then dividing the numerator by the denominator, i.e. multiplying the numerator by the reciprocal of the denominator. The method used here, though, is much simpler.

a $\dfrac{x + \frac{a^2}{x}}{x - \frac{a^4}{x^3}} = \dfrac{x^4 + a^2x^2}{x^4 - a^4}$

Multiply numerator and denominator by x^3, the LCM of x and x^3.

$= \dfrac{x^2\cancel{(x^2 + a^2)}}{(x^2 - a^2)\cancel{(x^2 + a^2)}}$

Factorise the denominator using difference of squares.

$= \dfrac{x^2}{x^2 - a^2}$

b $\dfrac{\frac{4}{x}+\frac{x}{2}-3}{\frac{x}{6}-\frac{1}{3}-\frac{4}{3x}}=\dfrac{24+3x^2-18x}{x^2-2x-8}$

To remove fractions from the numerator and denominator multiply both by $6x$.

$$=\frac{3(x^2-6x+8)}{(x-4)(x+2)}$$

Factorise the numerator and denominator before cancelling.

$$=\frac{3(x-4)(x-2)}{(x-4)(x+2)}$$

$$=\frac{3(x-2)}{x+2}$$

EXERCISE 2f

This exercise revises numerical fractions. Do not use a calculator.

1 Fill in the missing terms.

a $\dfrac{2}{5}=\dfrac{\square}{10}$ **b** $\dfrac{3}{7}=\dfrac{15}{\square}$ **c** $\dfrac{2}{9}=\dfrac{\square}{810}$

d $\dfrac{3}{2}=\dfrac{\square}{8}$ **e** $2=\dfrac{\square}{8}$

2 Find the value of

a $\frac{6}{7}+\frac{3}{14}$ **b** $\frac{1}{5}-\frac{1}{4}+\frac{1}{10}$ **c** $3\frac{1}{4}+2\frac{4}{9}$

d $3\frac{1}{4}-2\frac{4}{9}$ **e** $\frac{4}{5}+\frac{2}{5}+\frac{7}{10}$ **f** $3\frac{1}{2}+11\frac{2}{5}$

g $7\frac{2}{7}-5\frac{2}{5}$ **h** $107\frac{1}{4}-41\frac{2}{3}$ **i** $1001\frac{1}{3}+98\frac{1}{4}$

3 Simplify

a $12\times\frac{3}{4}$ **b** $\frac{2}{3}\times\frac{9}{8}$ **c** $4\frac{1}{4}\times\frac{8}{51}$

d $2\frac{1}{3}\times4\frac{1}{5}$ **e** $5\frac{2}{3}\times3$ **f** $5\frac{2}{3}\times4\frac{1}{2}$

g $120\times\frac{3}{5}$

4 Simplify

a $1\frac{1}{2}\times1\frac{1}{3}\times1\frac{1}{4}\times1\frac{1}{5}\times1\frac{1}{6}$ **b** $1\frac{2}{3}\times1\frac{2}{5}\times1\frac{2}{7}\times1\frac{2}{9}\times1\frac{2}{11}\times1\frac{2}{13}$

5 Simplify

a $2\frac{2}{5}\div1\frac{1}{3}$ **b** $\frac{3}{10}\div2\frac{2}{5}$ **c** $\frac{3}{4}\div\frac{5}{12}$

d $1\frac{2}{3}\div2$ **e** $2\frac{7}{10}\div7\frac{1}{5}$ **f** $4\frac{1}{3}\div3\frac{1}{4}$

EXERCISE 2g

This exercise involves algebraic fractions.

1 Fill in the missing terms.

a $\dfrac{2c}{ab}=\dfrac{6c^2}{\square}$ **b** $\dfrac{2mn}{\square}=\dfrac{m}{4nt}$ **c** $\dfrac{3a}{2b}=\dfrac{\square}{8bc}$ **d** $2ac=\dfrac{6ace}{\square}$

e $\dfrac{a-b}{3ab}=\dfrac{\square}{6a^2b}$ **f** $\dfrac{3}{17y}=\dfrac{\square}{51y^2}$ **g** $\dfrac{4}{13}=\dfrac{28x}{\square}$

2 Express each of these as a single fraction.

a $\frac{2}{a}+\frac{3}{a}$ **b** $\frac{a}{4}+\frac{a}{3}$ **c** $\frac{6}{x}-\frac{5}{x}$

d $\frac{y}{3}+\frac{y}{4}-\frac{y}{6}$ **e** $\frac{2}{a}-\frac{3}{b}$ **f** $\frac{1}{3x}+\frac{1}{5x}$

g $\frac{1}{4a}-\frac{1}{6a}-3$ **h** $\frac{b}{4}+\frac{3b}{8}+\frac{1}{2}$ **i** $\frac{x}{4}+\frac{5x}{12}-\frac{x}{3}$

j $\frac{x}{yz}+\frac{z}{xy}$ **k** $\frac{m}{n}+\frac{n}{m}$ **l** $\frac{6a^2}{9a}-\frac{b^2}{a^2}$

m $5+\frac{31}{3y}$ **n** $\frac{2}{x-1}-\frac{3}{x+1}$ **o** $\frac{7}{x}+\frac{2}{x+1}+1$

p $\frac{2b}{a}+\frac{a-b}{b}$ **q** $\frac{1}{a+b}+\frac{1}{a-b}$ **r** $\frac{3}{x-2}-\frac{2}{x+2}$

s $\frac{x}{a-x}-\frac{y}{a-y}$ **t** $\frac{u-v}{6}-\frac{u+v}{8}$ **u** $7-\frac{1}{7-x}$

3 Simplify

a $\frac{5}{6}(b-3c)+\frac{3}{8}(4b+3c)$ **b** $\frac{3}{4}(x+4)-\frac{2}{5}(3x-1)$

c $x-\frac{1}{3}(x+3)+\frac{1}{5}(x-2)+2$ **d** $\frac{1}{x+3}+\frac{3}{(x^2-9)}$

e $\frac{3(2x-3y)}{2}-\frac{4(3x+y)}{9}-\frac{3x-17}{18}$ **f** $\frac{6}{x^2-2x-8}+\frac{1}{x^2+5x+6}$

g $\frac{7}{x^2+x-12}-\frac{6}{x^2+2x-8}$ **h** $\frac{p+2}{2}-\frac{p}{p+2}-\frac{p^3-2p^2}{2p^2-8}$

i $\frac{1}{3a-1}+\frac{2}{a-1}+\frac{1}{a}$

4 Simplify

a $\frac{a}{b}\times\frac{b^2}{a^2}$ **b** $\frac{3x}{2y}\times\frac{6x^2y}{5z}$ **c** $\frac{ab^2}{2}\times 6a$

d $3\times\frac{2x^2}{9}$ **e** $3\times\frac{2x^2}{y}$ **f** $3\times\frac{x^2}{2y}$

g $\frac{ab^2}{4c^2d}\times\frac{2cd}{ab}$ **h** $\frac{18ab}{15bc}\times\frac{20ce}{24de}$ **i** $\frac{mn}{2}\times\frac{2}{mn}$

j $\frac{3ab^2}{5b^3c}\times\frac{15b^2c^2}{9a^2b}$ **k** $\frac{a-b}{c}\times\frac{c}{b-a}$ **l** $\frac{6}{a+b}\times\frac{a^2-b^2}{2}$

5 Simplify

a $\frac{m+n}{m}\times\frac{mn}{3m+3n}$ **b** $\frac{a^2-b^2}{ab+a^2}\times\frac{2a^2}{ab-a^2}$

c $\frac{3d^2-12}{9d^2}\times\frac{6d^3}{4d+8}$ **d** $\frac{cd}{c^2+cd}\times\frac{c^2-d^2}{d^4}$

e $\frac{13c^2}{15}\times\frac{16a^4}{39d^3}\times\frac{27d^4}{48a^2b^2c}$ **f** $\frac{a^2-b^2}{x^2-y^2}\times\frac{x+y}{a-b}$

EXERCISE 2g
(continued)

6 Simplify, expressing as a single fraction

a $\dfrac{a}{2b} \div \dfrac{b}{2a}$ **b** $c \div \dfrac{1}{1-d}$

c $\dfrac{12xy^3}{5xy} \div \dfrac{2xz}{3xyz}$ **d** $\dfrac{a^2-4}{a^2-3a+2} \div \dfrac{a}{a-1}$

e $\dfrac{a^2-b^2}{a^2+ab} \div \dfrac{2a-2b}{ab}$ **f** $\dfrac{u^2+3u-10}{3u^2+12u} \div \dfrac{u^2-25}{u^2-u-20}$

7 Simplify, expressing as a single fraction

a $\dfrac{1}{\frac{x}{y}}$ **b** $\dfrac{2}{\frac{a}{b}}$ **c** $\dfrac{1}{a+\frac{b}{c}}$ **d** $\dfrac{1}{\frac{x}{y}-z}$

e $\dfrac{x+1}{1-\frac{1}{x^3}}$ **f** $\dfrac{\frac{1}{b}+\frac{1}{a}}{\frac{a}{b}-\frac{b}{a}}$ **g** $1-\dfrac{1}{a}$ **h** $1-\dfrac{1}{1+\frac{1}{a}}$

i $\dfrac{\frac{2}{x^2}+\frac{3}{x}}{\frac{5}{x^2}-y}$ **j** $\dfrac{2-\frac{4}{x}-\frac{6}{x^2}}{1-\frac{3}{x}-\frac{4}{x^2}}$ **k** $\dfrac{5x-\frac{20}{x}}{3x-3-\frac{6}{x}}$ **l** $\dfrac{1-a^2}{a-1}$

8 Simplify, expressing as a single fraction

a $\dfrac{4x^2}{x^2-3x} \times \dfrac{2(x-3)}{x^3}$ **b** $\dfrac{3+x}{(2-x)(4+x)} \times \dfrac{(x+4)}{6(x+3)}$

c $\dfrac{x^2-1}{x^2-3x+2} \times \dfrac{x^2-4}{2(x+1)}$ **d** $\dfrac{2x+2}{x^2-x-6} \times \dfrac{4x^2+8x-60}{x+1}$

e $\dfrac{x^2-4x+3}{x^2+4x+3} \times \dfrac{x^2+6x+9}{x^2-9}$ **f** $\dfrac{3x^2+x}{x+4} \times \dfrac{x+4}{3x^2-2x-1}$

g $\dfrac{a^2-b^2}{a^2+2ab+b^2} \div \dfrac{4(a^2-ab)}{a^2+ab}$ **h** $\dfrac{x^2+3x+2}{x+3} \div \dfrac{x^2+4x+3}{x+2}$

i $\dfrac{x^2+7x+10}{x^2+3x-18} \div \dfrac{x^2+2x-15}{x^2+8x+12}$ **j** $\dfrac{x^3-xy^2}{(x+y)^2} \div \dfrac{(x-y)^2}{x^2y-y^3}$

EXERCISE 2h
(Extension)

1 Show that

$x^3-1=(x-1)(x^2+x+1)$
$x^4-1=(x-1)(x^3+x^2+x+1)$

Using the formula for the sum of a GP (see page 284) show that

$x^{n+1}-1=(x-1)(x^n+x^{n-1}+\cdots+x^2+x+1)$

2 Factorise $xy+x+y+1$.
Hence show that there are no positive integer solutions to $xy+x+y=30$.

3 Find the HCF of $1144x^n$ and $585x^{2n}$.

4 Simplify

a $x-1+\dfrac{1}{1+x}$ **b** $\dfrac{N(4N^2-1)+3(2N+1)^2}{N+1}$

c $\dfrac{(x+h)^3-x^3}{h}$ **d** $\dfrac{\frac{a}{b}+\frac{c}{d}}{1+\frac{ac}{bd}}$

5 Simplify

a $(x^2+1)^{\frac{1}{2}} - \dfrac{1}{(x^2+1)^{\frac{1}{2}}}$

b $(1+x)^{\frac{1}{3}} - x(1+x)^{-\frac{2}{3}}$

EXERCISE 2i (Miscellaneous)

1 Given $a=3$, $b=\frac{1}{4}$, $c=5$, $d=\frac{2}{7}$ and $e=2$, find the value of these, giving the answer as simply as possible.

a $\dfrac{a+c}{e}$ **b** $\dfrac{a+b}{c}$ **c** $\dfrac{a+c}{b}$ **d** $3d$

e $\dfrac{a+3b}{2d}$ **f** $\dfrac{b}{d}$ **g** $\dfrac{a-c}{c-a}$ **h** $12bcd$

i $b \div e$ **j** $7(b+d)$ **k** $a+b+ab$ **l** $10b^2$

m $\dfrac{12}{d^2}$ **n** $\dfrac{c-e}{e-c}$ **o** $\dfrac{(2b)^2}{3d}$ **p** $\sqrt{a-3b}$

2 Given $a=x+1$, $b=x^2$, $c=\frac{3}{x}$ and $d=4-\frac{1}{x}$, find the value of these, giving the answer as simply as possible.

a bc **b** bd **c** bd^2 **d** $4a-d$

e $c+d$ **f** $\dfrac{c}{d}$ **g** $c(a^2-b-1)$ **h** bc^2

i $\sqrt{b+2a-1}$ **j** $\dfrac{d}{c^2}$ **k** $\dfrac{c+3d}{3c+d}$ **l** $\dfrac{1-b}{a}$

3 Given $x=129$ and $y=71$, use factors to find the value of

a $\dfrac{x^2-y^2}{x-y}$ **b** $\dfrac{x+y}{x^2-y^2}$

c $x^2+2xy+y^2$

4 Simplify

a $\sqrt{(a-b)^2+4ab}$ **b** $\dfrac{2T-2t}{T^2-t^2}$

c $\dfrac{1-\frac{1}{t}}{1-t}$ **d** $\dfrac{T-t}{\frac{1}{T}-\frac{1}{t}}$

5 Express each of these as a single fraction.

a $\dfrac{1}{(x-h)^2} - \dfrac{1}{(x+h)^2}$ **b** $\dfrac{2}{(N+1)(N+3)} - \dfrac{2N+3}{(N+1)(N+2)}$

c $\dfrac{2n+1}{n^2(n+1)^2} - \dfrac{1}{n^2}$ **d** $\dfrac{1}{a+1} + \dfrac{2}{a-1} + \dfrac{3}{a^2-1}$

Test yourself

1 The degree of the polynomial $4x^6 + 7x^4 - \frac{1}{9}x^3 + x^2 - 12$ is

A 4 **B** 7 **C** 6 **D** 5 **E** 24

2 The sum of $a^3 + a^2b - ab^2 + 2$ and $2a^3 + 2a^2b - 4$ is

A $2a^6 + 2a^4b^2 - ab^2 - 2$ **B** $2a^6 + 4a^5b - 2a^3b^3 + 4ab^2 - 8$

C $3a^3 + 3a^2b - ab^2 - 2$ **D** $2a^9 - 8$

E $3a^6 + 3a^4b^2 - ab^2 - 8$

3 The highest common factor of $72a^3bc^2$ and $16ab^2d$ is

A $1152a^4b^3c^2d$ **B** $8abc^2d$ **C** $144a^3b^2c^2d$

D $8ab$ **E** 8

4 If $f(y) = 2 - y - 2y^2$ and $g(y) = 3y^2 - 2y + 4$, then $f(y)g(y)$ is equal to

A $-5y^2 + y - 2$ **B** $8 + 2y^2 - 6y^4$ **C** $-(6y^4 + 7y^3 + 4y^2 + 8y - 8)$

D $-6y^4 + y^3 - 8y + 8$ **E** $y^2 - 3y + 6$

5 The complete factorisation of $2p^3 - 2p^2 - 4p$ is

A $2(p^3 - p^2 - 2p)$ **B** $2p(p + 1)(p - 2)$ **C** 0, −1 or 2

D $4p^3\left(\frac{1}{2} - \frac{1}{2p} - \frac{1}{p^2}\right)$ **E** $2p^2(-3p - 1)$

6 The lowest common multiple of $6kl^2p$ and $15k^2mp$ is

A $3kp$ **B** $30k^2l^2mp$ **C** $90k^3l^2mp^2$ **D** $90klmp$ **E** $30k^2p$

7 $(3r + 1)(r - 2) - (r - 2)(r + 1)$ is equivalent to

A $2r^2 - 6r - 4$ **B** $-3r^4 + 8r^3 + 3r^2 - 12r - 4$ **C** $2r^2 - 4r$

D $2(r + 1)(r - 2)$ **E** 0

8 $\dfrac{pq - 2q}{p^2q - 4q}$ is equivalent to

A $\dfrac{1}{4 - p}$ **B** $\dfrac{2 - p}{2p}$ **C** $\dfrac{q - 2}{p(q - 4)}$ **D** $\dfrac{p - 2q}{p^2 - 4}$ **E** $\dfrac{1}{p + 2}$

9 $\dfrac{2z}{3(z - 1)} \div \dfrac{4z}{z^2 - 1}$ is equal to

A $\dfrac{8z^2}{3(z - 1)(z^2 - 1)}$ **B** $\dfrac{1}{3z}$ **C** $\dfrac{z - 1}{6}$

D $\dfrac{z + 1}{6}$ **E** $\dfrac{z^2 - 1}{6z - 1}$

10 $\dfrac{1}{2 - x} - \dfrac{2}{1 - x}$ is equal to

A -1 **B** $\dfrac{x - 3}{(x - 1)(x - 2)}$ **C** $-\dfrac{1}{(2 - x)(1 - x)}$

D $-\dfrac{1}{2} + x$ **E** $-\dfrac{3}{x - 2}$

Key points

Polynomials

A polynomial in x of degree n has the form

$a_n x^n + a_{n-1} x^{n-1} + \cdots + a_2 x^2 + a_1 x + a_0$

where $n \in \mathbb{Z}$ and $a_n \neq 0$.

Factorisation

$a(b + c) = ab + ac$
$(a + b)(c + d) = ac + ad + bc + bd$
$(a + b)(a - b) = a^2 - b^2$
$(a + b)^2 = a^2 + 2ab + b^2$
$(a - b)^2 = a^2 - 2ab + b^2$
$a^3 - b^3 = (a - b)(a^2 + ab + b^2)$
$a^3 + b^3 = (a + b)(a^2 - ab + b^2)$

$(x + a)(x + b) = x^2 + (a + b)x + ab$

$(a + b)^3 = a^3 + 3a^2b + 3ab^2 + b^3$
$(a - b)^3 = a^3 - 3a^2b + 3ab^2 - b^3$

$a^2 + b^2$ *cannot* be factorised.
$a^2 - b^2$ is the **difference of squares**.

$\dfrac{a - b}{b - a} = -1 \ (b \neq a)$

Fractions

- Fractions can be added and subtracted *only if* they have equal denominators.

  $$\frac{a}{b} + \frac{c}{d} = \frac{ad}{bd} + \frac{bc}{bd} = \frac{ad + bc}{bd}$$

  The LCM of the two denominators is the most efficient denominator to use.

- *Any* fractions can be multiplied or divided.

  $$\frac{a}{b} \times \frac{c}{d} = \frac{ac}{bd} \qquad \frac{a}{b} \div \frac{c}{d} = \frac{a}{b} \times \frac{d}{c} = \frac{ad}{bc}$$

  Cancel any factor common to the numerator and denominator before multiplying.

  Never cancel part of a bracket, only the whole bracket.

  Division by $\frac{a}{b}$ is the same as multiplication by $\frac{b}{a}$. So $\frac{x}{y} \div \frac{a}{b} = \frac{x}{y} \times \frac{b}{a}$.

  Multiplying or dividing both the numerator and denominator of a fraction by the *same* number or expression does not change the value of the fraction.

3 Equations

Before starting this chapter you will need to know

- how to handle algebraic expressions (Chapter 2).

3.1 Relationships

In Chapter 2 algebraic expressions, such as $x(x+1)+2x$, were studied.

✓ *Note* Expressions do not contain any equals sign.

A **single** expression can be

- simplified, or — $x(x+1)+2x = x^2+x+2x = x^2+3x$
- factorised, or — $x^2+3x = x(x+3)$
- evaluated for a particular value. — When $x=5$, $x^2+3x = 5^2+3\times 5 = 40$

Chapters 3 and 4 consider relationships between *two* expressions. These will be statements about the expressions, such as equations and inequalities. The statements *always* contain an equals sign (=) or an inequality sign ($<$, $>$, $\geqslant$, $\leqslant$).

Variables and unknowns

In algebra letters take the place of numbers.

There are two main situations where this occurs.

- The letter represents a **variable** and can take various values.
  For example, in a formula: $v = u + at$
  or in function notation: $f(x) = 2x+1$
  or in the equation of a graph: $y = 3x^2 - 4$
- The letter represents a specific **unknown** value (or values).
  For example, in an equation: $3x^2 - 2x - 1 = 0$
  or in an inequality: $2x > 5$

Equations, inequalities and identities

Consider these statements and try substituting values of x to see when they are true.

$x^2 - x = x(x-1)$ $\quad 3x - 1 = 0$ $\quad x^2 = 9$ $\quad x^2 = -4$

$x - 1 > 0$ $\quad x^2 + 1 > 0$ $\quad x^2 + 1 < 0$

Example 1 $x^2 - x \equiv x(x-1)$

This is true for all values of x. It is an **identity**. The symbol $\equiv$ can be used, rather than $=$. Read $\equiv$ as 'is identically equal to'.

➤ When an equation is true for all values of the variable it is called an **identity**. An identity is true for all values of the variable.

Example 2

a $3x - 1 = 0 \Rightarrow x = \frac{1}{3}$

This is an equation. The result holds for just one value of x. The number $\frac{1}{3}$ is the **root** of the equation. The **solution** is $x = \frac{1}{3}$.

b $x^2 = 9 \Rightarrow x = \pm 3$

This is an equation with two real roots, i.e. two possible values of x satisfy the equation. The solutions are $x = \pm 3$.

c $x^2 = -4$

This equation has no real roots. (It does, however, have a solution in the set of complex numbers.)

➤ An equation may be true for some real values of the unknown.

Example 3

a $x - 1 > 0 \Rightarrow x > 1$

This inequality holds for values of x where $x > 1$.

b $x^2 + 1 > 0$

This inequality is true for all real values of x. x^2 is always positive or zero, therefore $x^2 + 1$ is always positive.

c $x^2 + 1 < 0$

This inequality is not true for any real value of x. x^2 is always positive or zero, therefore $x^2 + 1$ cannot be negative.

➤ An inequality may be true for a set of values of the unknown.

This chapter deals with solving equations and rearranging formulae. Chapter 4 then covers solving inequalities and proving identities.

3.2 Solving linear equations

A **linear equation in x** is of the form $ax + b = 0$, $a \neq 0$, or can be arranged in this form. In linear equations, the highest power of the unknown is *one*. Linear equations have *one* root.

The graph of a linear equation is a straight line which (providing the gradient is non-zero) cuts the x-axis ($y = 0$) once.

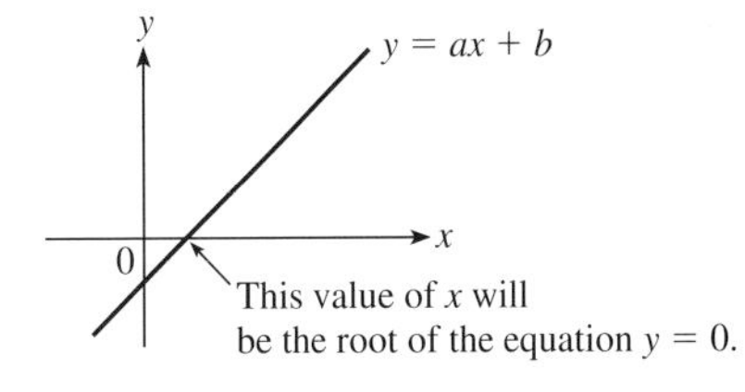

Technique for solving equations:
Do the same to both sides.

Since both sides of an equation are equal, any operation performed on both sides will not affect the equality. For example, if one side is multiplied by 2, so must the other side be, to maintain equality.

Example 4

In this example, a lot of steps are shown to illustrate the method clearly. With practice, it is possible to combine some of the steps to produce a more streamlined solution.

Solve $7x - 3 = 3(x + 3)$.

When x terms appear on both sides of a linear equation all x terms must be collected on one side and all other terms on the other side.

$7x - 3 = 3(x + 3)$ — Remove brackets.

$7x - 3 = 3x + 9$ — Collect all x terms on one side by subtracting $3x$ from both sides.

$7x - 3x - 3 = 3x - 3x + 9$ — Tidy up by collecting like terms.

$4x - 3 = 9$ — Collect all numbers (constant terms) on the other side by adding 3 to both sides.

$4x - 3 + 3 = 9 + 3$ — Tidy up.

$4x = 12$ — Divide both sides by 4.

$\frac{4x}{4} = \frac{12}{4}$

$x = 3$

The solution can be checked by substituting $x = 3$ in the original equation.

LHS $= 7x - 3 = 7 \times 3 - 3 = 18$

RHS $= 3(x + 3) = 3 \times (3 + 3) = 3 \times 6 = 18$

Example 5

In this example, an operation in brackets on the left indicates what is to be done to both sides of an equation.

Solve $3x - 5 = 2(x - 1) - (x + 7)$.

$3x - 5 = 2(x - 1) - (x + 7)$ — Simplify the RHS. *Note*: $-(x + 7) = -x - 7$.

$= 2x - 2 - x - 7$

So $3x - 5 = x - 9$ — Collect all terms in x on one side.

$(-x)$ $2x - 5 = -9$ — Collect all numbers (constant terms) on the other side.

$(+5)$ $2x = -9 + 5$

$= -4$

$(\div 2)$ $x = -\frac{4}{2}$

$= -2$

So the solution is $x = -2$.

The solution can be checked by substituting $x = -2$ in the original equation.

LHS $= (3 \times -2) - 5 = -6 - 5 = -11$

RHS $= (2 \times -3) - (-2 + 7) = -6 - 5 = -11$

Example 6 Solve $\frac{x}{2} + \frac{x-1}{3} = 7$.

$$\frac{x}{2} + \frac{x-1}{3} = 7$$

Multiply every term by 6 (the LCM of the denominators) to eliminate the fractions.

$$\overset{3}{\cancel{6}} \times \frac{x}{\underset{1}{\cancel{2}}} + \overset{2}{\cancel{6}} \times \frac{x-1}{\underset{1}{\cancel{3}}} = 6 \times 7$$

$$3x + 2(x - 1) = 42$$

Remove the brackets.

$$3x + 2x - 2 = 42$$

Collect like terms.

$$5x - 2 = 42$$

$$5x = 44$$

Divide both sides by 5.

$$x = \frac{44}{5} = 8\frac{4}{5}$$

Example 7 Solve $\frac{3}{x} + 2 = \frac{6}{x}$.

$$\frac{3}{x} + 2 = \frac{6}{x}$$

Multiply by x to eliminate the fractions. Each term must be multiplied by x.

$$\cancel{x} \times \frac{3}{\cancel{x}} + 2x = \cancel{x} \times \frac{6}{\cancel{x}}$$

$$3 + 2x = 6$$

$$2x = 3$$

$$x = \frac{3}{2}$$

Cross-multiplying

When two fractions are equal, the technique called cross-multiplying can be used.

$$\frac{3}{4} = \frac{6}{8} \quad \Leftrightarrow \quad 3 \times 8 = 6 \times 4$$

$$\frac{a}{b} = \frac{c}{d} \quad \Leftrightarrow \quad ad = bc \quad (b \neq 0, d \neq 0)$$

Example 8 Solve $\frac{x-1}{x+4} = \frac{x+3}{x-7}$.

$$\frac{x-1}{x+4} = \frac{x+3}{x-7}$$

Two equal fractions so cross-multiplying can be used.

$$(x - 1)(x - 7) = (x + 3)(x + 4)$$

Remove the brackets.

$$x^2 - 8x + 7 = x^2 + 7x + 12$$

Subtract x^2 from both sides.

$$-8x + 7 = 7x + 12$$

Adding $8x$ to both sides gives a positive coefficient to the x term.

$$7 = 15x + 12$$

$$-5 = 15x$$

The LHS and RHS can be interchanged to put the x term on the left.

$$15x = -5$$

$$x = -\frac{5}{15} = -\frac{1}{3}$$

Example 9

Solve $\frac{1}{5}(2x+7) - x = 6 - (1 - x)$.

$$\frac{1}{5}(2x+7) - x = 6 - (1 - x)$$

Remove brackets from the RHS.

$$\frac{1}{5}(2x+7) - x = 6 - 1 + x$$

Add x to both sides.

$$\frac{1}{5}(2x+7) = 5 + 2x$$

Multiply both sides by 5 to eliminate the fraction.

$$2x + 7 = 5(5 + 2x)$$

$$= 25 + 10x$$

Subtract $2x$ from both sides.

$$7 = 25 + 8x$$

Subtract 25 from both sides.

$$-18 = 8x$$

Divide both sides by 8.

$$\therefore \quad x = -\frac{18}{8} = -\frac{9}{4}$$

Example 10

A cleaner is paid a normal hourly rate during the week, time and a half for evenings and double time for weekends.

One week the cleaner works 32 hours during weekdays, 5 hours in the evening and 6 hours at the weekend.

The total pay for the week is £267.80. Find the normal hourly rate.

Solution

Let the normal hourly rate be £x per hour.

Choose a letter to represent the quantity to be found.

Then the evening rate is £$\frac{3x}{2}$ per hour and the weekend rate is £$2x$ per hour.

So $\quad 32x + 5 \times \frac{3x}{2} + 6 \times 2x = 267.8$

$$64x + 15x + 24x = 535.6$$

$$103x = 535.6$$

Form an equation from the information. No units in an equation. (Both sides are expressed in £.)

$$\therefore \quad x = \frac{535.6}{103} = 5.2$$

State the answer as a sum of money.

So the normal hourly rate is £5.20.

EXERCISE 3a

1 Solve these equations.

a $8x + 2 = x - 3$ **b** $2x + 1 = 3 - x$

c $3x + 1 = 4x - 2$ **d** $5x + 2 = 4 + x$

e $5 - 2x = 3 + 4x$ **f** $x + 7 + 5x - 8 = 3 + 2x$

g $4 - 3x = 6 - 4x$ **h** $3y + 3 + 4y = 7y + 2 - 2y$

i $4(a - 2) = 3(a - 1)$ **j** $4(b + 1) + 2(b + 3) = 10$

k $2(c - 2) - (1 - c) = 18$ **l** $2(d - 1) - 3(2 - d) = 3(d + 1)$

m $7 + 2(e - 3) = 1$ **n** $5m - 3(m + 2) = 0$

o $2(2v - 1) - 3(3v + 1) = 5$ **p** $5 - 3(2x - 5) = 7 - x$

q $8k - 7 = 4(k - 3) - 2(3k - 5) - (3 - 2k)$

2 Solve these equations.

a $\frac{a}{4} = 12$ **b** $\frac{2}{3}x = \frac{9}{8}$

c $\frac{a}{4} + 7 = 13$

d $\frac{2}{x} = \frac{3}{x+1}$

e $\frac{x}{3} + 4 = 2x + 7$

f $\frac{x}{2} + \frac{x}{3} + \frac{x}{6} = 5$

g $\frac{y}{2} + 5 = \frac{y}{5}$

h $\frac{6}{x} + \frac{3}{2x} = \frac{5}{2}$

i $\frac{3}{y} + 5 = 11$

j $\frac{3x}{4} - \frac{2}{3} = \frac{7}{12}$

k $\frac{7x+2}{5} = \frac{4x-1}{2}$

l $\frac{3x-13}{7} + \frac{11-4x}{3} = 0$

m $2x - \frac{1}{3}(x + 27) = 16$

n $\frac{1}{3}(1 - 2x) - \frac{1}{6}(4 - 5x) + \frac{13}{42} = 0$

o $6 - \frac{x-1}{2} = 3x - 11$

p $\frac{x}{4} + \frac{5x+8}{6} = \frac{2x+9}{3}$

q $0.4x = 1.3 - 0.2x - 1$

r $(x+1)(x+2) = x(x+7) - 6$

s $\frac{2x+1}{x-3} = \frac{2x+3}{x-1}$

t $\frac{2a-1}{3} - \frac{a+5}{4} = \frac{1}{2}$

u $3.2x + 0.99 = 3.13x + 0.15$

v $\frac{7}{6}(3x - 1) - 8\frac{1}{3} = \frac{3}{2}(2x - 5)$

w $\frac{x}{5} + 1\frac{1}{2}x - \frac{11}{20} = \frac{5x-1}{4}$

x $\frac{4x-3}{5} - \frac{5x-3}{8} = 1$

y $\frac{x+1}{2} - \frac{x-7}{5} = \frac{x+4}{3}$

z $\frac{3}{x^2 + 4x - 1} = \frac{6}{2x^2 - 3x + 5}$

3 The length of a swimming pool is 2.5 m greater than its width.
The pool's perimeter is 29 m. Find the length of the pool.

4 When an object travelling at a speed u is subject to a constant acceleration a, the object's speed v after time t has elapsed is given by the equation $v = u + at$.
A motorist driving at $14\,\text{ms}^{-1}$ brakes steadily for 3.5 s, reducing her speed by half.
Find the acceleration of the car during this time.

5 Anouk shares a bag of sweets with two friends.
She gives five sweets to Katie and a third of the remaining sweets to Phil, and is left with twelve for herself.
Find the number of sweets in the full bag.

6 The temperature, C, in degrees Celsius can be calculated from the temperature, F, in degrees Fahrenheit using the formula $C = \frac{5}{9}(F - x)$.
A cook has forgotten the value of x, but remembers that the boiling point of water is 100°C, which is equivalent to 212°F. Find the value of x.

7 For a village fête, Archna and Eddie grow the same number of plants, but Archna gives Eddie twelve of her plants for his stall before the fête opens.
Archna sells her remaining plants for £5.60 each, while Eddie sells all the plants on his stall for £4 each.
Both of them raise the same amount of money. Find the total number of plants sold.

3.3 Rearranging formulae

The method of 'doing the same to both sides' was used for solving linear equations. The same method is used for rearranging formulae.

Example 11 Rearrange $ax + b = c$ to give x in terms of a, b and c.

$$ax + b = c$$

The term with x has to be isolated on one side.

$$ax = c - b$$

$$x = \frac{c - b}{a}$$

Do this by subtracting b from both sides. Then, divide both sides by a.

Example 12 Solve for x: $sx + t = lx + k$.

x terms are on both sides. Collect all x terms on one side, the rest of the terms on the other. Do this by subtracting lx and t from both sides. When x appears in more than one term put it outside the bracket.

$$sx + t = lx + k$$

$$sx - lx = k - t$$

$$x(s - l) = k - t$$

$$x = \frac{k - t}{s - l}$$

Divide both sides by $(s - l)$.

Example 13 Give x in terms of a, b and c, where $\frac{x}{a} + \frac{x - 1}{b} = c$.

$$\frac{x}{a} + \frac{x - 1}{b} = c$$

Multiply every term by ab, the LCM of the denominators, to eliminate the fractions.

$$\cancel{a}b \times \frac{x}{\cancel{a}} + a\cancel{b} \times \frac{x - 1}{\cancel{b}} = ab \times c$$

$$bx + a(x - 1) = abc$$

Remove the bracket.

$$bx + ax - a = abc$$

Collect all x terms on one side, the rest of the terms on the other.

$$x(b + a) = abc + a$$

$$x = \frac{a(bc + 1)}{a + b}$$

x appears in more than one term; put it outside the bracket, and divide by $(a + b)$.

Example 14 Solve for x: $\frac{l}{x} + m = \frac{n}{x}$.

$$\frac{l}{x} + m = \frac{n}{x}$$

Eliminate the fractions by multiplying all terms by x.

$$l + mx = n$$

$$mx = n - l$$

Isolate the x term on one side.

$$x = \frac{n - l}{m}$$

Example 15 Solve for x: $\frac{x - s}{c - d} = \frac{t - x}{y}$.

$$\frac{x - s}{c - d} = \frac{t - x}{y}$$

Two equal fractions, so cross-multiply.

$$y(x - s) = (t - x)(c - d)$$

Remove brackets.

$$xy - sy = ct - dt - cx + dx$$

Collect all x terms on one side, the rest of the terms on the other; take x outside the bracket.

$$xy + cx - dx = ct - dt + sy$$

$$x(y + c - d) = ct - dt + sy$$

Divide by $(y + c - d)$.

$$x = \frac{ct - dt + sy}{y + c - d}$$

Example 16

Rearrange $T = 2\pi\sqrt{\frac{l}{g}}$ to make g the subject of the formula.

$$T = 2\pi\sqrt{\frac{l}{g}}$$

Square both sides to remove the root sign. *Note*: $(2\pi)^2 = 4\pi^2$

$$T^2 = 4\pi^2\frac{l}{g}$$

Multiply by g to eliminate the fraction.

$$T^2 g = 4\pi^2 l$$

$$g = \frac{4\pi^2 l}{T^2}$$

Example 17

This example illustrates the fact that there may be several possible forms of the answer when rearranging formulae. When checking an answer, you may have the correct answer but expressed in a different form.

Solve for t: $2(t + x) = y$.

$$2(t + x) = y$$

One method is to divide by 2, and then subtract x from both sides.

$$t + x = \frac{y}{2}$$

$$t = \frac{y}{2} - x$$

Alternatively

A second method is to remove the brackets, subtract $2x$ from both sides and then divide by 2.

$$2(t + x) = y$$

$$2t + 2x = y$$

$$2t = y - 2x$$

$$t = \frac{y - 2x}{2}$$

The two answers are equivalent.

EXERCISE 3b

1 Solve these equations for x.

a $ax - b = c$ **b** $a - x = b$ **c** $cx = d$ **d** $\frac{e}{x} = f$

e $g - hx = j$ **f** $\frac{k}{x} + l = m$ **g** $\frac{3}{x} + \frac{a}{x} = b$ **h** $\frac{x + n}{a} = b$

i $\frac{2x}{3} + b = d$ **j** $hx + jx = k$ **k** $mx + n = px$ **l** $\frac{1}{2}sx = t$

EXERCISE 3b *(continued)*

m $a(x+b)=c$ **n** $p(x+q)=rx$ **o** $3(ax+b)=2(cx+d)$

p $\dfrac{a}{b-x}=c$ **q** $\dfrac{t}{x}-p=\dfrac{s}{x}$ **r** $a(px+q)=c(r-sx)$

s $a=\dfrac{2b+3x}{3b-2x}$ **t** $a=\dfrac{x-b}{x+b}$ **u** $2x+2y+2mx-4my+1=0$

2 Solve these equations for x.

a $\sqrt{x}=a$ **b** $\sqrt{3x}=a$ **c** $3\sqrt{x}=a$

d $\sqrt{x}+a=b$ **e** $\sqrt{x+a}=b$ **f** $x^2=c$

g $x^2+c=d$ **h** $a\sqrt{x-b}=c$ **i** $a\sqrt{x}-1=b$

j $x=\dfrac{k}{x}$ **k** $\dfrac{d}{\sqrt{x}}=e$ **l** $\sqrt{\dfrac{x}{a}}=b$

m $\sqrt{x^2-c^2}+c=x$ **n** $x^{\frac{1}{3}}=y$ **o** $x^{\frac{2}{3}}=y$

p $x^{m/n}=p$ **q** $x^{-2}=q$ **r** $x^{-\frac{1}{4}}=s$

3 Transform these formulae to make the letter in the brackets the subject. Where there is more than one letter in the brackets, make each letter the subject in turn.

a $C=2\pi r$ (r) **b** $pv=c$ (p, v) **c** $v=u+at$ (u, a, t)

d $A=lb$ (b) **e** $\dfrac{pv}{t}=k$ (t, p) **f** $\dfrac{p_1v_1}{t_1}=\dfrac{p_2v_2}{t_2}$ (v_2, t_1)

g $I=\dfrac{PRT}{100}$ (P) **h** $A=\pi r^2$ (r) **i** $S=\frac{1}{2}gt^2$ (t)

j $S=4\pi r^2$ (r) **k** $d=\sqrt{y}$ (y) **l** $d=z^2$ (z)

m $a=\sqrt{\dfrac{4h}{3}}$ (h) **n** $t=2\pi\sqrt{y}$ (y) **o** $t=2\pi\sqrt{\dfrac{l}{g}}$ (l, g)

p $a^2+b^2=c^2$ (a) **q** $V=\frac{1}{3}\pi r^2h$ (h, r) **r** $A=\pi(R^2-r^2)$ (R, r)

s $\dfrac{1}{u}+\dfrac{1}{v}=\dfrac{1}{f}$ (u, v, f) **t** $A=P+\dfrac{PRT}{100}$ (P, T) **u** $s=\dfrac{n}{2}(a+l)$ (n, a)

v $A=\pi r\sqrt{h^2+r^2}$ (h) **w** $\dfrac{L}{E}=\dfrac{2a}{R-r}$ (R) **x** $k=\dfrac{brt}{a-b}$ (b)

y $V=\frac{1}{3}\sqrt{\dfrac{s^3}{8\pi}}$ (s) **z** $A=\frac{1}{2}m(v^2-u^2)$ (u)

3.4 Solving quadratic equations

A quadratic equation is of the form $ax^2+bx+c=0$, $a\neq 0$, or can be arranged in that form. In quadratic equations, the highest power of the unknown is *two*.
Quadratic equations have *two* roots: these may be

- two distinct real roots
- two equal roots or
- two complex roots (no real roots).

The graph of a quadratic equation cuts the x-axis ($y = 0$), at most, twice.

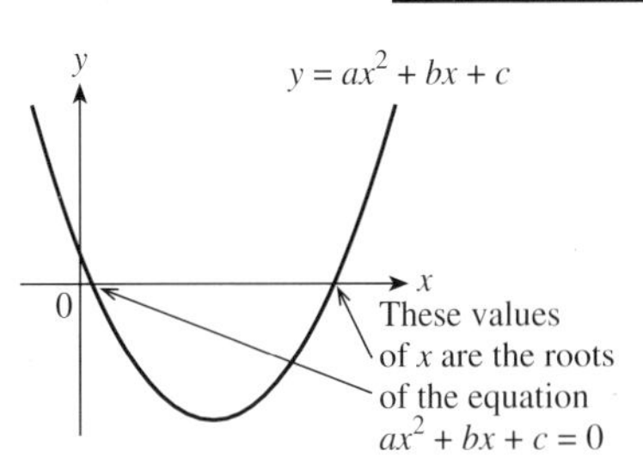

Three techniques for solving quadratic equations are covered in this chapter.

- Factorisation (this page)
- Completing the square (page 60)
- Using the quadratic formula (page 62)

Solving quadratic equations using factorisation

Example 18 Solve the equation $x^2 - 3x - 4 = 0$.

$x^2 - 3x - 4 = 0$

$(x - 4)(x + 1) = 0$

$\Rightarrow \quad x - 4 = 0$ or $x + 1 = 0$

$\therefore \quad x = 4$ or $x = -1$

Factorise. If the product of two numbers is zero, then one or other (or both) of the numbers must be zero.

So the solution of $x^2 - 3x - 4 = 0$ is $x = 4$ or $x = -1$.

Example 19 Find the values of x which satisfy the equation $3x^2 + 12x = 0$.

$3x^2 + 12x = 0$ — 3 is a common factor and can be divided out.

$x^2 + 4x = 0$ — x is a common factor which can be taken outside a bracket.

$x(x + 4) = 0$ — *Remember*: Do not divide through by x, which could be zero.

$\Rightarrow \quad x = 0$ or $x + 4 = 0$

$\therefore \quad x = 0 \qquad x = -4$

The values of x which satisfy the equation $3x^2 + 12x = 0$ are 0 and -4.

Example 20 Solve $x^2 - 25 = 0$.

$x^2 - 25 = 0$ — One method is to factorise using difference of squares.

$(x - 5)(x + 5) = 0$

$\Rightarrow \quad x - 5 = 0$ or $x + 5 = 0$

So $\quad x = \pm 5$

Alternatively

$x^2 - 25 = 0$

$x^2 = 25$ — Take square root of both sides.

$x = \pm\sqrt{25}$ — *Remember*: This can be +5 or −5.

$\therefore \quad x = \pm 5$

So the solution to $x^2 - 25 = 0$ is $x = \pm 5$.

Example 21 Solve $(x + 1)(2x + 3) = 4x^2 - 22$.

$$(x + 1)(2x + 3) = 4x^2 - 22$$

Multiply out brackets.

$$2x^2 + 5x + 3 = 4x^2 - 22$$

Put all of the terms on one side.

$$2x^2 + 5x + 3 - 4x^2 + 22 = 0$$

$$-2x^2 + 5x + 25 = 0$$

Multiply all terms by -1 so that the x^2 term is +ve.

$$2x^2 - 5x - 25 = 0$$

$$(2x + 5)(x - 5) = 0$$

$$\Rightarrow \quad 2x + 5 = 0 \quad \text{or} \quad x - 5 = 0$$

$$\therefore \quad x = -\tfrac{5}{2} \qquad x = 5$$

So the solution is $x = -\frac{5}{2}$ or $x = 5$.

Example 22 Solve $\dfrac{7}{x + 5} - \dfrac{1}{x - 3} = \dfrac{5}{3}$.

$$\frac{7}{x + 5} - \frac{1}{x - 3} = \frac{5}{3}$$

Multiply through by the LCM of the denominators: $3(x + 5)(x - 3)$.

$$7 \times 3(x - 3) - 3(x + 5) = 5(x + 5)(x - 3)$$

$$21x - 63 - 3x - 15 = 5(x^2 + 2x - 15)$$

$$= 5x^2 + 10x - 75$$

Arrange in the form $ax^2+bx + c = 0$, $a > 0$.

$$5x^2 - 8x + 3 = 0$$

$$(5x - 3)(x - 1) = 0$$

$$\Rightarrow \quad 5x - 3 = 0 \text{ or } x - 1 = 0$$

$$\therefore \quad x = \tfrac{3}{5} \qquad x = 1$$

So the solution is $x = \frac{3}{5}$ or $x = 1$.

Example 23 Find the values of x for which $\dfrac{2x + 1}{x - 4} = \dfrac{2(2x + 1)}{x - 2}$.

$$\frac{2x + 1}{x - 4} = \frac{2(2x + 1)}{x - 2}$$

Two equal fractions so use cross-multiplying.

$$(2x + 1)(x - 2) = 2(2x + 1)(x - 4)$$

$$2x^2 - 3x - 2 = 2(2x^2 - 7x - 4)$$

$$= 4x^2 - 14x - 8$$

Arrange in the form $ax^2 + bx + c = 0$, $a > 0$.

$$2x^2 - 11x - 6 = 0$$

$$(2x + 1)(x - 6) = 0$$

$$\Rightarrow \quad x = -\tfrac{1}{2} \text{ or } x = 6$$

So the values of x which satisfy the equation are $x = -\frac{1}{2}$ and $x = 6$.

Examples 24 and 25 involve quadratic equations in some function of x.

Example 24

This example involves a quadratic equation in $x^{\frac{1}{3}}$, most easily seen by substituting $y = x^{\frac{1}{3}}$. Alternatively, factorise the original equation: $(2x^{\frac{1}{3}} - 1)(x^{\frac{1}{3}} + 3) = 0$

Solve $2x^{\frac{2}{3}} + 5x^{\frac{1}{3}} - 3 = 0$.

Substituting $y = x^{\frac{1}{3}}$ gives

$$2y^2 + 5y - 3 = 0$$

$$(2y - 1)(y + 3) = 0$$

$$\Rightarrow \quad 2y - 1 = 0 \quad \text{or} \quad y + 3 = 0$$

$$y = \tfrac{1}{2} \qquad\qquad y = -3$$

$$\therefore \quad x^{\frac{1}{3}} = \tfrac{1}{2} \quad \text{or} \quad x^{\frac{1}{3}} = -3$$

$$x^{\frac{1}{3}} = \tfrac{1}{2} \Rightarrow x = \left(\tfrac{1}{2}\right)^3 = \tfrac{1}{8}$$

$$x^{\frac{1}{3}} = -3 \Rightarrow x = (-3)^3 = -27$$

So the solutions are $x = -27$ or $x = \frac{1}{8}$.

Example 25

This example involves a ***quartic equation*** *(highest power of x is 4) which is a quadratic equation in x^2.*

Solve $9x^4 - 10x^2 + 1 = 0$.

$$9x^4 - 10x^2 + 1 = 0$$

If preferred, the substitution $y = x^2$ can be made, giving $9y^2 - 10y + 1 = 0$.

$$(9x^2 - 1)(x^2 - 1) = 0$$

$$\Rightarrow \quad 9x^2 - 1 = 0 \quad \text{or} \quad x^2 - 1 = 0$$

$$x^2 = \tfrac{1}{9} \qquad\qquad x^2 = 1$$

$$\therefore \quad x = \pm\tfrac{1}{3} \qquad\qquad x = \pm 1$$

So the solutions to $9x^4 - 10x^2 + 1 = 0$ are $x = \pm\frac{1}{3}$ and $x = \pm 1$.

✓ ***Note*** Quartic equations have, at most, *four* real roots.

Example 26

Solve $x^3 - x = 0$.

This is a **cubic equation**, (highest power of x is 3).

$$x^3 - x = 0$$

x is a common factor and can be taken outside a bracket.

$$x(x^2 - 1) = 0$$

$$x(x + 1)(x - 1) = 0$$

$$\Rightarrow \quad x = 0 \text{ or } x = \pm 1$$

✓ ***Note*** Cubic equations have, at most, *three* real roots.

Completing the square

Writing a quadratic expression, $ax^2 + bx + c$, in the form $a(x + p)^2 + q$ is called completing the square.

Consider the form of expressions which are perfect squares:

- $(x + \mathbf{3})^2 = x^2 + \mathbf{6}x + 9$ — Notice **3** is $\frac{6}{2}$.
- $(x - \mathbf{5})^2 = x^2 - \mathbf{10}x + 25$ — Notice **−5** is $\frac{-10}{2}$.
- $(x + \boldsymbol{k})^2 = x^2 + \mathbf{2}\boldsymbol{k}x + k^2$ — Notice $\boldsymbol{k}$ is $\frac{2k}{2}$.

The constant in each bracket is half the coefficient of x.

A quadratic expression, such as $x^2 - 12x$, can be written as

$x^2 - 12x \equiv (x - 6)^2 - 36$

6 is half the coefficient of x. Subtracting $6^2 = 36$ from $(x - 6)^2$ makes both sides of the equation equal. Check this mentally.

> ➤ To complete the square for expressions of the form $x^2 + ax$, put $\frac{a}{2}$ (half the coefficient of x) at the end of the bracket and subtract $\left(\frac{a}{2}\right)^2$ (its square).

Example 27

This example illustrates possible cases for completing the square for expressions of the form $x^2 + ax$.

a $x^2 + 8x = (x + 4)^2 - 16$ — Half the coefficient of $x = \frac{8}{2} = 4$. Subtract $4^2 = 16$.

b $x^2 - 3x = \left(x - \frac{3}{2}\right)^2 - \frac{9}{4}$ — Half the coefficient of $x = \frac{-3}{2} = -\frac{3}{2}$. Subtract $\left(-\frac{3}{2}\right)^2 = \frac{9}{4}$.

c $x^2 + \frac{b}{a}x = \left(x + \frac{b}{2a}\right)^2 - \frac{b^2}{4a^2}$ — Half the coefficient of $x = \frac{b}{2a}$. Subtract $\left(\frac{b}{2a}\right)^2 = \frac{b^2}{4a^2}$.

Example 28

This example illustrates possible cases for completing the square for quadratic expressions $ax^2 + bx + c$.

a $x^2 - 2x + 4 \equiv (x - 1)^2 - 1 + 4$

$\equiv (x - 1)^2 + 3$

Completing the square: $x^2 - 2x \equiv (x - 1)^2 - 1$.

b $x^2 + 6x - 8 \equiv (x + 3)^2 - 9 - 8$

$\equiv (x + 3)^2 - 17$

c $x^2 + 5x - 1 \equiv \left(x + \frac{5}{2}\right)^2 - \frac{25}{4} - 1$

$\equiv \left(x + \frac{5}{2}\right)^2 - \frac{29}{4}$

d $2x^2 + 12x + 1 \equiv 2\left(x^2 + 6x + \frac{1}{2}\right)$
$\equiv 2\left((x+3)^2 - 9 + \frac{1}{2}\right)$
$\equiv 2\left((x+3)^2 - 8\frac{1}{2}\right)$
$\equiv 2(x+3)^2 - 17$

If the coefficient of x^2 is not 1, take the coefficient outside the bracket first.

e $-x^2 - 6x + 7 \equiv -(x^2 + 6x - 7)$
$\equiv -((x+3)^2 - 9 - 7)$
$\equiv -((x+3)^2 - 16)$
$\equiv 16 - (x+3)^2$

Here the coefficient of x^2 is -1.

Completing the square is a useful method for

- finding maximum and minimum values
- sketching curves
- solving quadratic equations, although other methods are preferable.

It is essential at a higher level, in calculus, for certain integrals.

Example 29

Use the method of completing the square to solve $x^2 - 5x - 2 = 0$.

$$x^2 - 5x - 2 = \left(x - \frac{5}{2}\right)^2 - \frac{25}{4} - 2$$
$$= \left(x - \frac{5}{2}\right)^2 - \frac{33}{4}$$

So the equation $x^2 - 5x - 2 = 0$ can be written as $\left(x - \frac{5}{2}\right)^2 - \frac{33}{4} = 0$.

$$\left(x - \frac{5}{2}\right)^2 - \frac{33}{4} = 0$$

Add $\frac{33}{4}$ to both sides.

$$\left(x - \frac{5}{2}\right)^2 = \frac{33}{4}$$

Square root both sides, remembering $\pm$ sign.

$$x - \frac{5}{2} = \pm\sqrt{\frac{33}{4}}$$
$$= \pm\frac{\sqrt{33}}{2}$$

Add $\frac{5}{2}$ to both sides.

$$x = \frac{5}{2} \pm \frac{\sqrt{33}}{2}$$

Express as a single fraction.

$$= \frac{5 \pm \sqrt{33}}{2}$$

So the solution of $x^2 - 5x - 2 = 0$ is $x = \dfrac{5 \pm \sqrt{33}}{2}$.

Example 30

Solve $ax^2 + bx + c = 0$ by the method of completing the square.

$$ax^2 + bx + c = 0$$

Divide through by a.

$$x^2 + \frac{b}{a}x + \frac{c}{a} = 0$$

Complete the square.

$$\left(x + \frac{b}{2a}\right)^2 - \frac{b^2}{4a^2} + \frac{c}{a} = 0$$
$$\left(x + \frac{b}{2a}\right)^2 = \frac{b^2}{4a^2} - \frac{c}{a}$$

Express the fractions with a common denominator, $4a^2$.

$$= \frac{b^2 - 4ac}{4a^2}$$

Square root both sides, remembering $\pm$ sign.

So $\quad x + \frac{b}{2a} = \pm\sqrt{\frac{b^2 - 4ac}{4a^2}}$

Note: $\sqrt{4a^2} = 2a$

$$= \pm\frac{\sqrt{b^2 - 4ac}}{2a}$$

$\therefore \quad x = -\frac{b}{2a} \pm \frac{\sqrt{b^2 - 4ac}}{2a}$

The fractions have a common denominator so can be combined.

$$= \frac{-b \pm \sqrt{b^2 - 4ac}}{2a}$$

$x = \frac{-b \pm \sqrt{b^2 - 4ac}}{2a}$ is the **quadratic equation formula**.

Using the quadratic equation formula

Example 30 led to the quadratic equation formula:

➤

$$ax^2 + bx + c = 0 \Leftrightarrow x = \frac{-b \pm \sqrt{b^2 - 4ac}}{2a}$$

The quantity under the root sign, $b^2 - 4ac$, is called the **discriminant** of the quadratic equation $ax^2 + bx + c = 0$. The discriminant gives useful information about the roots of the quadratic equation; see the table on page 66.

➤

To solve a quadratic equation using the quadratic equation formula:

- Arrange the equation in the form $ax^2 + bx + c = 0$.
- Compare the equation to be solved with $ax^2 + bx + c = 0$ to find a, b and c.
- Substitute the values of a, b and c in the formula. Take great care with the signs.

Example 31

Solve the equation $x^2 + 8x + 5 = 0$ giving the answer both exactly (i.e. in surd form) and correct to 3 significant figures.

$x^2 + 8x + 5 = 0$

Compare $x^2 + 8x + 5 = 0$ with $ax^2 + bx + c = 0$.

$a = 1, b = 8, c = 5$

With practice this line can be omitted.

$$x = \frac{-8 \pm \sqrt{8^2 - 4 \times 1 \times 5}}{2 \times 1}$$

$$= \frac{-8 \pm \sqrt{64 - 20}}{2}$$

$$= \frac{-8 \pm \sqrt{44}}{2}$$

$\sqrt{44} = \sqrt{4 \times 11} = 2\sqrt{11}$.

$$= \frac{-8 \pm 2\sqrt{11}}{2}$$

Both terms of the numerator can be divided by 2.

$$= -4 \pm \sqrt{11}$$

The **exact answer** includes surds.

Exact solution is $x = -4 \pm \sqrt{11}$.

Use the calculator to find the values of x correct to the required accuracy.

Correct to 3 significant figures, the solution is $x = -0.683$ or $x = -7.32$.

Example 32 Solve the equation $2x^2 - 5x - 6 = 0$, giving the answer both exactly (i.e. in surd form) and correct to 3 significant figures.

$2x^2 - 5x - 6 = 0$ — Compare $2x^2 - 5x - 6 = 0$ with $ax^2 + bx + c = 0$.

$a = 2, b = -5, c = -6$ — With practice this line can be omitted.

$$x = \frac{-(-5) \pm \sqrt{(-5)^2 - 4 \times 2 \times (-6)}}{2 \times 2}$$

Take care with signs under the root sign.

$$= \frac{5 \pm \sqrt{25 + 48}}{4}$$

$$= \frac{5 \pm \sqrt{73}}{4}$$

The **exact** answer includes surds.

Exact solution is $x = \dfrac{5 \pm \sqrt{73}}{4}$.

Use a calculator to find the values of x correct to the required accuracy.

Correct to 3 significant figures, the solution is $x = -0.886$ or $x = 3.39$.

Example 33 An open box with volume $48\,\text{cm}^3$ is to be made by cutting 4 cm squares from each corner of a square piece of metal and folding up the sides. Find the dimensions, to the nearest mm, of the piece of metal required.

Let x cm be the side of the square.

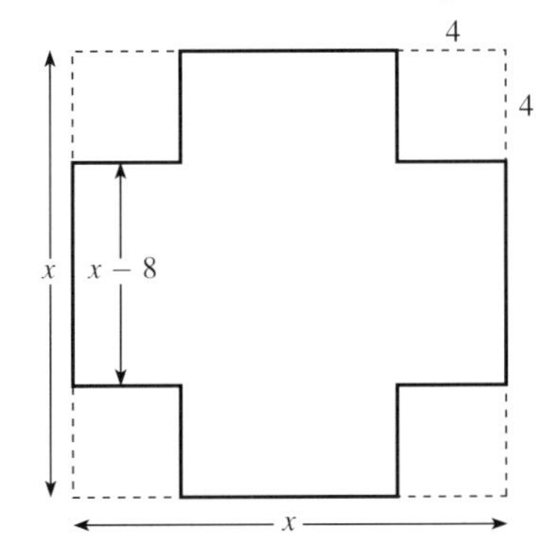

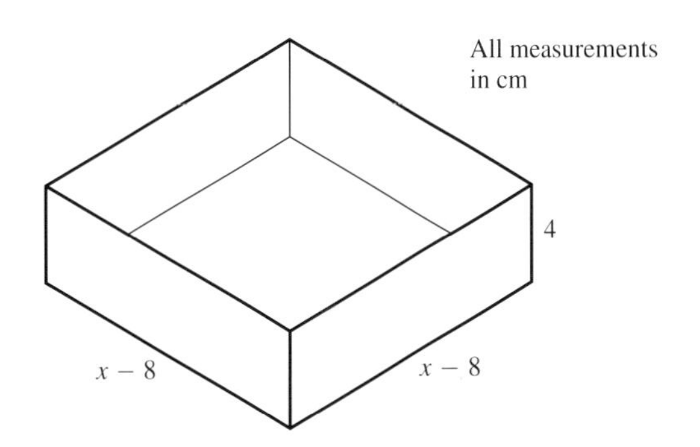

Then volume $= 4(x - 8)^2\text{cm}^3$

But volume $= 48\,\text{cm}^3$

So $4(x - 8)^2 = 48$ — No units are written in an equation (both sides are in cm^3).

$(x - 8)^2 = 12$ — Take square root. Remember $\pm$ signs.

$x - 8 = \pm\sqrt{12}$

$x = 8 \pm \sqrt{12}$

The length of the side of the square must allow two 4 cm squares to be cut out.
So $x > 8$ and $x = 8 - \sqrt{12}$ is not a possible solution.
So $x = 8 + \sqrt{12}$ is the solution.

The length of the side of the piece of metal is 11.5 cm to the nearest millimetre.

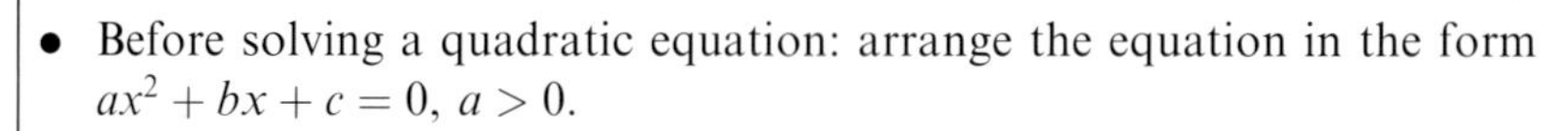

- Before solving a quadratic equation: arrange the equation in the form $ax^2 + bx + c = 0$, $a > 0$.
- Always look for a common factor.
  If there is a numerical one, divide through by it before proceeding.
  Do not divide through by an unknown quantity which could be zero.
- Try to factorise, remembering particularly that the form $ax^2 + bx = 0$ gives $x(ax + b) = 0$ and difference of squares $x^2 - a^2 = 0$ gives $(x - a)(x + a) = 0$.
- For cases where factorisation is difficult, or not possible, use the formula on page 62.

EXERCISE 3c

1 Solve these equations.

a $(x - 2)(2x + 1) = 0$ **b** $x^2 - 7x + 12 = 0$ **c** $y^2 - 5y + 6 = 0$
d $y^2 - 16 = 0$ **e** $3x^2 - 27x = 0$ **f** $6x^2 = 10x$
g $x^2 - 4x - 21 = 0$ **h** $x^2 + x - 12 = 0$ **i** $x^2 - 6x + 9 = 0$
j $x^2 + 5x + 6 = 0$ **k** $2x^2 - 7x + 6 = 0$ **l** $3e^2 + 4e - 4 = 0$
m $3d^2 - 5d - 8 = 0$ **n** $3e^2 - 4e - 4 = 0$ **o** $12f^2 - f - 6 = 0$
p $5g^2 + 29g - 6 = 0$ **q** $49 - y^2 = 0$ **r** $25x^2 = 9$
s $x^3 - 6x^2 = 0$ **t** $90x^2 - 40 = 0$ **u** $6y^2 = 150$

2 Solve the equations.

a $3a^2 + 2 = 5a$ **b** $b(2b - 5) + 3 = 0$
c $2c^2 = 7c - 3$ **d** $2(d^2 - 3d + 3) = d + 1$
e $3(e + 1)^2 = 1 - e$ **f** $3f = 2(f^2 - 1)$
g $(g + 3)(2 - g) = g^2$ **h** $h^2 - h = 0$
i $6k^2 = 35 + k$ **j** $2l^2 + 4l = 0$
k $4m^2 - 16m = 0$ **l** $100t - t^3 = 0$
m $u^3 - 7u^2 = 0$ **n** $251w^2 = 251$
o $17x^2 - 51x + 34 = 0$ **p** $24y^2 - 48y + 24 = 0$
q $3(1 - 6k^2) = 25k$ **r** $(3x + 1)(x + 3) = 19 - 2(x + 2)^2$

3 Solve these by completing the square, giving an exact answer.

a $x^2 + 2x = 5$ **b** $x^2 - 4x = 7$ **c** $t^2 - 10t - 2 = 0$
d $s^2 + 6s - 3 = 0$ **e** $r^2 + 5r - 1 = 0$ **f** $t^2 - 3t - 7 = 0$
g $a^2 - a - 1 = 0$ **h** $b^2 + 7b + 3 = 0$ **i** $2x^2 - x - 1 = 0$
j $3x^2 = 6x + 4$

4 Solve these, giving the answer in an exact form and, if appropriate, correct to 3 significant figures.

a $x^2 - x - 1 = 0$ **b** $2x^2 + 7x + 3 = 0$ **c** $2x^2 - 7x + 3 = 0$
d $2x^2 + 7x - 3 = 0$ **e** $2x^2 - 7x - 3 = 0$ **f** $3 + 7x - 2x^2 = 0$
g $x^2 - 5 = 0$ **h** $6x^2 - x - 4 = 0$ **i** $(5x + 2)(x - 1) = x(2x + 1)$
j $(3x - 1)(2x + 7) = 1$

5 Solve

a $x^2 - x = 0$

b $x^3 - x^2 = 0$

c $(x-1)(2x-1)(3x-1) = 0$

d $x^3 - x = 0$

e $x^4 - 16 = 0$

f $(x+k)(x^2 - l^2) = 0$

6 Solve these equations.

a $x^4 - 2x^2 - 3 = 0$

b $y^{\frac{2}{3}} - 2y^{\frac{1}{3}} - 3 = 0$

c $2z + 3z^{\frac{1}{2}} - 2 = 0$

d $x^6 = 7x^3 - 12$

e $\frac{20}{x^2} - \frac{1}{x} = 1$

f $12 = a^4 - 11a^2$

7 The square of Adjua's age six years ago is equal to her age in six years' time. Find her present age.

8 The diagram shows the floor plan of a room. All lengths are given in metres.

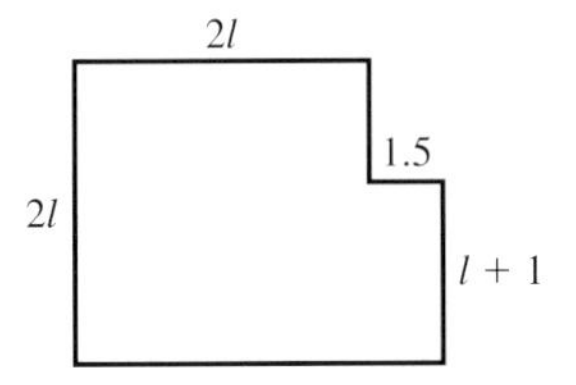

An architect uses this plan to design a room with a floor area of $22.5\,\text{m}^2$. Find the value of l correct to 3 significant figures.

9 A factory produces metal discs of radius $(r-1)$ mm and negligible thickness for making washers, and metal spheres of radius r mm for ball bearings. The total surface area of a disc (both sides) and a ball bearing is $132\pi\,\text{mm}^2$. (Surface area of a sphere is $4\pi r^2$.) Find r.

10 A ball is thrown in the air. After t seconds, its height, s, in metres above ground is given by the equation $2s = -10t^2 + 16t + 3$.

a Find t when the ball is 4.5 metres above the ground.

b Comment on the physical interpretation of the solution to part **a**.

11 A jar of jam weighs 750 g. There are $5n$ jars in a carton and $n + 3$ cartons in a pallet. A grocer has 3 full pallets, 4 cartons and 12 jars in the stockroom, with a total mass of 534 kg (excluding the mass of the pallets and cartons themselves). Find the number of jars in a carton and the number of cartons in a pallet.

3.5 Sketching quadratic functions: Use of the discriminant

The graph of any equation of the form $ax^2 + bx + c$ is a parabola.

- If $a > 0$ the parabola is ∪-shaped.
- If $a < 0$ the parabola is ∩-shaped.

The turning point on a parabola is called its **vertex**.

To sketch the parabola, first solve $ax^2 + bx + c = 0$.

	Discriminant		
	$b^2 - 4ac > 0$	$b^2 - 4ac = 0$	$b^2 - 4ac < 0$
Number of roots	Two distinct real roots	One repeated real root (2 equal roots)	No real roots (2 complex roots)
Intersection with the x-axis	Two distinct points	Curve touches x-axis (or curve meets x-axis in two coincident points)	Curve and x-axis do not meet
Sketch for $a > 0$	y, c, x, 0, α, β, Vertex	y, c, x, 0, α	y, c, x, 0
Sketch for $a < 0$	y, Vertex, c, x, α, 0, β	y, α, x, 0, c	y, x, 0, c

The value of the discriminant, $b^2 - 4ac$, can be used to determine whether the parabola cuts, touches or does not cut the x-axis. The roots of the equation, α and β, if they are real, show where the parabola cuts the x-axis; the constant, c, shows where it cuts the y-axis.

If α and β are real, the axis of symmetry of the parabola will be midway between α and β.

Example 34 State the number of distinct real roots of given equations.

a $3x^2 - 2x - 5 = 0$

Compare $3x^2 - 2x - 5 = 0$ with $ax^2 + bx + c = 0$.

$b^2 - 4ac = (-2)^2 - 4 \times 3 \times (-5) = 64 > 0$

$a = 3, b = -2, c = -5.$

Discriminant > 0.

Therefore the equation $3x^2 - 2x - 5 = 0$ has two distinct real roots.

b $x^2 - 2x + 1 = 0$

$a = 1, b = -2, c = 1.$

$b^2 - 4ac = (-2)^2 - 4 \times 1 = 0$

Discriminant $= 0$. Therefore the equation $x^2 - 2x + 1 = 0$ has a repeated root. That is, there is just one distinct root.

c $x^2 + 4 = 0$

$a = 1, b = 0, c = 4.$

$b^2 - 4ac = 0 - 4 \times 4 = -16 < 0$

Discriminant < 0. Therefore the equation $x^2 + 4 = 0$ has no real roots.

Example 35 By calculating the discriminant of $x^2 + 4x + 8 = 0$, or otherwise, show that $x^2 + 4x + 8$ is always positive.

$x^2 + 4x + 8 = 0$

$a = 1, b = 4, c = 8.$

Discriminant $= b^2 - 4ac$

$= 16 - 4 \times 1 \times 8 = -16 < 0$

Alternatively, completing the square,
$x^2 + 4x + 8 = (x + 2)^2 + 4$
$(x + 2)^2 \geqslant 0$
$\therefore \quad x^2 + 4x + 8$ is always positive.

Since the discriminant is less than zero, the graph of $y = x^2 + 4x + 8$ does not meet the x-axis. $a > 0$ so the parabola is ∪-shaped.

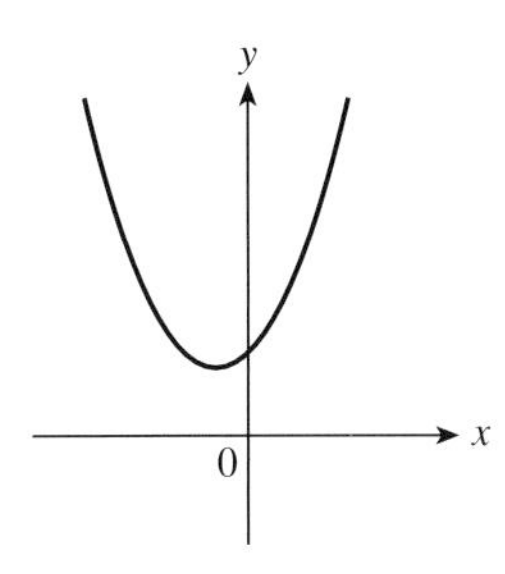

The graph lies above the x-axis so $x^2 + 4x + 8$ is always positive.

Example 36 Find the values of k for which $2(k-1)x^2 + 2kx + k - 1 = 0$ has equal roots.

Equal roots ⇒ discriminant = 0

$a = 2(k-1), b = 2k, c = k - 1.$

$$\begin{aligned} b^2 - 4ac &= 4k^2 - 4 \times 2(k-1)(k-1) \\ &= 4k^2 - 8(k^2 - 2k + 1) \\ &= 4k^2 - 8k^2 + 16k - 8 \\ &= -4k^2 + 16k - 8 \end{aligned}$$

The discriminant, $b^2 - 4ac$, is a quadratic expression in k so $b^2 - 4ac = 0$ introduces a second quadratic equation.

But $b^2 - 4ac = 0$, so

$-4k^2 + 16k - 8 = 0$

$k^2 - 4k + 2 = 0$

$a = 1, b = -4, c = 2.$

$$\Rightarrow \quad k = \frac{4 \pm \sqrt{4^2 - 4 \times 1 \times 2}}{2} = \frac{4 \pm \sqrt{8}}{2} = \frac{4 \pm 2\sqrt{2}}{2} = 2 \pm \sqrt{2}$$

Therefore the values of k for which $2(k-1)x^2 + 2kx + k - 1 = 0$ has equal roots are $k = 2 \pm \sqrt{2}$.

Example 37 Sketch $y = 3x^2 + 5x - 2$.

Consider $\quad 3x^2 + 5x - 2 = 0$

Discriminant $= 5^2 - 4 \times 3 \times (-2) = 25 + 24 > 0$ $\therefore$ curve cuts x-axis in two distinct points.

$$(3x - 1)(x + 2) = 0$$

$\Rightarrow \quad x = \frac{1}{3}$ or $x = -2$

Curve cuts x-axis at $(-2, 0)$ and $(\frac{1}{3}, 0)$.

Coefficient of x^2 term $= 3 > 0$ $\therefore$ curve is ∪-shaped.

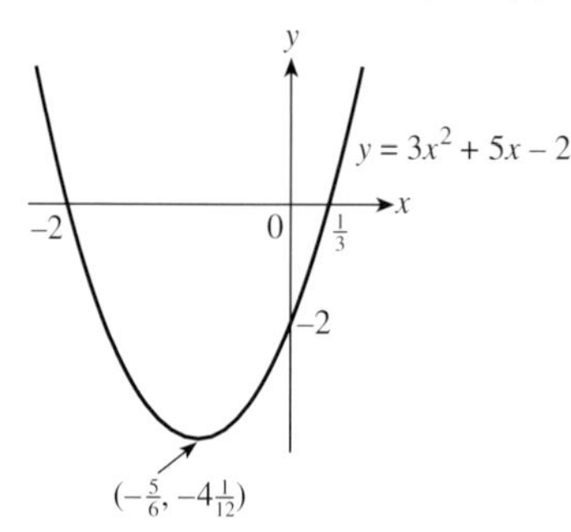

The graph has an axis of symmetry midway between the roots so the vertex should be to the **left** of the y-axis in this case.

When $x = 0$, $y = -2$ $\therefore$ curve cuts y-axis at $(0, -2)$.

Example 38 Use the method of completing the square to

a solve the quadratic equation $x^2 + 8x - 1 = 0$
b find the minimum value of $x^2 + 8x - 1$ and the value of x for which this occurs
c sketch the curve $y = x^2 + 8x - 1$, showing where the curve cuts the axes.

Solution

a $x^2 + 8x - 1 \equiv (x + 4)^2 - 16 - 1$ — Complete the square.

$$\equiv (x + 4)^2 - 17$$

So the equation $x^2 + 8x - 1 = 0$ can be written as $(x + 4)^2 - 17 = 0$.

Solving this:

$(x + 4)^2 - 17 = 0$ — Add 17 to both sides.

$(x + 4)^2 = 17$ — Take square root of both sides.

$x + 4 = \pm\sqrt{17}$ — *Remember*: This can be $+\sqrt{17}$ or $-\sqrt{17}$.

$x = -4 \pm \sqrt{17}$

b $x^2 + 8x - 1 \equiv (x + 4)^2 - 17$ — A square number cannot be –ve.

$(x + 4)^2 \geqslant 0$ for all values of x so the minimum value for $(x + 4)^2$ is zero and this occurs when $x = -4$.

When $x = -4$, $y = (x + 4)^2 - 17 = -17$.

So the minimum value of $x^2 + 8x - 1$ is -17 and this occurs when $x = -4$.

✓ ***Note*** the minimum value and the value of x where it occurs give the coordinates of the vertex of the parabola.

c $y = x^2 + 8x - 1$

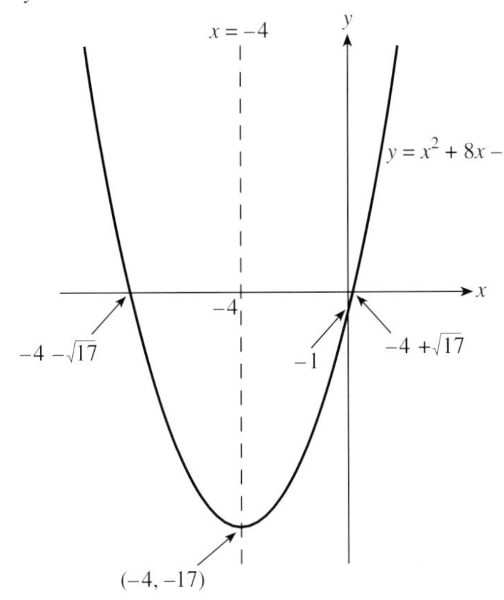

$a > 0 \quad \therefore$ parabola is ∪ shaped.

From part **b**, the graph has its vertex, a minimum point, at $(-4, -17)$.

When $x = 0$, $y = -1$.
$\therefore$ curve cuts y-axis at $y = -1$.

When $y = 0$, $x = -4 \pm \sqrt{17}$.
$\therefore$ curve cuts x-axis at $x = -4 \pm \sqrt{17}$.

The axis of symmetry (shown with a dotted line), is midway between the roots $-4 - \sqrt{17}$ and $-4 + \sqrt{17}$, i.e. $x = -4$ or $x + 4 = 0$.

➤ The information given by the **completed square form**:

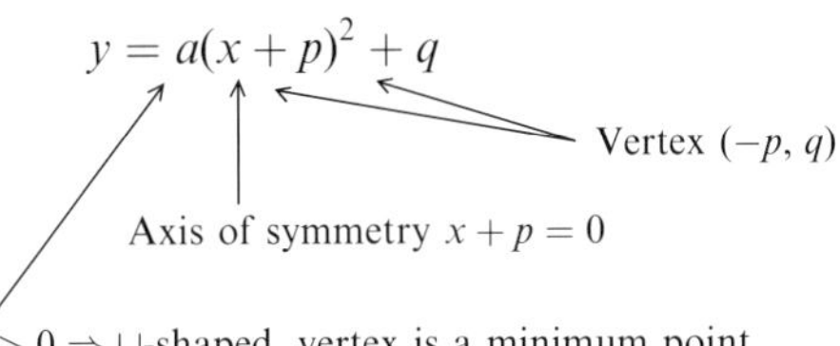

$a > 0 \Rightarrow$ ∪-shaped, vertex is a minimum point.
$a < 0 \Rightarrow$ ∩-shaped, vertex is a maximum point.

Example 39 Sketch $y = (x - 1)(x - 3)$, showing where the curve cuts the axes and the coordinates of the vertex.

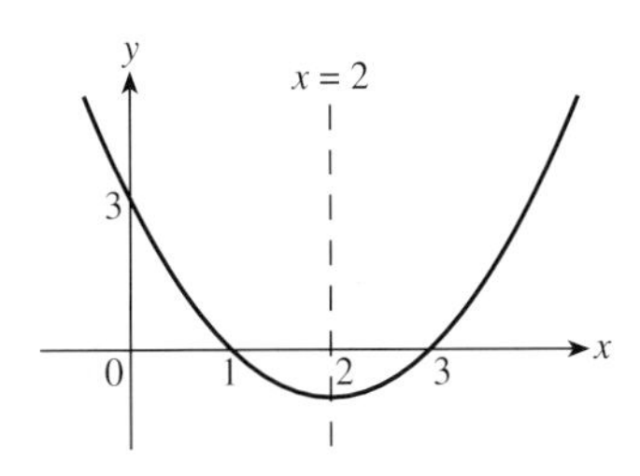

Coefficient of x^2 is +ve.
$\therefore$ ∪-shaped

$y = 0 \Rightarrow x = 1$ or $x = 3$
$\therefore$ intercepts on x-axis are $(1, 0)$ and $(3, 0)$

$x = 0 \Rightarrow y = 3$
$\therefore$ intercept on y-axis is $(0, 3)$

Axis of symmetry (shown dotted) is midway between the roots, i.e. at $x = 2$.

When $x = 2$, $y = (2 - 1)(2 - 3) = -1$.

$\therefore$ by symmetry, the vertex is at $(2, -1)$.

Example 40 Use the method of completing the square to sketch the curve $y = 7 - 6x - x^2$.

$7 - 6x - x^2 \equiv 16 - (x + 3)^2$ 　Complete the square.

So $\quad y = -(x + 3)^2 + 16$

The coefficient of x^2 is $-$ve so the parabola has a maximum point.

Maximum point is $(-3, 16)$. 　Parabola is ∩-shaped

Axis of symmetry is $x + 3 = 0$.

When $x = 0$, $y = 7$.

So, the intercept on y-axis is 7.

The curve cuts the x-axis where $y = 0$.

$$16 - (x + 3)^2 = 0$$

$$(x + 3)^2 = 16$$

$$x + 3 = \pm 4$$

$$x = -7 \text{ or } x = 1$$

So curve cuts x-axis at $(-7, 0)$ and $(1, 0)$.

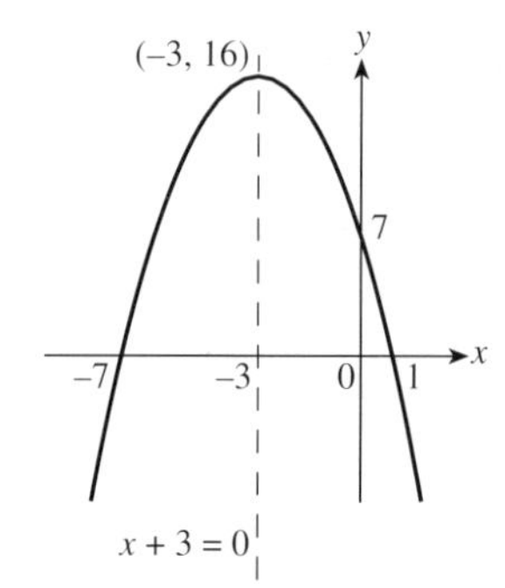

Factorising a quadratic expression using the discriminant

The discriminant, $b^2 - 4ac$, can be used to decide whether $ax^2 + bx + c$ can be factorised.

$b^2 - 4ac$	$ax^2 + bx + c$
> 0 and a perfect square	can be factorised with integers
> 0 and not a perfect square	can be factorised with surds
$= 0$	can be factorised as a perfect square
< 0	cannot be factorised with real numbers

If the solution of a quadratic equation is $x = \frac{2}{5}$ and $x = -\frac{4}{7}$, then, working backwards, the equation must be $(5x - 2)(7x + 4) = 0$. So, given the solution, one can work backwards to the factorised form.

Example 41 Factorise $2x^2 - 3x - 20$.

The discriminant of $2x^2 - 3x - 20 = 0$ is $3^2 + 4 \times 2 \times 20 = 169 = 13^2$.

Since the discriminant is a perfect square, the expression can be factorised using integers. Solving $2x^2 - 3x - 20 = 0$ gives

$$x = \frac{3 \pm \sqrt{169}}{4}$$

$$= \frac{3 \pm 13}{4}$$

$\therefore \quad x = 4$ or $x = -\frac{5}{2}$ 　$x = 4$ or $x = -\frac{5}{2} \Leftrightarrow (x - 4)(2x + 5) = 0$.

So (working backwards): $2x^2 - 3x - 20 = (x - 4)(2x + 5)$

3.6 Location of roots

Some equations are difficult, or impossible, to solve algebraically, e.g. $x^4 - 2x^3 - 4 = 0$.

An approximate solution can be found by plotting the graph of $y = x^4 - 2x^3 - 4$. The roots of the equation are the values of x where the graph crosses the x-axis, i.e. where $y = 0$. The graph shows that there is one root between $x = -1$ and $x = -2$ and another between $x = 2$ and $x = 3$.

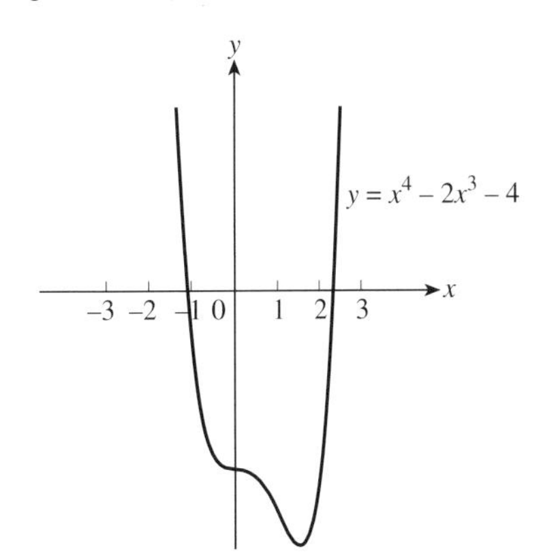

Notice from the graph that, for each root, the curve is above the x-axis on one side of the root and below on the other.

Using function notation, with $f(x) = x^4 - 2x^3 - 4$:

$f(-2) = 28 > 0 \quad f(-1) = -1 < 0$ Notice the change in sign between $f(-2)$ and $f(-1)$.

$f(2) = -4 < 0 \quad f(3) = 23 > 0$ Notice the change in sign between $f(2)$ and $f(3)$.

So, if two values of x, x_1 and x_2, can be found such that $f(x_1)$ and $f(x_2)$ have *different* signs, then, providing the curve is continuous,* i.e. there are no breaks in the curve, there will be at least one root between x_1 and x_2. (The converse is *not* necessarily true. See Question 5 in Exercise 3e.)

Example 42 Show that $x^3 + 3 = 2x$ has a root between -1 and -2.

$$x^3 + 3 = 2x$$

$$x^3 - 2x + 3 = 0$$

Arrange with zero on RHS.

Let $f(x) = x^3 - 2x + 3$.

Use function notation. The function is a polynomial, so it is continuous.

$$f(-2) = (-2)^3 - 2 \times (-2) + 3 = -1 < 0$$

$$f(-1) = (-1)^3 - 2 \times (-1) + 3 = 4 > 0$$

To show that $f(x) = 0$ has a root between -1 and -2 show that $f(-1)$ and $f(-2)$ have different signs.

The function is continuous and $f(-2)$ and $f(-1)$ have different signs.
So $x^3 + 3 = 2x$ has a root between -1 and -2.

EXERCISE 3d

1 Find, by completing the square, the maximum or minimum values of each of these. State the value of x for which each maximum or minimum occurs.

a $x^2 - 2x + 3$ **b** $x^2 + 6x - 7$ **c** $8 + 6x - x^2$
d $4 - 2x - x^2$ **e** $x^2 + 3x - 1$ **f** $x^2 - 5x - 7$
g $3 - x - x^2$ **h** $9 + 3x - x^2$ **i** $2x^2 + 8x + 1$
j $3x^2 - x + 4$ **k** $6 - x - 2x^2$ **l** $1 + 12x - 6x^2$

2 Use the method of completing the square to find the maximum or minimum values of each of these functions and then sketch the curves, $y = f(x)$, marking the coordinates of the vertex and the intercept on the y-axis.

a $f(x) = x^2 - 2x - 1$ **b** $f(x) = x^2 + 4x + 9$ **c** $f(x) = 3 + 6x - x^2$

*All polynomials are continuous functions.

EXERCISE 3d
(continued)

3 Find the relation between a and b if $ax^2 + bx + 1 = 0$ has equal roots (i.e. one repeated root).

4 Find the value(s) of k if these equations have equal roots.

a $x^2 - 2x + k = 0$ b $4x^2 + kx + 9 = 0$ c $x^2 + (2k + 10)x + k^2 + 5 = 0$

5 If $x^2 + mx + n$ is a perfect square, show that $m^2 = 4n$.

6 Find an equation whose roots are

a 2, 3 b 3, −5 c 0, −6 d p, q

7 Show that $2x^3 + x - 4 = 0$ has a root between 1 and 2.

8 a Show that $x^3 - 7x + 1 = 0$ has a root between 0 and 1.

b Show that $x^3 - 7x + 1 = 0$ has a root between 0.143 and 0.144. Hence state a root of $x^3 - 7x + 1 = 0$ correct to 2 d.p.

9 Given that $f(x) = 3 + x - x^4$, show that the equation $f(x) = 0$ has roots a and b where $-2 < a < -1$ and $1 < b < 2$.

10 Show that $x^3 - 5x - 3 = 0$ has roots in the intervals $[-2, -1]$, $[-1, 0]$ and $[2, 3]$.

11 Show that $x^4 = 3x^3 - x + 1$ has a root between 2 and 3.

12 Calculate the possible values of k if $(k + 1)x^2 + kx + k + 1 = 0$ has a repeated root.

13 By completing the square show that $x^2 + 2x + 5$ is positive for all real values of x.

14 Show that $x^2 + 2px + 2p^2$ is positive for all real values of x.

EXERCISE 3e
(Extension)

1 Solve these equations.

a $9x = \dfrac{4}{x+1}$ b $\dfrac{2x-1}{1-x} = \dfrac{x-2}{x+3}$ c $\dfrac{4}{x+1} - \dfrac{2}{x-2} = -1$

d $\dfrac{x+10}{x-5} - \dfrac{10}{x} = \dfrac{11}{6}$ e $\dfrac{15}{x+1} - \dfrac{8}{x-2} = \dfrac{3}{x-5}$ f $\dfrac{1}{x-1} = \dfrac{x+1}{2x+7}$

2 Solve these equations for x.

a $(x - a)^3 - b^2(x - a) = 0$ b $x^3 + a^2x = 0$

c $x^4 - a^4 = 0$ d $(x - p)^3 = q^3$

e $x^5 + k^2x = 0$ f $x^6 - 7k^3x^3 - 8k^6 = 0$

3 Transform these formulae to make the letter in the brackets the subject.

a $\dfrac{y-k}{K-k} = \dfrac{x-h}{H-h}$ (y) b $2x - 3y - 3mx + 2my - 2m + 4 = 0$ (m)

c $\dfrac{c}{t} = \dfrac{x-ct}{t^2}$ (x) d $3mc = (4 + 3m)(c - 4)$ (c)

e $x - \dfrac{c}{t} = -t^2(x + ct)$ (x) f $\dfrac{R-r}{R+r} = \dfrac{r+a}{r+b}$ (R)

4 Solve $(b + 1)x^2 - (b^2 + b + 1)x + b = 0$ for x.

5 Explain, with the aid of sketches, for the equation $f(x) = 0$, how

a given $f(x_1) > 0$ and $f(x_2) < 0$, $x_1 < x_2$, there could be
 i more than one root α such that $x_1 < \alpha < x_2$
 ii no root α such that $x_1 < \alpha < x_2$

b there could be a root α and yet no values x_1 and x_2, such that $f(x_1)$ and $f(x_2)$ have different signs.

6 a Show that a necessary and sufficient condition for α and β to be the roots of a quadratic equation is $x^2 - (\alpha + \beta)x + \alpha\beta = 0$.

b By comparing $x^2 - (\alpha + \beta)x + \alpha\beta = 0$ with $ax^2 + bx + c = 0$ show that
 i the sum of the roots of $ax^2 + bx + c = 0$ is $-\dfrac{b}{a}$
 ii the product of the roots of $ax^2 + bx + c = 0$ is $\dfrac{c}{a}$.

c Show that if α, β and γ are the roots of the cubic equation $ax^3 + bx^2 + cx + d = 0$ then
 i $\alpha + \beta + \gamma = -\dfrac{b}{a}$
 ii $\alpha\beta + \beta\gamma + \gamma\alpha = \dfrac{c}{a}$
 iii $\alpha\beta\gamma = -\dfrac{d}{a}$.

EXERCISE 3f (Miscellaneous)

1 Solve for x.

a $3x + 4 = 6 - 7x$ b $2(x + 1) - (3x - 4) = 8 - (x + 2)$
c $x^2 - 4 = 0$ d $x^2 - 4x = 0$
e $x^3 - 4x = 0$ f $x^3 = 7x^2$
g $x^3 - x^2 - 20x = 0$ h $x^4 - 81 = 0$
i $x^4 - 17x^2 + 16 = 0$ j $9x^4 + 5x^2 - 4 = 0$
k $x^5 - x^3 = 0$ l $x^4 - 1 = 0$

2 Solve for x.

a $ax - b = 2x$ b $x^2 + y^2 = r^2$ c $\dfrac{ax + b}{cx + d} = k$ d $l = \frac{1}{2}\sqrt{\dfrac{2}{x}}$

3 Solve for x.

a $x^2 + kx = 0$ b $x^2 - a^2 = 0$ c $x^3 + kx^2 = 0$ d $(x - a)^2 = b^2$

4 Multiply $x^{\frac{2}{3}} + 2x^{\frac{1}{3}} + 1$ by $x^{\frac{1}{3}} - 2$. Check the answer by substituting $x = 8$.

5 Show, either by calculating the discriminant or by completing the square, that

a $x^2 - 8x + 20$ is never zero b $12 - 4x - x^2 = 0$ has two distinct real roots

6 Use the method of completing the square to sketch

a $y = x^2 + 10x + 4$ b $y = 6 + x - x^2$
c $y = 2x^2 - 4x + 1$ d $y = 4 - 2x - 4x^2$

7 Find p, q and r such that $5x^2 - 2x + 1 \equiv p(x - q)^2 + r$. Hence, find the minimum value of $5x^2 - 2x + 1$ and the value of x for which it occurs.

8 Find the value of k for which $6x^2 + 2x + k = 0$ has equal roots.

9 The graphs of five quadratic functions are shown. Find an equation for each graph.

a

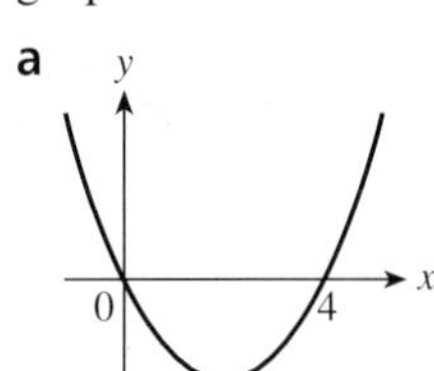

b

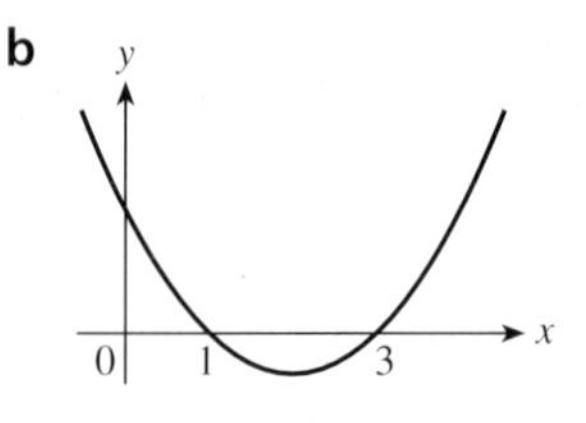

c

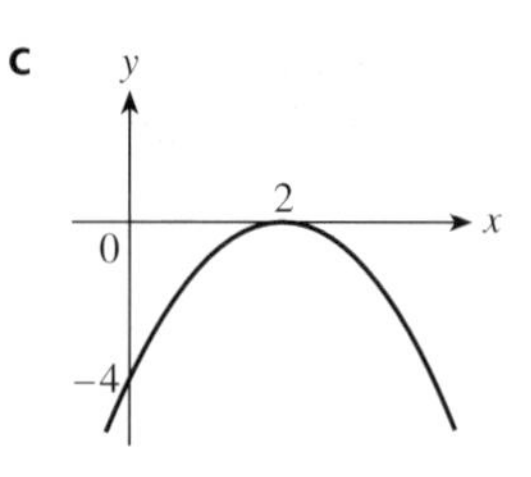

d

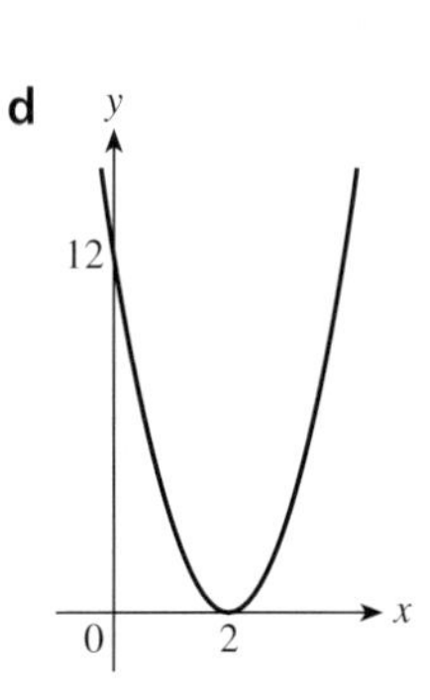

e

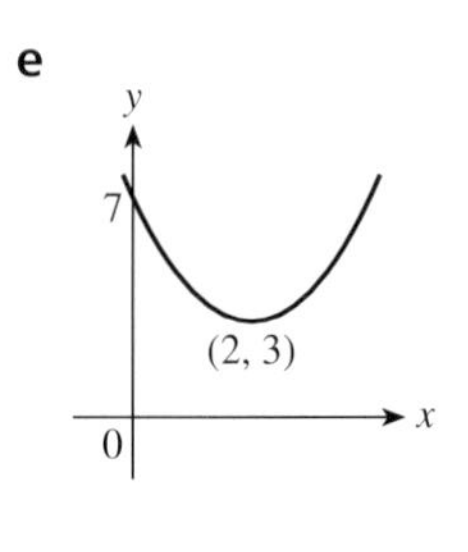

Test yourself

1 If $2x + 1 = 3(x + 3) - 2(7 - x)$ then x is equal to

A $\frac{2}{3}$ **B** 2 **C** 3 **D** $3\frac{1}{3}$ **E** -2

2 The vertex of the parabola $y = x^2 + 6x + 2$ is at

A (6, 2) **B** (3, 2) **C** (3, −7) **D** (−3, −4) **E** (−3, −7)

3 If $3k^2 - 5k = 2$ then k is equal to

A 0 or $1\frac{2}{3}$ **B** -2 or $\frac{1}{3}$ **C** -3 or 2 **D** $-\frac{1}{3}$ or 2 **E** $\frac{2}{3}$ or 1

4 If $\dfrac{x^2 - a}{x^2} = 2b - b^2$ then x is equal to

A $\dfrac{\pm\sqrt{a}}{b - 1}$ **B** $\pm\sqrt{\dfrac{b^2 - 2b - a}{2}}$ **C** $\dfrac{\pm a}{\sqrt{b + 1}}$

D $\pm\sqrt{\dfrac{a}{b^2 - 2b}}$ **E** none of these

5 If $\dfrac{y + 2}{y - 1} = \dfrac{y + 10}{y + 1}$ then y is equal to

A -1 or -2 **B** 1 or -10 **C** 2 **D** $-2\frac{2}{3}$ **E** $1\frac{1}{2}$

6 The roots of $2x^2 - 4x - 3 = 0$ are

A $2 \pm \sqrt{2}$ **B** $1 \pm \dfrac{\sqrt{10}}{2}$ **C** 1 and $1\frac{1}{2}$ **D** $1 \pm \sqrt{5}$ **E** $-\frac{1}{2}$ and 3

7 Given that $2x^2 + kx + 8 = 0$ has equal roots and $k > 0$, $k =$

A 0 **B** $2\sqrt{2}$ **C** 64 **D** 8 **E** 4

Key points

Cross-multiplying

$\frac{a}{b} = \frac{c}{d} \Leftrightarrow ad = bc \quad (b \neq 0, d \neq 0)$

Solving equations

Linear equations

- Do the same to both sides.
- Collect all the terms in the unknown on one side.

Quadratic equations

- Factorisation $(x - \alpha)(x - \beta) = 0 \Rightarrow x = \alpha$ or $x = \beta$
- Completing the square: $x^2 - kx + c = 0 \Rightarrow \left(x - \frac{k}{2}\right)^2 - \frac{k^2}{4} + c = 0$
- Formula: $ax^2 + bx + c = 0 \Rightarrow x = \frac{-b \pm \sqrt{b^2 - 4ac}}{2a}$

Rearranging formulae

- Do the same to both sides.
- Collect all the terms in the unknown on one side.

Discriminant of a quadratic equation

$b^2 - 4ac$ is the discriminant of the equation $ax^2 + bx + c = 0$

- $b^2 - 4ac > 0 \Rightarrow 2$ distinct real roots
- $b^2 - 4ac = 0 \Rightarrow 1$ repeated real root (2 equal roots)
- $b^2 - 4ac < 0 \Rightarrow$ No real roots.

Sketching a quadratic function

For $y = ax^2 + bx + c$

- $a > 0 \Rightarrow$ curve is ∪-shaped and has a minimum point.
- $a < 0 \Rightarrow$ curve is ∩-shaped and has a maximum point.
- The axis of symmetry is $x = -\frac{b}{2a}$.
- The discriminant indicates in how many points the curve cuts the x-axis.

For the completed-square form $y = a(x + p)^2 + q$

- The vertex is at $(-p, q)$.
- The axis of symmetry is $x = -p$.

Location of roots

- Locate a root of $f(x) = 0$ by looking for a change in sign in $f(x)$.
- For a continuous function $f(x)$, the equation $f(x) = 0$ will have at least one root between x_1 and x_2 if $f(x_1)$ and $f(x_2)$ have *different* signs.

4 Inequalities, Identities and the Modulus Function

Before starting this chapter you will need to know

- how to solve linear and quadratic equations (Chapter 3)
- how to sketch quadratic functions (Chapter 3).

4.1 Linear inequalities

Consider the true statements $3 < 4$ and $-3 < 2$.

- Certain operations carried out on both sides of an inequality will not affect the truth of the statement.
- For some other operations, the direction of the inequality sign must be reversed for the statement to remain true.
- Other operations should not be carried out since the inequality may or may not still be true.

EXERCISE 4a

1 Perform these operations on the inequality $3 < 4$.

In each case, state if the resulting inequality is true.

a Add 4 to both sides.

b Subtract 100 from both sides.

c Multiply both sides by 6.

d Divide both sides by -1.

e Square both sides.

f Take the reciprocal of both sides.

g Cube both sides.

2 Repeat Question **1** for the inequality $-3 < 2$.

The results of this exercise can be summarised as follows.

Linear inequalities are solved by doing the same to both sides, bearing in mind the situations where the sign must be reversed and avoiding unsafe operations.

Inequality *unaffected*:

- When adding same quantity to (or subtracting from) both sides
- When multiplying (or dividing) both sides by the same *positive* quantity
- Providing they are positive, squaring both sides

Inequality *true if sign is reversed*:

- When multiplying (or dividing) both sides by the same *negative* quantity
- Providing they are positive, taking the reciprocal of both sides

Unsafe operations:

- If either of the quantities is negative, squaring both sides or taking their reciprocals

Example 1 shows two methods of solving an inequality and that both solutions give the same answer.

Example 1

Solve $7x + 13 < 2x - 7$.

As with linear equations, all x terms must be collected on one side, with the rest of the terms on the other side.

$7x + 13 < 2x - 7$

$7x - 2x < -7 - 13$ — Do this first by subtracting $2x$ and 13 from both sides.

$5x < -20$

$x < -4$ — Now, divide by 5. Division is by a positive quantity, so no need to reverse the sign.

Alternatively

$7x + 13 < 2x - 7$ — This time, subtract $7x$ and add 7. This will result in $-5x$ on RHS

$13 + 7 < 2x - 7x$

$20 < -5x$ — Now, divide by -5. Division is by a *negative* quantity, so the sign must be *reversed.*

$-4 > x$

$x < -4$ — *Note*: x is written on the LHS.

✓ ***Note*** It is usually possible, and makes sense, to avoid multiplying or dividing by a negative number by keeping the coefficient of x positive, as in the first solution.

Example 2

Find the range of values for which $2 < 3x - 4 \leqslant 7$. Illustrate the solution on a number line.

Consider this as two separate inequalities: $2 < 3x - 4$ and $3x - 4 \leqslant 7$.

$2 < 3x - 4$	$3x - 4 \leqslant 7$	To isolate x, add 4 to both sides.
$6 < 3x$	$3x \leqslant 11$	Divide each side by 3.
$2 < x$	$x \leqslant \frac{11}{3}$	Rewrite with x on the LHS.

For both inequalities to hold $x > 2$ and $x \leqslant \frac{11}{3}$.

The two resulting inequalities can be shown on two separate number lines.

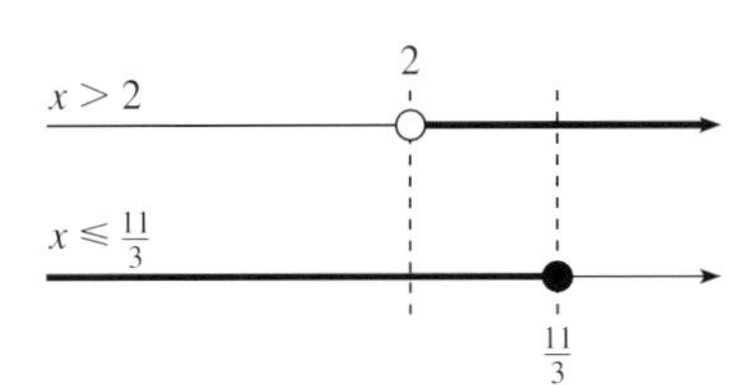

Note: The empty circle indicates that x cannot equal 2. The full circle indicates that x can equal $\frac{11}{3}$.

For both inequalities to hold, $2 < x \leqslant 3\frac{2}{3}$.

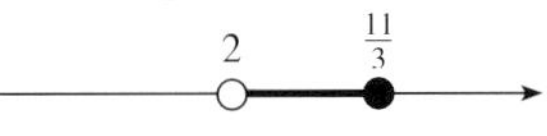

Combine this into a single number line.

EXERCISE 4b

1 Solve these inequalities.

a $3x + 4 < 2$ **b** $4 + 2x \geqslant 3$ **c** $2 \geqslant 7x - 5$

d $7 < 1 - 2x$ **e** $2a - 1 < 6a - 12$ **f** $3b + 4 > 6b + 5$

g $5c + 1 \geqslant 2c - 1$ **h** $2d + 9 \geqslant 5d - 2$ **i** $3 - 5e \leqslant 7 - 3e$

j $5f - 3 > 5 - 3f$ **k** $7 + 2(h - 3) < 1$ **l** $5 - (2 - 3x) \leqslant 9$

m $1 - (4x + 1) < 8$ **n** $7 + 2(5 - 3x) > 6x$

EXERCISE 4b *(continued)*

2 Solve these inequalities.

a $4(g-2) > 3(g-1)$ **b** $2(2x-1) < 3(3x+1)$

c $2+3(x-4) < 3(2x-5)$ **d** $x+4(3-2x) \geqslant 2-2(4-3x)$

3 Solve these inequalities. Illustrate each solution on a number line.

a $-1 < 2x+1 < 11$ **b** $4 \leqslant 7x-3 \leqslant 11$ **c** $6 < 4-x < 7$

d $-1 < 5x+3 \leqslant 7$ **e** $3x < 5x+1 \leqslant 2x+9$ **f** $2-x < 5+2x < 8$

4.2 Quadratic (and other) inequalities

Consider the inequalities $x^2 < 4$ and $x^2 > 9$ and the numbers on the number line that would satisfy them.

$x^2 < 4 \Leftrightarrow -2 < x < 2$

-2 $+2$

$x^2 > 9 \Leftrightarrow x < -3$ or $x > 3$

-3 $+3$

✓ ***Note*** $x < -3$ or $x > 3$. These inequalities represent two *separate* parts of the number line; they must *not* be combined in a single inequality.

These solutions can be illustrated graphically. (The bold lines show where the inequality holds.)

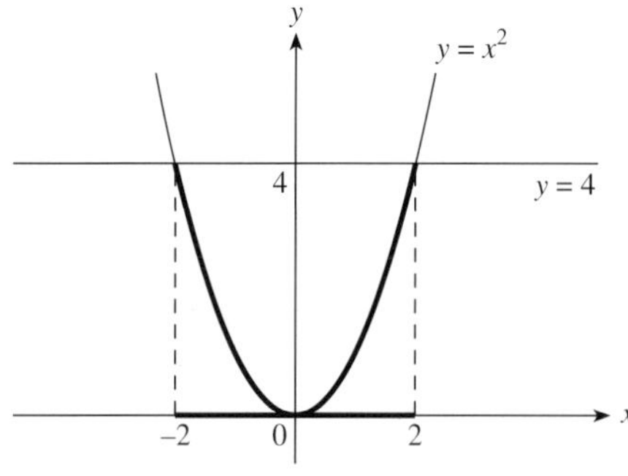

x^2 is less than 4 when the curve $y = x^2$ is *below* the line $y = 4$.
This occurs when $-2 < x < 2$.

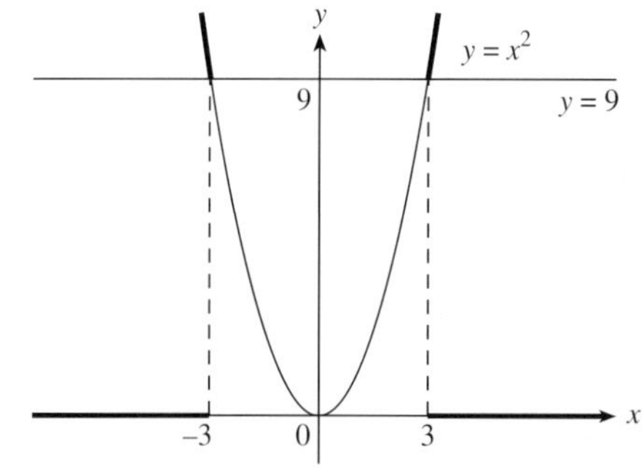

x^2 is greater than 9 when the curve $y = x^2$ is *above* the line $y = 9$.
This occurs when $x < -3$ or $x > 3$.

So $\quad x^2 < a^2 \Leftrightarrow -a < x < a \quad (a > 0)$

and $\quad x^2 > a^2 \Leftrightarrow x < -a \quad$ or $\quad x > a \quad (a > 0)$

For inequalities such as $x^2 - x - 2 > 0$, a graphical approach can be used. Solving the inequality, in this example, means finding the values of x for which $y = x^2 - x - 2 > 0$, i.e. for which the curve is above the x-axis.

To sketch $y = x^2 - x - 2$

$y = x^2 - x - 2 = (x - 2)(x + 1)$

When $y = 0$, $x = -1$ or $x = 2$. So the curve cuts the x-axis at $x = -1$ and $x = 2$.

The coefficient of x^2 is +ve, so the graph is ∪-shaped.

The values of y are *greater than zero*, i.e. $x^2 - x - 2 > 0$, when the curve is *above* the x-axis. That is, when $x < -1$ and $x > 2$.

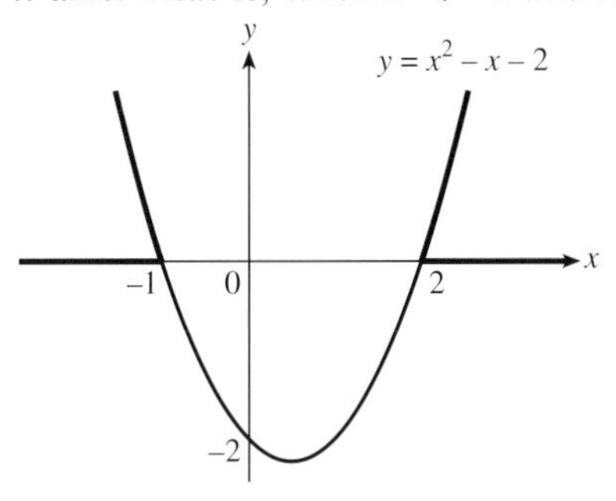

✓ ***Note*** If the inequality had been reversed, i.e. $x^2 - x - 2 < 0$ the solution would be $-1 < x < 2$.

Any real solution to a quadratic inequality, $f(x) > 0$ or $f(x) < 0$, is either the range of values *between* the roots of $f(x) = 0$ or the range of values *outside* the roots.

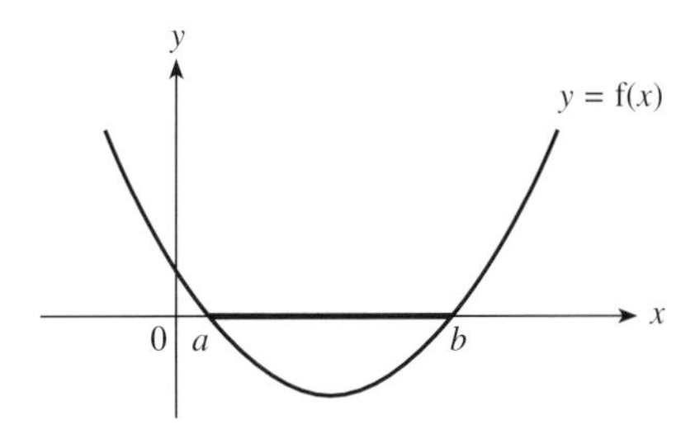

$f(x) < 0$ between the roots: $a < x < b$

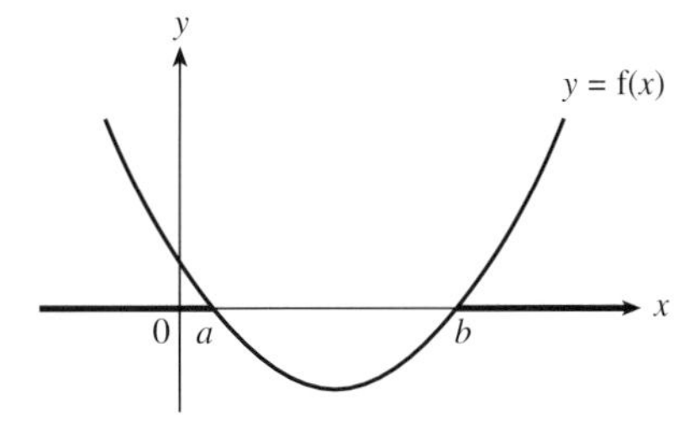

$f(x) > 0$ outside the roots: $x < a$ and $x > b$

➤ **To solve a quadratic inequality**

- Arrange the inequality with $ax^2 + bx + c$ on one side and zero on the other.
- Solve $ax^2 + bx + c = 0$.
- Sketch $y = ax^2 + bx + c$, marking only the intercepts on the x-axis.
- Look at the inequality sign to decide on the range of values of x required to make the inequality true. (This range will either be between the roots or be outside the roots of $ax^2 + bx + c = 0$.)

Example 3 Solve $6 - x - x^2 < 0$.

Consider $\quad 6 - x - x^2 = 0$

$$(3 + x)(2 - x) = 0$$

$\therefore \quad x = -3$ or $x = 2$

A sketch of $y = 6 - x - x^2$ is required. Solve $ax^2 + bx + c = 0$.

Coefficient of x^2 term is $-$ve, so curve is ∩-shaped.

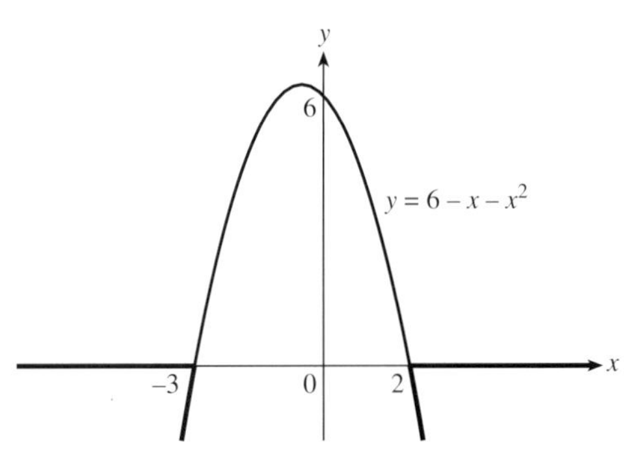

Sketch $y = ax^2 + bx + c$ marking the intercepts on the x-axis.

$y < 0$ when the curve is below the x-axis, i.e. for values of x outside the roots.

So $\quad 6 - x - x^2 < 0$ when $\quad x < -3$ or $x > 2$.

$\therefore \quad x < -3$ or $x > 2$.

Example 4 Solve $(3x - 1)(x + 1) \leqslant x(2x - 3) - 5$.

$(3x - 1)(x + 1) \leqslant x(2x - 3) - 5$

Remove the brackets.

$3x^2 + 2x - 1 \leqslant 2x^2 - 3x - 5$

Rearrange with $ax^2 + bx + c$ on LHS and zero on RHS.

$x^2 + 5x + 4 \leqslant 0$

$x^2 + 5x + 4 = 0$

A sketch of $y = x^2 + 5x + 4$ is required. Solve $ax^2 + bx + c = 0$

So $\quad (x + 1)(x + 4) = 0$

$\therefore \quad x = -1$ or $x = -4$

Coefficient of x^2 term is $+$ve, so curve is ∪-shaped.

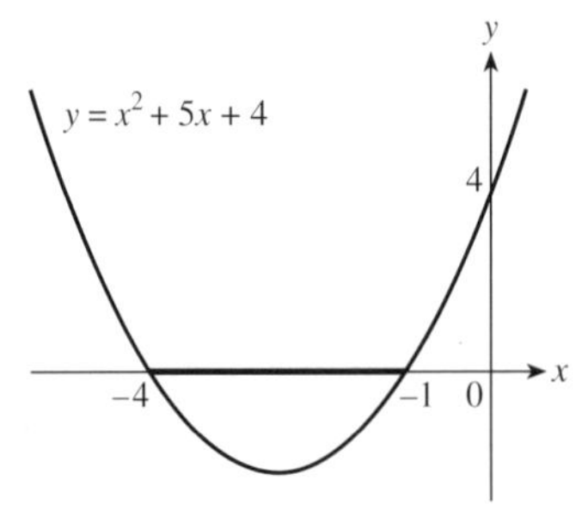

Sketch $y = ax^2 + bx + c$ marking the intercepts on the x-axis.

So $\quad x^2 + 5x + 4 \leqslant 0$

$\therefore \quad -4 \leqslant x \leqslant -1$

$y \leqslant 0$ when the curve is below the x-axis, i.e. for values of x between the roots.

The solution is $-4 \leqslant x \leqslant -1$.

✓ ***Note*** For a quadratic inequality with sign $\geqslant$ or $\leqslant$ the roots *are* included, so use $\geqslant$ or $\leqslant$ in the answer. For sign $>$ or $<$ the roots are excluded so use $>$ or $<$.

Polynomial inequalities with more than two linear factors can also be solved by a sketching method.

Example 5 Solve $(x-2)(x+1)(x+4) > 0$.

Sketching $y=(x-2)(x+1)(x+4)$

Sketch $y=(x-2)(x+1)(x+4)$ marking the intercepts on the x-axis. $y>0$ when the curve is above the x-axis.

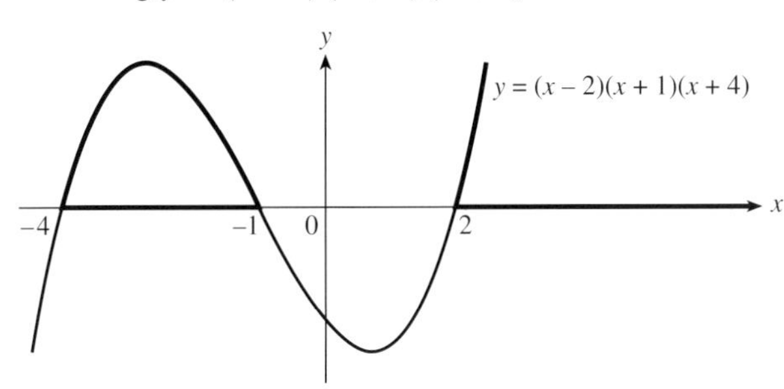

So $(x-2)(x+1)(x+4) > 0 \Rightarrow -4 < x < -1$ or $x > 2$.

EXERCISE 4c

1 Solve these inequalities.

a $(x-2)(x-3) < 0$ **b** $(x+4)(x-5) > 0$ **c** $(2x+1)(x-1) \geqslant 0$

d $(2x-5)(3-2x) \leqslant 0$ **e** $x^2 - x > 0$ **f** $6 + x - x^2 < 0$

g $x^2 - 3x + 2 < 0$ **h** $x^2 - 7x - 18 > 0$ **i** $x^2 - x - 6 \geqslant 0$

j $4x - 3x^2 < 0$ **k** $y^2 - 7y + 12 > 0$ **l** $y^2 - 4y - 5 \geqslant 0$

m $6y^2 - 7y + 2 \leqslant 0$ **n** $3 - 5y - 8y^2 > 0$ **o** $2u^2 + 7u + 3 \leqslant 0$

p $2v^2 + 7v - 4 < 0$ **q** $4x^2 + 4x + 1 \geqslant 0$ **r** $9 + 6x + x^2 < 0$

2 Solve these inequalities.

a $3x^2 - 2 < 5x$ **b** $4x + 5 < 9x^2$

c $5x - x^2 > 4$ **d** $4(x-1) \geqslant x^2$

e $(x+1)^2 \leqslant 6x^2 + x + 1$ **f** $(x-5)^2 + 5(2x-3) > 2x(x+3) - 6$

3 Solve

a $(x-1)(x-2)(x+3) \leqslant 0$ **b** $(x-1)(2x-1)(4-x) > 0$

c $(5x-1)(x-1)^2 < 0$ **d** $(x^2-1)(x^2-4) \leqslant 0$

4.3 Identities

An identity is true for all values of the variable.

Example 6

This example shows one method of proving an identity: to start with one side and by algebraic manipulation show that it is equal to the other side.

Prove that $x^2 + 2x - 2 \equiv (x+1)(x-1) + 2(x+1) - 3$.

RHS $\equiv (x+1)(x-1) + 2(x+1) - 3$ — Start with the RHS as it can be simplified.

$\equiv x^2 - 1 + 2x + 2 - 3$ — Show, by simplifying, that it equals the LHS.

$\equiv x^2 + 2x - 2$

$\equiv$ LHS

To find unknowns in an identity use either **substitution** (as in Example 7) or **equating coefficients** (as in Example 8).

Example 7 Find A and B given that $6x + 9 \equiv A(x + 1) + B(x - 2)$.

Use substitution.

$6x + 9 \equiv A(x + 1) + B(x - 2)$

Since this is an identity and thus true for all values of x, any value can be substituted.

Putting $x = -1$

$-6 + 9 = A \times 0 - 3B$

$3 = -3B$

$B = -1$

Putting $x = -1$ eliminates one of the terms on RHS since it makes the bracket $(x + 1)$ zero.

Putting $x = 2$

$12 + 9 = 3A + B \times 0$

$21 = 3A$

$A = 7$

Putting $x = 2$ eliminates the other term on the RHS since it makes the bracket $(x - 2)$ zero.

So $A = 7$ and $B = -1$, and $6x + 9 \equiv 7(x + 1) - (x - 2)$.

This can easily be checked by multiplying out the RHS.

Example 8

In an identity, the expressions on the LHS and RHS are identically equal, therefore the coefficients of the x^3, x^2 and x terms must be equal. Similarly, the constant terms must be equal.

Find A, B and C given that $4x^3 - 2x^2 - 3x - 12 \equiv Ax(x^2 + 1) + Bx^2(x - 2) + C(x + 2)$.

$$4x^3 - 2x^2 - 3x - 12 \equiv Ax(x^2 + 1) + Bx^2(x - 2) + C(x + 2)$$
$$\equiv Ax^3 + Ax + Bx^3 - 2Bx^2 + Cx + 2C$$
$$\equiv (A + B)x^3 - 2Bx^2 + (A + C)x + 2C$$

Multiplying out brackets and collecting like terms makes it easier to compare coefficients. With practice, the coefficients can be worked out mentally.

Equating constant terms $\quad -12 = 2C \quad \Rightarrow C = -6$

Equating coefficients of x terms $\quad -3 = A + C \Rightarrow A = 3$

Equating coefficients of x^2 terms $\quad -2 = -2B \quad \Rightarrow B = 1$

So $A = 3$, $B = 1$, $C = -6$.

EXERCISE 4d

1 Find the values of A and B in these identities.

a $5x - 14 \equiv A(x - 1) + B(x - 4)$
b $2x + 6 \equiv A(x + 2) + B(x + 4)$
c $-x \equiv A(x - 3) - B(x - 2)$
d $5x + 17 \equiv A(x + 2) - B(x - 5)$
e $2x - 4 \equiv A(3 + x) + B(7 - x)$
f $5x - 7 \equiv A(x - 1) + B(2x - 3)$
g $8x + 1 \equiv A(3x - 1) + B(2x + 3)$

2 Find the values of A, B and C in these identities.

a $6x^2 - 25x + 23 \equiv A(x - 1)(x - 2) + B(x - 2)(x - 3) + C(x - 3)(x - 1)$
b $4x^2 - 2x + 4 \equiv Ax(x + 2) + B(x + 2)(x - 2) + Cx(x - 2)$
c $4x^2 + 4x - 26 \equiv A(x + 2)(x - 4) + B(x - 4)(x - 1) + C(x - 1)(x + 2)$
d $2x^2 - 22x + 53 \equiv A(x - 5)(x - 3) + B(x - 3)(x + 2) + C(x + 2)(x - 5)$
e $2 \equiv A(x - 1)(x + 1) + Bx(x + 1) + Cx(x - 1)$
f $2x^2 + 9x - 10 \equiv A(x - 3)(x + 4) + B(x + 2)(x + 4) + C(x + 2)(x - 3)$

3 Show that these are identities, i.e. true for all values of x.

a $(2x + 3)(x - 7) - 2(x + 8)(x - 2) = 11 - 23x$

b $\dfrac{1}{2x + 1} + \dfrac{3}{x - 4} = \dfrac{7x - 1}{(2x + 1)(x - 4)}$

4.4 The modulus function

The notation $|x|$ means the magnitude of x, ignoring the sign. So, for example, $|6| = 6$ and $|-7| = 7$.

➤

$\lvert x\rvert = x$	if $x \geqslant 0$
$\lvert x\rvert = -x$	if $x < 0$

For $|x|$ read 'mod x'.

✓ ***Note*** $|a| = |b| \Leftrightarrow a^2 = b^2$.

The modulus function can be used to express a range.

➤

$\lvert x\rvert < a \Leftrightarrow -a < x < a$	$\lvert x\rvert > a \Leftrightarrow x < -a$ or $x > a$

$|x| < 1 \Leftrightarrow -1 < x < 1$

$|x| \geqslant 1 \Leftrightarrow x \leqslant -1$ or $x \geqslant 1$

−1 1 −1 1

✓ ***Remember*** 'Empty' circles indicate that x cannot be equal to -1 or $+1$. 'Full' circles indicate x can be equal to -1 or $+1$.

- $|x - a| = x - a$ for $x \geqslant a$ and $|x - a| = -(x - a) = a - x$ for $x < a$
- $|x - b| \leqslant a \Leftrightarrow -a \leqslant x - b \leqslant a$
- $|x - b| \leqslant a \Leftrightarrow -a + b \leqslant x \leqslant a + b$

Sketching functions involving modulus signs

To sketch $y = |f(x)|$

- Sketch the curve $y = f(x)$, using a dashed line for points below the x-axis.
- Reflect any part of the curve below the x-axis in the x-axis.

The solution is the solid line; the dashed line just acts as a guide.

To sketch $y = f(|x|)$

- Sketch $y = f(x)$ for x greater than or equal to 0.
- Reflect the parts of the curve to the right of the y-axis in the y-axis.

✓ ***Note*** Be careful not to confuse $y = |f(x)|$ and $y = f(|x|)$.

Examples 9 and 10 involve examples of $y = |f(x)|$.
For an example of $y = f(|x|)$ see Example 9 in Chapter 7 (page 134).

Example 9 Sketch $y = |x|$.

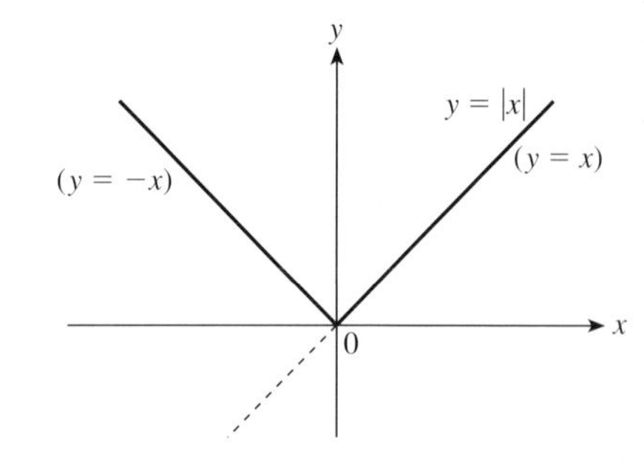

The right-hand branch of $y = |x|$ has equation $y = x$.
The left-hand branch is the negative of x, i.e. $y = -x$.

To draw $y = |x|$, $y = x$ is drawn, with points below the x-axis (where y is $-$ve) shown as a dashed line. The dashed line is then reflected in the x-axis.

Example 10 Sketch $y = |3x + 1|$.

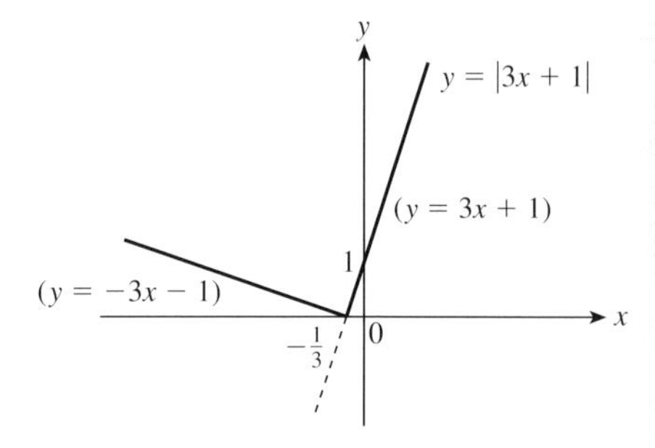

The graph of $y = |3x + 1|$ has the right-hand branch with equation $y = 3x + 1$.
The left-hand branch is the negative of $3x + 1$, i.e. $y = -3x - 1$.

To draw $y = |3x + 1|$, $y = 3x + 1$ is drawn, with points below the x-axis (where y is $-$ve) shown as a dashed line. The dashed line is then reflected in the x-axis.

EXERCISE 4e

For all sketches in this exercise, use the method above and then use a graphical calculator to check the solution. Note that in computer languages and on graphical calculators |x| is usually written as ABS(x).

1 For these inequalities, find the range of values for which the inequality is true and illustrate the range on a number line.

a $|x| < 2$ **b** $|x| \geqslant 3$ **c** $|x - 1| < 5$

2 Sketch these curves.

a $y = |2x|$ **b** $y = |x - 4|$ **c** $y = |2x + 1|$ **d** $y = |2 - x|$
e $y = |x - 2|$ **f** $y = |x| - 2$ **g** $y = 2 - |x|$

Equations and inequalities with modulus signs

Equations and inequalities with modulus signs can be solved graphically or algebraically. If both sides are positive, the technique of squaring both sides can be used.

Example 11

*This example illustrates both situations. In part **a** squaring cannot be used so the equation and the inequality are solved graphically. Part **b** could be solved using either method.*

Solve **a** $|2x - 3| = x + 3$ and $|2x - 3| \leqslant x + 3$
b $|2x - 3| = 5$ and $|2x - 3| \geqslant 5$

a *For the equality* $|2x - 3| = x + 3$

Since $x + 3$ is not always +ve both sides *cannot* be squared.

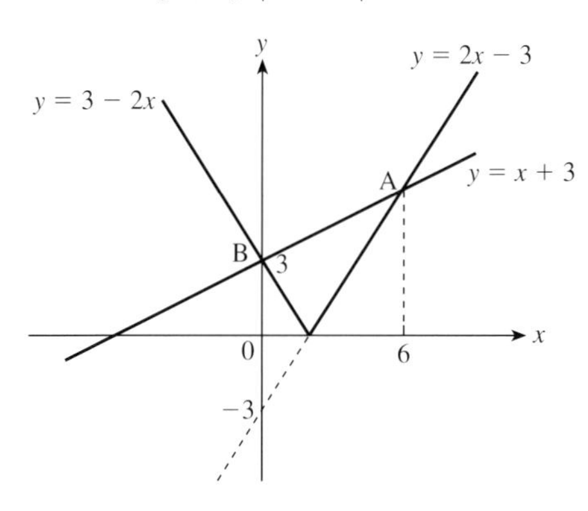

Sketch $y = |2x - 3|$ and $y = x + 3$ and find their points of intersection.

At A, $2x - 3 = x + 3$

$\therefore \quad x = 6$

At B, $3 - 2x = x + 3$

$3x = 0$

$\therefore \quad x = 0$

So $y = |2x + 3|$ and $y = x + 3$ intersect at $x = 0$ and $x = 6$.

For the inequality $|2x - 3| \leqslant x + 3$

From the graph, $|2x - 3| \leqslant x + 3 \Rightarrow 0 \leqslant x \leqslant 6$

The inequality holds when the graph of $y = |2x - 3|$ is below the graph of $y = x + 3$ or where the graphs intersect.

b *For the equality* $|2x - 3| = 5$

$(2x - 3)^2 = 5^2$

$4x^2 - 12x + 9 = 25$

$4x^2 - 12x - 16 = 0$

$x^2 - 3x - 4 = 0$

$(x - 4)(x + 1) = 0$

$\Rightarrow \quad x = -1 \quad \text{or} \quad x = 4$

$|2x - 3| = 5$ could be solved by finding the points of intersection of $y = |2x - 3|$ and $y = 5$. However, since both sides are +ve, they can be squared.

So $y = |2x - 3|$ and $y = 5$ intersect at $x = -1$ and $x = 4$.

For the inequality $|2x - 3| \geqslant 5$

Use $|x| \geqslant a \Leftrightarrow x \geqslant a \quad \text{or} \quad x \leqslant -a$

$|2x - 3| \geqslant 5$

$\Rightarrow \quad 2x - 3 \geqslant 5 \quad \text{or} \quad 2x - 3 \leqslant -5$

$2x \geqslant 8 \qquad 2x \leqslant -2$

$\therefore \quad x \geqslant 4 \qquad x \leqslant -1$

So $x \leqslant -1$ or $x \geqslant 4$.

Example 12

This example shows both methods.

Solve $|2x - 3| = |x|$ and $|2x - 3| > |x|$.

For the equality $|2x - 3| = |x|$

Graphically

At A, $2x - 3 = x$

$x = 3$

At B, $3 - 2x = x$

$3x = 3$

$x = 1$

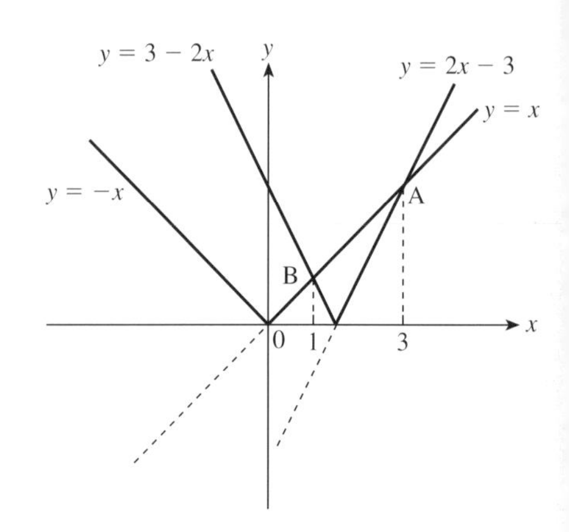

Algebraically

$$|2x - 3| = |x|$$
$$(2x - 3)^2 = x^2$$
$$4x^2 - 12x + 9 = x^2$$
$$3x^2 - 12x + 9 = 0$$
$$x^2 - 4x + 3 = 0$$
$$(x - 1)(x - 3) = 0$$
$$\Rightarrow \quad x = 1 \quad \text{or} \quad x = 3$$

Solutions to $|2x - 3| = |x|$ are $x = 1$ and $x = 3$.

For the inequality $|2x - 3| > |x|$

From the graph, $|2x - 3| > |x| \Rightarrow x < 1$ or $x > 3$.

The inequality holds where the graph of $y = |2x - 3|$ is above the graph of $y = |x|$.

EXERCISE 4f

In this exercise, both questions use the same expressions. Your answers to Question 1 should help you to answer Queston 2.

1 Solve these equations.

a $|x + 1| = 4$

b $|2x - 1| = 5$

c $|3 - x| = 0$

d $|1 - 2x| = 3$

e $|6x - 5| = 7$

f $|x + 3| = |1 - x|$

g $|x + 3| = |3x - 1|$

h $|2x + 1| = |1 - 4x|$

i $|x + 3| = 2|x - 1|$

j $|2x - 4| = x$

k $|3x + 2| = 2 - x$

l $|1 - 3x| - |2x + 1| = 0$

2 Solve these inequalities.

a $|x + 1| < 4$

b $|2x - 1| \geqslant 5$

c $|3 - x| > 0$

d $|1 - 2x| \leqslant 3$

e $|6x - 5| < 7$

f $|x + 3| \leqslant |1 - x|$

g $|x + 3| \geqslant |3x - 1|$

h $|2x + 1| \leqslant |1 - 4x|$

i $|x + 3| > 2|x - 1|$

j $|2x - 4| < x$

k $|3x + 2| \geqslant 2 - x$

l $|1 - 3x| - |2x + 1| \leqslant 0$

EXERCISE 4g (Extension)

1 Solve

a $x^2 + 7x > 6 + 2x^3$

b $x^2(x - 3) < 1 - 3x$

2 Certain operations applied to both sides of an inequality require the inequality sign to be reversed for the statement to remain true.

Explain why the sign has to be reversed when multiplying by a negative number.

Explain also why taking reciprocals of and squaring both sides is unsafe.

3 Find the values of A, B and C in these identities.

a $8 - x \equiv A(x - 2)^2 + B(x - 2)(x + 1) + C(x + 1)$

b $2x^3 - 15x^2 - 10 \equiv A(x - 2)(x + 1) + B(x + 1)(2x^2 + 1) + C(2x^2 + 1)(x - 2)$

c $22 - 4x - 2x^2 \equiv A(x - 1)^2 + B(x - 1)(x + 3) + C(x + 3)$

d $3x^2 + 6x - 4 \equiv A(x + 1)^2 + B$

e $5x^2 + 7x + 9 \equiv A(x + 1)^2 + B(x + 1) + C$

f $x^2 + 1 \equiv A(x - 2)^2 + B(x - 2) + C$

4 Solve these equations.

a $|4 - x| = 1 + |x + 1|$

b $2|x| - 5 = x$

5 Solve these inequalities.

a $|4 - x| > 1 + |x + 1|$

b $2|x| - 5 < x$

EXERCISE 4h (Miscellaneous)

1 Equations and inequalities fall into one of three categories: they are either true for *all* values of x, true for *some* values of x or *not true for any* value of x.
Decide the category for each of these.

a $x^2 + 2x + 2 = (x + 1)^2 + 1$

b $(2x + 1)^2 > 5$

c $9x^2 \geqslant 6x - 1$

d $x^2 + 2x > x^2 - 2x$

e $3x + 7 < 2(x - 4) + x + 4$

f $3x + 5 = 7 - 3x$

g $x^2 = x$

h $x(x + 1) + 7 = 5 + x + x^2$

i $(x + 1)^2 = x^2 + x$

j $(x + 1)^2 = x^2 + 2x + 1$

k $(x + 1)^2 = x^2 + 2x + 2$

2 Solve these inequalities.

a $3y + 7 < 2 - 4(1 - y)$

b $|x - 3| \geqslant 6$

c $x^2 > 4$

d $x^2 \leqslant 100$

e $(x - 1)(x + 2) > 0$

f $x^2 - 3x - 10 < 0$

g $(x - 5)^2 > 3$

h $2x^2 + 7x - 4 \geqslant 0$

3 Find A and B in this identity.

$5x + 31 \equiv A(x + 2) + B(x - 1)$

4 Find A, B and C in the identity

$5x + 31 \equiv A(x + 2)(x - 1) + B(x - 1)(x - 5) + C(x - 5)(x + 2)$.

5 Show that $x^2 + 2kx + 9 \geqslant 0$ for all real values of x, if $k^2 \leqslant 9$.

6 Find the range of values of k that give each of these equations two distinct real roots.

a $x^2 + 3x + k = 0$ **b** $3x^2 + kx + 2 = 0$ **c** $k(x^2 + 1) = x - k$

7 Find the range of values of k that give these equations no real roots.

a $x^2 + 6x + k = 0$ **b** $2x^2 + kx + 1 = 0$ **c** $(k + 1)x^2 + 4kx + 9 = 0$

Test yourself

1 The range of values satisfying $-7 \leqslant 2x - 5 < 7$ is

A $-1 \leqslant x < 6$

B $-3 \leqslant x < 2$

C $x \leqslant -1$ or $x > 6$

D $x \geqslant -3\frac{1}{2}$

E $-\frac{7}{10} \leqslant x < \frac{7}{10}$

2 The range of values satisfying $y^2 - 2y - 8 > 0$ is

A $3 - \sqrt{17} < y < 3 + \sqrt{17}$

B $y < -2$

C $y > -2$

D $y < -2$ or $y > 4$

E $-2 < y < 4$

3 $|x - 4| > 2$ can be expressed as

A $x < -2$ or $x > 6$

B $x < 2$ or $x > 6$

C $2 < x < 6$

D $|4 - x| < 2$

E $|x| > 6$

4 If $x^2 - 3x + 5 \equiv Px(x - 5) + Q(x + 1)(x - 5) + Rx$ then P, Q and R have values

A $-1, 3, 2$

B $0, 1, 1$

C $2, 1, 3$

D $2, -1, 3$

E $3, -1, 2$

Key points

Solving inequalities

Linear inequalities
Do the same to both sides (e.g. add, subtract, multiply, divide) but reverse the inequality sign if multiplying or dividing by a negative number.

Quadratic inequalities and those involving other polynomials
Sketch the graph of the quadratic or other polynomial and use the sketch to decide on the range of values of x required to make the inequality true.

To solve a quadratic inequality

- Arrange the inequality with $ax^2 + bx + c$ on one side and zero on the other.
- Solve $ax^2 + bx + c = 0$.
- Sketch $y = ax^2 + bx + c$, marking only the intercepts on the x-axis.
- Look at the inequality sign to decide on the range of values of x required to make the inequality true. (This range will either be between the roots or be outside the roots of $ax^2 + bx + c = 0$.)

Solving identities

An identity is true for all values of the variable.

- To prove the truth of an identity, one method is to start with one side and by algebraic manipulation show that it is equal to the other side.
- To find unknowns either substitute values or equate (compare) coefficients.

Modulus function

$|x| = x$ if $x \geqslant 0$

$|x| = -x$ if $x < 0$

$|x| < a \Leftrightarrow -a < x < a$

$|x| > a \Leftrightarrow x < -a$ or $x > a$

$|x - a| = x - a$ for $x \geqslant a$ and $|x - a| = -(x - a) = a - x$ for $x < a$

$|x - b| \leqslant a \Leftrightarrow -a \leqslant x - b \leqslant a$

$|x - b| \leqslant a \Leftrightarrow -a + b \leqslant x \leqslant a + b$

5 Simultaneous Equations

Before starting this chapter you will need to know

- how to sketch graphs: linear and quadratic (Chapter 3)
- how to solve linear and quadratic equations (Chapter 3).

A graphical calculator should not be used in this chapter to find solutions. However it is a useful tool to check a solution once it has been obtained or to illustrate the solution graphically.

5.1 Simultaneous equations: Linear equations

Equations such as $3x + 2 = 7$ were solved in Chapter 3. These equations had *one* unknown and there was *one* equation to solve.

This chapter deals with sets of equations with two (or more) unknowns.

Consider pairs of values which satisfy $x + y = 8$.

x	-1	0	1.2
y	9	8	6.8

There is an infinite number of such pairs, x and y. These pairs can be plotted and in this case a straight line is obtained.

Similarly if $2x - y = 1$ there is an infinite number of pairs of values of x and y which satisfy the equation.

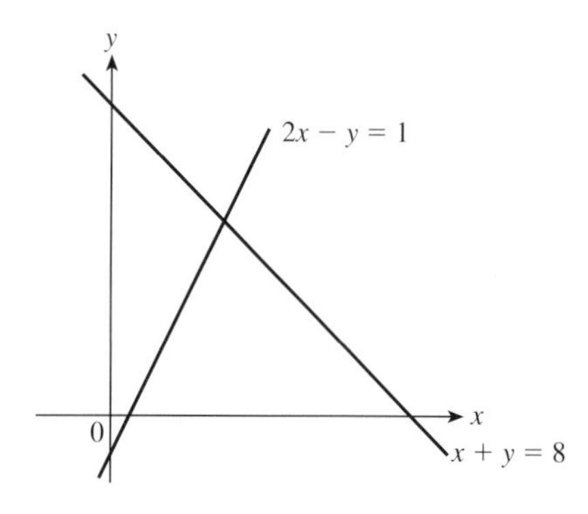

Solving equations simultaneously means finding the values that satisfy both (or all) equations simultaneously.

The point of intersection of the lines is the solution of the equations. These values of x and y satisfy *both* equations simultaneously.

In this case there are *two* unknowns, x and y, and *two* equations are needed to find a solution. With *three* unknowns, *three* equations would be needed.

Two methods for solving simultaneous linear equations are explained:

- Elimination
- Substitution (see p. 93).

Solving two linear simultaneous equations: Elimination method

Example 1 Solve the simultaneous equations $x + y = 8$ and $2x - y = 1$.

$$x + y = 8 \quad (1)$$
$$2x - y = 1 \quad (2)$$

Notice that the y terms in both equations have matching coefficients with *different* signs.

(1) + (2) $\quad 3x = 9$

Add the equations to eliminate the y terms.

$\therefore \quad x = 3$

Substituting in (1) $\quad 3 + y = 8$

Substitute $x = 3$ in equation (1) to give the value of y.

$\therefore \quad y = 5$

Checking in (2) $\quad$ LHS $= 2x - y$
$= 2 \times 3 - 5$
$= 1 =$ RHS

Check that the solution is correct by substituting $x = 3$ and $y = 5$ in equation (2).

So the solution is $x = 3$, $y = 5$.

✓ ***Note*** Always substitute and check in *different* equations.
If one line is used for substitution, use the other for checking.

Example 2 Solve the simultaneous equations $2x + 5y = 12$ and $2x - 3y = -4$.

$$2x + 5y = 12 \quad (1)$$
$$2x - 3y = -4 \quad (2)$$

Notice that the x terms have matching coefficients with the *same* sign

(1) − (2) $\quad 5y - (-3y) = 12 - (-4)$

Subtract the equations to eliminate the x terms.

$8y = 16$

$\therefore \quad y = 2$

Substituting in (2) $\quad 2x - 6 = -4$

Substitute $y = 2$ in equation (2) to give the value of x.

$\therefore \quad 2x = 2$

$\therefore \quad x = 1$

Checking in (1) $\quad$ LHS $= 2x + 5y$
$= 2 \times 1 + 5 \times 2$
$= 12 =$ RHS

Check that the solution is correct by substituting $x = 1$ and $y = 2$ in equation (1).

So the solution is $x = 1$, $y = 2$.

Example 3 Find the point of intersection of the lines $3x + 2y = 2$ and $x - 3y = -14$.

$$3x + 2y = 2 \quad (1)$$
$$x - 3y = -14 \quad (2)$$

The solution of the simultaneous equations will give the point of intersection of the lines.

(2) × 3 $\quad 3x - 9y = -42 \quad (3)$

Neither the x terms nor the y terms have matching coefficients.
To match up the x coefficients multiply all the terms in (2) by 3.

(1) − (3) $\quad 2y - (-9y) = 2 - (-42)$

$11y = 44$

$\therefore \quad y = 4$

The matching coefficients in (1) and (3) have the *same* sign so *subtract* (3) from (1) (or vice versa) to eliminate the x terms.

Substituting in (2) $\quad x - 12 = -14$

Substitute $y = 4$ in equation (2) to give the value of x.

$\therefore \quad x = -2$

Checking in ① LHS $= 3x + 2y$

$= 3 \times (-2) + 2 \times 4$

$= 2 = $ RHS

Check that the solution is correct by substituting $x = -2$ and $y = 4$ in equation ①.

So the solution is $x = -2$, $y = 4$ and the point of intersection of the lines is $(-2, 4)$.

Example 4 Solve the simultaneous equations $3x = -7 + 2y$ and $5y = 8 - 2x$.

$3x = -7 + 2y$ ①

$5y = 8 - 2x$ ②

Rearrange the equations to line up x and y terms on the LHS.

$3x - 2y = -7$ ③

$2x + 5y = 8$ ④

To match the y coefficients, multiply equation ③ by 5 and equation ④ by 2. (Or match up x coefficients by multiplying equation ③ by 2 and equation ④ by 3.)

③ × 5 $15x - 10y = -35$ ⑤

④ × 2 $4x + 10y = 16$ ⑥

⑤ + ⑥ $19x = -19$

∴ $x = -1$

The y coefficients in ⑤ and ⑥ now match with *different* signs, so *add* equations ⑤ and ⑥ to eliminate the y terms.

Substituting in ① $-3 = -7 + 2y$

$2y = 4$

∴ $y = 2$

Substitute $x = -1$ in ① to give the value of y.

Checking in ② LHS $= 5y = 10$

RHS $= 8 - 2x$

$= 8 - (-2)$

$= 10$

LHS = RHS

Check that the solution is correct by substituting $x = -1$, $y = 2$ in equation ②. Use the original equations for checking as they will be correct (unless miscopied!).

So the solution is $x = -1$, $y = 2$.

EXERCISE 5a

1 Solve these simultaneous equations, by elimination.

a $x + y = 6$, $x - y = 2$

b $2c + d = 23$, $c - d = 1$

c $5x - 3y = 23$, $2x + 3y = 26$

d $-g + 6h = 15$, $g - 4h = -9$

e $x + 3y = 8$, $x - 2y = 3$

f $5r - 2s = 14$, $3r - 2s = 6$

g $5t - 3u = 9$, $5t + 2u = 19$

h $-x + 5y = 39$, $-x + 2y = 18$

i $5x + 6y = 14$, $x - 6y = 10$

j $3x + 2y = 7$, $5x + y = 7$

k $n - 6p - 1 = 0$, $3n + 2p - 13 = 0$

l $3x - 4y = 4$, $2x + 2y = 5$

2 Solve these simultaneous equations, by elimination.

a $s + 2t = 8$, $5s - 3t = 1$

b $3a - y = 5$, $2a - 10y = 1$

c $b + 2x = 3$, $4b + 3x = 2$

d $3z - 2y - 5 = 0$, $4z + 3y - 1 = 0$

e $4x + 3y = 5$, $3x + 2y = 4$

f $4r - 3q = 11$, $3r + 2q = 4$

g $3p - 2q = 5$, $2p - 3q = 0$

h $4r - 5s = 1$, $2r - 3s = 1$

i $7x - 11y = 21$, $5x - 3y = 15$

j $7x - 3y = 18$, $2x + 5y = 11$

Solving two linear simultaneous equations: Substitution method

Substitution is an alternative, more general, method of solving simultaneous equations.

Example 5 Solve the simultaneous equations $y = 3x + 4$ and $y = 2 - 7x$.

$$y = 3x + 4 \quad (1)$$
$$y = 2 - 7x \quad (2)$$

For the solution, the values of y must be equal. Hence the expressions for y can be put equal to each other.

So $3x + 4 = 2 - 7x$

$10x = -2$

$\therefore \quad x = -\frac{1}{5}$

Choose the equation that makes for the easiest substitution. Substitute $x = -\frac{1}{5}$ in equation (1).

Substituting in (1) $\quad y = 3 \times (-\frac{1}{5}) + 4 = 3\frac{2}{5}$

Check by substituting $x = -\frac{1}{5}$ and $y = 3\frac{2}{5}$ in equation (2).

Checking in (2) $\quad \text{LHS} = 3\frac{2}{5}$

$\text{RHS} = 2 + \frac{7}{5} = 3\frac{2}{5}$

$\text{LHS} = \text{RHS}$

So the solution is $x = -\frac{1}{5}$, $y = 3\frac{2}{5}$.

Example 6 Solve the simultaneous equations $y - 2x = 5$ and $6y - 5x = 23$.

$$y - 2x = 5 \quad (1)$$
$$6y - 5x = 23 \quad (2)$$

Rearrange one of the equations to express one unknown in terms of the other.

In this case (1) can easily be arranged to express y in terms of x.

Rearranging (1) $\quad y = 2x + 5$

Substitute this expression for y in the other equation, to solve for x.

Substituting in (2) $\quad 6(2x + 5) - 5x = 23$

$12x + 30 - 5x = 23$

$7x = -7$

$\therefore \quad x = -1$

Substituting in (1) $\quad y - 2 \times (-1) = 5$

Substitute $x = -1$ in (1) to give the value of y.

$y + 2 = 5$

$\therefore \quad y = 3$

Checking in (2) $\quad \text{LHS} = 6 \times 3 - 5 \times (-1)$

$= 18 + 5$

$= 23 = \text{RHS}$

Check by substituting $x = -1$ and $y = 3$ in equation (2).

So the solution is $x = -1$, $y = 3$.

➤ Before solving simultaneous equations, look at the coefficients.

- If there are fractional or decimal coefficients in any equation, multiply all terms in the equation by a suitable number, so that all coefficients are whole numbers.
- If there is a common factor in all the coefficients of an equation, divide through by that factor before proceeding.

Example 7

This example involves fractional coefficients.

Solve the simultaneous equations $\frac{x}{3} - \frac{y}{4} = 0$ and $\frac{x}{2} + \frac{3y}{10} = 5\frac{2}{5}$.

$$\frac{x}{3} - \frac{y}{4} = 0 \quad ①$$

$$\frac{x}{2} + \frac{3y}{10} = 5\frac{2}{5} \quad ②$$

Eliminate fractions by multiplying each equation by the LCM of its denominators: multiply equation ① by 12 and equation ② by 10.

① × 12 $\quad 4x - 3y = 0 \quad$ ③

② × 10 $\quad 5x + 3y = 54 \quad$ ④

Coefficients of y match, but signs are *different* so *add* to eliminate the y terms.

③ + ④ $\quad 9x = 54$

∴ $\quad x = 6$

Substituting in ③ $\quad 4 \times 6 - 3y = 0$

$3y = 24$

∴ $\quad y = 8$

Substitute $x = 6$ in equation ③ to give the value of y.

Checking in ② $\quad \text{LHS} = \frac{6}{2} + \frac{3 \times 8}{10}$

$= 3 + \frac{12}{5}$

$= 5\frac{2}{5} = \text{RHS}$

Since the substitution was in ③ (which was derived from ①), check by substituting $x = 6$ and $y = 8$ in the other equation, i.e. ②.

So the solution is $x = 6$, $y = 8$.

Example 8

This example includes a common factor. When solving money problems express all sums of money in the same units. Pence are used here to avoid decimals.

Of 23 articles bought, some cost £2.50 each, and the rest cost £3.00 each. The total cost was £61. Find how many of each article were bought.

Let numbers of articles bought at £2.50 and £3 be x and y respectively.

Then $\quad x + y = 23 \quad$ ①

23 articles were bought.

and $\quad 250x + 300y = 6100 \quad$ ②

② ÷ 50 $\quad 5x + 6y = 122 \quad$ ③

① × 5 $\quad 5x + 5y = 115 \quad$ ④

Divide ② by 50, the HCF of the coefficients. (It is easier to work with smaller numbers.)

③ − ④ $\quad y = 7$

Substituting in ① $\quad x + 7 = 23$

∴ $\quad x = 16$

Checking in ② $\quad \text{LHS} = 250 \times 16 + 300 \times 7$

$= 4000 + 2100$

$= 6100 = \text{RHS}$

Or check in equation ③, which is a simpler form of equation ②.

So 16 articles at £2.50 and 7 at £3 were bought.

Example 9 Here are the tariffs of two mobile phone companies:

Company 1: £6 per month plus 2 pence per minute on a call

Company 2: No monthly fee but 5 pence per minute on a call.

a Find the number of minutes during one month for which the charge would be the same.

Zöe uses her mobile phone for 150 minutes per month on average. Jon's monthly total is always more than 250 minutes.

b Find which company would provide the better deal for each of these potential customers.

Solution

a Let C pence be the charge of the service in one month.

£6 = 600 pence

Let t minutes be the time of calls in one month.

For Company 1 $\quad C = 600 + 2t$

For Company 2 $\quad C = 5t$

To find the value of t for which the charges are the same, solve the equations simultaneously.

The charges are the same, so $\quad 5t = 600 + 2t$

$3t = 600$

$\therefore \quad t = 200$

So the charge would be the same for calls totalling 200 minutes.

b For $t > 200$ Company 1 has a lower charge than Company 2.

For $t = 200$ charges are the same.

For $t < 200$ Company 2 has a lower charge than Company 1.

So for Zöe, who uses her mobile on average for 150 minutes a month, Company 2 offers the better deal.

For Jon, who uses the mobile for more than 250 minutes a month, Company 1 offers the better deal.

One approach is to draw graphs for the two companies showing charge C, against time, t.

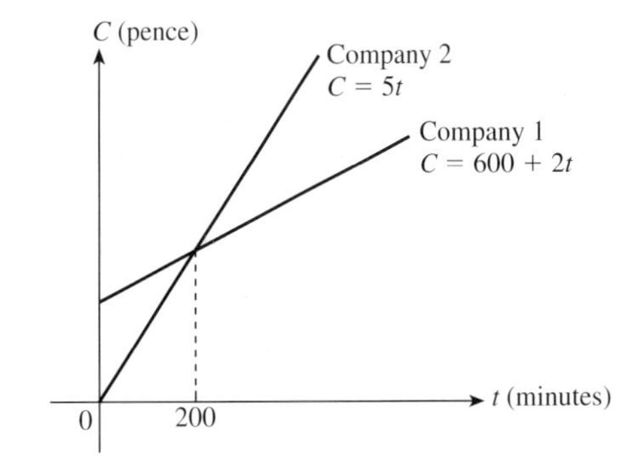

EXERCISE 5b

1 Solve these by the most appropriate method, elimination or substitution.

a $y = 2x + 1$, $3y + 10x = 7$ **b** $x + y = 11$, $3x - 5y = 1$ **c** $2x + y = 1$, $3x + 2y = 3$ **d** $x = 3 - 7y$, $2x + 9y = 11$

e $5x + 7y = 52$, $3x - 8y = 19$ **f** $2s + 3x = 31$, $3s + 4x = 44$ **g** $2x - 3y = 4$, $5x + 2y = 1$ **h** $3x + 4y = 2$, $5x - 3y = 1$

2 Solve these simultaneous equations for x and y.

a $7x - 8y = 9$, $11x + 3y = -17$ **b** $7x + 4y = 9$, $2x + 3y = 1$ **c** $3x + 2y = 5x + 2y = 7$

d $3x + 2y - 5 = 0$, $5x - 3y - 21 = 0$ **e** $ax + by = m$, $cx + dy = n$

3 Find the point of intersection for each of these pairs of lines.

a $y = 5x$, $y = 3 - x$ **b** $y = 4x + 5$, $y = 3x + 6$ **c** $2x - 3y + 5 = 0$, $4x + 5y - 1 = 0$ **d** $4y - 2x = 7$, $5y - 3x = 6$

EXERCISE 5b
(continued)

4 2 kg of apples and 3 kg of pears cost £7.60; 3 kg of apples and 2 kg of pears cost £7.40.
Find the price of each fruit per kilogram.

5 An entomologist wishes to find the average mass of a particular species of beetle. He has several live specimens, which must be weighed in plastic bottles. One bottle containing eight beetles has a mass of 5.7g; three bottles containing a total of thirty beetles have a total mass of 20.7g.

Find the average masses of

a the beetles

b the specimen bottles

6 Mariko has ten more sweets than Brian. If she gives him a quarter of her sweets, he will have six more than her.

Find the number of sweets each child has.

7 A fast train leaves Manchester for London, a journey of 330 km, at 12 noon. A slow train, travelling half as fast, leaves London for Manchester at the same time. They pass each other at 2 p.m.

Find the speed of each train.

8 Siobhan is five years older then her brother. Six years ago, her brother was half her age.

Find the age of each child.

9 The momentum of a body with mass m travelling at a speed v is mv and its kinetic energy is $\frac{1}{2}mv^2$. The momentum of a certain object is $3\,\text{kg}\,\text{m}\,\text{s}^{-1}$ and its kinetic energy is 3 J.

Find the mass and the speed of the object.

10 ABC is a right-angled triangle. The base BC is 12 cm long and the hypotenuse AC is 6 cm longer than the shortest side AB.

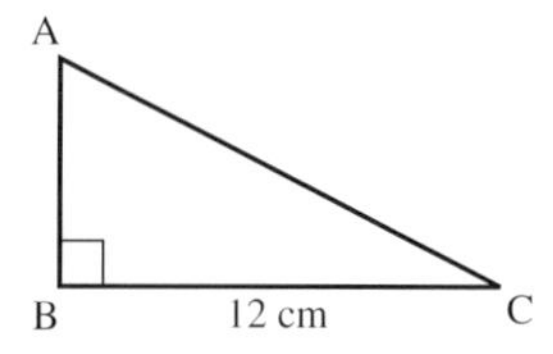

Find the lengths of AB and AC.

11 In a football league, teams score two points for a win, one for a draw and none for losing. At the end of the season, Exton Park have a total of 18 points, having won x matches and drawn y. Wyeville United have a total of 20 points, having won $2y$ matches and drawn $x - 3$.

Find the number of matches won and drawn by each team.

12 One mobile telephone company charges £4 per month plus a pence per minute for calls; a second company charges £10 per month plus b pence per minute for calls. A customer who makes 120 minutes of calls per month has the same monthly bill from each company; a customer who makes 400 minutes of calls per month pays only half as much if he uses the second company rather than the first.

Find a and b.

13 A student can complete a maths question in five minutes and a biology question in twelve minutes. A certain day's maths and biology homework consists of eleven questions altogether and takes an hour-and-a-half.

Find how many questions were set in each subject.

14 A swimmer in a river can swim 1km in 15 minutes when swimming with the current, but the same distance takes an hour against the current.

Find the speeds of

a the swimmer

b the current

5.2 Solving simultaneous equations: One linear and one quadratic

Plotting two *linear* equations on the same axes usually gives a single point of intersection.

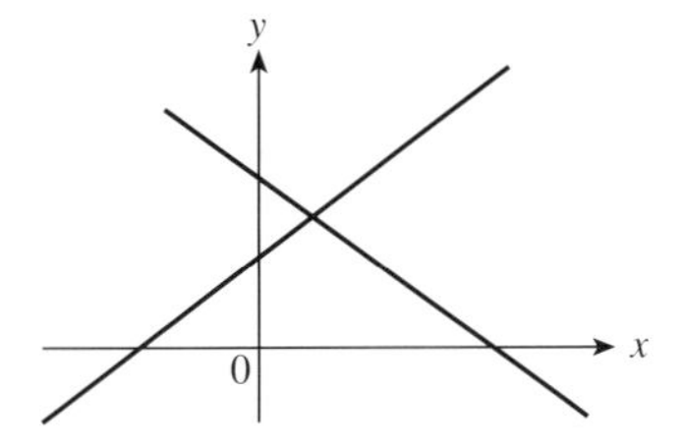

Plotting one *linear* and one *quadratic* equation will lead to no points of intersection or one or two.

Consider the possible points of intersection of a parabola and a general straight line:

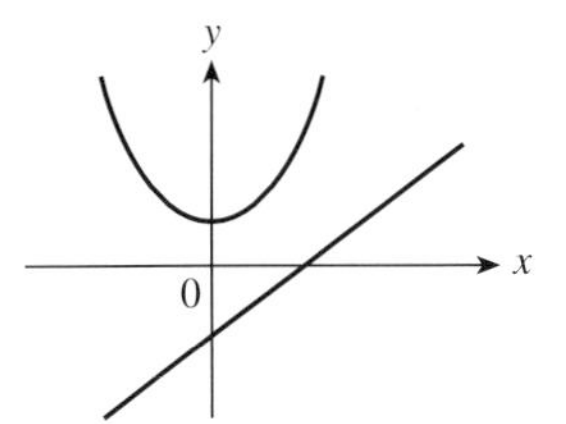

No point of intersection
The line misses the curve altogether.

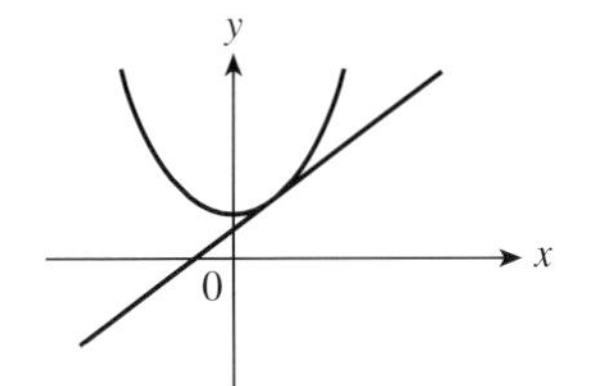

One point of intersection (or two coincident points)
The line is a tangent to the curve.

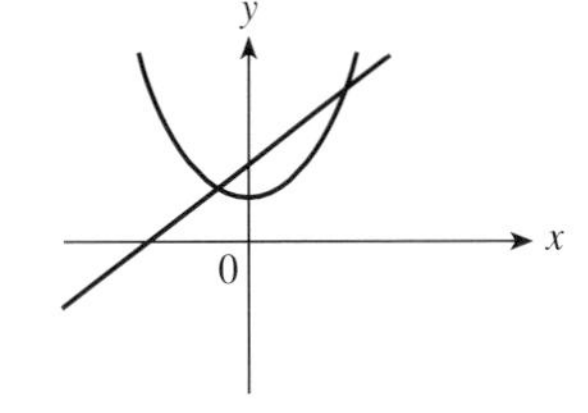

Two points of intersection
The line cuts the curve in two distinct points.

Simultaneous equations with one linear and one quadratic equation are usually solved by

- rearranging the linear equation to give one variable in terms of the other
- substituting in the quadratic equation.

Most of the examples in this section are illustrated graphically. It is not necessary to follow the details of the sketches, nor to know the names of the curves; it does, however, give geometrical meaning to solving the equations.

Example 10 Solve the simultaneous equations $y = x^2$ and $y = x + 2$.

$$y = x + 2 \quad ①$$

Equation ① is linear.

$$y = x^2 \quad ②$$

Equation ② is quadratic.

$$\Rightarrow \quad x^2 = x + 2$$

For the solution, the values of y must be equal. Hence the expressions for y can be put equal to each other.

$$x^2 - x - 2 = 0$$

$$(x - 2)(x + 1) = 0$$

$$\Rightarrow \quad x = 2 \text{ or } x = -1$$

Substitute values of x in the linear equation ① to obtain corresponding values of y, and then check in ②.

When $x = 2$, $y = 4$.

When $x = -1$, $y = 1$.

So solution is $x = -1$, $y = 1$ or $x = 2$, $y = 4$.

Corresponding values of the unknowns must be given in pairs.

Illustrating the solution graphically:

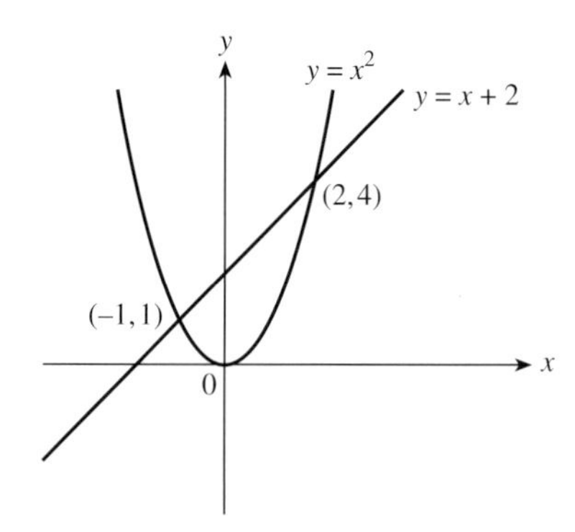

The points of intersection are $(-1, 1)$ and $(2, 4)$.

✓ ***Note*** The linear equation should be used for substitution when solving simultaneous equations (one linear, one quadratic). If the quadratic equation is used, some solutions may be obtained which do not satisfy the linear equation.

The parabola is only one of the forms of quadratic curves.

Equations of the form $xy = c$ or $ax^2 \pm by^2 = c$ give hyperbolas, circles and ellipses.

Examples 11–13 illustrate lines intersecting with hyperbolas. Exercise 5c (on page 101) contains examples of lines intersecting with circles and ellipses, as well as parabolas and hyperbolas.

Example 11

Solve the simultaneous equations $x - 2y = 8$ and $xy = 24$.

$$x - 2y = 8 \qquad ①$$

$$xy = 24 \qquad ②$$

Equation ① is linear.

Equation ② is quadratic.

Rearranging ① $\qquad x = 8 + 2y$

Rearrange the linear equation to give one unknown in terms of the other. In this case it is easier to give x in terms of y. Then substitute in the quadratic equation.

Substituting in ② $\qquad (8 + 2y)y = 24$

$$2y^2 + 8y - 24 = 0$$

$$y^2 + 4y - 12 = 0$$

$$(y + 6)(y - 2) = 0$$

$$\Rightarrow \qquad y = -6 \text{ or } y = 2$$

Multiply out and put all terms on one side, and then divide through by 2.

Substituting in ①

Substitute values of y in the linear equation to obtain corresponding values of x.

When $y = -6$, $x = -4$.

When $y = 2$, $x = 12$.

So the solutions are $x = -4$, $y = -6$ and $x = 12$, $y = 2$.

Corresponding values of the unknowns must be given in pairs.

Checking in ② $\qquad (-4) \times (-6) = 24$

$$12 \times 2 = 24$$

Illustrating the solution graphically:

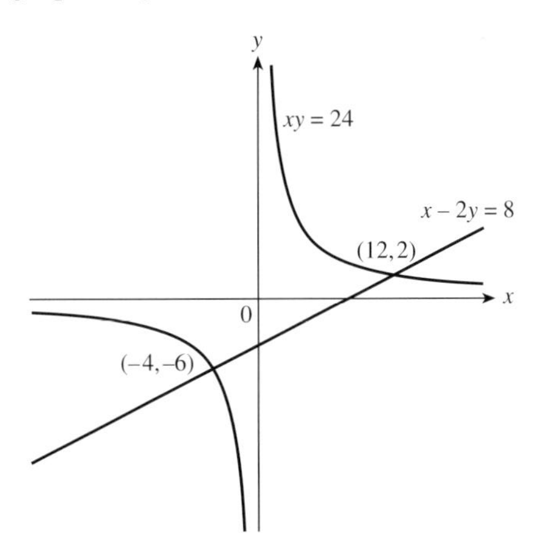

There are two solutions to the pair of equations: $x = -4$, $y = -6$ and $x = 12$, $y = 2$.

The graphs intersect at $(-4, -6)$ and $(12, 2)$.

Example 12

Solve the simultaneous equations $2x + y = 5$ and $x^2 - y^2 = 3$.

$$2x + y = 5 \quad ①$$

Equation ① is linear.

$$x^2 - y^2 = 3 \quad ②$$

Equation ② is quadratic.

Rearranging ① $\quad y = 5 - 2x$

Rearrange the linear equation to give one variable in terms of the other. Express y in terms of x to avoid using fractions, and then substitute in the quadratic equation ②.

Substituting in ② $\quad x^2 - (5 - 2x)^2 = 3$

Multiply out $(5 - 2x)(5 - 2x)$.

$$x^2 - (25 - 20x + 4x^2) = 3$$

Keep the result in a bracket since it has to be subtracted.

$$3x^2 - 20x + 28 = 0$$

Put all terms on one side.

$$(3x - 14)(x - 2) = 0$$

Factorise or use the formula.

$\Rightarrow \quad x = \frac{14}{3}$ or $x = 2$

Substitute values of x in the linear equation to obtain corresponding values of y.

Substituting in ①

When $x = \frac{14}{3}$, $y = 5 - \frac{28}{3} = -\frac{13}{3}$.

When $x = 2$, $y = 1$.

So the solutions are $x = \frac{14}{3}$, $y = -\frac{13}{3}$ or $x = 2$, $y = 1$.

Give answers in pairs of x and y. Check by substituting in ②.

Illustrating the solution graphically, points of intersection are (2, 1) and $\left(\frac{14}{3}, -\frac{13}{3}\right)$.

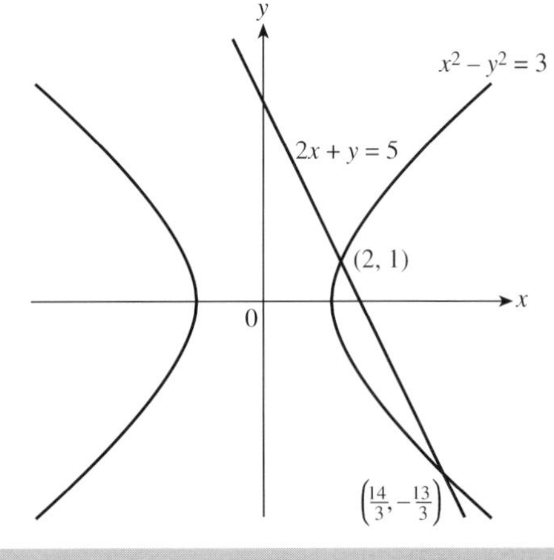

Example 13

This example shows two methods: using fractions, and avoiding fractions. The standard method of rearranging the linear equation and substituting in the quadratic equation may involve substituting algebraic fractions (as in part **a***). Sometimes algebraic fractions can be avoided by squaring the linear equation (it may need to be rearranged first) and matching terms (as in part* **b***).*

Solve the simultaneous equations $3x - 2y = 1$ and $3x^2 - 2y^2 + 5 = 0$.

a *Using fractions* $\quad 3x - 2y = 1 \quad ①$

Linear

$$3x^2 - 2y^2 + 5 = 0 \quad ②$$

Quadratic

Rearranging ① $\quad x = \dfrac{1 + 2y}{3}$

Rearrange to give x in terms of y or y in terms of x.

Substituting in ② $3\left(\frac{1+2y}{3}\right)^2 - 2y^2 + 5 = 0$

$$\frac{\overset{1}{\cancel{3}}(1+2y)(1+2y)}{\underset{1}{\cancel{3}} \times 3} - 2y^2 + 5 = 0$$

$$\frac{1+4y+4y^2}{3} - 2y^2 + 5 = 0$$

$$1 + 4y + 4y^2 - 6y^2 + 15 = 0$$

$$2y^2 - 4y - 16 = 0$$

$$y^2 - 2y - 8 = 0$$

$$(y-4)(y+2) = 0$$

$\Rightarrow$ $y = 4$ or $y = -2$

Substituting for x in ② avoids problems with the minus sign.

Multiply through by 3 to eliminate the fraction.

Divide through by 2.

Substituting in ①

When $y = 4$, $3x - 8 = 1$, and so $x = 3$.

When $y = -2$, $3x - (-4) = 1$, and so $x = -1$.

So the solutions are $x = 3$, $y = 4$ or $x = -1$, $y = -2$.

Substitute values of y in the linear equation to obtain corresponding values of x.

b *Avoiding fractions* $3x - 2y = 1$ ① Linear

$3x^2 - 2y^2 + 5 = 0$ ② Quadratic

Rearranging ① $3x = 1 + 2y$

Rearrange the linear equation to give one unknown in terms of the other.

Squaring $9x^2 = (1+2y)^2$

$= 1 + 4y + 4y^2$

Square both sides to give an expression for $9x^2$.

② × 3 $9x^2 - 6y^2 + 15 = 0$

$9x^2 = 6y^2 - 15$

Multiply ② by 3 to give another expression for $9x^2$.

So $6y^2 - 15 = 1 + 4y + 4y^2$

Put the expressions for $9x^2$ equal to each other.

$$2y^2 - 4y - 16 = 0$$

$$y^2 - 2y - 8 = 0$$

Divide through by 2.

$$(y-4)(y+2) = 0$$

$\Rightarrow$ $y = 4$ or $y = -2$

Now proceed as in part **a**.

EXERCISE 5c

1 Solve for x and y

a $y = x^2$
$y = x + 6$

b $y = x^2$
$y = 3 - 2x$

c $y + x^2 = 8x$
$y = 2x$

d $y + 1 = x$
$y = x^2 - 6x + 5$

e $x - y = 0$
$x^2 + y^2 = 18$

f $x^2 + y^2 = 20$
$2y - x = 0$

2 Solve

a $y = \frac{8}{x}$
$y = 7 + x$

b $xy = 4$
$y = 2x + 2$

c $x^2 + y^2 = 25$
$y = x + 1$

d $x^2 + 4y^2 = 4$
$x = 2 - 2y$

e $y^2 = 4x$
$2x + y = 4$

f $4y^2 - 3x^2 = 1$
$x - 2y = 1$

EXERCISE 5c *(continued)*

3 Solve

a $x^2 + xy + y^2 = 7$
$2x + y = 1$

b $x^2 + 5x + y = 4$
$x + y = 8$

c $x^2 - xy - y^2 = -11$
$2x + y = 1$

d $x^2 + y^2 + 4x + 6y - 40 = 0$
$x - y = 10$

5.3 Intersection of linear and quadratic curves: Three cases of the discriminant

The discriminant can be used to test for the number of points of intersection of a linear and a quadratic graph.

When the linear equation is rearranged and substituted into the quadratic equation a further quadratic equation is formed. The number of roots of this equation will correspond to the number of points in which the line and curve intersect.

Discriminant	*Number of roots*	*Intersection of curve and line*
$b^2 - 4ac > 0$	Two distinct real roots	Two distinct points
$b^2 - 4ac = 0$	One real root (or two equal roots)	Line is tangent to curve. Line meets curve in two coincident points.
$b^2 - 4ac < 0$	No real roots	Line and curve do not intersect.

Example 14

To find points of intersection, the equations in this example are solved simultaneously. Parts a–c relate to the three alternatives for the discriminant: < 0, $= 0$ and > 0. Part d is a special case.

Find the coordinates of the points of intersection with $y = x^2$ of these lines.

a $x + y = 12$ b $x + y = -8$ c $x + y = -\frac{1}{4}$ d $x = 3$

Solution

a
$x + y = 12$ ① — ① is linear
$y = x^2$ ② — ② is quadratic

From ① $y = 12 - x$ — Rearrange the linear equation.

So $x^2 = 12 - x$ — The two expressions for y are equal.

$x^2 + x - 12 = 0$ ③ — Solve the quadratic. Note that $b^2 - 4ac > 0$.

$(x - 3)(x + 4) = 0$

$\Rightarrow$ $x = 3$ or $x = -4$

When $x = 3$, $y = 9$. — Substitute in the linear equation for values of y.

When $x = -4$, $y = 16$.

There are two distinct points of intersection: (3, 9) and (−4, 16).

b $x + y = -8$ ① Linear

$y = x^2$ ② Quadratic

From ① $y = -8 - x$ Rearrange the linear equation.

So $x^2 = -8 - x$ The two expressions for y are equal.

$x^2 + x + 8 = 0$ *Note*: $b^2 - 4ac < 0$.

$\therefore \quad x = \dfrac{-1 \pm \sqrt{1 - 32}}{2}$

There are no real roots so there are no points of intersection.

c $x + y = -\frac{1}{4}$ ① Linear

$y = x^2$ ② Quadratic

From ① $y = -\frac{1}{4} - x$ Rearrange the linear equation.

So $x^2 = -\frac{1}{4} - x$ The two expressions for y are equal.

$4x^2 = -1 - 4x$ Multiply through by 4.

$4x^2 + 4x + 1 = 0$ *Note*: $b^2 - 4ac = 0$.

$(2x + 1)(2x + 1) = 0$

$\therefore \quad x = -\frac{1}{2}$ One repeated root.

Substituting in ①, when $x = -\frac{1}{2}$, $y = \frac{1}{4}$. Substitute in the linear equation.

There is one point of intersection. The root is repeated so the line is a tangent to the curve at $\left(-\frac{1}{2}, \frac{1}{4}\right)$.

d $x = 3$ Linear

$y = x^2$ Quadratic

When $x = 3$, $y = 3^2 = 9$. There is one point of intersection (3, 9).
This is not a repeated root, so line is not a tangent to the curve.

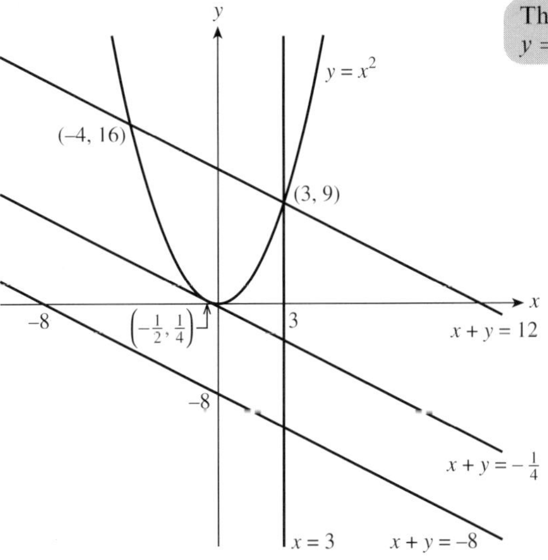

The four lines and their intersections with $y = x^2$ can be illustrated graphically.

Example 15 Find the values of k for which $kx + y = 4$ is a tangent to the curve $y = x^2 + 8$.

$$kx + y = 4 \quad ①$$ Linear

$$y = x^2 + 8 \quad ②$$ Quadratic

From ① $y = 4 - kx$ Rearrange the linear equation.

Graphs intersect when $x^2 + 8 = 4 - kx$ Put the two expressions for y equal to each other.

$$x^2 + kx + 4 = 0 \quad ③$$

For the line to be a tangent to the curve, ③ must have equal roots, that is $b^2 - 4ac = 0$.

So $k^2 - 16 = 0$

$\therefore$ $k = \pm 4$ Substitute $k = \pm 4$ in equation ①.

So $y + 4x = 4$ and $y - 4x = 4$ are tangents to the curve $y = x^2 + 8$.

The solution can be illustrated graphically.

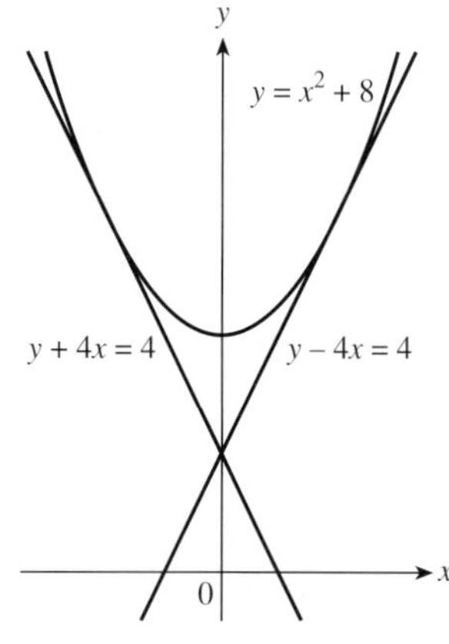

Example 16 Find the range of values of k for which $y = 2x + k$ meets $2x^2 + y^2 = 3$ in two distinct points.

$$y = 2x + k \quad ①$$

$$2x^2 + y^2 = 3 \quad ②$$

To find the points of intersection solve these equations simultaneously.

Substituting ① in ② $2x^2 + (2x + k)^2 = 3$

$$2x^2 + 4x^2 + 4kx + k^2 = 3$$

$$6x^2 + 4kx + k^2 - 3 = 0$$

For the line and the curve to intersect in two distinct points, the discriminant of this equation must be +ve.

For two distinct points of intersection, $b^2 - 4ac > 0$

So $16k^2 - 4 \times 6(k^2 - 3) > 0$

$(\div 8)$ $2k^2 - 3k^2 + 9 > 0$

$$k^2 < 9$$

Solve this inequality.

$\therefore$ $-3 < k < 3$.

EXERCISE 5d

1 Find the value of k for which $y = 3x + 1$ is a tangent to the curve $x^2 + y^2 = k$.

2 Find the range of values of k for which $y = x - 3$ meets $x^2 - 3y^2 = k$ in two distinct points.

3 Show that the line $y = x - 4$ touches the curve $x^2 + y^2 = 8$.

4 Find the value of k for which $y = kx + 1$ is a tangent to the curve $y^2 = 8x$.

5 Show that $y = x + c$ is a tangent to $x^2 + y^2 = 4$ if, and only if, $c^2 = 8$.
(Show that if $y = x + c$ is a tangent then $c^2 = 8$, and also that if $c^2 = 8$ then $y = x + c$ is a tangent.)

6 A rectangular photograph has an area of 600 cm² and a perimeter of 1m.
Find its dimensions.

7 The square of Richard's age is equal to his mother's age.
When he is twice as old as he is now, she will be $3\frac{1}{2}$ times as old as he is.
Find the ages of

a Richard **b** his mother.

8 The hypotenuse of a right-angled triangle measures 17 cm.
The shortest side is 7 cm shorter than the middle side.
Find the lengths of the sides.

9 The sides of a cuboid measure 1 cm, a cm and b cm.
Its volume is 12 cm³ and its surface area is 38 cm².
Find a and b.

5.4 Extension material for simultaneous equations

For simultaneous linear equations with more than two unknowns, the elimination method is usually used.

Example 17

Solve
$$x + y + z = 7$$
$$2x + 3y - z = 0$$
$$3x + 4y + 2z = 17$$

Solution

	$x + y + z = 7$	①
	$2x + 3y - z = 0$	②
	$3x + 4y + 2z = 17$	③
① + ②	$3x + 4y = 7$	④
2 × ②	$4x + 6y - 2z = 0$	⑤
③ + ⑤	$7x + 10y = 17$	⑥
7 × ④	$21x + 28y = 49$	⑦
3 × ⑥	$21x + 30y = 51$	⑧
⑧ − ⑦	$2y = 2$	
∴	$y = 1$	

Look for matching coefficients. The z coefficients in lines ① and ② match with different signs. Add lines ① and ② to eliminate the z terms.

To obtain another equation with no z term line multiply ② by 2 and add to line ③.

Now solve the equations in lines ④ and ⑥.

Substituting in ④ $3x + 4 = 7$

∴ $x = 1$

Substituting in ① $z = 5$

Checking in ③ $3 \times 1 + 4 \times 1 + 2 \times 5 = 17$

So the solution is $x = 1$, $y = 1$, $z = 5$.

④ = ① + ② and ① have been used for substitution so ③ should be used for the check.

Intersection of two quadratic curves

Two quadratic curves meet in up to four points.

Example 18

This example illustrates a circle and hyperbola meeting in four points.

Find the points of intersection of $xy = 6$ and $x^2 + y^2 = 13$.

$$xy = 6 \quad ①$$
$$x^2 + y^2 = 13 \quad ②$$

From ① $\quad x = \dfrac{6}{y}$ — Rearrange ① to give x in terms of y or y in terms of x.

Substituting in ② $\quad \left(\dfrac{6}{y}\right)^2 + y^2 = 1$

$$\frac{36}{y^2} + y^2 = 13$$

Multiply through by y^2.

$$36 + y^4 = 13y^2$$
$$y^4 - 13y^2 + 36 = 0$$
$$(y^2 - 4)(y^2 - 9) = 0$$

This is a quadratic in y^2. Substitute $z = y^2$ if preferred to give $z^2 - 13z + 36 = 0$.

$\Rightarrow \quad y = \pm 2 \quad \text{or} \quad y = \pm 3$

When $y = 2$, $x = 3$. When $y = -2$, $x = -3$.

When $y = 3$, $x = 2$. When $y = -3$, $x = -2$.

Substitute in ①. Avoid substituting in equations with x^2 or y^2.

Remember to check that all solutions satisfy both equations.

The solution can be illustrated graphically.

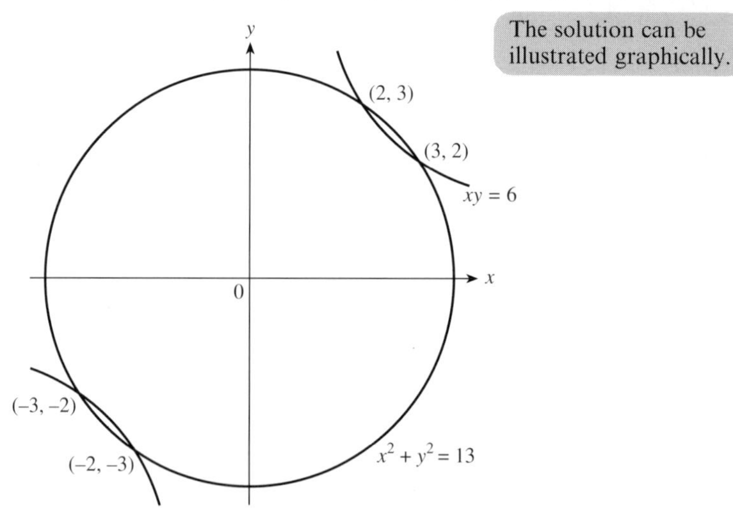

The points of intersection are (2, 3), (−2, −3), (3, 2) and (−3, −2).

EXERCISE 5e (Extension)

1 Solve these equations.

a
$$x + y - z = 8$$
$$4x - y + 3z = 26$$
$$2x + y - 4z = 8$$

b
$$2x + y + z = 8$$
$$5x - 3y + 2z = 23$$
$$7x + y + 3z = 20$$

c
$$x + z = 2y$$
$$9x + 3z = 8y$$
$$2x + 3y + 5z = 36$$

d
$$\tfrac{1}{4}x + \tfrac{1}{6}y + \tfrac{1}{3}z = 8$$
$$\tfrac{1}{2}x - \tfrac{1}{9}y + \tfrac{1}{6}z = 5$$
$$\tfrac{1}{3}x + \tfrac{1}{2}y - z = 7$$

2 Simultaneous linear equations may have one solution, no solution or an infinite number of solutions.

For these simultaneous linear equations, decide how many solutions there are. Illustrate each with a sketch.

a $y = 2x - 1$
$x + y = 5$

b $4x + 3y = 1$
$16x + 12y = 4$

c $x + 3y = 2$
$3x + 9y = 8$

3 Express x and y in terms of the other variables.

a $2y = x + 4c$
$5y = x + 25c$

b $ty = x + t^2$
$Ty = x + T^2$ (where $t \neq T$)

c $xy = 1$
$t^2x - y = t^3 - \dfrac{1}{t}$

d $x^2 - y^2 = 16a^2$
$y = 3x - 12a$

4 Find all possible pairs of real solutions for each of these pairs of simultaneous equations.

a $x^4 = 3y + 1$
$x^2 = y - 1$

b $x^4 - 4y = 14$
$x^2 - 2y = 3$

c $x^4 = y^2 - 19$
$x^2 = \dfrac{y^2}{10} - 1$

5 Solve these simultaneous equations.

$2(x - y) = (y + 1)^2$

$\dfrac{1}{x} = \dfrac{2}{y + 11}$

6 Solve these pairs of simultaneous equations.

a $x^2 + y^2 = 65$
$xy = 28$

b $xy = 35$
$\dfrac{1}{x} + \dfrac{1}{y} = \dfrac{12}{35}$

c $x^2 + 4y^2 = 52$
$xy = 12$

7 The combined resistance R_T for two resistors R_1 and R_2 is given by $R_T = R_1 + R_2$ if the resistors are in series and by

$$\frac{1}{R_T} = \frac{1}{R_1} + \frac{1}{R_2}$$

if they are in parallel. A pair of resistors have a combined resistance of 9 ohms in series and 2 ohms in parallel. Find the resistance of each resistor.

8 A rectangular wooden board has sides a m and ab m.
Its area is $1.5\,\text{m}^2$ and its perimeter is 7 m. Find a and b.

9 Show that the line $y = mx$ meets the curve $x^2 + y^2 + 2gx + 2fy + c = 0$ in two real points, if $(g + fm)^2 \geqslant c(1 + m^2)$.

10 Solve for x and y.

a $3x^2 - 2y^2 + 5 = 0$
$3x - 2y = 1$

b $2x^2 + 3y^2 + x = 13$
$2x + 3y = 7$

c $2x^2 - 3xy - 2y^2 = 12$
$2x - 3y = 4$

d $5x^2 - 5xy + 2y^2 = 12$
$3x - 2y + 2 = 0$

EXERCISE 5f (Miscellaneous)

1 Solve these.

a $4x + 3y = 1$
$3x + 2y = 1$

b $17x - 2y = 28$
$9x - 5y = 3$

c $x + y = 7$
$x^2 - 2xy + y^2 = 1$

d $3x - y = 5$
$2x^2 + y^2 = 129$

e $5x - 3y = 6$
$3x - 4y = 1$

f $3x - 5y = 5x - 3y = 16$

2 Find the point of intersection of $y = 4x - 1$ and $3y - 8x + 2 = 0$.

3 Find the points of intersection of $y = 4x - 1$ and $3x^2 - xy + 2y^2 = 18$.

4 Prove that the line $y = 2x + \frac{5}{4}$ touches the curve $y^2 = 10x$.

5 Find the points of intersection of $x - y = 2$ with $x^2 - 4y^2 = 5$.

6 Find the possible values of k if $y = 2x + k$ meets $y = x^2 - 2x - 7$

a in two distinct real points

b in just one point

7 Find the range of values of k for which $kx + y = 3$ meets $x^2 + y^2 = 5$ in two distinct points.

8 Find the values of k for which $y = kx - 2$ is a tangent to the curve $y = x^2 - 8x + 7$.

9 Find the range of values of k for which $y = 2x + k$ and $x^2 + y^2 = 4$ do not intersect.

10 A magician asks a volunteer to think of two different positive integers without telling her what they are. She then asks him to calculate x, the sum of the larger number with the square of the smaller, and y, the difference between the numbers. The volunteer tells her that $x = 9$ and $y = 3$. Find the original numbers.

11 A climbing centre has 14 fixed staff plus one additional staff member for every six climbers. There are twice as many climbers as staff altogether. Find the number of

a climbers

b staff

12 The temperature in a certain town fell 5°C from Monday to Tuesday. The mean temperature for the two days was 14.5°C. Find the temperature on each day.

13 In a casino, a gambler must give the banker a £20 stake at the beginning of the evening. Each time he wins a game, his amount in the bank is multiplied by a factor a; each time he loses, his amount in the bank is reduced by £b. One evening, a gambler wins his first game and loses the next ten, and finishes with £10 in the bank. A second gambler loses his first two games and wins the next one, and finishes with £30.

Find two possible pairs of values for a and b.

14 A hollow cylinder has volume $12\,\text{cm}^3$ and curved surface area $12\,\text{cm}^2$. Find

a the radius of its base

b its height

15 If 1 is added to the denominator of a certain fraction, the result is equal to $\frac{1}{3}$. If 1 is subtracted from the numerator of the original fraction, the result is equal to $\frac{1}{4}$. Find the fraction.

Test yourself

1 The simultaneous equations

$4x + y = 0$

$2y - 3x = 11$

have solutions

A $x = 1,\ y = -4$ **B** $x = \frac{11}{24},\ y = \frac{11}{6}$ **C** $x = \frac{11}{14},\ y = -3\frac{1}{7}$

D $x = -1,\ y = 4$ **E** none of these

2 A pair of simultaneous equations with one linear and one quadratic

A always has one pair of real solutions

B may have no real solutions

C always has two pairs of real solutions

D may have up to four pairs of real solutions

E always has either one or two pairs of real solutions

3 Given that $2x - 4y = 3$ and $x + 3y = 4$ then $x + y =$

A 3 **B** -1 **C** -7

D 1.8 **E** none of these

4 What are the solutions of these simultaneous equations?

$x - 2y = 4y - 6$

$\frac{x+1}{y} = 4$

A $x = 9,\ y = \frac{5}{2}$ **B** $x = 9,\ y = 21$ **C** $x = 30,\ y = 6$

D $x = 4,\ y = \frac{5}{4}$ **E** $x = 4,\ y = \frac{3}{5}$

5 The simultaneous equations

$\frac{1 - 3x}{y} = 2y + 1$

$x + 3y = 3$

have solutions

A $x = 3,\ y = 2$ and $x = -3,\ y = -2$ **B** $x = 1,\ y = 0$ and $x = -3,\ y = 2$

C $x = 30,\ y = 6$ **D** $x = -2,\ y = 1$ and $x = -\frac{3}{2},\ y = \frac{3}{2}$

E $x = -3,\ y = 2$

6 The angles in a scalene triangle, in ascending order, are θ, 2θ and ϕ. The largest angle is 5° more than the next one. θ and ϕ are

A 30° and 70° **B** $58\frac{1}{3}$° and $121\frac{2}{3}$° **C** 35° and 75°

D 45° and 90° **E** $22\frac{1}{2}$° and 45°

7 If the line $y = 3x - k$ is a tangent to the curve $y = 2x^2 - 5$ then $k =$

A $\frac{29}{4}$ **B** $-\frac{1}{2}$ **C** $\frac{49}{8}$ **D** $-\frac{31}{8}$ **E** 0

8 The square of Billy's age is four times his grandmother's age.
When Billy is $1\frac{1}{2}$ times as old as he is now, his grandmother will be 90.
The ages of Billy and his grandmother are

A not deducible without more information **B** 16 and 64
C $22\frac{1}{2}$ and $78\frac{3}{4}$ **D** 15.5 (1 d.p.) and 60 **E** 18 and 81

9 The number of real solutions of the simultaneous equations

$$x^2 + y^2 = 19$$
$$3x^2 - y^2 = 47$$

is

A 0 **B** 1 **C** 2 **D** 3 **E** 4

10 The area of a rectangular room measuring a m by b m is $8\,\text{m}^2$ more than the area of a square room of side a m.
The perimeter of the rectangular room is 1.25 times that of the square room.
a and b are

A 2 and 3 **B** 2 and 6 **C** 3 and $4\frac{1}{2}$ **D** 4 and 6 **E** 8 and 9

➤➤➤ Key points

Solving simultaneous equations

Two methods of solving simultaneous equations: elimination or substitution.

For two linear equations *either* method can be used.
For one linear and one quadratic equation, the substitution method is usually more suitable. The linear equation is rearranged.

- **Elimination**
  Match the coefficients of terms with the same letter.
  If matching terms have the *same* sign then *subtracting* the equations will eliminate those terms.
  If matching terms have *different* signs then *adding* the equations will eliminate those terms.
- **Substitution**
  Rearrange one of the equations to express one unknown in terms of the other.
  Substitute in the other equation.

Before solving simultaneous equations, look at the coefficients.

- If there are fractional or decimal coefficients in any equation, multiply all terms in the equation by a suitable number, so that all coefficients are whole numbers.
- If there is a common factor in all the coefficients of an equation, divide through by that factor before proceeding.

Always check the answer.

6 Further Work on Polynomials

Before starting this chapter you will need to know

- how to multiply polynomials (see Chapter 2).

6.1 Binomial expansion using Pascal's triangle

The binomial expansion is a method of raising a binomial expression (i.e. one with two terms)* to any power.

Consider

$$(a+b)^0 = \mathbf{1}$$
$$(a+b)^1 = \mathbf{1}a + \mathbf{1}b$$
$$(a+b)^2 = \mathbf{1}a^2 + \mathbf{2}ab + \mathbf{1}b^2$$
$$(a+b)^3 = \mathbf{1}a^3 + \mathbf{3}a^2b + \mathbf{3}ab^2 + \mathbf{1}b^3$$

The table of coefficients looks like this

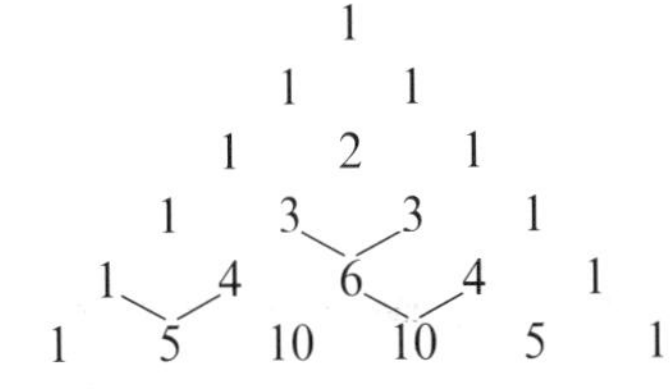

and so on.

Each entry in the table is the sum of the two above, so the next row would be 1, 6, 15, 20, 15, 6, 1.

> *This triangle is known as the Chinese triangle – Jia Xian, a Chinese mathematician, was using it in the mid-eleventh century – or* ***Pascal's triangle*** *after the mathematician and philosopher, Blaise Pascal (1623–1662).*

Notice that in the expansion of $(a+b)^3$ the first term is a^3 (or a^3b^0). In the second term, $3a^2b$, the power of a is *reduced* by one, and the power of b *increased* by one, and so on.

The coefficients in each row of Pascal's triangle are symmetrical.

In the expansion of $(a+b)^n$

- there are $n+1$ terms.
- the coefficients of the first two terms are 1 and n.
- the sum of the powers of a and b in each term is n.

Example 1

Expand, using Pascal's triangle:

a $(a+b)^6 = a^6 + 6a^5b + 15a^4b^2 + 20a^3b^3 + 15a^2b^4 + 6ab^5 + b^6$

The seventh row of the triangle gives the coefficients: 1, 6, 15, 20, 15, 6, 1. The letters in the terms are a^6, a^5b, a^4b^2 ....

b $(1+x)^5 = 1 + 5x + 10x^2 + 10x^3 + 5x^4 + x^5$

The coefficients are 1, 5, 10, 10, 5, 1. $a = 1$, $b = x$

*A *monomial* expression has one term. A *triomial* expression has three terms. A *polynomial* expression has many terms.

c $(2x-3)^4 = (2x)^4 + 4(2x)^3(-3) + 6(2x)^2(-3)^2 + 4(2x)(-3)^3 + (-3)^4$
$= 16x^4 - 96x^3 + 216x^2 - 216x + 81$

Here $a = 2x$, $b = -3$. Note how, with b –ve, the signs of the terms alternate.

✓ *Note* Putting $x = 1$ in both LHS and RHS of parts **b** and **c** will give some check that the expansion is correct.

EXERCISE 6a

1 Expand

a $(1+x)^4$ **b** $(1-x)^5$ **c** $(1+x)^6$ **d** $(1-x)^6$

2 Expand

a $(1+2x)^4$ **b** $(1-3y)^5$ **c** $(1+4z)^3$ **d** $\left(1-\frac{x}{2}\right)^3$

e $(a+b)^7$ **f** $(a^2-b^2)^5$ **g** $(a-b)^3(a+b)^3$

3 Expand

a $(x+y)^4$ **b** $(x+y)^5$ **c** $(3+x)^4$ **d** $(x-2)^3$

e $\left(2-\frac{x}{2}\right)^3$ **f** $\left(\frac{1}{x}+x^2\right)^3$ **g** $(2-x^3)^4$

4 **a** Expand

i $(a+b)^3$ **ii** $(a-b)^3$

b Hence, or otherwise, simplify, leaving surds in the answer where appropriate

i $(1+\sqrt{2})^3 + (1-\sqrt{2})^3$ **ii** $(1+\sqrt{2})^3 - (1-\sqrt{2})^3$

iii $(\sqrt{6}+\sqrt{2})^3 - (\sqrt{6}-\sqrt{2})^3$

5 Simplify, leaving surds in the answer where appropriate

a $(2+\sqrt{3})^4 + (2-\sqrt{3})^4$ **b** $(2+\sqrt{6})^4 - (2-\sqrt{6})^4$

c $(\sqrt{2}+\sqrt{3})^4 + (\sqrt{2}-\sqrt{3})^4$

6.2 Division of polynomials

Consider $36 \div 5$. $\frac{36}{5} = 7\frac{1}{5}$ or $\frac{36}{5} = 7$ remainder 1.

This can be expressed as

$$36 = 5 \times 7 + 1$$

(36: Dividend; 5: Divisor; 7: Quotient; 1: Remainder)

Consider $(x^2 + x - 3) \div (x - 1)$.

$$x^2 + x - 3 = (x-1)(x+2) - 1$$

(x^2+x-3: Dividend; $x-1$: Divisor; $x+2$: Quotient; -1: Remainder)

A method is needed to find the quotient and remainder in all situations.

The method of long division in algebra has much in common with long division of integers.

$$\begin{array}{r} 341 \\ 23\overline{)7846} \\ \underline{69} \\ 94 \\ \underline{92} \\ 26 \\ \underline{23} \\ 3 \end{array}$$

The result of this division can be written as

$7846 = 23 \times 341 + 3$

or $\frac{7846}{23} = 341$ remainder 3

or $\frac{7846}{23} = 341\frac{3}{23}$

Consider dividing $(x^2 + x - 3)$ by $(x - 1)$.

$$\begin{array}{r} x + 2 \\ x - 1\overline{)x^2 + x - 3} \\ \underline{x^2 - x\phantom{{}-3}} \\ 2x - 3 \\ \underline{2x - 2} \\ -1 \end{array}$$

Divisor ($x - 1$), Quotient ($x + 2$), Dividend ($x^2 + x - 3$), Remainder (-1)

The divisor and dividend should always be arranged in descending powers of the variable.

- Divide the term on the left of the dividend (x^2) by the term on the left of the divisor (x). This gives
  $$\frac{x^2}{x} = x$$
  This is the first term of the quotient.
- Multiply the whole divisor $(x - 1)$ by this term of the quotient (x). The result is $x^2 - x$. Write this below the dividend, lining up like terms. Then subtract it from the dividend.
- Bring down from the dividend the next term (-3). (Sometimes more than one term needs to be brought down.) This forms the new dividend.
- Repeat the process. Divide the term on the left of the new dividend $(2x)$ by the term on the left of the divisor (x). This gives
  $$\frac{2x}{x} = 2$$
  This is the second term of the quotient.
- Multiply the whole divisor $(x - 1)$ by this term of the quotient (2). This result is $2x - 2$. Write this below the dividend and subtract it from the new dividend $(2x - 3)$. The result is -1.
- The process cannot be repeated as x cannot be divided into -1. So -1 is the remainder. So
  $$x^2 + x - 3 \equiv (x - 1)(x + 2) - 1$$
- Finally, check the division by multiplying.

➤ The **algorithm (set of instructions) for division of polynomials**

- Arrange the divisor and dividend in descending powers of the variable, lining up like terms, and leaving gaps in the dividend for 'missing' terms.
- Divide the term on the left of the dividend by the term on the left of the divisor. The result is a term of the quotient.
- Multiply the whole divisor by this term of the quotient and subtract the product from the dividend.
- Bring down as many terms as necessary to form a new dividend.
- Repeat the instructions until all terms of the dividend have been used.

Example 2 Divide $x^3 - 3x^2 + 6x + 5$ by $x - 2$.

$$\begin{array}{r l}
 & x^2 - x + 4 \\
x - 2 \,) & x^3 - 3x^2 + 6x + 5 \\
 & \underline{x^3 - 2x^2} \\
 & \quad -x^2 + 6x \\
 & \quad \underline{-x^2 + 2x} \\
 & \qquad\quad 4x + 5 \\
 & \qquad\quad \underline{4x - 8} \\
 & \qquad\qquad + 13
\end{array}$$

So $x^3 - 3x^2 + 6x + 5 \equiv (x - 2)(x^2 - x + 4) + 13$.

This can also be written as

$$\frac{x^3 - 3x^2 + 6x + 5}{x - 2} \equiv x^2 - x + 4 + \frac{13}{x - 2} \quad x \neq 2$$

Example 3 Divide $3x^4 - 2x^2 - 1$ by $x + 1$.

$$\begin{array}{r l}
 & 3x^3 - 3x^2 + x - 1 \\
x + 1 \,) & 3x^4 \qquad\quad - 2x^2 \qquad - 1 \\
 & \underline{3x^4 + 3x^3} \\
 & \quad -3x^3 - 2x^2 \\
 & \quad \underline{-3x^3 - 3x^2} \\
 & \qquad\qquad x^2 \\
 & \qquad\qquad \underline{x^2 + x} \\
 & \qquad\qquad\quad -x - 1 \\
 & \qquad\qquad\quad \underline{-x - 1} \\
 & \qquad\qquad\qquad 0
\end{array}$$

There are no terms in x^3 or x in the dividend, so gaps must be left.

There is no remainder so $(x + 1)$ is a factor of $3x^4 - 2x^2 - 1$.

So $3x^4 - 2x^2 - 1 \equiv (x + 1)(3x^3 - 3x^2 + x - 1)$.

Example 4 Divide $x^3 - y^3$ by $x - y$.

$$\begin{array}{r l}
 & x^2 + xy + y^2 \\
x - y \,) & x^3 \qquad\qquad\quad - y^3 \\
 & \underline{x^3 - x^2y} \\
 & \quad x^2y \\
 & \quad \underline{x^2y - xy^2} \\
 & \qquad\quad xy^2 - y^3 \\
 & \qquad\quad \underline{xy^2 - y^3} \\
 & \qquad\qquad 0
\end{array}$$

There are no terms with x^2 or x in the dividend, so gaps must be left.

No remainder

So $x^3 - y^3 \equiv (x - y)(x^2 + xy + y^2)$

or $\dfrac{x^3 - y^3}{x - y} \equiv x^2 + xy + y^2 \qquad x \neq y$

Example 5 Divide $2x^3 + 3x^2 - 4x + 1$ by $x^2 + 2$.

$$\begin{array}{r l}
 & 2x + 3 \\
x^2 + 2 \,\big)\!\! & \overline{2x^3 + 3x^2 - 4x + 1} \\
 & \underline{2x^3 \qquad\quad + 4x \quad\;\;} \\
 & \qquad 3x^2 - 8x + 1 \\
 & \qquad \underline{3x^2 \qquad\;\; + 6} \\
 & \qquad\qquad -8x - 5
\end{array}$$

So $2x^3 + 3x^2 - 4x + 1 \equiv (x^2 + 2)(2x + 3) - 8x - 5$

or $\dfrac{2x^3 + 3x^2 - 4x + 1}{x^2 + 2} \equiv 2x + 3 - \dfrac{8x + 5}{x^2 + 2}$

The minus sign in front of the fraction means the whole fraction is subtracted. $-8x - 5 = -(8x + 5)$

Alternative method of division

With practice, long division in algebra can be avoided. Instead, a method of building up the quotient can be used.

Consider dividing $(x^3 + x^2 - 9x + 6)$ by $(x - 2)$.

$$x^3 + x^2 - 9x + 6 = (x - 2)(? \quad ? \quad ?)$$

Once mastered, this method is easier than it looks!

The quotient bracket can be built up, term by term.

To obtain x^3 (the first term of the dividend), the quotient must start with x^2.

$$x^3 + x^2 - 9x + 6 = (x - 2)(x^2 \quad ? \quad ?)$$

Dividend Divisor Quotient

Consider now how the term, x^2, of the dividend will be obtained. It will come from two products:

$$-2 \times x^2 = -2x^2 \quad \text{and} \quad x \times x \text{ term}$$

In divisor In quotient In divisor In quotient

$-2x^2$ will need $3x^2$ added to it to give the x^2 required.

To obtain $3x^2$, the x term of the quotient will have to be $3x$.

$$x^3 + x^2 - 9x + 6 = (x - 2)(x^2 + 3x \quad ?)$$

Check that this gives $x^3 + x^2$.

Consider now how the x term, $-9x$, of the dividend will be obtained. It will come from two products:

$$-2 \times 3x = -6x \quad \text{and} \quad x \times \text{constant term}$$

In divisor ↗ In quotient ↖ In divisor ↗ In quotient ↖

$-6x$ will need $-3x$ more to give the $-9x$ required.

To obtain $-3x$ the constant term of the quotient will have to be -3.

So $x^3 + x^2 - 9x + 6 = (x - 2)(x^2 + 3x - 3)$.

There is no remainder because $-2 \times -3 = 6$.

Check the division by multiplying the divisor by the quotient.

For a complicated example such as $(x^5 - x^4 - 2x^2 - 9x + 3)$ divided by $(x^2 + 3)$ the method of building up the quotient is to be recommended.

A simpler method of division

When the degree of the polynomials in the numerator and denominator are the same, the division can be carried out more simply.

Example 6 Divide $x + 2$ by $x + 1$.

Both numerator and denominator are of degree 1.

$$\frac{x+2}{x+1} = \frac{x+1+1}{x+1}$$

Rewrite the numerator so that it starts with a multiple of the denominator.

$$= \frac{x+1}{x+1} + \frac{1}{x+1}$$

$$= 1 + \frac{1}{x+1}$$

Example 7 Express $\dfrac{3x-5}{x+2}$ in the form $A + \dfrac{B}{x+2}$.

Rewrite the numerator so that it starts with a multiple of the denominator, $x + 2$.

$$\frac{3x-5}{x+2} = \frac{3(x+2)-11}{x+2} = 3 - \frac{11}{x+2}$$

Example 8 Express $\dfrac{4x^2-3x}{x^2+5}$ in the form $A + \dfrac{Bx+C}{x^2+5}$ where A, B and C are constants.

$$\frac{4x^2-3x}{x^2+5} = \frac{4(x^2+5)-3x-20}{x^2+5}$$

$$= 4 - \frac{3x+20}{x^2+5}$$

The minus sign in front of the fraction means the whole fraction is subtracted; $-3x - 20 = -(3x + 20)$.

EXERCISE 6b

1 Find the quotient when each of these polynomials is divided by the expression in brackets.

a $x^3 + 4x^2 + x - 6$ $(x - 1)$

b $x^3 + 4x^2 - 9x - 36$ $(x + 3)$

c $x^3 + 3x^2 + 3x + 2$ $(x + 2)$

d $x^3 - 3x^2 - 10x + 24$ $(x - 4)$

e $2x^3 + x^2 - 13x + 6$ $(x - 2)$

f $x^3 - 3x - 2$ $(x - 2)$

g $x^3 - x^2 - 4$ $(x - 2)$

h $2x^3 - x - 1$ $(x - 1)$

i $2x^3 - 5x^2 + 5x + 4$ $(2x + 1)$

j $2x^3 + 5x^2 - 14x + 3$ $(2x - 3)$

k $4x^3 + 6x^2 - 18x + 7$ $(2x - 1)$

l $2x^3 + x^2 + 18x + 9$ $(2x + 1)$

2 Repeat Question 1 for these expressions.

a $8x^3 - 24x + 9$ $(2x - 3)$

b $2x^4 - 9x^3 + 13x^2 - 15x + 9$ $(x - 3)$

c $x^4 - x^3 + 2x^2 + x - 3$ $(x + 1)$

d $x^4 + x^3 - 14x^2 + 4x + 6$ $(x - 3)$

e $12x^4 - 7x^2 + 1$ $(2x + 1)$

3 Find the quotient and, if it exists, the remainder when these polynomials are divided by the expression in brackets.

a $x^3 + 3x^2 + 6x + 1$ $(x + 1)$

b $x^3 + 5x^2 - 6x - 2$ $(x + 1)$

c $x^3 - 6x^2 + 11x - 6$ $(x - 1)$

d $x^3 - 3x^2 - x - 1$ $(x + 2)$

e $2x^3 - x + 51$ $(x + 3)$

f $2x^3 - x^2 - 4x + 12$ $(x + 2)$

g $3x^3 + 8x^2 - 6x + 12$ $(3x - 1)$

h $2x^3 + 5x^2 - 7x + 4$ $(x + 4)$

4 Express these as a constant plus a proper fraction as in Examples 6–8.

a $\dfrac{x + 9}{x + 5}$ **b** $\dfrac{x - 2}{x + 8}$ **c** $\dfrac{2x + 1}{x - 3}$ **d** $\dfrac{x^2 - 5}{x^2 + 3}$

e $\dfrac{x^2 - 5}{x^2 + 3x}$ **f** $\dfrac{x^2 - 5x}{x^2 + 3x}$ **g** $\dfrac{2 - x}{x + 5}$ **h** $\dfrac{1 - 3x}{x - 1}$

5 Find the quotient when these polynomials are divided by the expression in brackets.

a $x^4 - 2x^3 - 4x^2 + 7x - 2$ $(x^2 + x - 2)$

b $x^4 + 3x^3 + 3x - 1$ $(x^2 + 1)$

c $3x^4 - 2x^3 + 7x^2 - 4x + 2$ $(x^2 + 2)$

d $2a^3 - 7a^2 - a + 2$ $(a^2 - 3a - 2)$

6 Copy and complete these identities.

a $x^3 + x^2 - 5x + 3 \equiv (x^2 - 2x + 1)(\ldots)$

b $x^3 + x^2 - 10x + 8 \equiv (x^2 + 3x - 4)(\ldots)$

c $x^4 - 2x^3 + 4x^2 - 2x + 3 \equiv (x^2 + 1)(\ldots)$

d $x^4 + 3x^3 - 7x^2 - 9x + 12 \equiv (x^2 - 3)(\ldots)$

e $2x^4 - 3x^3 + 7x^2 - 12x - 4 \equiv (x^2 + 4)(\ldots)$

f $2x^4 + 8x^3 - 9x^2 + 4x - 5 \equiv (2x^2 + 1)(\ldots)$

g $12x^4 + 6x^3 - 23x^2 - 4x + 10 \equiv (3x^2 - 2)(\ldots)$

h $2x^4 + 11x^3 + 2x^2 - 25x + 12 \equiv (x^2 + 4x - 3)(\ldots)$

i $x^4 + x^3 + 7x - 3 \equiv (x^2 + 2x - 1)(\ldots)$

EXERCISE 6b *(continued)*

7 Find the quotient and the remainder when these polynomials are divided by the expression in brackets.

a	$x^4 + x^2 - 10$	$(x^2 - 2)$
b	$x^4 + 4x^3 + 7x^2 + 12x + 4$	$(x^2 + 3)$
c	$2x^4 - 10x^3 + 11x^2 - 25x$	$(2x^2 + 5)$
d	$6x^4 + 15x^3 - 13x^2 + 10x - 6$	$(3x^2 - 2)$
e	$8x^4 - 4x - 16$	$(2x^2 - 4)$
f	$x^4 - 17x^2 - 12x + 4$	$(x^2 + 4x + 1)$
g	$2x^4 - 2x^3 - 7x^2 + 25x$	$(2x^2 + 4x - 3)$
h	$8x^4 + 15x - 30$	$(2x^2 - x + 4)$
i	$3x^4 + 8x^3 + 14x^2 - x + 6$	$(3x^2 + 2x + 1)$

6.3 Remainder and factor theorems

When $f(x) = x^2 + x - 3$ is divided by $(x - 1)$ there is a quotient and a remainder.

$$f(x) \equiv x^2 + x - 3 \equiv (x - 1) \times \text{Quotient} + \text{Remainder}$$

Substituting $x = 1$ gives

$x = 1$ is chosen to make the bracket $(x - 1)$ zero.

$$f(1) = 1^2 + 1 - 3 = 0 \times \text{Quotient} + \text{Remainder}$$

$$f(1) = -1 = \text{Remainder}$$

So the remainder has been found without carrying out the division.

The remainder $= f(1)$. The quotient has not been found.

Check: $x^2 + x - 3 \equiv (x - 1)(x + 2) - 1$

The remainder theorem gives a quick way of finding remainders, without the need to carry out long division.

- The remainder on division by $x - 1$ is $f(1)$.
- The remainder on division by $x + 2$ is $f(-2)$.
- The remainder on division by $2x - 1$ is $f\left(\frac{1}{2}\right)$. $\left(2x - 1 = 0 \Leftrightarrow x = \frac{1}{2}\right)$

Example 9

In this example, to illustrate the method, more steps are shown than necessary.

Find the remainder when $2x^3 + x - 7$ is divided by $x + 2$.

Let $f(x) = 2x^3 + x - 7$

Define the expression as $f(x)$ so that function notation can be used.

$$f(x) = 2x^3 + x - 7 \equiv (x + 2) \times \text{Quotient} + \text{Remainder}$$

Putting $x = -2$

$x = -2$ is chosen to make the bracket $(x + 2)$ zero.

$$f(-2) = 2 \times (-2)^3 + (-2) - 7 = \text{Remainder}$$

$\therefore$ the remainder is -25.

So, if polynomial $f(x)$ is divided by $(x - a)$ the remainder is $f(a)$.
The remainder theorem states this in a more general form.

Remainder Theorem

If $f(x)$ is divided by $(ax - b)$ the remainder is $f\left(\frac{b}{a}\right)$.

Note: $x = \frac{b}{a} \Leftrightarrow ax - b = 0$

If there is *no* remainder on division, then the divisor is a **factor**.

So, if $f(a) = 0$ then $(x - a)$ is a factor of $f(x)$.

The factor theorem (a corollary of the remainder theorem) states this in a more general form.

Factor Theorem

$f(a) = 0 \Leftrightarrow (x - a)$ is a factor of $f(x)$.

$f\left(\frac{b}{a}\right) = 0 \Leftrightarrow (ax - b)$ is a factor of $f(x)$.

Example 10

Find the remainder when $2x^3 - 3x^2 + x + 5$ is divided by $2x - 1$.

Let $f(x) = 2x^3 - 3x^2 + x + 5$

Define the expression as $f(x)$ so that function notation can be used.

The remainder on division by $2x - 1$ is $f(\frac{1}{2})$.

$2x - 1 = 0 \Leftrightarrow x = \frac{1}{2}$

$$\begin{aligned} f(\tfrac{1}{2}) &= 2 \times (\tfrac{1}{2})^3 - 3 \times (\tfrac{1}{2})^2 + \tfrac{1}{2} + 5 \\ &= \tfrac{1}{4} - \tfrac{3}{4} + \tfrac{1}{2} + 5 \\ &= 5 \end{aligned}$$

So the remainder is 5.

Example 11

When the expression $x^3 + ax^2 + 2x + 1$ is divided by $x - 2$, the remainder is three times as great as when the expression is divided by $x - 1$. Find a.

Let $f(x) = x^3 + ax^2 + 2x + 1$

$f(2) = 8 + 4a + 4 + 1 = 13 + 4a$

$f(2)$ is the remainder on division by $x - 2$.

$f(1) = 1 + a + 2 + 1 = 4 + a$

$f(1)$ is the remainder on division by $x - 1$.

But $f(2) = 3f(1)$

$$\begin{aligned} \text{So} \quad 13 + 4a &= 3(4 + a) \\ &= 12 + 3a \\ \therefore \quad a &= -1 \end{aligned}$$

Factorising polynomials

Steps for factorising a polynomial in x

- Put the expression equal to $f(x)$ so that function notation can be used.
- Find one factor. $(x - a)$ will be a factor if $f(a) = 0$
  Try $f(1)$ first. If $f(1) = 0$ then $(x - 1)$ is a factor.
  If $f(1) \neq 0$, try $f(-1)$. If $f(-1) = 0$ then $(x + 1)$ is a factor.
  If $f(-1) \neq 0$, list (at least mentally) other possible factors and test until one factor is found.
- When one factor is found, divide the expression by that factor.
- Repeat the process until the polynomial is fully factorised.

Example 12

Show that $(x + 1)$ is a factor of $x^3 + 2x^2 - 5x - 6$ and hence factorise the expression fully.

Let $f(x) = x^3 + 2x^2 - 5x - 6$

Define the expression as $f(x)$ so that function notation can be used.

$$f(-1) = (-1)^3 + 2(-1)^2 - 5 \times (-1) - 6$$
$$= -1 + 2 + 5 - 6 = 0$$

$(x + 1)$ is a factor of $f(x)$ if, and only if, $f(-1) = 0$.

$\therefore$ $(x + 1)$ is a factor.

The function can now be divided by $(x + 1)$ giving $x^2 + x - 6$.

$$x^3 + 2x^2 - 5x - 6 \equiv (x + 1)(x^2 + x - 6)$$
$$\equiv (x + 1)(x + 3)(x - 2)$$

The expression is fully factorised when no further factors can be found.

Example 13

Factorise $x^3 - 3x^2 - 4x + 12$.

Possible factors are:

$(x \pm 1)$, $(x \pm 2)$, $(x \pm 3)$, $(x \pm 4)$, $(x \pm 6)$, $(x \pm 12)$

If this cubic expression has a linear factor then the bracket would start with x and end with a factor of 12.

Try $(x \pm 1)$ first.

Let $f(x) = x^3 - 3x^2 - 4x + 12$

Use function notation.

$$f(1) = 1 - 3 - 4 + 12 \neq 0$$

Try possible values, a, until some value gives $f(a) = 0$.

$\therefore$ $(x - 1)$ is *not* a factor.

$$f(-1) = -1 - 3 + 4 + 12 \neq 0$$

$\therefore$ $(x + 1)$ is *not* a factor.

$$f(2) = 8 - 12 - 8 + 12 = 0$$

Then $(x - a)$ is factor.

$\therefore$ $(x - 2)$ is a factor.

$$x^3 - 3x^2 - 4x + 12 = (x - 2)(x^2 - x - 6)$$
$$= (x - 2)(x - 3)(x + 2)$$

Algebraic division can be used if necessary.

Example 14

List the possible linear factors of $2x^3 + 3x^2 - 5$.

To obtain $2x^3$ the linear factor must contain only x or $2x$. Similarly, to obtain 5, it must contain 1 or 5.

The possible factors of $2x^3 + 3x^2 - 5$ are

$(x \pm 1)$, $(2x \pm 1)$, $(x \pm 5)$, $(2x \pm 5)$

Example 15

Factorise fully $f(x) = x^3 + x^2 + x - 3$. Hence solve $f(x) = 0$.

$f(x) = x^3 + x^2 + x - 3$

$f(1) = 1 + 1 + 1 - 3 = 0$

$\Rightarrow \quad (x - 1)$ is a factor

So $x^3 + x^2 + x - 3 = (x - 1)(x^2 + 2x + 3)$.

$x^2 + 2x + 3$ cannot be factorised.

$f(x) = 0 \Rightarrow (x - 1)(x^2 + 2x + 3) = 0$

$\Rightarrow \quad x = 1 \quad \text{or} \quad x^2 + 2x + 3 = 0$

The discriminant of $x^2 + 2x + 3 = 0$, $b^2 - 4ac = 4 - 12 = -8 < 0$.

$\therefore \quad x^2 + 2x + 3 = 0$ has no real roots so $f(x) = 0 \Rightarrow x = 1$.

Example 16

Factorise $x^3 + y^3$.

Substituting $x = -y$ makes the expression zero.

Let $f(x) = x^3 + y^3$.
Since $f(-y) = (-y)^3 + y^3 = 0$,
$x + y$ is a factor.

$\therefore \quad (x + y)$ is a factor

$x^3 + y^3 = (x + y)(x^2 - xy + y^2)$

EXERCISE 6c
(Factor theorem)

1 Find the values of $f(0)$, $f(1)$, $f(-1)$, $f(2)$ and $f(-2)$ and state one factor of each expression.

a $f(x) = x^3 + 3x^2 - 4x - 12$

b $f(x) = 3x^3 - 2x - 1$

c $f(x) = x^5 + 2x^4 + 3x^3$

d $f(x) = x^4 - 4x^2 + 3$

2 Show that

a $x - 1$ is a factor of $f(x) = x^5 - 3x^2 + 2$

b $x + 2$ is a factor of $f(x) = 2x^3 - 3x^2 - 12x + 4$

c $2x - 1$ is a factor of $f(x) = 2x^3 + x^2 - 3x + 1$

3 Find the values of a in these expressions when

a $x^3 + x^2 + ax + 8$ is divisible by $x - 1$

b $x^4 - 3x^2 + 2x + a$ is divisible by $x + 1$

c $x^5 + 4x^4 - 6x^2 + ax + 2$ is divisible by $x + 2$

4 Show that $x - 1$ is a factor of $x^3 - 7x + 6$, and find the other factors of the expression.
Hence solve $x^3 - 7x + 6 = 0$.

5 Find a factor of $f(x)$ using the factor theorem and hence factorise $f(x)$.

a $f(x) = x^3 - x^2 - 4x + 4$

b $f(x) = x^3 + 2x^2 - 5x - 6$

c $f(x) = x^3 - 2x^2 - 5x + 6$

d $f(x) = 2x^3 + x^2 - 8x - 4$

EXERCISE 6c *(continued)*

6 Solve $f(x) = 0$ for the functions in Question 5.

7 Show that $2x^3 + x^2 - 13x + 6$ is divisible by $x - 2$, and find the other factors of the expression.
Hence solve $2x^3 + x^2 - 13x + 6 = 0$.

8 Find the values of a and b so that $x^3 + ax^2 + bx - 6$ is divisible by $x - 1$ and $x + 2$.
Factorise the expression.

9 Find the values of a and b so that $2x^4 + 3x^3 + ax^2 - x + b$ is divisible by $x + 1$ and $2x - 1$.
Factorise the expression.

10 **a** Factorise $x^2 - 3x - 4$.

b Show that $x^2 - 3x - 4$ is a factor of $f(x)$ where
$f(x) = x^4 - 3x^3 - 12x^2 + 24x + 32$.

c Solve $f(x) = 0$.

EXERCISE 6d
(Remainder theorem)

1 Find the remainders when

a $x^3 + 3x^2 - 4x + 2$ is divided by $x - 1$

b $x^3 - 2x^2 + 5x + 8$ is divided by $x - 2$

c $x^5 + x - 9$ is divided by $x + 1$

d $x^3 + 3x^2 + 3x + 1$ is divided by $x + 2$

e $4x^3 - 5x + 4$ is divided by $2x - 1$

f $4x^3 + 6x^2 + 3x + 2$ is divided by $2x + 3$

2 Find the values of a in these expressions when

a $x^3 + ax^2 + 3x - 5$ has remainder -3 when divided by $x - 2$

b $x^3 + x^2 - 2ax + a^2$ has remainder 8 when divided by $x - 2$

c $x^3 - 3x^2 + ax + 5$ has remainder 17 when divided by $x - 3$

d $x^5 + 4x^4 - 6x^2 + ax + 2$ has remainder 6 when divided by $x + 2$

3 Find the values of a and b if $x^4 + ax^3 + bx^2 - 2x + 8$ has remainder 6 when divided by $x - 1$ and remainder -24 when divided by $x + 2$.

4 The expression $ax^2 + bx + c$ is divisible by $x - 1$, has remainder 2 when divided by $x + 1$, and has remainder 8 when divided by $x - 2$.
Find the values of a, b and c.

5 $x - 1$ and $x + 1$ are factors of the expression $x^3 + ax^2 + bx + c$, and it leaves a remainder of 12 when divided by $x - 2$.
Find the values of a, b and c.

6 The remainder when $2x^3 + ax^2 + 4$ is divided by $x - 2$ is five more than when it is divided by $x - 1$.
Find a.

7 The remainder when $ax^4 + 3x^2 - x + 2$ is divided by $x + 2$ is eight times the remainder when it is divided by $x - 1$.
Find a.

8 The remainders when $2x^3 + ax^2 + (a+6)x - 5$ is divided by $2x + 1$ and by $x - 1$ are equal.
Find a.

9 Show that the remainder when $x^3 + ax^2 - 2x$ is divided by $x - 2$ is four times the remainder when it is divided by $x + 1$.

10 Find the remainder when these expressions are divided by $x + 1$.

a $x^{17} + x^{15}$ **b** $x^{18} + x^{16}$

11 Show that $x + 2$ cannot be a factor of $x^{2n} + 4$.

12 For what values of n $(n > 0)$ is $x + 1$ a factor of $x^n + 1$?

EXERCISE 6e (Extension)

1 Show that $x - p$ is a factor of $(x - q)^7 + (q - p)^7$.

2 When $px^2 + qx + r$ is divided by $x + 1$, $x + 2$ and $x - 1$ the remainders are -6, -4 and 8 respectively.
Find p, q and r.

3 Expand

a $(2 + x + x^2)^3$ **b** $(3 + x - 2x^2)^3$ **c** $(1 - x + x^2)^4$

4 Expand as far as the term in x^2

a $(1 - x - x^2)^4$ **b** $(1 + 2x + 3x^2)^5$ **c** $(2 + x - x^2)^6$

5 Use a binomial expansion to simplify these.

a $(\sqrt{3} + \sqrt{2})^5 + (\sqrt{3} - \sqrt{2})^5$ **b** $(2\sqrt{2} + 1)^4 - (2\sqrt{2} - 1)^4$

6 Prove that $x^4 + x^3 - 3x^2 - 4x - 4$ is divisible by $x^2 - 4$.

7 Prove that $x^5 - 7x^3 - 12x + 18$ is divisible by $x^2 + 2x - 3$.

8 Show that $12x^3 + 16x^2 - 5x - 3$ is divisible by $2x - 1$ and find the factors of the expression.

9 Factorise these.

a $2x^3 + 11x^2 + 17x + 6$ **b** $2x^3 - x^2 + 2x - 1$

10 Find the value of a if $2x^2 - x - 6$, $3x^2 - 8x + 4$ and $ax^3 - 10x - 4$ have a common factor.

11 Find the values of a and b if $ax^4 + bx^3 - 8x^2 + 6$ has remainder $2x + 1$ when divided by $x^2 - 1$.

12 The remainders when $f(x) = 2x^3 - 3x^2 + ax + b$ is divided by $x + 1$, $x - 1$ and $x - 2$ respectively form an arithmetic progression.
Find a and b.

EXERCISE 6f
(Miscellaneous)

1 Divide $2x^3 + 7x^2 + 15x + 6$ by $2x + 1$.
Hence show that $2x^3 + 7x^2 + 15x + 6 = 0$ has only one real root.

2 Divide $x^3 - 9x + 10$ by $x - 2$.
Hence find the solutions to $x^3 - 9x + 10 = 0$ in the set

a $\mathbb{Z}$ (integers) **b** $\mathbb{Q}$ (rational numbers) **c** $\mathbb{R}$ (real numbers)

3 Given that $x^3 - 2x^2 + x - 12 \equiv (x - 3)(x^2 + ax + b)$, find the values of a and b.

4 Find the first three terms in these expansions in ascending powers of x.

a $(1 + x)^4$ **b** $(1 - 2x)^3$ **c** $\left(1 + \frac{x}{3}\right)^5$ **d** $(2 - x)^4$ **e** $\left(x + \frac{1}{x}\right)^6$

5 Given that $x + 2$ is a factor of $x^3 - 2x^2 + ax + 6$, find a.

6 **a** Find the first three terms in the expansion, in ascending powers of x, of $(1 - x)^4$.

b Repeat part **a** for $(1 + 3x)^5$.

c Hence find the coefficient of x^2 in the expansion of $(1 - x)^4(1 + 3x)^5$.

7 Given that $x - 1$ and $x + 3$ are factors of $x^3 - x^2 + ax + b$, find a and b.

8 Factorise fully $2x^4 - x^3 - 5x^2 - 2x$.
Hence solve $2x^4 - x^3 - 5x^2 - 2x = 0$.

9 Given that $f(x) = x^3 - 10x + 12$

a show that $f(2) = 0$

b solve $f(x) = 0$

10 The remainder when $2x^3 + ax^2 - x - 4$ is divided by $x - 2$ is 6.
Find a.

11 The remainders when $3x^9 - ax + b$ is divided by $x - 1$ and by $x + 1$ are equal.

a Find a.

b Show that b can take any value.

12 **a** Expand $(1 + x)^4$ in ascending powers of x.

b Hence, or otherwise, show that $(1 + x)^4 - (1 - x)^4 = 8x(1 + x^2)$.

c Hence solve $(1 + x)^4 - (1 - x)^4 = 0$.

13 When the polynomial $f(x) = 2x^3 + ax^2 + bx + c$ is divided by x, $x - 1$ and $2x + 1$ the remainders are 5, 10 and 1 respectively.
Find a, b and c.

Test yourself

1 $x - 2$ is a factor of

A $x^3 - 2x^2 - 4x - 8$ **B** $2x^4 - 4x^2$ **C** $4x^3 + 2x^2 - 16$

D $3x^5 - 10x^3 - 5x^2 + 4$ **E** $5x^3 - 7x^2 - 12x + 4$

2 The coefficient of y^3 in the expansion of $(1 + y)^6$ is

A 120 **B** 15 **C** 20

D 60 **E** 1

3 The remainder when a polynomial of degree 7 is divided by a polynomial of degree 3

A is of degree 4

B is of degree 2

C may be of degree 1 or 2

D may be of any degree up to and including 7

E may be of any degree up to and including 2

4 One of the linear factors of $2t^3 - 3t^2 - 5t + 6$ is

A $2t - 3$ **B** $t - 2$ **C** $t + 3$

D $t + 1$ **E** $t + 2$

5 The quotient when $x^4 - 2x^3 - 3x^2 - 4x - 4$ is divided by $x + 1$ is

A $x^3 - 2x^2 - 3x - 4$ **B** $x^3 - 3x^2 - 4$ **C** $-x^3 - 3x - 4$

D zero **E** $x^3 - x^2 - 4x + 4$

6 If $x + 1$ is a factor of $a^2x^3 - 4x^2 + ax + 10$, then

A $a = 2$ or -3 **B** $a = -2$ **C** $a = \pm\sqrt{6}$

D $a = 4$ **E** none of these

7 When $rx^3 + r^2x^2 + r^3x + r^4$ is divided by $x - r$, the remainder is

A $4r^4$ **B** zero **C** $r^3 + r^2 + r$

D $-r^5 + 2r^4$ **E** -1

8 If $ax^3 - 4x^2 + bx - 5$ leaves a remainder of -12 when divided by $x + 1$ and a remainder of -8 when divided by $x - 3$, then

A $a + b = -9$ **B** $a = -1, b = -2$ **C** $a^3 + b = -3$

D $a = 1, b = 2$ **E** $a = 4, b = 5$

➤➤➤ Key points

The binomial expansion

The coefficients of the terms of a binomial expression can be obtained from Pascal's triangle. For example:

$$
\begin{array}{ccccccccc}
 & & & & 1 & & & & \\
 & & & 1 & & 1 & & & \\
 & & 1 & & 2 & & 1 & & \\
 & 1 & & 3 & & 3 & & 1 & \\
1 & & 4 & & 6 & & 4 & & 1
\end{array}
$$

$$(a+b)^4 = \boxed{1}a^4 + \boxed{4}a^3b + \boxed{6}a^2b^2 + \boxed{4}ab^3 + \boxed{1}b^4$$

Division of polynomials

- Arrange the divisor and dividend in descending powers of the variable, lining up like terms, and leaving gaps in the dividend for 'missing' terms.
- Divide the term on the left of the dividend by the term on the left of the divisor. The result is a term of the quotient.
- Multiply the whole divisor by this term of the quotient and subtract the product from the dividend.
- Bring down as many terms as necessary to form a new dividend.
- Repeat the instructions until all terms of the dividend have been used.

Remainder theorem

If $f(x)$ is divided by $(ax - b)$ then the remainder is $f\left(\frac{b}{a}\right)$.

Factor theorem

$f(a) = 0 \Leftrightarrow (x - a)$ is a factor of $f(x)$. $f\left(\frac{b}{a}\right) = 0 \Leftrightarrow (ax - b)$ is a factor of $f(x)$.

Factorising polynomials

- Put the expression equal to $f(x)$ so that function notation can be used.
- Find one factor. $(x - a)$ will be a factor if $f(a) = 0$
  Try $f(1)$ first. If $f(1) = 0$ then $(x - 1)$ is a factor.
  If $f(1) \neq 0$, try $f(-1)$. If $f(-1) = 0$ then $(x + 1)$ is a factor.
  If $f(-1) \neq 0$, list (at least mentally) other possible factors and test until one factor is found.
- When one factor is found, divide the expression by that factor.
- Repeat the process until the polynomial is fully factorised.

7 Graphs

Before starting this chapter you will need to know

- about function notation (Chapter 2)
- about the modulus function (Chapter 4).

A calculator or computer may be used for checking sketches. It is important to understand the techniques of curve sketching and transformation of curves with and without technological aids.

7.1 Graphs of standard functions

The graphs of standard functions should be known.

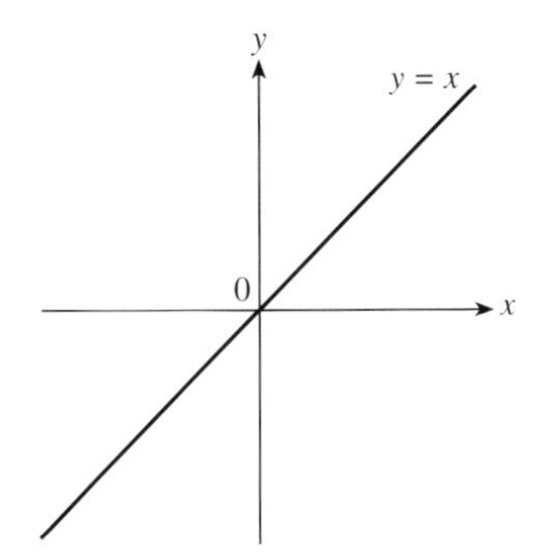

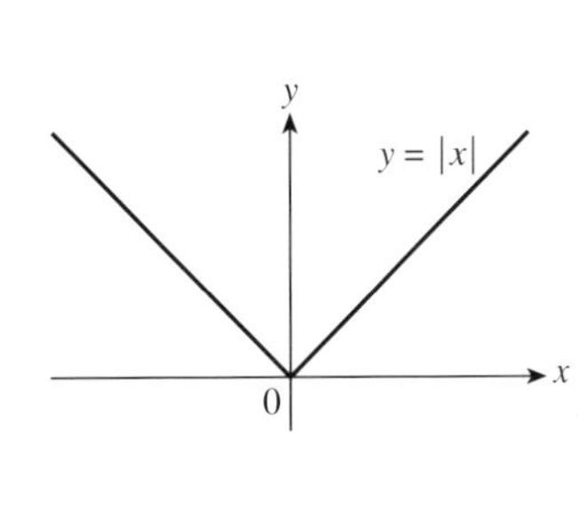

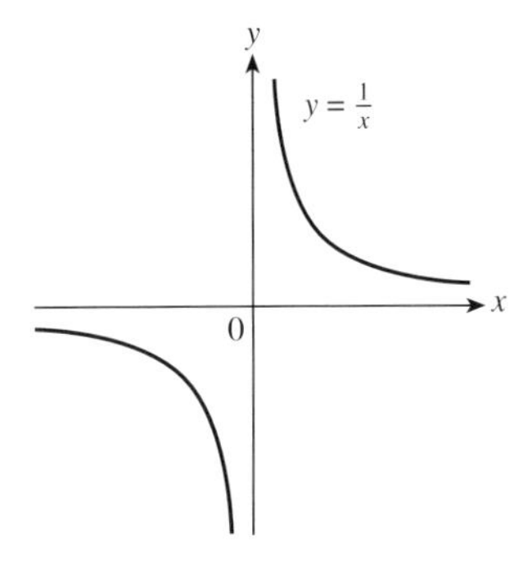

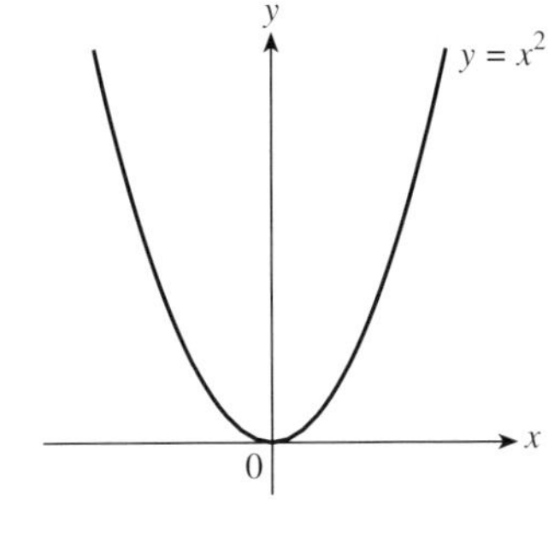

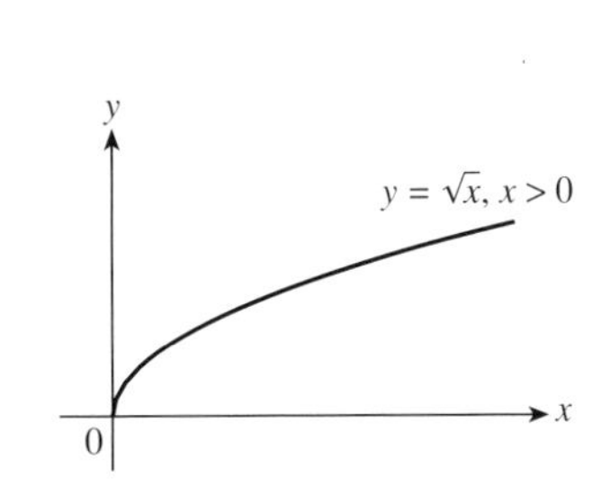

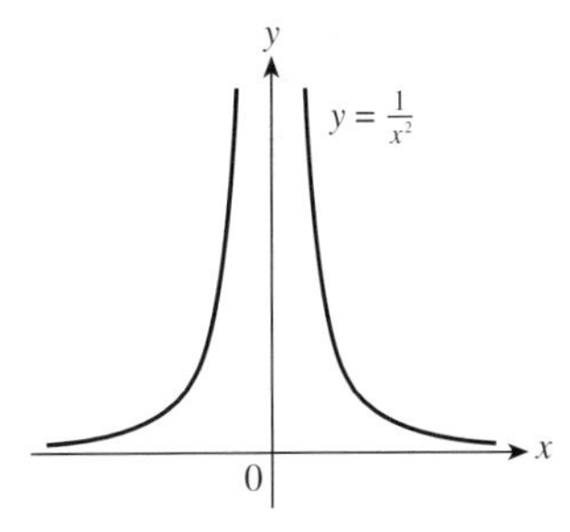

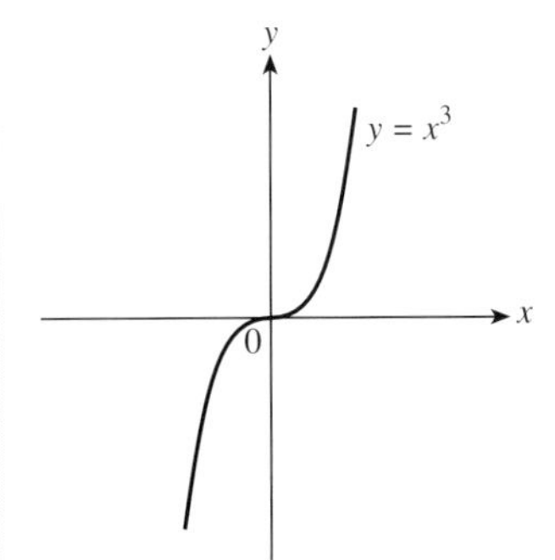

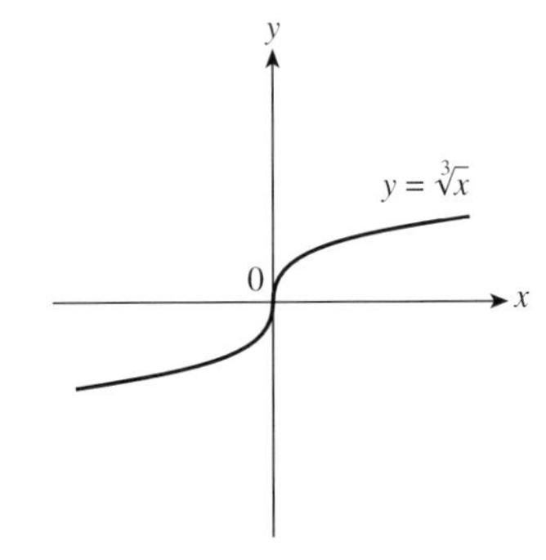

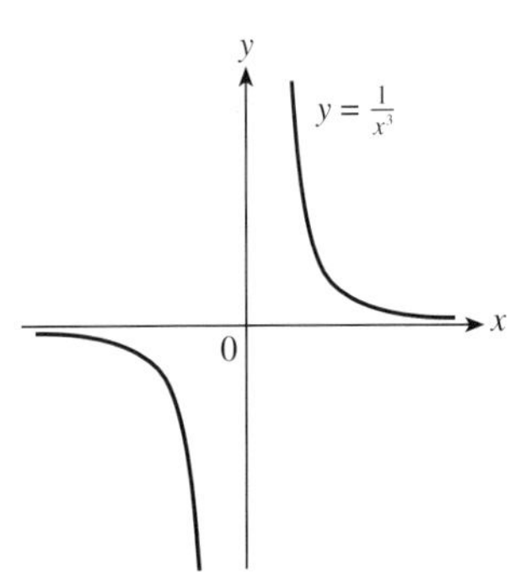

$y = x^{2n}$

For $n > 0$, curves intersect at $x = 0$ and $x = \pm 1$.

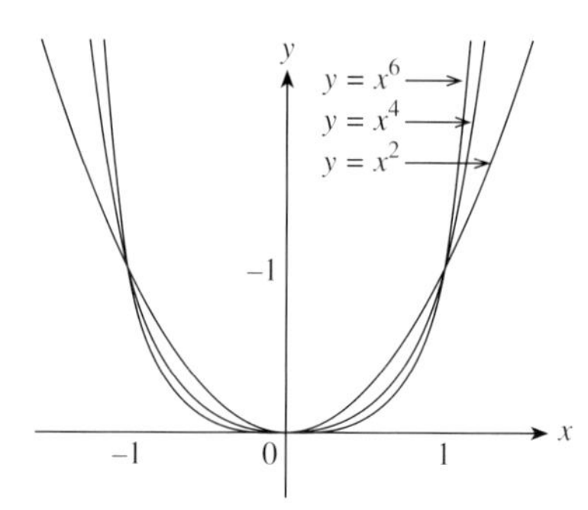

At $x = 0$ or $x = \pm 1$, $x^2 = x^4 = x^6$

For $-1 < x < 1$, $x^6 < x^4 < x^2$

For $x < -1$ and $x > 1$, $x^2 < x^4 < x^6$

$y = x^{2n+1}$

For $n > 0$, curves intersect at $x = 0$ and $x = \pm 1$

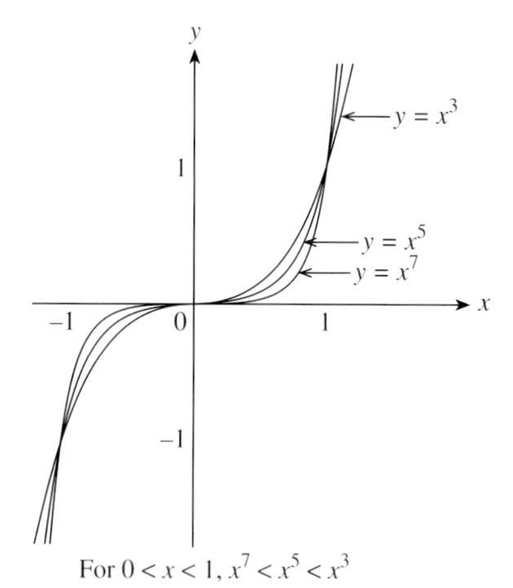

For $0 < x < 1$, $x^7 < x^5 < x^3$

For $x = 0$ or $x \pm 1$, $x^7 = x^5 = x^3$

For $x > 1$, $x^3 < x^5 < x^7$

There are similar results for $x < 0$

$y = a^x$

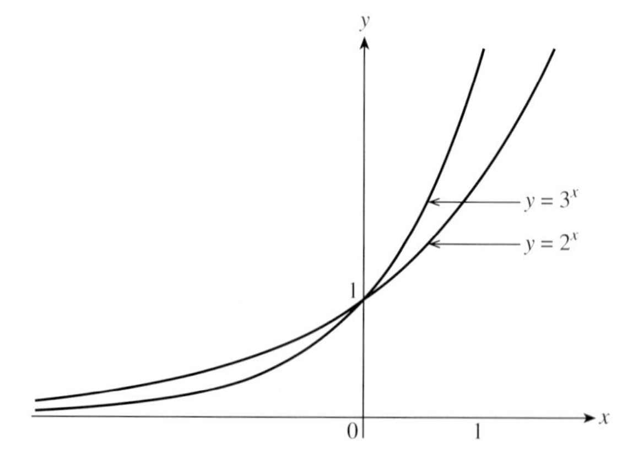

Continuous and discontinuous curves

Curves without a break, such as $y = x^2$ and $y = x^3$ are called **continuous**.

The graphs of $y = \frac{1}{x}$, $y = \frac{1}{x^2}$ and $y = \frac{1}{x^3}$ have breaks in the curves at $x = 0$. The curves that cannot be drawn without taking the pencil off the paper are called **discontinuous**. When $x = 0$, the graphs shoot off to plus or minus infinity. The line $x = 0$ (the y-axis) is an **asymptote** to each curve. For very large positive and negative values of x, the curve approaches the x-axis but *never* reaches it. The x-axis is also an asymptote to each curve.

✓ ***Note*** As a curve approaches an asymptote it becomes closer and closer to the asymptote but never reaches it. An asymptote which is not the x- or y-axis is shown with a dashed line. (See Example 11 on page 135.)

Asymptotes are discussed more fully in Chapter 18.

7.2 Transformation of graphs

Translating, reflecting and stretching the standard curves is one useful approach to sketching curves.

Example 1 Consider $y = x^2$ and $y = x^2 + 3$.

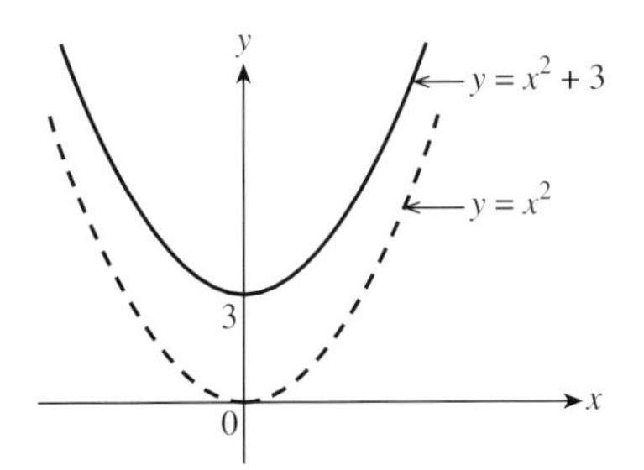

For $y = x^2 + 3$ all points of $y = x^2$ have been moved up 3 units.

The graph of $y = x^2$ has been translated by $\binom{0}{3}$.

➤ $y = f(x) + a$ is a translation $\binom{0}{a}$ of $y = f(x)$.

Add 3 to the function ⇒ move **up** 3.
Subtract 3 from the function ⇒ move **down** 3.

Example 2 Consider $y = x^2$ and $y = (x-3)^2$.

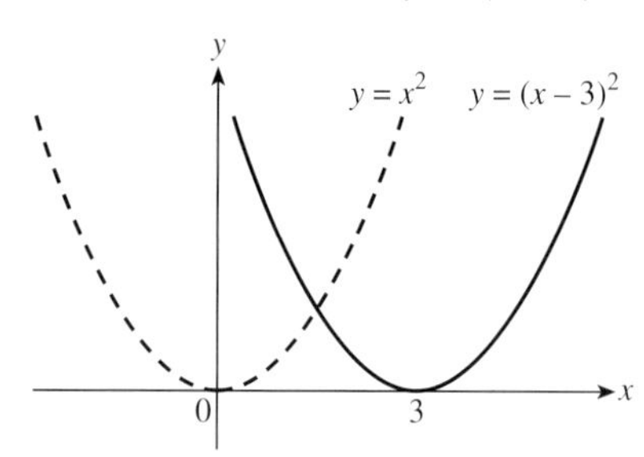

For $y = (x-3)^2$ all points of $y = x^2$ have been moved 3 units to the right. (Putting $x = 3$ gives $y = 0$.)

The graph of $y = x^2$ has been translated by $\binom{3}{0}$.

➤ $y = \mathrm{f}(x-a)$ is a translation $\binom{a}{0}$ of $y = \mathrm{f}(x)$.

Replace $\boldsymbol{x}$ by $x - 3 \Rightarrow$ move **right** 3.
Replace $\boldsymbol{x}$ by $x + 3 \Rightarrow$ move **left** 3.

Example 3 *This example combines the two previous results.*

Consider $y = x^2$ and $y = (x+1)^2 - 4$.
$(x+1)^2 - 4$ is a quadratic expression in completed square form.

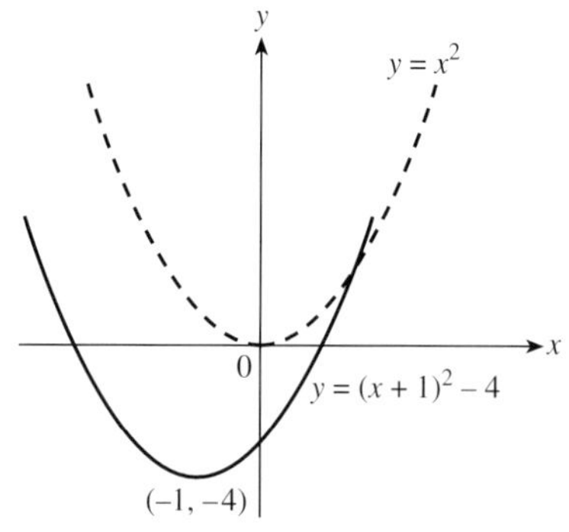

Since x has been replaced by $x + 1$, the graph of $y = x^2$ moves 1 unit to the left.

Since 4 has been subtracted, the graph then moves down 4.

So $y = x^2$ is translated $\binom{-1}{-4}$ to give $y = (x+1)^2 - 4$.

There will be a minimum point at $(-1, -4)$.

➤ $y = \mathrm{f}(x-a) + b$ is a translation $\binom{a}{b}$ of $y = \mathrm{f}(x)$.

Example 4 Consider $y = x^2$ and $y = -x^2$.
For $y = -x^2$ all points of $y = x^2$ have been reflected in the x-axis.

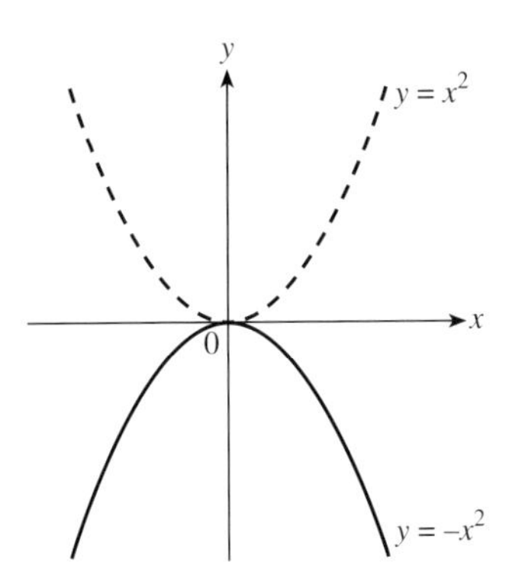

➤ $y = -f(x)$ is a reflection in the x-axis ($y = 0$) of $y = f(x)$.

Example 5 Consider $y = x^3 + 1$ and $y = (-x)^3 + 1 = -x^3 + 1$.
For $y = -x^3 + 1$ all points of $y = x^3 + 1$ have been reflected in the y-axis.
In the equation, x has been replaced by $-x$.

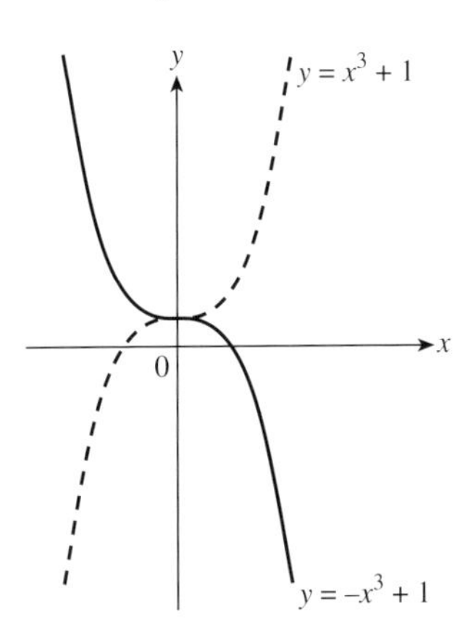

➤ $y = f(-x)$ is a reflection in the y-axis ($x = 0$) of $y = f(x)$.

Although the sine curve is not studied until later (in Chapter 15, section 15.4) it is used for the next two examples because it provides a better illustration of stretches than other functions.

Example 6 Consider $y = \sin x$ and $y = 2\sin x$.
For $y = 2\sin x$ all points of $y = \sin x$ have had their y-coordinate multiplied by 2.
This transformation is a stretch parallel to the y-axis of scale factor 2.

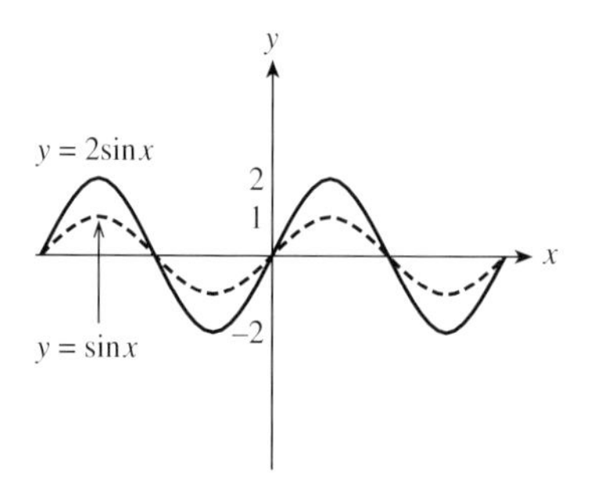

➤ $y = af(x)$ is a stretch parallel to the y-axis of scale factor a.

$a > 1 \Rightarrow$ curve is stretched away from x-axis.
$0 < a < 1 \Rightarrow$ curve is compressed towards x-axis.

Example 7 Consider $y = \sin x$ and $y = \sin 2x$.

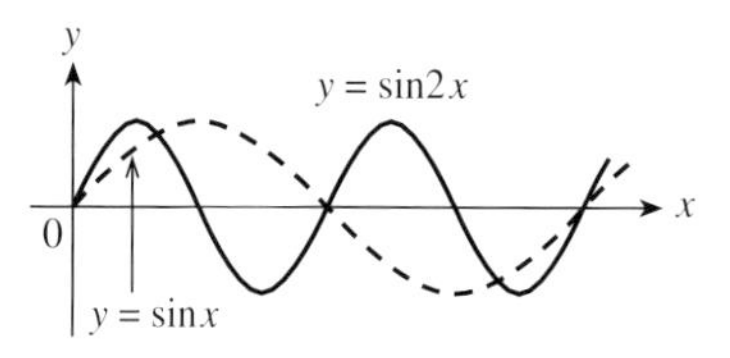

For $y = \sin 2x$ all the points of $y = \sin x$ have had their x-coordinate multiplied by $\frac{1}{2}$.
This transformation is a stretch parallel to the x-axis of scale factor $\frac{1}{2}$.

Similarly, for $y = \sin \frac{1}{2}x$ all the points of $y = \sin x$ have had their x-coordinate multiplied by 2.

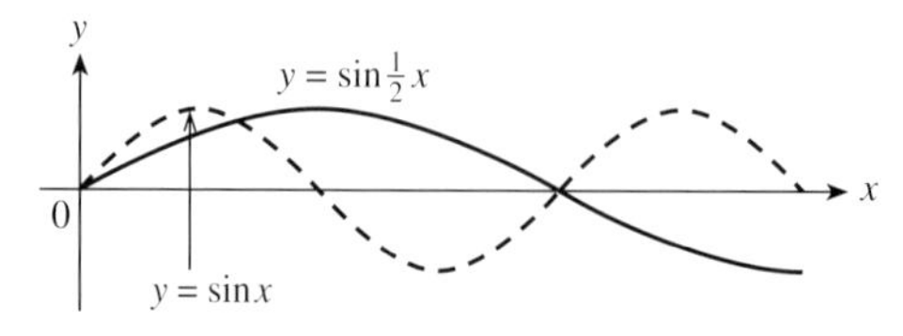

This transformation is a stretch parallel to the x-axis of scale factor 2.

➤ $y = f(ax)$ is a stretch parallel to the x-axis of scale factor $\frac{1}{a}$.

$a > 1 \Rightarrow$ curve is compressed towards y-axis.
$0 < a < 1 \Rightarrow$ curve is stretched away from y-axis.

7.3 Curve sketching 1

Sketching a curve means showing its general shape and marking certain important features. Only if an accurate **plot** of a graph is required should a large number of points be tabulated.

A graphics calculator should be used with care; it can mislead. There is no substitute for knowing functions and their graphs and practising curve sketching techniques.

When a graph is to be sketched, consider these points:

- Is the graph a *standard function* or a *transformation* of one?
- Where does the curve *cross the axes*?
  Putting $x = 0$ will give the intercepts on the y-axis.
  Putting $y = 0$ will give the intercepts on the x-axis.

A second section on curve sketching, in Chapter 10, extends this work further.

Example 8 $f(x) = x^2 + 2$

a Sketch $y = f(x)$ and $y = f(x + 3)$ on the same axes, marking the coordinates of the vertex of each parabola.

b Find an expression for the function $f(x + 3)$ in the form $ax^2 + bx + c$.

c Find the point of intersection of $y = f(x)$ and $y = f(x + 3)$

Solution

a

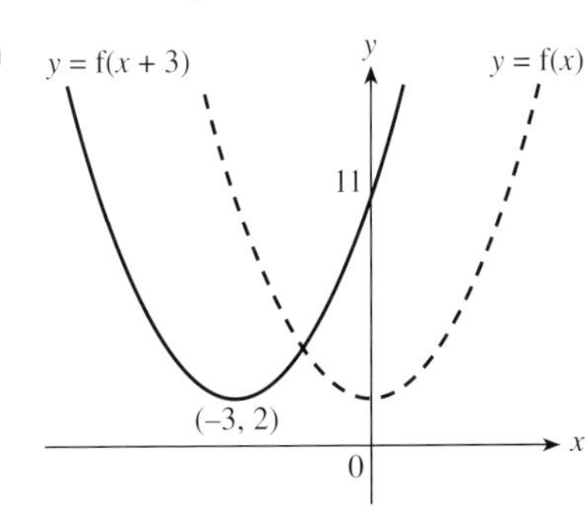

To obtain the graph of $y = x^2 + 2$, $y = x^2$ is translated $\binom{0}{2}$, vertex at (0, 2).

$f(x + 3)$ is a translation of $f(x)$ three units to the left.

The vertex is at (–3, 2).

$f(x + 3)$ is $f(x)$ translated by $\binom{-3}{0}$.

b $f(x + 3) = (x + 3)^2 + 2$

$= x^2 + 6x + 11$

To obtain the function $f(x + 3)$ substitute $(x + 3)$ for x in $f(x) = x^2 + 2$.

c The two curves intersect where $f(x) = f(x + 3)$.

Note: When $x = 0$, $f(x + 3) = 11$, $\therefore$ curve cuts y-axis at (0, 11).

So $x^2 + 2 = x^2 + 6x + 11$

$6x = -9$

$x = -\frac{3}{2}$

When $x = -\frac{3}{2}$, $y = \frac{9}{4} + 2 = \frac{17}{4}$, so the curves intersect at $\left(-\frac{3}{2}, \frac{17}{4}\right)$.

Example 9 $f(x) = (x - 1)^2 - 4$. Sketch the graphs of

a $y = f(x)$ **b** $y = |f(x)|$ **c** $y = f(|x|)$

Solution

a When $x = 0$, $y = -3$.

Curve cuts y-axis when $x = 0$.

So the curve cuts the y-axis at $y = -3$.

When $y = 0$

$$(x - 1)^2 - 4 = 0$$
$$(x - 1)^2 = 4$$
$$x - 1 = \pm 2$$
$$\therefore \quad x = 1 \pm 2$$

Curve cuts x-axis when $y = 0$.

So the curve cuts the x-axis at $x = 3$ and $x = -1$.

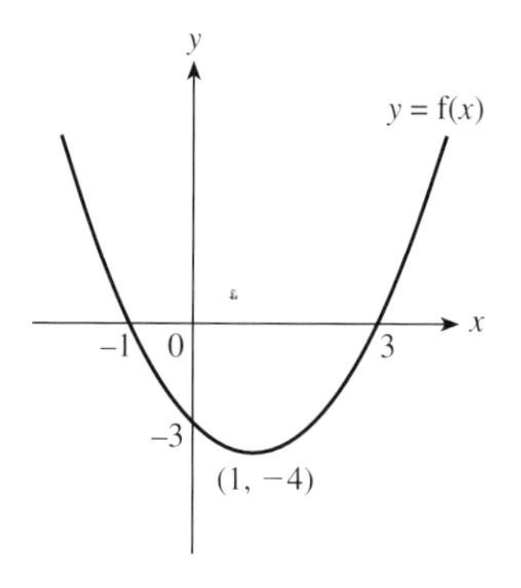

$y = x^2$ has been translated 1 unit right and 4 down.

Vertex (0, 0) of $y = x^2$ has moved to (1, −4).

b

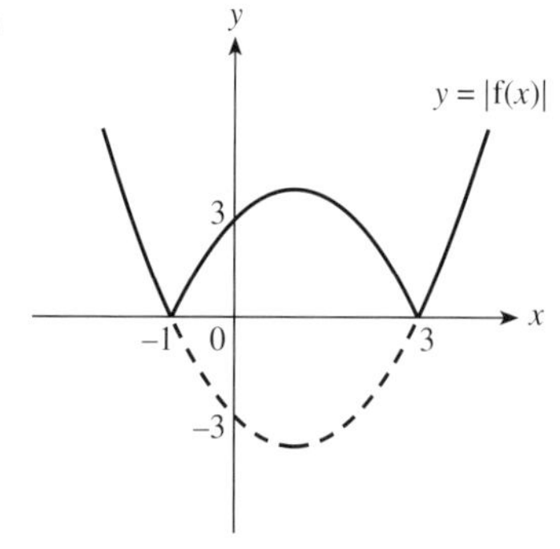

For $f(x)$ +ve, i.e. for the curve above the x-axis $|f(x)| = f(x)$.

For $f(x)$ −ve, i.e. for the curve below the x-axis $|f(x)| = -f(x)$.

The portion of the curve below the x-axis, shown with a dotted line, must be reflected in the x-axis.

Try drawing $y = |(x - 1)^2 - 4|$ on a graphics calculator. *Note*: $|x| = \text{ABS}(x)$.

c

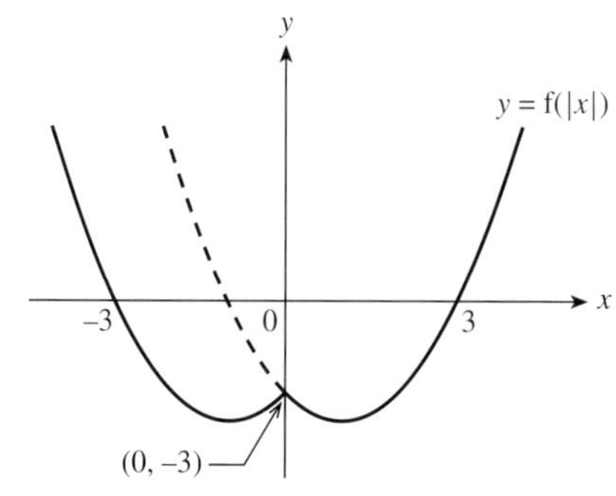

For x +ve i.e. to the right of the y-axis $f(|x|) = f(x)$.

For x −ve, i.e. to the left of the y-axis $f(|x|) = f(-x)$.

So the curve to the right of the y-axis is reflected in the y-axis.

Try drawing $y = (|x| - 1)^2 - 4$ on a graphics calculator.

Example 10 Sketch, on the same axes, $y = \sqrt{x}$ and $y = \sqrt{x+2}$, stating the values of x for which the graphs can be drawn.

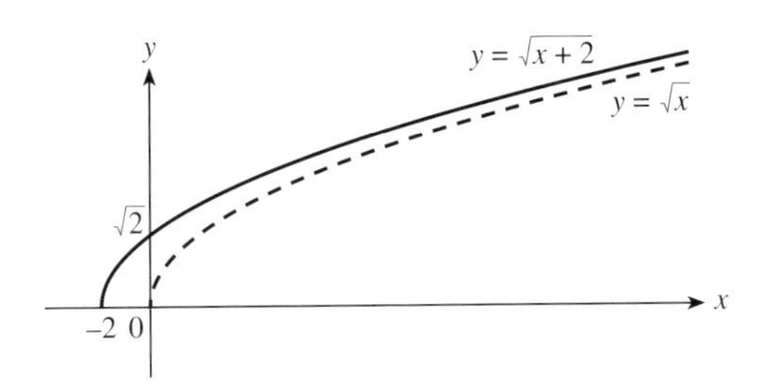

Note: $\sqrt{a}$ means the positive square root of a.

Replacing x by $x + 2$ shifts the curve **left** by **2** units.

$y = \sqrt{x}$ can be drawn for $x \geqslant 0$

$y = \sqrt{x+2}$ can be drawn for $x \geqslant -2$

The graph cannot be drawn for values of x which make the number under the root sign negative.

Example 11 Sketch $y = f(x)$ given that $f(x) = \dfrac{1}{x-3} + 4$ for $x \neq 3$.

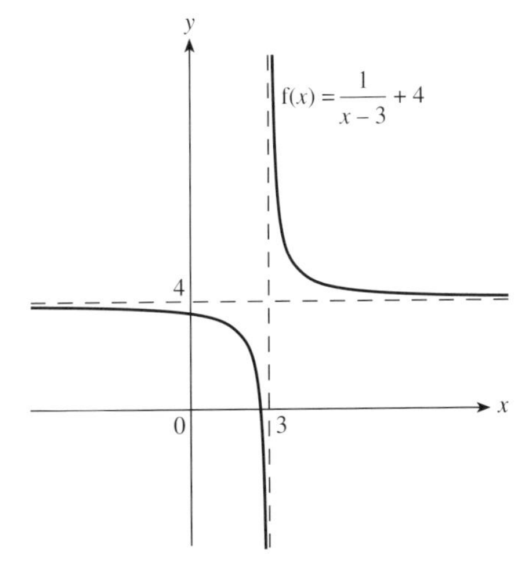

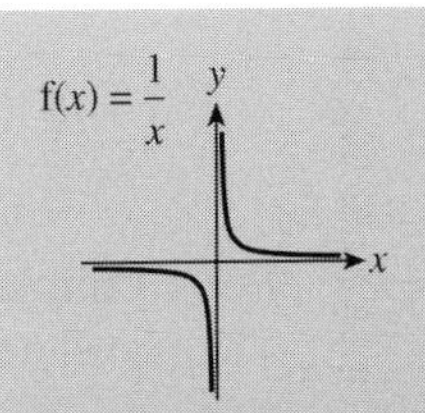

The graph of $\frac{1}{x}$ is translated 3 to the right and 4 up.
First draw the asymptotes, $x = 3$ and $y = 4$.
Then add the translated curve.

$f(x)$ is a translation $\binom{3}{4}$ of $\dfrac{1}{x}$.

Example 12 Sketch $y = f(x)$ given that $f(x) = 2 + 2\sin 3x$.

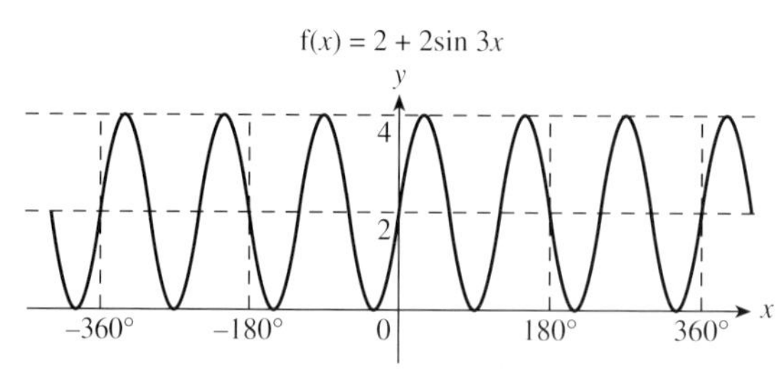

$f(x)$ is a stretch parallel to the x-axis (scale factor $\frac{1}{3}$) of $\sin x$, followed by a stretch parallel to the y-axis (scale factor 2), followed by a translation $\binom{0}{2}$.

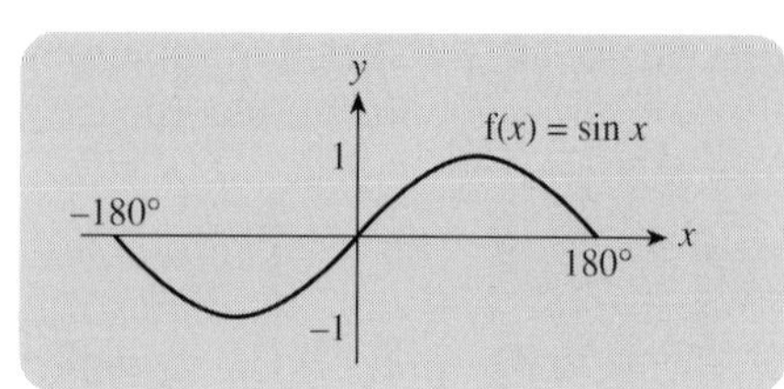

'Stretch' (squash), parallel to x-axis, scale factor $\frac{1}{3}$, for $f(x) = \sin 3x$.

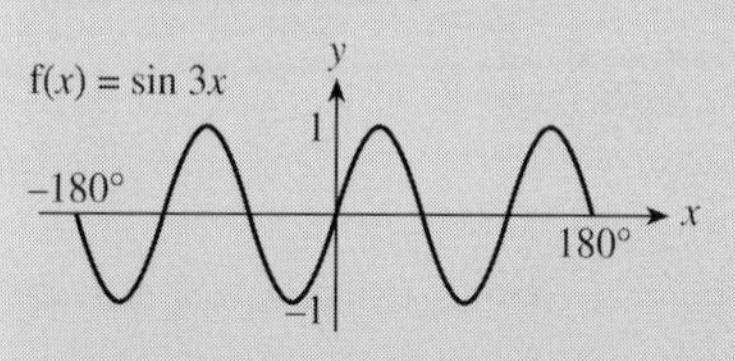

Stretch, parallel to the y-axis, scale factor 2, for $f(x) = 2\sin 3x$.

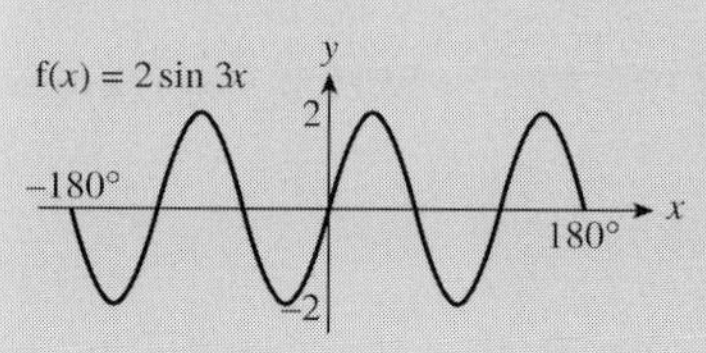

Translation 2 units up gives $f(x) = 2 + 2\sin 3x$.

For Example 12, the stretches must be carried out *before* the translation. The translation *followed* by the stretches would give $y = 2(\sin 3x + 2)$.

A graphical calculator can provide a useful double check when learning curve sketching techniques. However, resist the temptation to have a 'quick look first'. It is important to do the sketch before checking on a graphical calculator or computer. It is not always possible to use a calculator: see questions 14–17 of Exercise 7a.

EXERCISE 7a

1 Sketch $y = x^2$ and use transformations of graphs to sketch, on the same axes

a $y = x^2 + 3$ **b** $y = (x - 2)^2$

2 Sketch $y = x^2$ and use transformations of graphs to sketch, on the same axes

a $y = -x^2$ **b** $y = 4 - x^2$

3 Sketch $y = x^3$ and, on the same axes

a $y = x^3 - 3$ **b** $y = (x + 2)^3$

4 Sketch $y = x^3$ and, on the same axes

a $y = 2x^3$ **b** $y = 4 + x^3$

5 Sketch $y = \dfrac{1}{x^2}$ and, on the same axes

a $y = \dfrac{1}{x^2} + 5$ **b** $y = \dfrac{3}{x^2}$ **c** $y = -\dfrac{1}{x^2}$ **d** $y = 4 - \dfrac{1}{x^2}$

6 Sketch $y = \dfrac{1}{x}$ and, on the same axes

a $y = \dfrac{1}{x} + 2 \quad x \neq 0$ **b** $y = \dfrac{1}{x-1} \quad x \neq 1$

7 Sketch $y = \dfrac{1}{x}$ and, on the same axes

a $y = \dfrac{2}{x} \quad x \neq 0$ **b** $y = \dfrac{1}{x+3} + 2 \quad x \neq -3$

8 Sketch $y = |x|$ and, on the same axes

a $y = |x| + 3$ **b** $y = |x - 3|$ **c** $y = -|x|$ **d** $y = 2|x|$

9 Given $f(x) = x^2$ sketch these graphs, each on a separate diagram, and find an expression, giving y in terms of x, for each function.

a $y = f(x) - 1$ **b** $y = f(x + 1)$ **c** $y = f(2x)$ **d** $y = 2 + f(x + 3)$

10 Given $f(x) = \sqrt{x}$ for $x \geqslant 0$, sketch these graphs, each on a different diagram, stating the values of x for which each graph can be drawn, and find an expression, giving y in terms of x, for each of the functions.

a $y = f(x) - 1$ **b** $y = f(x + 1)$ **c** $y = -f(x)$ **d** $y = 2 + f(x + 3)$

11 Given $f(x) = |x| + 2$ sketch, on the same axes, the graphs of

a $y = f(x)$ **b** $y = f(x) - 1$ **c** $y = f(x + 1)$ **d** $y = -f(x)$

12 Given $f(x) = |x| + 2$ sketch, on the same axes, the graphs of

a $y = f(x)$ **b** $y = f(2x)$ **c** $y = 2f(x)$

13 Sketch the graph of $y = f(x)$ where $f(x) = (x + 2)^3$.
On the same axes, show the graphs of $y = |f(x)|$ and $y = f(|x|)$.

14 Copy this sketch of $y = g(x)$ and, on the same axes, sketch $y = -g(x)$, $y = g(-x)$ and $y = -g(-x)$.

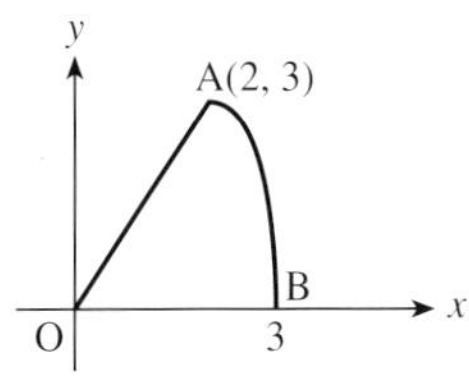

Mark the images of points A and B under the transformations, stating their coordinates.

EXERCISE 7a *(continued)*

15 Copy this sketch of $y = \text{f}(x)$ and, on the same axes, sketch $y = -\text{f}(x)$, $y = \text{f}(x - 3)$, $y = \text{f}(-x)$, $y = \text{f}(3 - x)$.

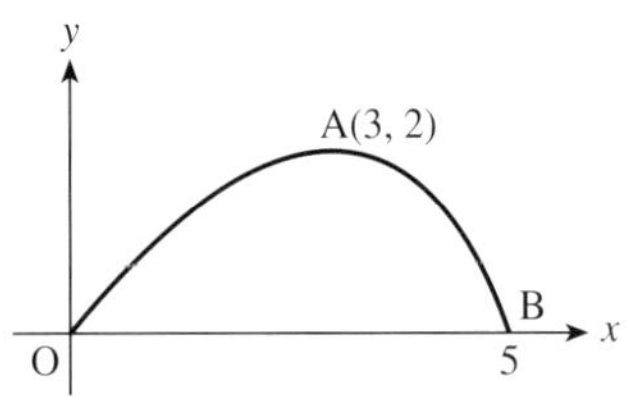

Mark the images of points O, A and B under the transformations, stating their coordinates.

16 The graph shows a sketch of $y = \text{g}(x)$.

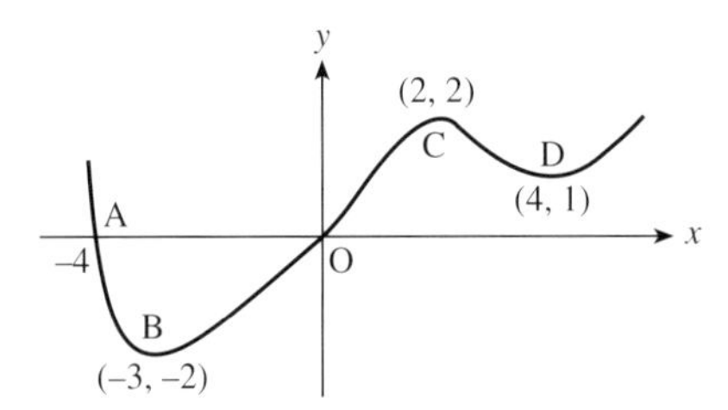

a Copy the sketch and, on the same axes, sketch $y = 2\text{g}(x)$ and $y = -\text{g}(x)$.

b Mark the images of points A, B, C, D and O under the transformations, stating their coordinates.

c Describe each transformation geometrically, i.e. in terms of translations, reflections and stretches.

17 **a** Copy the original sketch of $\text{g}(x)$ in Question 16 and, on the same axes, sketch $y = \text{g}(x - 1)$ and $y = \text{g}(x) + 3$.

b Mark the images of points A, B, C, D and O under the transformations, stating their coordinates.

c Describe each transformation geometrically, i.e. in terms of translations, reflections and stretches.

18 Express $x^2 + 2x + 8$ in the form $(x + a)^2 + b$, either by completing the square or by equating coefficients.
Hence sketch the parabola $y = x^2 + 2x + 8$, marking the coordinates of the vertex and the intercept on the y-axis.

19 Express these in completed square form and hence sketch each parabola, marking the coordinates of the vertex and the intercept on the y-axis.

a $y = x^2 - 2x + 4$ **b** $y = x^2 + 4x - 5$ **c** $y = x^2 - 6x + 3$

d $y = x^2 + x + 1$ **e** $y = 7 - 2x - x^2$

20 By solving the equation $x^2 = x^4$, find the points of intersection of $y = x^2$ and $y = x^4$. Sketch $y = x^2$ and $y = x^4$ showing where the curves intersect.

21 Sketch $y = x^3$ and $y = x^5$ showing clearly their points of intersection.

22 The graph of a function is reflected in the x-axis and then translated $\binom{3}{2}$. After the transformations its equation is

$$y = 2 - \frac{1}{(x-3)^2}$$

Find the original function.

23 a Copy the sketch of $y = \mathrm{f}(x)$ and, on the same axes, sketch $y = |\mathrm{f}(x)|$ and $y = \mathrm{f}(|x|)$.

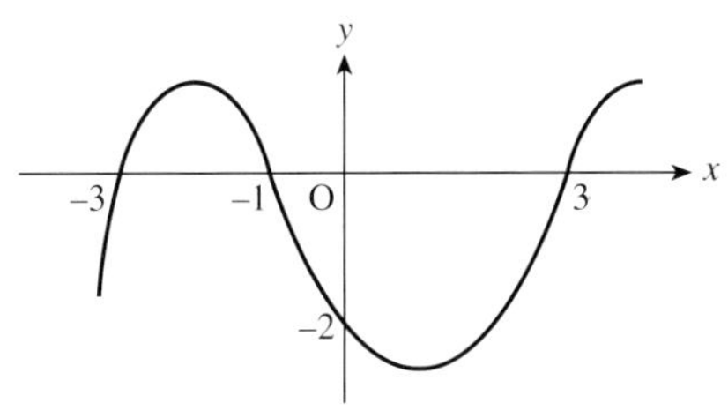

b Mark the points where the curves meet the axes and state their coordinates.

Test yourself

1 A sketch of the graph $y = mx + c$, with $m < 0$ and $c > 0$, could be

A

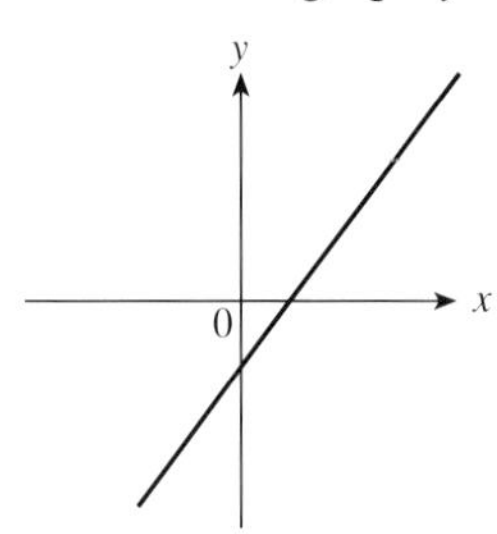

B

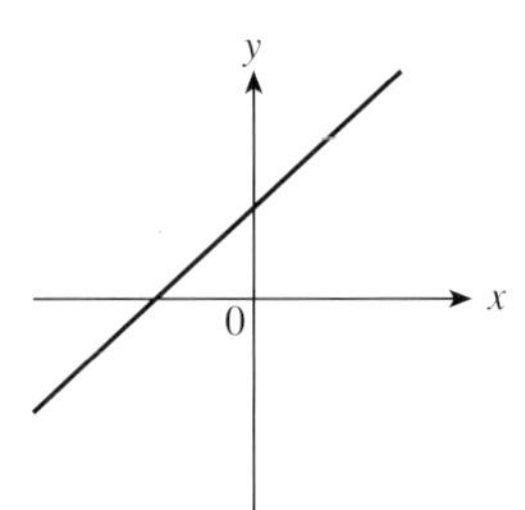

C

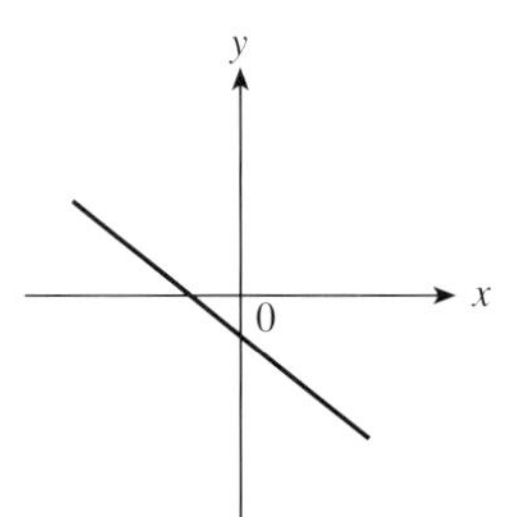

D

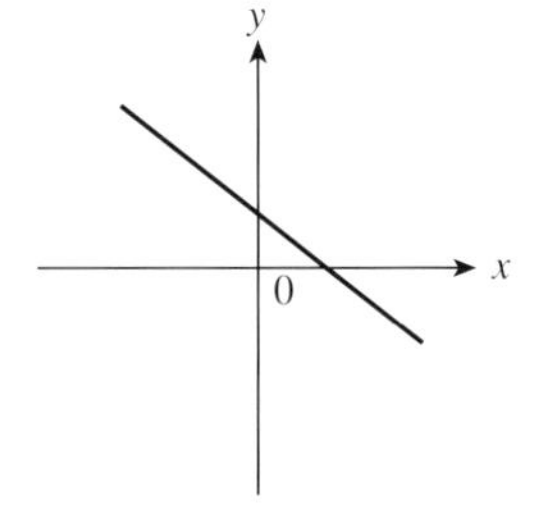

E

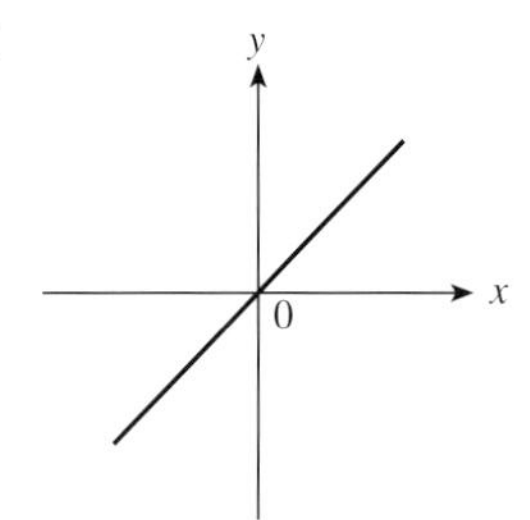

2 The equation of this graph could be

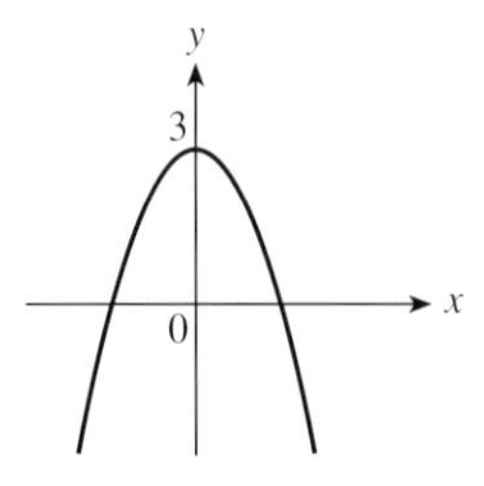

A $y = x^2 + 3$ **B** $y = x^2 - 3$ **C** $y = 3 - x^2$

D $y = (x - 3)^2$ **E** $y = -(x^2 + 3)$

3 This is the graph of $y = g(x)$.

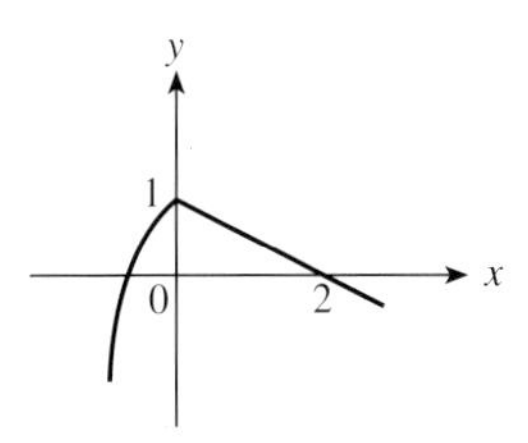

The graph of $y = g(x + 2)$ looks like

A

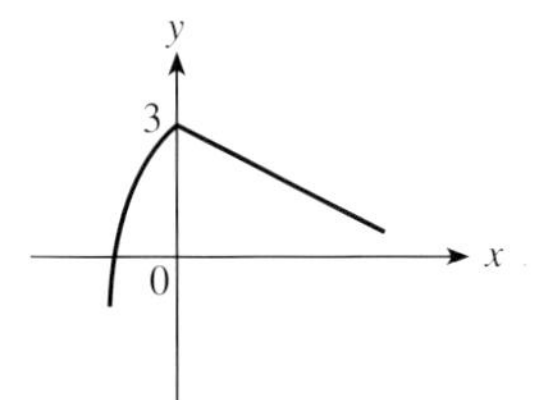

B

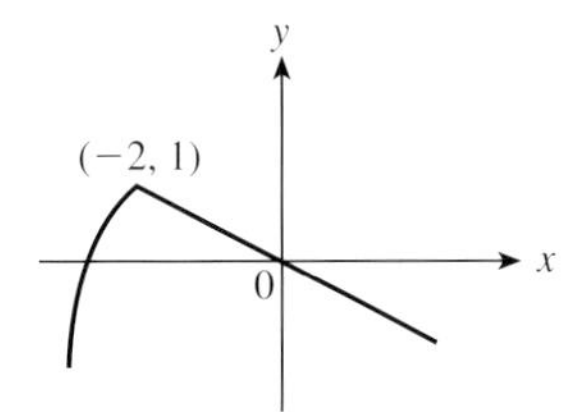

C

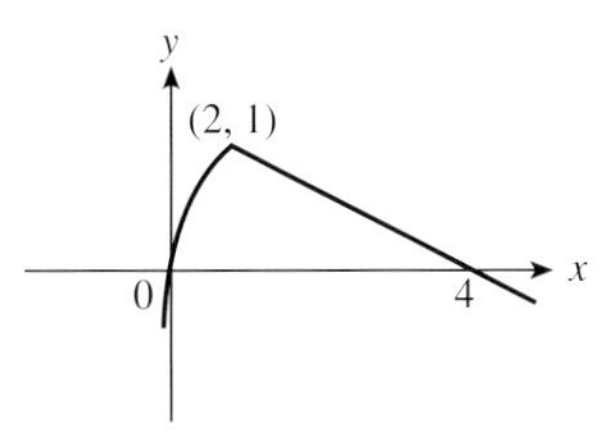

D

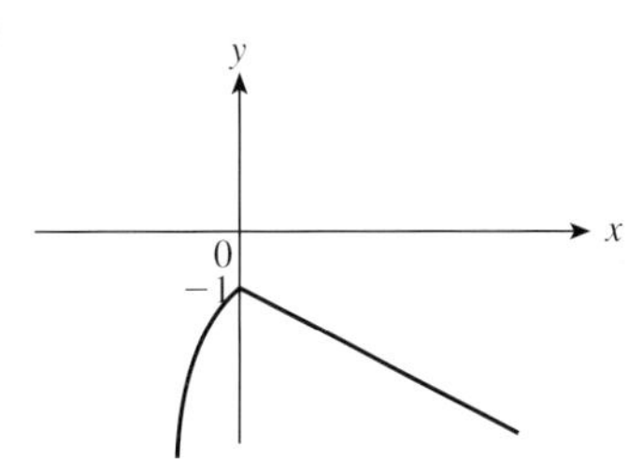

E

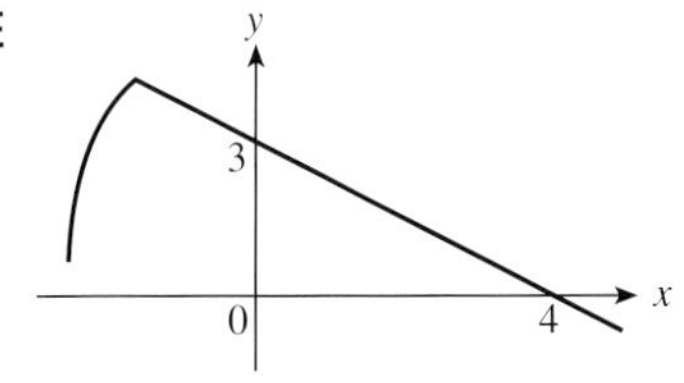

4 The graph of $y = x^2 - 6x + 3$ is a translation of $y = x^2$ of

A $\begin{pmatrix} -3 \\ -6 \end{pmatrix}$ **B** $\begin{pmatrix} -3 \\ 3 \end{pmatrix}$ **C** $\begin{pmatrix} 3 \\ -6 \end{pmatrix}$ **D** $\begin{pmatrix} 3 \\ 9 \end{pmatrix}$ **E** $\begin{pmatrix} 3 \\ 3 \end{pmatrix}$

5 This is the graph of $y = f(x)$.

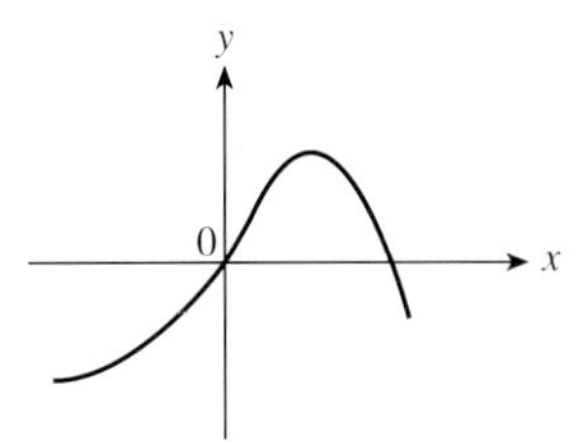

The graph of $y = f(-x)$ looks like

A

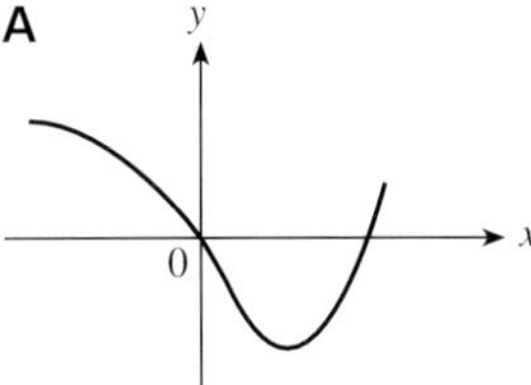

B

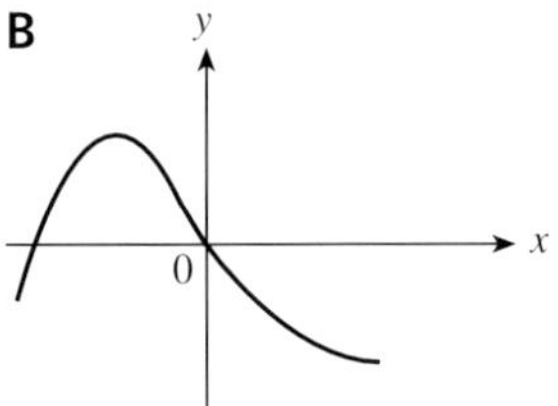

C

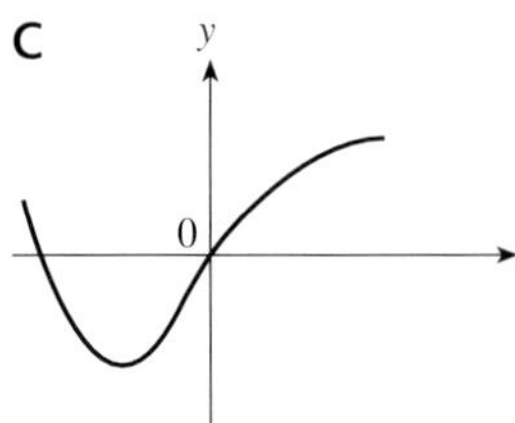

D

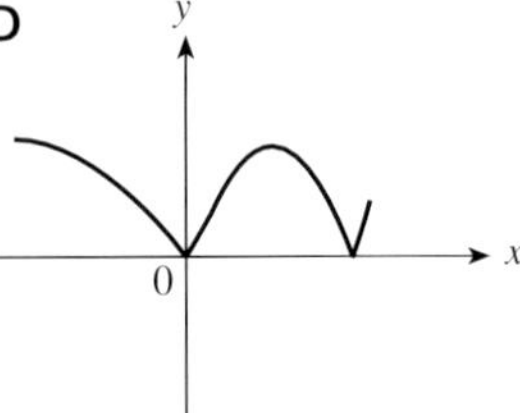

E

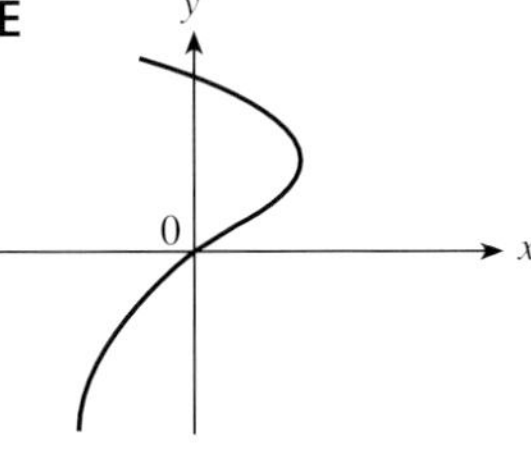

6 If $y = f(x)$ has a single vertex, at (2, 3), then $y = f(2x) - 1$ will have its vertex at

A (4, 2) **B** (3, 3) **C** (2, 5) **D** (1, 2) **E** (1, 4)

7 The equation of this graph could be

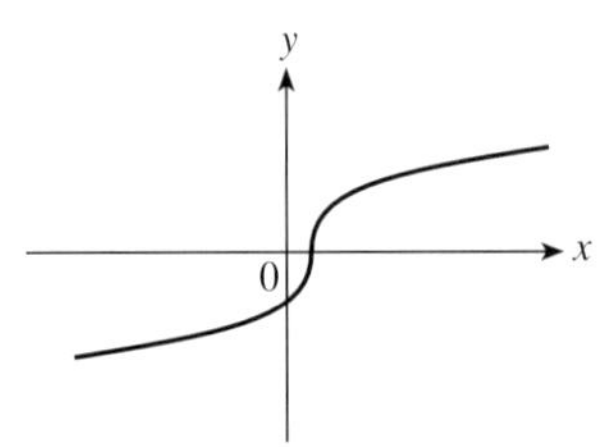

A $y = \sqrt{x}$ **B** $y = \sqrt[3]{x}$ **C** $y = \sqrt{|x|}$ **D** $y = \sqrt[3]{x+1}$ **E** $y = \sqrt[3]{x-1}$

Key points

Curve sketching

A sketch of a graph shows the general shape and marks certain important features, e.g. intercepts with axes, vertices.

Many curves can be sketched from knowledge of standard curves (see pages 119–20) and transformations.

Transformation of graphs

All these transformations apply to $y = f(x)$. Assume $a > 0$.

- $y = f(x) + a$ is a translation $\binom{0}{a}$.
  Adding a to the function moves the graph a units up.
- $y = f(x) - a$ is a translation $\binom{0}{-a}$.
  Subtracting a from the function moves the graph a units down.
- $y = f(x - a)$ is a translation $\binom{a}{0}$.
  Subtracting a from x (i.e. replacing x by $x - a$) moves the graph a units to the right.
- $y = f(x + a)$ is a translation $\binom{-a}{0}$.
  Adding a to x (i.e. replacing x by $x + a$) moves the graph a units to the left.
- $y = f(x - a) + b$ is a translation $\binom{a}{b}$.
- $y = -f(x)$ is a reflection in the x-axis.
- $y = f(-x)$ is a reflection in the y-axis.
- $y = af(x)$ is a stretch parallel to the y-axis with scale factor a.
- $y = f(ax)$ is a stretch parallel to the x-axis with scale factor $\frac{1}{a}$.

For $y = f(|x|)$ sketch $y = f(x)$ for $x > 0$ and reflect the parts of the curve to the right of the y-axis in the y-axis.

For $y = |f(x)|$ sketch $y = f(x)$ with a dotted line where $y < 0$.
Reflect the dotted line in the x-axis.

8 Coordinate Geometry and the Straight Line

Before starting this chapter you will need to know

- how to solve linear and quadratic equations (Chapter 3)
- how to solve simultaneous equations (Chapter 5).

8.1 Introduction

The position of a point can be specified by an origin and a number of coordinates.

- On a line (1D), an origin and one number are needed to identify a point.
  The number line is an example of this.
- On a plane (2D), an origin and two numbers are needed to identify a point.
  The Cartesian system, named after René Descartes (1596–1650), draws two axes at right angles to each other through the origin. Two coordinates are used: one in each of the two directions of the axes.
- Similarly, in 3D, an origin and three numbers are needed to identify a point.
  The most frequently used system is three perpendicular axes drawn through the origin.
  Three coordinates are needed to identify a point.
- In n dimensions, an origin and n numbers are needed to identify a point.

There are other systems for identifying the position of points in 2D and 3D, e.g. polar coordinates, and position vectors.

In 1998, Richard Borcherds was awarded a Fields medal for creating a rich new area of research known as 'vertex algebras' that links pure mathematics with theoretical physics. With these new techniques, he has proved the so-called 'moonshine conjectures' of the 'Monster Group' – whimsical labels for an abstract symmetrical snowflake that lives in 196 883-dimensional space and has 808 017 424 794 512 875 886 459 904 961 710 757 005 005 754 368 000 000 000 symmetries. That's more than the sun has atoms.

Superstring theory suggests that our universe may be part of a 26-dimensional space. The rest of this chapter is restricted to coordinate geometry in two dimensions!

8.2 Coordinate geometry of a plane

- The horizontal axis (across the page) is the x-axis. This can be written Ox.
- The vertical axis (up and down the page) is the y-axis. This can be written Oy.
- The point, O, where the axes meet is the origin. This is the zero point on both axes.
- The x-coordinate (or **abscissa**) of a point, P, is its directed distance, +ve or −ve, from the y-axis.
- The y-coordinate (or **ordinate**) of a point, P, is its directed distance, +ve or −ve, from the x-axis.

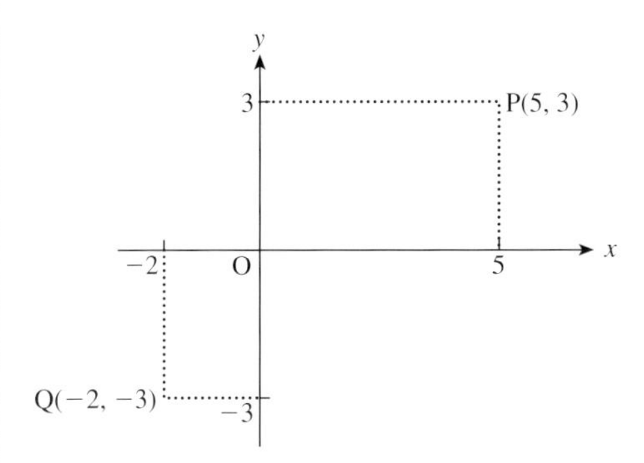

In the diagram P is the point (5, 3). Q is the point (−2, −3).

8.3 The length of a line segment

In mathematics a line is understood to be a straight line extending indefinitely in both directions.

A finite part of a line is called a **line segment**. AB is a line segment of the line l.

The length of a line segment can be calculated

- using numerical coordinates, or
- algebraically.

To find the length of the line joining A(2, 1) to B(5, 6), AC and CB are drawn parallel to the x-axis and y-axis respectively.

Pythagoras' theorem can then be applied to the right-angled triangle ABC.

$$\text{AB}^2 = \text{AC}^2 + \text{BC}^2$$

$$= (5-2)^2 + (6-1)^2$$

$$= 9 + 25$$

$$\therefore \quad \text{AB} = \sqrt{34}$$

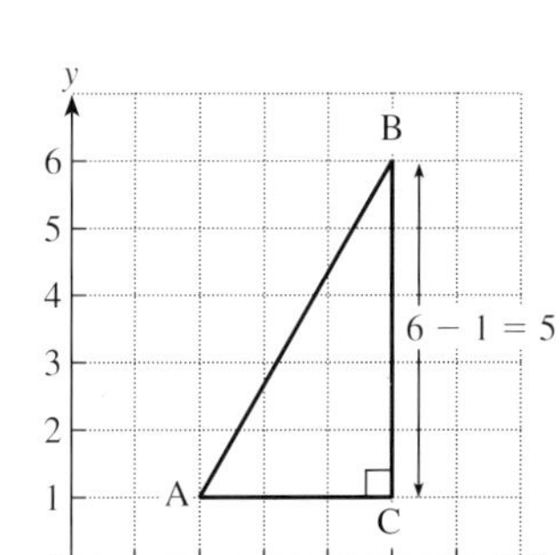

A similar method is used to find the length of the line joining $A(x_1, y_1)$ to $B(x_2, y_2)$.

Suffices are often used for points whose coordinates are unknown. (x_1, y_1) is read as 'x one, y one'.

$AC = x_2 - x_1$

$BC = y_2 - y_1$

Using Pythagoras' theorem

$AB^2 = (x_2 - x_1)^2 + (y_2 - y_1)^2$

$\therefore \quad AB = \sqrt{(x_2 - x_1)^2 + (y_2 - y_1)^2}$

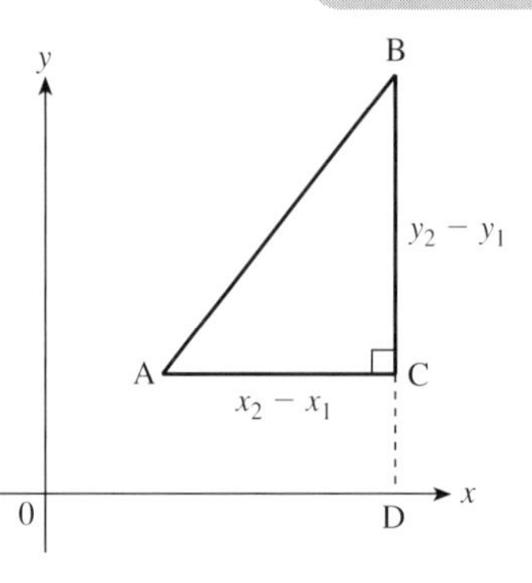

$BC = BD - CD$
$= y_2 - y_1$

➤ The length of the line segment joining (x_1, y_1) to (x_2, y_2) is $\sqrt{(x_2 - x_1)^2 + (y_2 - y_1)^2}$.

Example 1 Find the length of the line segment joining A(2, −4) to B(−6, −8).

$AB = \sqrt{((-6-2)^2 + (-8-(-4))^2}$

$= \sqrt{(-8)^2 + (-4)^2}$

$= \sqrt{80} = 4\sqrt{5}$

The formula can be used with
$x_1 \; y_1$ $x_2 \; y_2$
A(2, −4)   B(−6, −8)

The same result is obtained if the coordinates of A are (x_2, y_2) and of B are (x_1, y_1).

$\sqrt{80} = \sqrt{16} \times \sqrt{5} = 4\sqrt{5}$

Example 2 Prove that the triangle with vertices A(3, 7), B(1, −4) and C(−2, −3) is isosceles.

One method of proving that a triangle is isosceles is to show that two sides have equal length. A sketch can often help to decide which sides to test for equality.

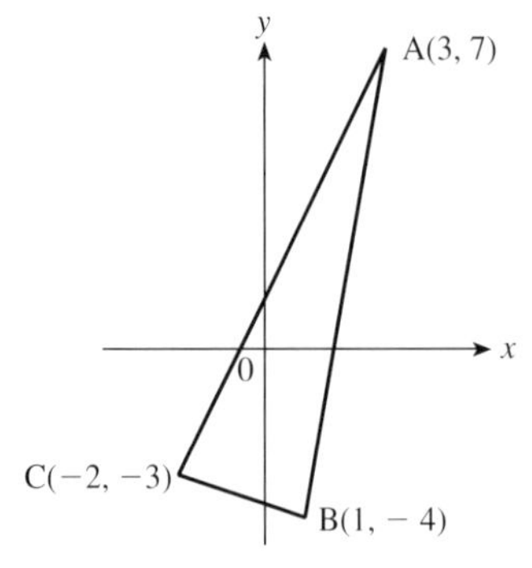

Draw a sketch. The sketch shows that AB and AC are likely to be the equal sides.

$AB^2 = (3-1)^2 + (7-(-4))^2$

$= 2^2 + 11^2 = 125$

$AC^2 = (3-(-2))^2 + (7-(-3))^2$

$= 5^2 + 10^2 = 125$

Since $AB^2 = AC^2$

$AB = AC$

so $\triangle ABC$ is isosceles.

Substitute in the formula $\sqrt{(x_2 - x_1)^2 + (y_2 - y_1)^2}$.

$y_2 - y_1 = 7 - (-4) = 7 + 4 = 11$
Note: Take care with the signs.

There is no need to take square roots. AB and AC are both +ve, so $AB^2 = AC^2 \Rightarrow AB = AC$.

8.4 The mid-point of a line segment

To find the mid-point of the line segment joining A(2, 1) to B(8, 11), let M(x, y) be the mid-point of AB.

Draw ML parallel to BC and MN parallel to AC.

Then L and N are the mid-points of AC and BC respectively, so AL = LC and BN = NC.

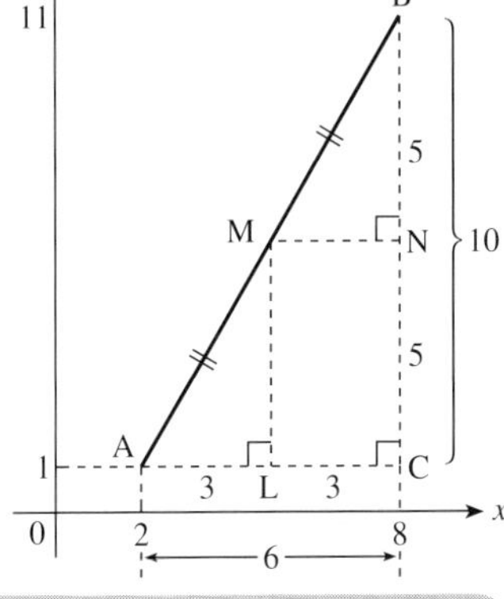

$$AL = LC$$

$$\therefore \quad AL = 3$$

$$BN = NC$$

$$\therefore \quad NC = 5$$

From the diagram

$$x = 2 + 3 = 5 \quad \text{and} \quad y = 1 + 5 = 6$$

so M is the point (5, 6).

An intuitive geometrical approach:
Since M is halfway between A and B its coordinates must be the arithmetic means of the coordinates of A and B

$$x = \frac{2+8}{2} = 5 \quad y = \frac{1+11}{2} = 6$$

A similar method is used to find the mid-point, M(x, y), of the line segment joining A(x_1, y_1) to B(x_2, y_2).

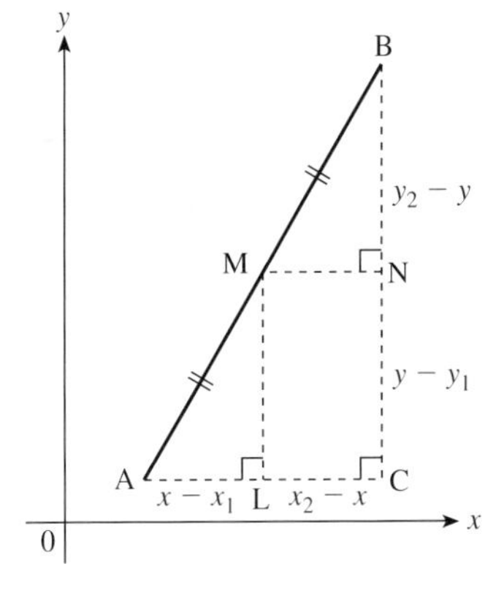

$$AL = LC$$

So $\quad x - x_1 = x_2 - x$

$$2x = x_1 + x_2$$

$$x = \frac{x_1 + x_2}{2}$$

Similarly, BN = NC.

So $\quad y_2 - y = y - y_1$

$$2y = y_1 + y_2$$

$$y = \frac{y_1 + y_2}{2}$$

➤ The mid-point of the line joining (x_1, y_1) to (x_2, y_2) is the point $\left(\frac{x_1 + x_2}{2}, \frac{y_1 + y_2}{2}\right)$.

Example 3 Find the mid-point of the line segment joining (−9, 6) and (3, −1).

$x_1 \quad y_1 \qquad x_2 \quad y_2$
(−9, 6) (3, −1)

Using the formula above the mid-point is $\left(\frac{-9+3}{2}, \frac{6+(-1)}{2}\right)$, i.e. $(-3, 2\frac{1}{2})$.

EXERCISE 8a

1 Find the lengths of the straight lines joining these pairs of points.

a A(3, 2) and B(8, 14) b C(−1, 3) and D(4, 7) c E(4, 2) and F(6, −10)

d G(p, q) and H(r, s) e J(−6, −1) and K(3, −4) f L(6, 9) and M(6, 13)

g N(1, 2) and P(5, 2) h Q(−4, −2) and R(3, −7) i S(−6, 1) and T(6, 6)

2 Find the coordinates of the mid-points of the line segments in Question 1.

3 Find the distance of the point (−15, 8) from the origin.

4 P, Q, R are the points (5, −3), (−6, 1) and (1, 8) respectively.
Show that triangle PQR is isosceles, and find the coordinates of the mid-point of the base.

5 Repeat Question 4 for the points L(4, 4), M(−4, 1) and N(1, −4).

6 For each triangle ABC, show that it is right-angled, state which side is the hypotenuse, find the area, and find tan A.

a A(13, −4), B(7, 4), C(3, 1) b A(−1, 2), B(0, −11), C(3, 1)

7 Find h if the point (h, 0) is equidistant from the points (−1, 7) and (−3, −2).

8 A and B are the points (−1, −6) and (5, −8) respectively.
Which of these points lie on the perpendicular bisector of AB?

P(3, −4) Q(4, 0) R(5, 2) S(6, 5)

9 Three of these four points lie on a circle whose centre is at the origin.

A(−1, 7) B(5, −5) C(−7, 5) D(7, −1)

Which are they, and what is the radius of the circle?

10 A and B are the points (12, 0) and (0, −5) respectively. Find the length of AB, and the length of the median, through the origin O, of the triangle OAB.

11 Find a and b if the point (6, 3) is the mid-point of the line joining ($2a$, $2a - b$) and ($a - 2b$, $4a + 3b$).

12 The point (3, k) is a distance of 5 units from (0, 1).
Find the two possible values of k.

13 Find the perimeter of triangle ABC where A is (7, 0), B is (4, 3) and C (10, 1), giving the answer as simply as possible.

14 One test that a quadrilateral is a parallelogram is to show that its diagonals bisect each other. Use this test to show that ABCD is a parallelogram where A is (0, 5), B is (7, 7), C is (4, 3) and D is (−3, 1).

15 The points A, B, C, D, E and F are (−1, −2), (2, 0), (3, 5), (7, −1), (8, 4) and (11, 6) respectively.
By considering the distances between the points, state which four points form

a a square b a rhombus c a kite (two possibilities)

8.5 The gradient of a line

The gradient of a straight line measures how steep the line is. The gradient is defined as

$$\frac{\text{increase in } y}{\text{increase in } x}$$

in moving between two points on the line. The gradient of a line can be positive, negative, zero or infinite.

- **Positive gradient (+ve)**

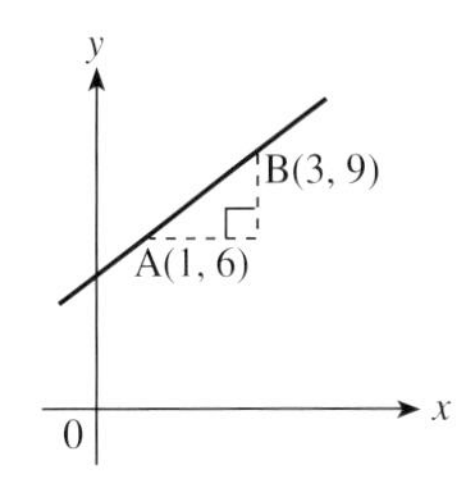

The increase in x from A to B $= 3 - 1 = 2$.
The increase in y from A to B $= 9 - 6 = 3$.

So the gradient of AB $= \frac{3}{2}$.

As x increases, so does y, so the gradient is +ve.

A +ve gradient line goes from bottom left to top right.

- **Negative gradient (−ve)**

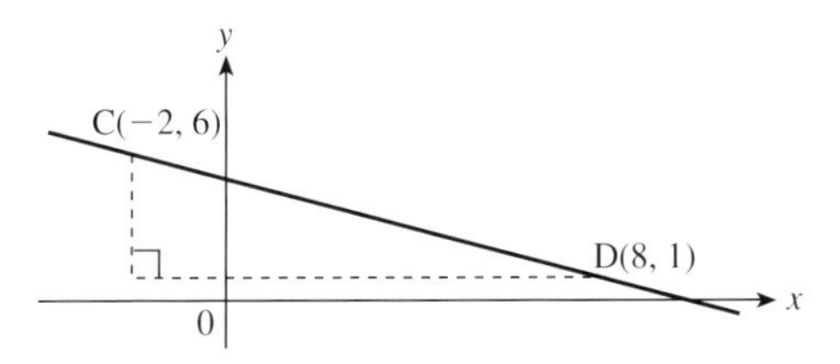

A −ve gradient line goes from top left to bottom right.

The increase in x from C to D $= 8 - (-2) = 10$.
The 'increase' in y from C to D $= 1 - 6 = -5$.

✓ ***Note*** As y is actually decreasing, the 'increase' from C to D is −ve.

So the gradient of CD $= \frac{-5}{10} = -\frac{1}{2}$.

As x increases, y decreases, so the gradient is −ve.

In general, this diagram shows how to find the gradient, m, of the line through $A(x_1, y_1)$ and $B(x_2, y_2)$.

➤ Gradient, $m = \dfrac{y_2 - y_1}{x_2 - x_1}$

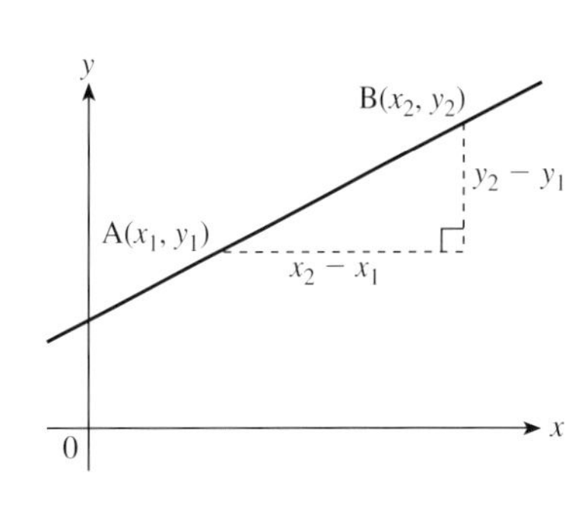

Example 4 Find the gradient of the line through the points (2, −1) and (4, −5).

$$\begin{matrix} x_1 & y_1 & & x_2 & y_2 \\ (2, & -1) & & (4, & -5) \end{matrix}$$

$$\text{Gradient} = \frac{-5-(-1)}{4-2} = \frac{-4}{2} = -2$$

The same result is obtained with $\begin{matrix} x_1 & y_1 \\ (4, & -5) \end{matrix}$ and $\begin{matrix} x_2 & y_2 \\ (2, & -1) \end{matrix}$
i.e. the *order* of points does not matter because $\dfrac{y_2 - y_1}{x_2 - x_1} = \dfrac{y_1 - y_2}{x_1 - x_2}$

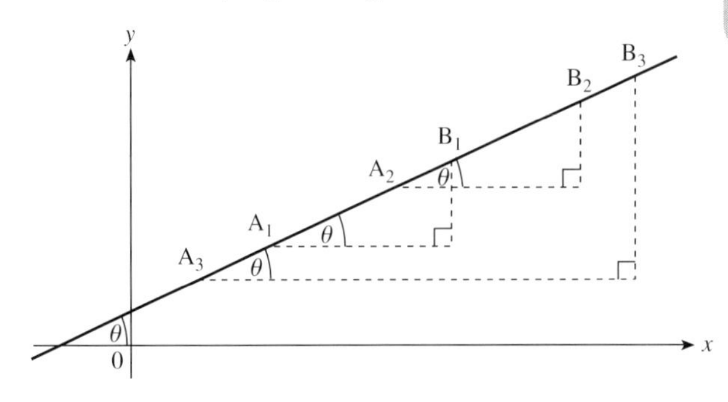

Any pair of points on the line will give the same result for the gradient because the resulting triangles are all similar.

Gradient as tan θ

The gradient of a line is the tangent of the angle made by the line and the +ve direction of the x-axis.

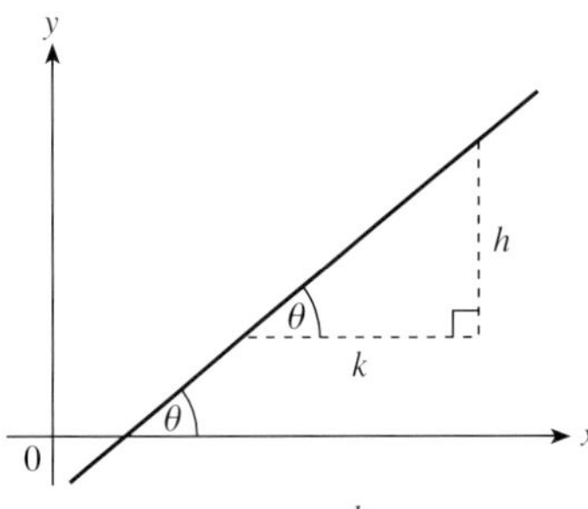

$\text{Gradient} = \tan\theta = \dfrac{h}{k}$

When θ is acute, $\tan\theta$ and the gradient are both +ve.

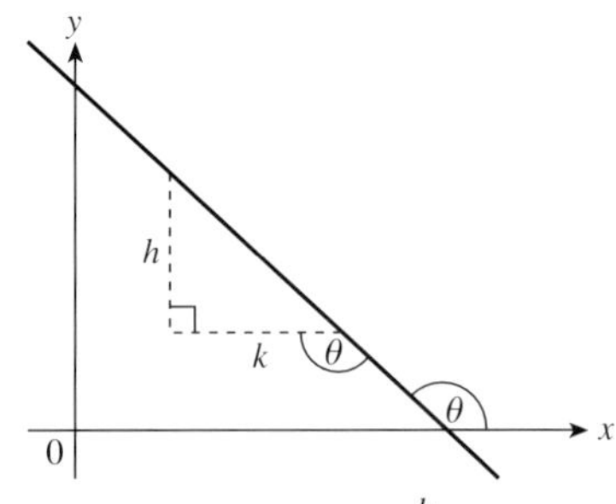

$\text{Gradient} = \tan\theta = -\dfrac{h}{k}$

When θ is obtuse, $\tan\theta$ and the gradient are both −ve.

✓ ***Note*** To avoid distorting the angle θ, the same scale must be used on both axes.

Special cases: Zero and infinite gradients

Zero gradient: line parallel to x-axis

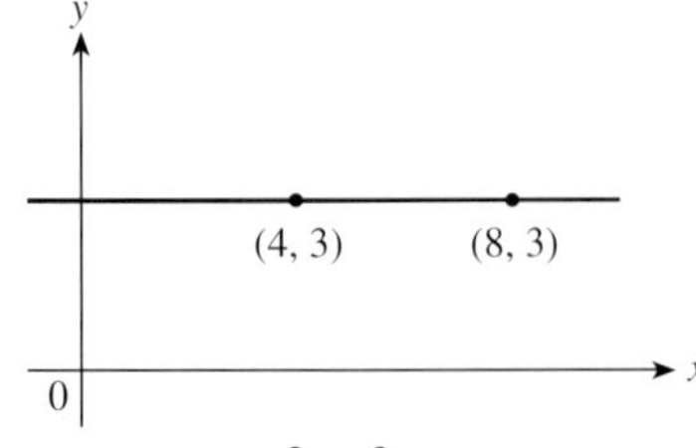

$$\text{Gradient} = \frac{3-3}{8-4} = 0$$

Infinite gradient: line parallel to y-axis

$$\text{Gradient} = \frac{8-3}{4-4} = \frac{5}{0} \text{ undefined}$$

Division by zero is undefined.
The gradient of the line is infinite.

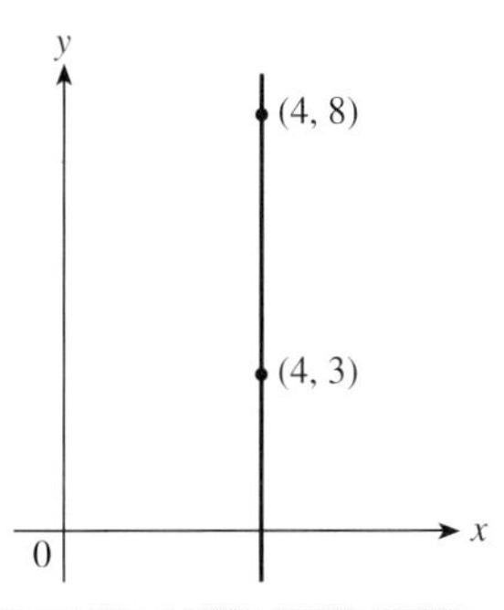

A sketch of points can help to avoid problems with infinite gradients.

8.6 Parallel and perpendicular lines

- **Parallel lines**: lines are parallel $\Leftrightarrow$ lines have equal gradient
- **Perpendicular lines**: lines at right angles to each other

Imagine rotating the rectangle OAPB through 90° anticlockwise to OA′P′B′.

When the line segment OP, where P is the point (a, b), is rotated through 90° anticlockwise to OP′, the point P′ will have coordinates $(-b, a)$.

The gradient, m, of $\text{OP} = \frac{b}{a}$

The gradient, m', of $\text{OP}' = -\frac{a}{b}$

$$mm' = \frac{b}{a} \times -\frac{a}{b} = -1$$

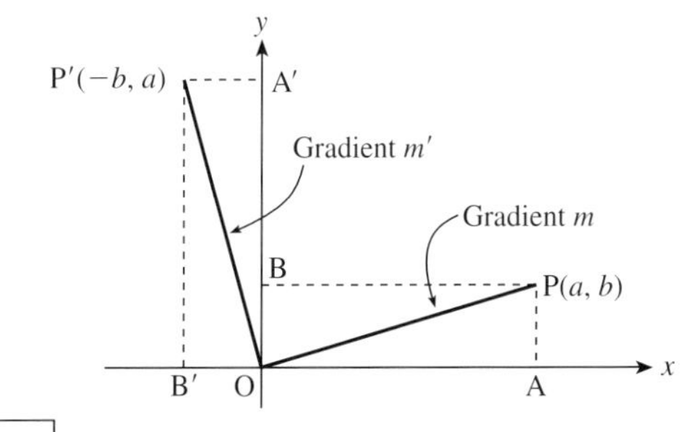

If two lines have gradients m and m' then
$mm' = -1 \quad \Leftrightarrow$ the lines are perpendicular
$m = m' \quad \Leftrightarrow$ the lines are parallel

Example 5 Find the gradient of the line perpendicular to the line joining A(3, 4) to B(7, −8).

$$\text{Gradient of AB} = \frac{-8-4}{7-3} = -3$$

So, the gradient of the line perpendicular to AB is $\frac{1}{3}$.

$-3 \times \frac{1}{3} = -1$

Note Given a gradient $\frac{a}{b}$, to find the perpendicular gradient, take the reciprocal $\left(\frac{b}{a}\right)$, and then reverse the sign $\left(-\frac{b}{a}\right)$.

Examples of gradients of pairs of lines which are perpendicular: 2 and $-\frac{1}{2}$; $\frac{p}{q}$ and $-\frac{q}{p}$; $\frac{7}{4}$ and $-\frac{4}{7}$.

8.7 Equation of a curve

The Cartesian equation of a curve is a relationship connecting the x and y values of points on the curve.

For example, $y = 3x + 1$, $x^2 + y^2 = 9$, $5x + 2y^7 = 7$.

These equations are satisfied by an infinite number of pairs of values of x and y, so there are an infinite number of points on each curve.

For an equation, pairs of values of x and y can be tabulated. These pairs can be plotted as points and the points joined by a smooth curve to give a graph.

Curves can also be plotted on a graphical calculator.

Consider $y = 3x + 1$.

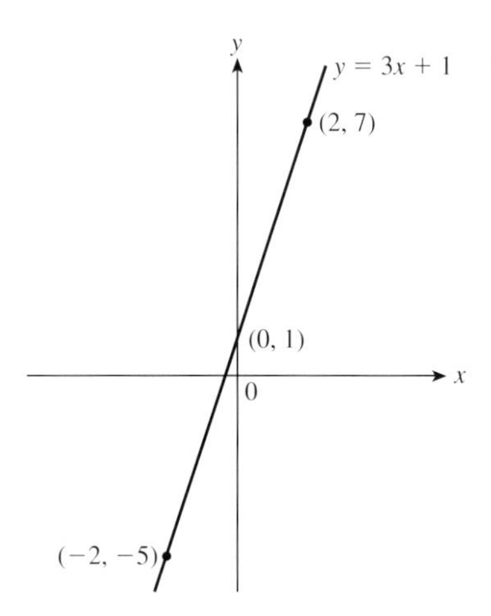

$y = 3x + 1$ is the equation of a straight line, so three points are sufficient (two to define the line, one for a check).

x	-2	0	2
y	-5	1	7

The points $(-2, -5)$, $(0, 1)$ and $(2, 7)$ are plotted and a straight line through the points, extended at both ends, is drawn.

Now consider $y = x^2$.

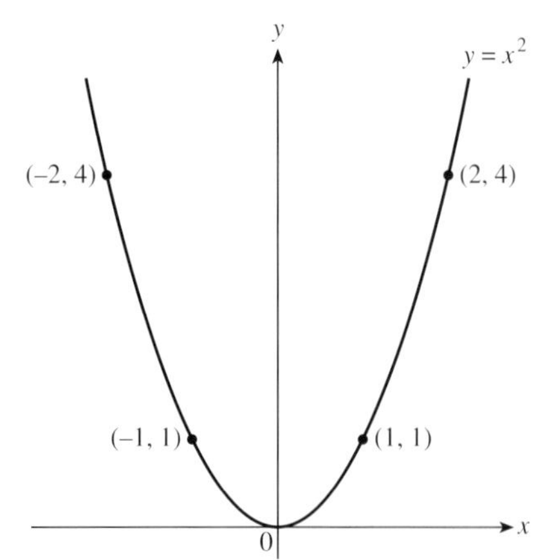

$y = x^2$ is the equation of a curve.
Many points are needed for an accurate graph.
Five points will give a rough idea of the shape.

x	-2	-1	0	1	2
y	4	1	0	1	4

The points $(-2, 4)$, $(-1, 1)$, $(0, 0)$, $(1, 1)$ and $(2, 4)$ are plotted and a smooth curve drawn through the points.

For an accurate graph more points would need to be worked out.

To test if a point lies on a curve

To test if a point lies on a curve, substitute the values of its coordinates into the equation. The point lies on the curve if, and only if, the equation is satisfied.

Example 6 Does (3, −4) lie on the line $y = -2x + 3$ or on the curve $x^2 + y^2 = 25$?

$y = -2x + 3$

When $x = 3$ $\quad y = -6 + 3$

$= -3$

If (3, −4) lies on the line then when $x = 3$ is substituted in the equation, $y = -4$ should result.

$\therefore$ (3, −4) does not lie on $y = -2x + 3$.

The result is $y = -3$, so the point does *not* lie on the line.

For the curve $x^2 + y^2 = 25$, when $x = 3$ and $y = -4$.

$$\begin{aligned} \text{LHS} &= x^2 + y^2 \\ &= 3^2 + (-4)^2 \\ &= 9 + 16 = 25 = \text{RHS} \end{aligned}$$

Start with one side of the equation (LHS in this case) and show that it equals the other side.

$\therefore$ (3, −4) does lie on the curve $x^2 + y^2 = 25$.

8.8 Equation of a straight line

A straight line can be defined by

- one point on the line and its gradient
- two points on the line.

In these two cases, equations of lines will be found numerically and algebraically.

To find the equation of a line given one point on the line and its gradient

Consider the equation of a line passing through A(3, 4) with gradient 2.

Let P(x, y) be any point on the line.

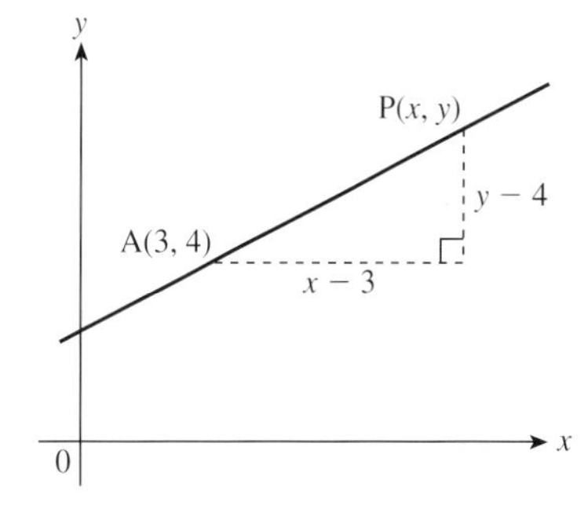

Gradient of AP $= \dfrac{y-4}{x-3}$

But gradient = 2

So $\quad \dfrac{y-4}{x-3} = 2$

$$\begin{aligned} y - 4 &= 2(x - 3) \\ y - 4 &= 2x - 6 \\ y &= 2x - 2 \end{aligned}$$

Now consider the equation of a line passing through A(x_1, y_1) with gradient m.

Let P(x, y) be any point on the line.

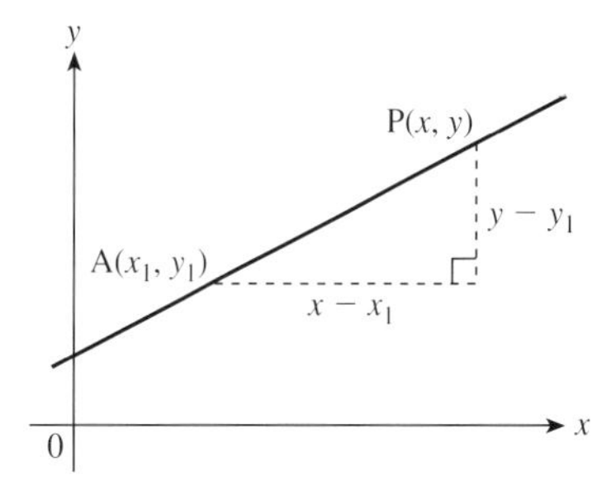

Gradient of AP $= \dfrac{y-y_1}{x-x_1}$

But gradient $= m$

So $\quad \dfrac{y-y_1}{x-x_1} = m$

$\therefore \quad y - y_1 = m(x - x_1)$

➤ The equation of the line through (x_1, y_1) with gradient, m, is $y - y_1 = m(x - x_1)$.

To find the equation of a line given two points on the line

Consider the equation of the line passing through A(−2, 7) and B(6, 3).
Let P(x, y) be any point on the line.

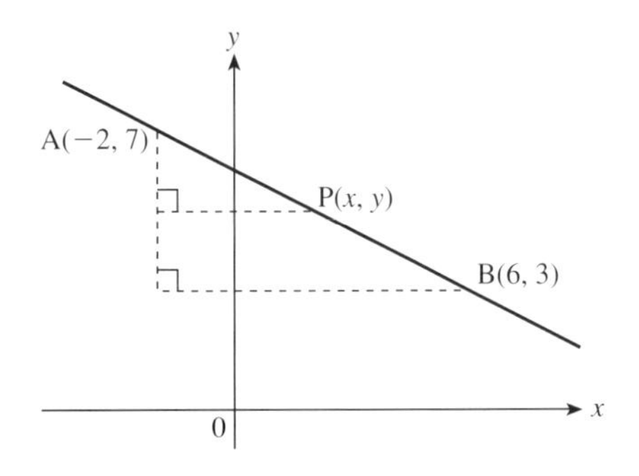

$$\text{Gradient of AB} = \frac{3-7}{6-(-2)} = \frac{-4}{8} = -\frac{1}{2}$$

$$\text{Gradient of AP} = \frac{y-7}{x-(-2)} = \frac{y-7}{x+2}$$

But the gradients are equal, so

$$\frac{y-7}{x+2} = -\frac{1}{2}$$

$$2y - 14 = -x - 2$$

$$2y + x = 12$$

Now consider the equation of the line through A(x_1, y_1) and B(x_2, y_2).
Let P(x, y) be any point on the line.

$$\text{Gradient of AB} = \frac{y_2 - y_1}{x_2 - x_1}$$

$$\text{Gradient of AP} = \frac{y - y_1}{x - x_1}$$

But the gradients are equal, so

$$\frac{y - y_1}{x - x_1} = \frac{y_2 - y_1}{x_2 - x_1}$$

Rearranging

$$\frac{y - y_1}{y_2 - y_1} = \frac{x - x_1}{x_2 - x_1}$$

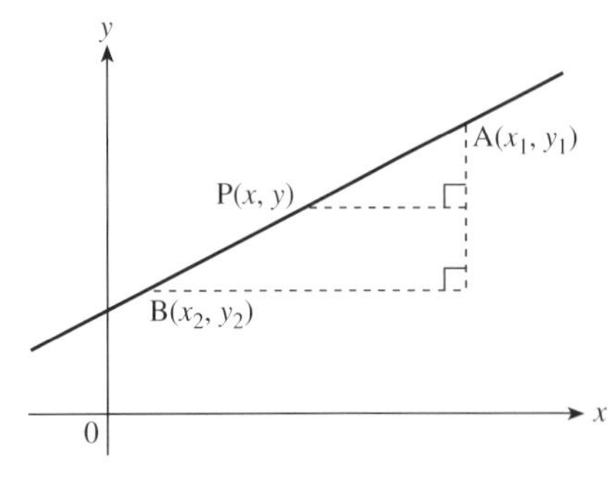

➤ The equation of the line through (x_1, y_1) and (x_2, y_2) is $\frac{y - y_1}{y_2 - y_1} = \frac{x - x_1}{x_2 - x_1}$.

Use of this formula can be avoided. Given two points on a line, the equation of the line can be found by

- finding the gradient, $m = \frac{y_2 - y_1}{x_2 - x_1}$ and
- using $y - y_1 = m(x - x_1)$

Example 7

The two possible methods are illustrated in this example.

Find the equation of the line passing through (3, −4) and (−1, −2).

Using $y - y_1 = m(x - x_1)$

$$\begin{matrix} x_1 & y_1 & & x_2 & y_2 \\ (3, & -4) & & (-1, & -2) \end{matrix}$$

$$\text{Gradient} = \frac{y_2 - y_1}{x_2 - x_1}$$

$$= \frac{-2 - (-4)}{-1 - 3} = \frac{2}{-4} = -\tfrac{1}{2}$$

So equation is

$$y - (-4) = -\tfrac{1}{2}(x - 3)$$

$$2y + 8 = 3 - x$$

Multiply both sides by 2 to eliminate the fractions, taking care with signs.

So the equation of the line is $2y + x + 5 = 0$.

Using $\dfrac{y - y_1}{y_2 - y_1} = \dfrac{x - x_1}{x_2 - x_1}$

Equation is

$$\frac{y - (-4)}{-2 - (-4)} = \frac{x - 3}{-1 - 3}$$

$$\frac{y + 4}{2} = \frac{x - 3}{-4}$$

$$2y + 8 = 3 - x$$

Multiply both sides by 4.

So the equation of the line is $2y + x + 5 = 0$.

✓ ***Note*** The equation of a line is normally given with integer coefficients. For example, $2y + x + 5 = 0$ in preference to $y + \frac{1}{2}x + \frac{5}{2} = 0$

Forms of equations of straight lines

An equation gives a straight line if, and only if, it can be expressed in the form $ax + by + c = 0$.

The only possible terms are x terms, y terms and a constant. There must be no squares, reciprocals, etc.

$ax + by + c = 0$ is the general form of the equation of a straight line.

One frequently used form of the equation of a straight line is $y = mx + c$.

Consider the line through $(0, c)$ with gradient m.

Using $y - y_1 = m(x - x_1)$

$y - c = mx$

$y = mx + c$

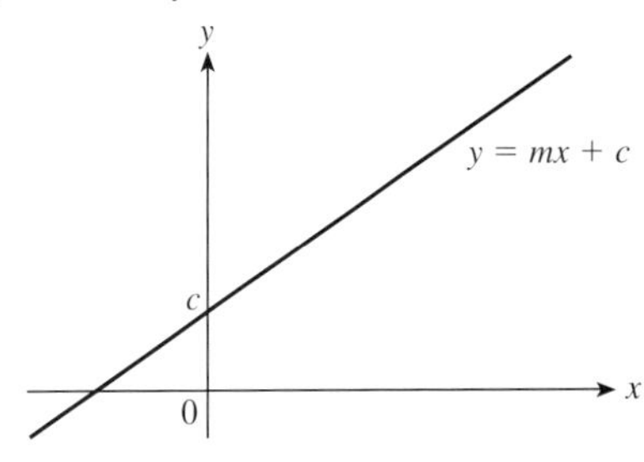

➤ The equation of a line with gradient m and intercept c on the y-axis is $y = mx + c$.

By arranging the equation of any straight line in the form $y = mx + c$, the gradient and intercept on the y-axis can be found directly.

Example 8 Find the gradient and intercept on the y-axis of the line with equation $3y - 2x + 7 = 0$

$3y - 2x + 7 = 0$

Arrange the equation with y alone on the LHS.

$3y = 2x - 7$

$(\div 3) \quad y = \frac{2}{3}x - \frac{7}{3}$

Compare with $y = mx + c$ (Gradient m, Intercept on y-axis c)

So, the line has gradient $\frac{2}{3}$ and intercept on the y-axis $-\frac{7}{3}$.

Example 9 Find the equation of the line with gradient $\frac{1}{7}$ and intercept on the y-axis -5.

$m = \frac{1}{7}$ and $c = -5$, so the equation is

$y = \frac{1}{7}x - 5$

or

$(\times 7) \quad 7y = x - 35$

Substitute for m and c.
$y = mx + c$ (Gradient m, Intercept on y-axis c)

Forms of equations of straight lines

$y = mx + c$	Line gradient m; intercept on y-axis, c
$y = mx$	Line gradient m, passes through the origin
$y = x + c$	Line gradient 1, makes an angle of 45° with the x-axis; intercept on y-axis, c
$y = k$	Line parallel to the x-axis through $(0, k)$
$y = 0$	x-axis
$x = k$	Line parallel to the y-axis through $(k, 0)$
$x = 0$	y-axis
$ax + by + c = 0$	General form of the equation of a straight line

Sketching straight lines

A sketch of a straight line should show where the line cuts the axes.

- To find the intercept on the x-axis, put $y = 0$.
- To find the intercept on the y-axis, put $x = 0$.

Example 10 Sketch $y = 2x - 8$.

When $x = 0$, $y = -8$, so the line intercepts the y-axis at $(0, -8)$.

When $y = 0$, $x = 4$, so the line intercepts the x-axis at $(4, 0)$.

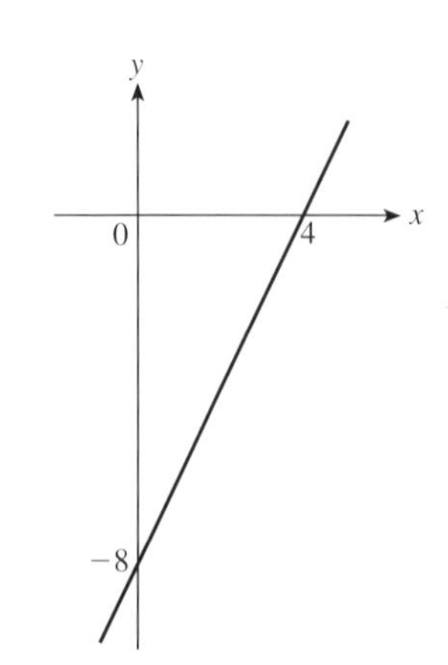

EXERCISE 8b

1 Find the gradients of the lines joining these pairs of points.

a (4, 3) and (8, 12) **b** (−2, −3) and (4, 6) **c** (5, 6) and (10, 2)

d (−3, 4) and (8, −6) **e** (−5, 3) and (−2, 3) **f** (p, q) and (r, s)

g $(0, a)$ and $(a, 0)$ **h** $(0, 0)$ and (a, b)

i $\left(-2\frac{1}{2}, -\frac{1}{2}\right)$ and $\left(4\frac{1}{2}, -1\right)$ **j** (−7, −3) and (−1, −4)

2 Write down the gradients of the lines perpendicular to lines of gradient

a 3 **b** $\frac{1}{4}$ **c** −6 **d** $-\frac{2}{3}$ **e** $2m$ **f** $-\dfrac{b}{a}$ **g** $-\dfrac{m}{2}$

3 Find if AB is parallel or perpendicular (or neither) to PQ in these cases.

a A(1, 4), B(6, 6), P(2, −1), Q(12, 3)

b A(−1, −1), B(0, 4), P(−4, 3), Q(6, 1)

c A(0, 3), B(7, 2), P(6, −1), Q(−1, −2)

d A(4, 3), B(8, 4), P(7, 1), Q(6, 5)

e A(3, 1), B(7, 3), P(−3, 2), Q(1, 0)

f A(−6, −1), B(−6, 3), P(2, 0), Q(2, −5)

g A(−6, −1), B(−6, 3), P(3, 1), Q(6, 1)

4 Determine whether these points lie on the given curves.

a $y = 6x + 7$, (1, 13) **b** $y = 2x + 2$, (13, 30) **c** $3x + 4y = 1$, $\left(-1, \frac{1}{2}\right)$

d $y = x^3 - 6$, (2, −2) **e** $xy = 36$, (−9, −4) **f** $x^2 + y^2 = 25$, (3, 4)

5 Find the coordinates of the points on the curve $y = 2x^2 - x - 1$ for which

a $x = 2$ **b** $x = -3$ **c** $x = 0$

6 Find the x-coordinates of the points on the line $y = 2x + 3$ for which the y-coordinates are

a 7 **b** 3 **c** −2

7 Find the points at which these lines cut the x-axis and the y-axis.

a $y = 3x - 6$ **b** $2y + 5x = 8$ **c** $\dfrac{x}{3} - \dfrac{y}{4} = 1$ **d** $y - 2x = 0$

8 Sketch these lines, on the same axes, labelling each line.

a $y = 2x$ **b** $y = 3$ **c** $y = -x$ **d** $x + 2 = 0$ **e** $y = \frac{1}{2}x$

9 Sketch on separate diagrams, showing the intercepts with the axes, these straight lines.

a $3y = 2x + 6$ **b** $x - 4y + 2 = 0$ **c** $3x + y + 6 = 0$ **d** $7x = 3y + 5$

10 Write down the equations of the straight lines through the origin having gradients

a $\frac{1}{3}$ **b** −2 **c** m

11 Rearrange these equations in the form $y = mx$ and hence write down the gradients of the lines they represent.

a $4y = x$ **b** $5x + 4y = 0$ **c** $3x = 2y$ **d** $\dfrac{x}{4} = \dfrac{y}{7}$ **e** $\dfrac{x}{p} - \dfrac{y}{q} = 0$

EXERCISE 8b
(continued)

12 Find the equations of the straight lines with

a gradient 3 and intercept on the y-axis 2

b gradient 3 and passing through $(0, -1)$

c gradient $\frac{1}{5}$ and intercept on the y-axis 2

d gradient $\frac{1}{5}$ and passing through $(0, 4)$

13 Arrange these equations in the form $y = mx + c$. Hence write down the gradient and the intercept on the y-axis for each line.

a $3y = 2x + 6$ **b** $x - 4y + 2 = 0$ **c** $3x + y + 6 = 0$

d $7x = 3y + 5$ **e** $y + 4 = 0$ **f** $lx + my + n = 0$

14 Find the equations of the straight lines of given gradients, passing through the given points.

a $4, (1, 3)$ **b** $3, (-2, 5)$ **c** $\frac{1}{3}, (2, -5)$

d $-\frac{3}{4}, (7, 5)$ **e** $\frac{1}{2}, \left(\frac{1}{3}, -\frac{1}{2}\right)$ **f** $a, (3, 2a)$

15 Find the equations of the straight lines joining these pairs of points.

a $(1, 6)$ and $(5, 9)$ **b** $(3, 2)$ and $(7, -3)$ **c** $(-3, 4)$ and $(8, 1)$

d $(-1, -4)$ and $(4, -3)$ **e** $\left(\frac{1}{2}, 2\right)$ and $\left(3, \frac{1}{3}\right)$ **f** $(k, 3h)$ and $(3k, h)$

16 Find the equation of the straight line through

a $(5, 4)$, parallel to $3x - 4y + 7 = 0$

b $(-2, 3)$, parallel to $5x - 2y - 1 = 0$

c $(4, 0)$, perpendicular to $x + 7y + 4 = 0$

d $(-2, -3)$, perpendicular to $4x + 3y - 5 = 0$

17 Calculate the area of the triangle formed by the line $3x - 7y + 4 = 0$ and the axes.

18 Find a if the line joining $(3, a)$ to $(-6, 5)$ has gradient $\frac{1}{3}$.

19 Given that $ax + 3y + 2 = 0$ and $2x - by - 5 = 0$ are perpendicular lines, find the ratio $a:b$.

20 Show that A$(-3, 1)$, B$(1, 2)$, C$(0, -1)$, D$(-4, -2)$ are the vertices of a parallelogram.

21 Show that P$(1, 7)$, Q$(7, 5)$, R$(6, 2)$, S$(0, 4)$ are the vertices of a rectangle. Calculate the lengths of the diagonals, and find their point of intersection.

22 Show that D$(-2, 0)$, E$\left(\frac{1}{2}, 1\frac{1}{2}\right)$ and F$\left(3\frac{1}{2}, -3\frac{1}{2}\right)$ are the vertices of a right-angled triangle, and find the length of the shortest side, and the mid-point of the hypotenuse.

8.9 Intersection of graphs

The intersection of two graphs consists of the points common to both graphs. To find these points, the equations of the graphs have to be solved simultaneously. (See Chapter 5.)

Example 11 Find the point of intersection of the two lines $y = 1 - x$ and $y = 2x - 8$.

$$y = 1 - x \quad ①$$
$$y = 2x - 8 \quad ②$$

Solve the equations of the two lines simultaneously.

The two lines intersect where

$$1 - x = 2x - 8$$

The two expressions for y must be equal.

$$3x = 9$$
$$\therefore \quad x = 3$$

Substituting in ① $\quad y = 1 - 3 = -2$

Check $x = 3$, $y = -2$ in ②.

The values $x = 3$, $y = -2$ satisfy both equations, so $(3, -2)$ lies on both lines.

So the point of intersection is $(3, -2)$.

Example 12 A and B are the points (2, 5) and (8, 4) respectively. Find the equation of the median through the origin, O, of the triangle OAB.

The required median is OM where M is the mid-point of AB.

The medians of a triangle are the lines joining the vertices to the mid-points of the opposite sides.

The mid-point, M, is at $\left(\frac{2+8}{2}, \frac{5+4}{2}\right) = \left(5, 4\frac{1}{2}\right)$.

OM passes through (0, 0) and $\left(5, 4\frac{1}{2}\right)$.

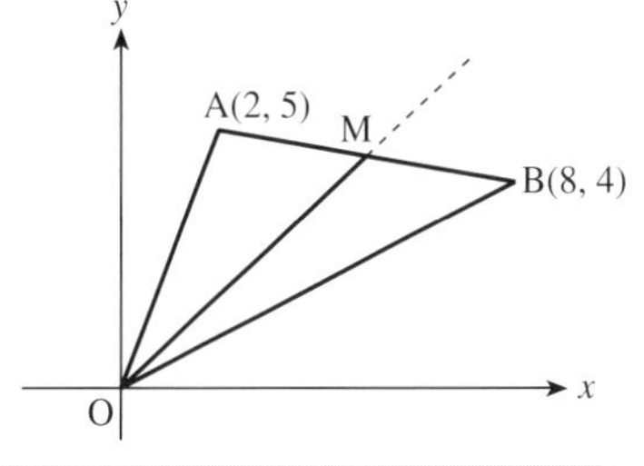

So the gradient of OM $= \frac{4\frac{1}{2} - 0}{5 - 0} = \frac{9}{10}$

$\begin{matrix} x_1 & y_1 \\ (0, & 0) \end{matrix} \quad \begin{matrix} x_2 & y_2 \\ (5, & 4\frac{1}{2}) \end{matrix}$ using gradient $\frac{y_2 - y_1}{x_2 - x_1}$

$\therefore$ Equation of OM is $y = \frac{9}{10}x$.

Using $y - y_1 = m(x - x_1)$.

Example 13 Find the equation of the perpendicular bisector of the line joining A(−2, 5) to B(−8, −3).

The perpendicular bisector of AB

- passes through the mid-point of AB
- is perpendicular to AB so the product of the gradients of AB and the bisector is −1.

Mid-point of AB $= \left(\frac{-2 + (-8)}{2}, \frac{5 + (-3)}{2}\right) = (-5, 1)$

$\begin{matrix} & x_1 & y_1 \\ \text{A}(& -2, & 5) \end{matrix} \quad \begin{matrix} & x_2 & y_2 \\ \text{B}(& -8, & -3) \end{matrix}$
Using $\left(\frac{x_1 + x_2}{2}, \frac{y_1 + y_2}{2}\right)$

Gradient of AB $= \frac{-3 - 5}{-8 - (-2)} = \frac{-8}{-6} = \frac{4}{3}$

Using $\frac{y_2 - y_1}{x_2 - x_1}$

So, the gradient of a line perpendicular to AB is $-\frac{3}{4}$.

$mm' = -1$

So, the perpendicular bisector passes through (−5, 1) with gradient $-\frac{3}{4}$.

$\therefore$ the equation is $\quad y - 1 = -\frac{3}{4}(x - (-5))$

Using $y - y_1 = m(x - x_1)$

$$4y - 4 = -3x - 15$$
$$4y + 3x + 11 = 0$$

Example 14 The points A, B, C and D are (7, 10), (5, 9), (2, 3) and (8, 6) respectively. Prove that ABCD is a trapezium with AB parallel to CD. Show that CD = 3AB.

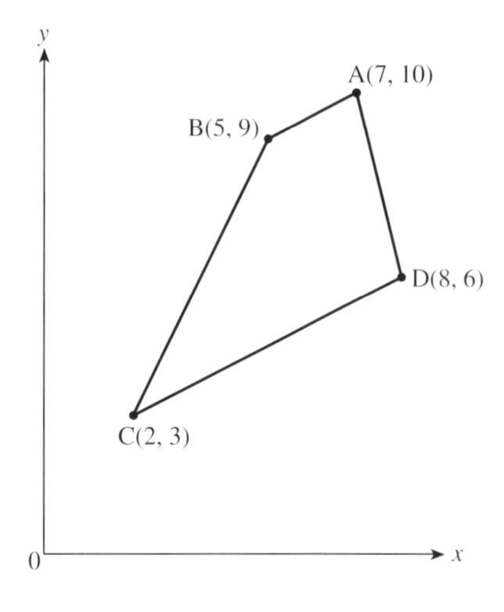

Gradient of CD $= \dfrac{6-3}{8-2} = \dfrac{3}{6} = \dfrac{1}{2}$

Gradient of AB $= \dfrac{10-9}{7-5} = \dfrac{1}{2}$

Gradient AB = Gradient CD, so AB || CD.

$$\begin{aligned} CD &= \sqrt{(8-2)^2 + (6-3)^2} \\ &= \sqrt{36+9} \\ &= \sqrt{45} \\ &= 3\sqrt{5} \\ AB &= \sqrt{(7-5)^2 + (10-9)^2} \\ &= \sqrt{2^2 + 1^2} \\ &= \sqrt{5} \end{aligned}$$

Note: This question can be solved using vector geometry. See Book 2.

$\therefore$ CD = 3AB. So ABCD is a trapezium with AB parallel to CD and CD = 3AB.

EXERCISE 8c

1 Find the points of intersection of these pairs of straight lines.

a $x + y = 0$
$y = -7$

b $y = 5x + 2$
$y = 3x - 1$

c $3x + 2y - 1 = 0$
$4x + 5y + 3 = 0$

d $5x + 7y + 29 = 0$
$11x - 3y - 65 = 0$

2 Find the equation of the straight line joining the origin to the mid-point of the line joining A(3, 2) and B(5, −1).

3 For the line segments joining these pairs of points find the mid-point, the gradient, the perpendicular gradient, and the equation of the perpendicular bisector.

a (3, 5) and (7, 7)

b (−2, 4) and (−4, 8)

c (−1, 3) and (−2, −5)

d (p, q) and $(7p, 3q)$

4 Given the points A(−4, 8) and B(0, −2), find the equation of the perpendicular bisector of AB.

5 Find the equation of the perpendicular bisector of PQ where P is (7, 3) and Q is (−6, 1).

6 **a** Find the equation of the straight line l through P(7, 5) perpendicular to the straight line AB whose equation is $3x + 4y - 16 = 0$.

b Find the point of intersection of the line AB with the line l in part **a**.

c Hence find the perpendicular distance from P to AB.

7 Find the perpendicular distance from (2, 4) to the line $y = 2x + 10$.

8 **a** Find the equation of the straight line joining the points A(7, 0) and B(0, 2).

b Find the equation of the line AC such that the x-axis bisects angle BAC.

9 A line is drawn through the point (2, 3) making an angle of 45° with the positive direction of the x-axis, and it meets the line $x = 6$ at P. Find the distance of P from the origin O, and the equation of the line through P perpendicular to OP.

10 Prove that the points (−5, 4), (−1, −2) and (5, 2) lie at three of the corners of a square. Find the coordinates of the fourth corner, and the area of the square.

11 The vertices of a quadrilateral ABCD are A(4, 0), B(14, 11), C(0, 6) and D(−10, −5). Prove that the diagonals AC, BD bisect each other at right angles, and that the length of BD is four times that of AC.

12 The coordinates of the vertices A, B, C of the triangle ABC are (−3, 7), (2, 19), (10, 7) respectively.

a Prove that the triangle is isosceles.

b Calculate the length of the perpendicular from B to AC, and use it to find the area of the triangle.

13 A triangle ABC, has A at the point (7, 9), B at (3, 5), C at (5, 1).
Find the equation of the line joining the mid-points of AB and AC.
Find also the area of the triangle enclosed by this line and the axes.

14 One side of a rhombus is the line $y = 2x$, and two opposite vertices are the points (0, 0) and $\left(4\frac{1}{2}, 4\frac{1}{2}\right)$. Find the equations of the diagonals, the coordinates of the other two vertices and the length of the side.

15 Here are two possible methods of proving that three points A, B and C are collinear (i.e. lie on the same line).

a Prove that AB + BC = AC (assuming B lies between A and C).
Use this method to show that P, Q and R are collinear where P is (2, 6), Q is (4, 9) and R is (−6, −6).

b Prove that AB and BC are parallel. Then since B is a point in common, A, B and C must be collinear. Use this method to show that L, M and N are collinear where L is (0, 4), M is (3, 13) and N is (−1, 1).

16 Which of these sets of points are collinear?

a (−1, −1), (1, 7) and (2, 11)

b (0, 5), (3, −1) and (7, −11)

c (−2, 14), (2, −6) and (1, −1)

17 Find all possible values of a and b given that $y = ax + 14$ is the perpendicular bisector of the line joining (1, 2) to (b, 6).

18 Find a and b given that $y + 4x = 11$ is the perpendicular bisector of the line joining (a, 2) to (6, b).

8.10 Extension material on coordinate geometry

Many geometrical results can be proved using coordinate geometry.

Example 15 Prove that the sum of the squares of the distance of any point, P, from two opposite vertices of a rectangle is equal to the sum of the squares of its distance from the other two vertices.

To prove the result for any rectangle and any point, a general rectangle and a general point must be chosen. It is often possible, however, to choose a simple version, e.g. to place the rectangle in a convenient position on the grid. A simple system reduces the complexity of the algebra without losing any rigour.

Proof Consider the rectangle OABC with vertices (0, 0), $(a, 0)$, (a, b) and $(0, b)$ respectively.

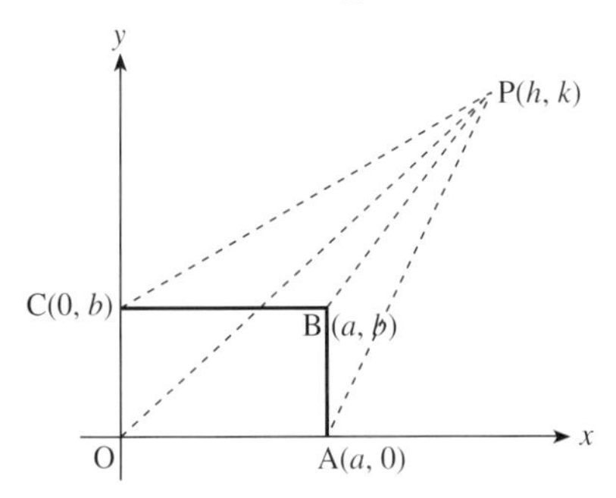

Without loss of generality the rectangle can be placed with one vertex at the origin and sides along the axes.

Let the point, P, have coordinates (h, k).

Make P a general point by using letters for its coordinates.

To prove $PA^2 + PC^2 = PO^2 + PB^2$

State what is to be proved.

$$\begin{aligned} PA^2 + PC^2 &= (h-a)^2 + (k-0)^2 + (h-0)^2 + (k-b)^2 \\ &= h^2 - 2ah + a^2 + k^2 + h^2 + k^2 - 2bk + b^2 \\ &= 2h^2 + 2k^2 - 2ah - 2bk + a^2 + b^2 \end{aligned}$$

Write down and simplify an expression for the LHS.

$$\begin{aligned} PO^2 + PB^2 &= h^2 + k^2 + (h-a)^2 + (k-b)^2 \\ &= h^2 + k^2 + h^2 - 2ah + a^2 + k^2 - 2bk + b^2 \\ &= 2h^2 + 2k^2 - 2ah - 2bk + a^2 + b^2 \end{aligned}$$

Write down and simplify an expression for the RHS.

So LHS = RHS and the result is therefore proved.

EXERCISE 8d (Extension)

1. Prove that the mid-point of the hypotenuse of any right-angled triangle is equidistant from its vertices.

2. Find the equations of the lines which pass through the point of intersection of the lines $x - 3y = 4$ and $3x + y = 2$, and are respectively parallel and perpendicular to the line $3x + 4y = 0$.

3. ABC is a triangle and L and M are the mid-points of the sides AB and AC respectively. Show that LM is parallel to BC and that $LM = \frac{1}{2}BC$.

4 The three straight lines $y = x$, $2y = 7x$ and $x + 4y - 60 = 0$ form a triangle. Find the equations of the three medians, and calculate the coordinates of their point of intersection.

5 The points D(2, −3), E(−1, 7) and F(3, 5) are the mid-points of the sides BC, CA, AB respectively of a triangle. Find the equations of its sides.

6 Prove that the points (1, −1), (−1, 1) and ($\sqrt{3}$, $\sqrt{3}$) are the vertices of an equilateral triangle. Find the coordinates of the point of intersection of the medians of this triangle.

7 The points A(−7, −7), B(8, −1), C(4, 9) and D are the vertices of the parallelogram ABCD. Find the coordinates of D. Prove that ABCD is a rectangle and find its area.

8 A, B and C are the points (1, 6), (−5, 2) and (3, 4) respectively.
Find the equations of the perpendicular bisectors of AB and BC.
Hence find the coordinates of the circumcentre of the triangle ABC.

9 Prove that the medians of a triangle are concurrent (i.e. meet in a point).

10 Find the circumcentre of the triangle with vertices (3, 0), (7, 8) and (3, 12).

11 Prove that the figure obtained by joining the mid-points of consecutive sides of any quadrilateral is a parallelogram.

12 Prove that the sum of the squares of the lengths of the diagonals of a parallelogram is equal to the sum of the squares of the lengths of its sides.

13 Find the equation of the straight line joining the feet of the perpendiculars drawn from the point (1, 1) to the lines $3x - 3y - 4 = 0$ and $3x + y - 6 = 0$.

14 Through the point A(1, 5) is drawn a line parallel to the x-axis to meet at B the line PQ whose equation is $3y = 2x - 5$. Find the length of AB and the sine of the angle between PQ and AB; hence show that the length of the perpendicular from A to PQ is $18 \div \sqrt{13}$. Calculate the area of the triangle formed by PQ and the axes.

EXERCISE 8e (Miscellaneous)

1 Find these equations.

a The line joining the points (2, 4) and (−3, 1)

b The line through (3, 1) parallel to the line $3x + 5y = 6$

c The line through (3, −4) perpendicular to the line $5x - 2y = 3$

2 **a** Find the equation of the line joining A(−3, 2) and B(6, 8).

b The line AB meets the line $3x + 2y - 21 = 0$ at M.
Find the coordinates of M and show that M divides AB in the ratio 2:1.

3 **a** Find the equation of the line passing through the point A(4, −2) and perpendicular to the line l whose equation is $2x - y - 5 = 0$.

b Find the coordinates of the foot of the perpendicular from A to the line l.

c Hence find the perpendicular distance from A to l.

4 The coordinates of P, Q and R are (5, 9), (14, −3) and (2, 3) respectively.

a Show that triangle PQR is a right-angled triangle.

b Find angle PQR correct to 3 significant figures.

EXERCISE 8e
(continued)

5 The area of any quadrilateral with perpendicular diagonals of lengths d_1 and d_2 is given by $\frac{1}{2}d_1d_2$.
Show that the area of the quadrilateral ABCD where the points A, B, C and D have coordinates $(-1, 4)$, $(3, 7)$, $(5, 2)$ and $(-5, -17)$ respectively is 80 units^2.

6 The points D, E and F have coordinates $(5, -2)$, $(2, 9)$ and $(9, 2)$ respectively.

a Find the equation of l, the perpendicular bisector of EF.

b Find the coordinates of the point where l meets DE.

7 A rhombus has three of its vertices at the points $(3, 9)$, $(2, 2)$ and $(7, -3)$.

a Find the coordinates of the fourth vertex.

b Find the area of the rhombus.

8 The pairs A and B have coordinates (h, k) and $(3h, -5k)$, respectively.

a Find the coordinates of the mid-point of AB.

b Find the gradient of AB.

c Hence find the equation of the perpendicular bisector of AB.

9 Given that P and Q are the points $(s, 2s)$ and $(3s, 8s)$ respectively, find the equation of the perpendicular bisector of PQ.

10 a Given that the point P has coordinates $(h-1, 3h+4)$, find the coordinates P_1, P_2 and P_3 when $h = 1$, 2 and 3 respectively.

b Show that P_1, P_2 and P_3 are collinear and find the equation of the line on which the points lie.

c Show that the equation found in part **b** can also be obtained by putting $x = h - 1$ and $y = 3h + 4$ and eliminating h.

11 The line l has equation $4y + 3x = 12$.

a Find the coordinates of the intercepts of l on the axes.

b Hence or otherwise find the equation of the reflection of l in the x-axis, the y-axis, and the line $y = x$.

c Find the area of the triangle enclosed by the line l and the axes.

12 a Sketch $y = |3x - 4|$.

b Find the area enclosed by $y = |3x - 4|$ and $y = 5$, and the area enclosed by $y = |3x - 4|$ and $y = 2x + 4$

13 a Sketch on the same axes, for $x \geqslant 0$: $y = |2x + 6|$ and $y = |3x - 6|$.

b Find, for $x \geqslant 0$, the points of intersection of the two equations.

c Find the area in the first quadrant, enclosed between $y = |2x + 6|$ and $y = |3x - 6|$.

14 Find the coordinates of the points at which these curves cut the y-axis and the x-axis.

a $y = x^2 - x - 12$ **b** $y = 6x^2 - 7x + 2$ **c** $y = x^2 - 6x + 9$

d $y = x^3 - 9x^2$ **e** $y = (x+1)(x-5)^2$ **f** $y = (x^2 - 1)(x^2 - 9)$

15 The parabola $y = x^2 + 4$ meets the straight line $y = 5x + 10$ at the points A and B.

a By solving these simultaneous equations find the coordinates of A and B.

$y = x^2 + 4$

$y = 5x + 10$

b Find the length AB.

16 The parabola $y = x^2 + 2x - 7$ meets the line $y = 17 - 3x$ at the points P and Q. Find the length of PQ.

17 The three points O(0, 0), A(−4, 6) and B(3, 7) are the vertices of a triangle. Find the largest angle of the triangle.

18 Given that a triangle has vertices (2, 3), (4, 9) and (5, 2)

a find the perimeter of the triangle, leaving surds in the answer

b show that the triangle is right-angled.

Test yourself

1 The coordinates of the mid-point of (3, 4) and (a, b) are

A $(a+3, b+4)$ **B** $\left(\frac{a+b}{2}, \frac{7}{2}\right)$ **C** $(a-3, b-4)$

D $\left(\frac{a+3}{2}, \frac{b+4}{2}\right)$ **E** $\left(\frac{a-4}{2}, \frac{b-3}{2}\right)$

2 One side of a rectangle has gradient $\frac{4}{7}$. An adjacent side has gradient

A $\frac{4}{7}$ **B** $\frac{7}{4}$ **C** -1 **D** $-1\frac{3}{4}$ **E** $\frac{3}{7}$

3 The line $2x + 3y + 4 = 0$ passes through the point

A $\left(0, \frac{3}{4}\right)$ **B** (4, 0) **C** (−8, 4) **D** (2, −3) **E** $\left(\frac{2}{3}, -3\right)$

4 The line passing through $(1, \sqrt{3})$ and $(2\sqrt{3}, 6)$ has gradient

A $-\frac{\sqrt{3}}{6}$ **B** -6 **C** $\frac{1+2\sqrt{3}}{6}$ **D** $5-\sqrt{2}$ **E** $\sqrt{3}$

5 The line parallel to $2x + 4y = 3$ passing through the point (3, −2) has equation

A $4x + 3y = 6$ **B** $11x + 12y = 9$ **C** $y = 2x - 8$

D $x + 2y = -1$ **E** $2y = x - 7$

6 The distance between the points $(3, p)$ and $(2p, 4)$ is

A $\sqrt{3p^2 - 7}$ **B** $p + 1$ **C** $\sqrt{5(p^2 - 4p + 5)}$

D $10p$ **E** $\sqrt{5p^2 - 22p + 25}$

7 The x-coordinate of the point of intersection of the lines $3y - 4x + 8 = 0$ and $2y - 3x + 5 = 0$ is

A -31 **B** 1 **C** -1 **D** $\frac{31}{17}$ **E** 31

8 The line passing through (3, 1) and (11, −3) has equation

A $y - 2x + 19 = 0$ **B** $x + 2y - 5 = 0$ **C** $y - 2x + 25 = 0$

D $x + 2y + 5 = 0$ **E** $y - 2x - 19 = 0$

9 The line $y = 2 - 3x$ intersects the curve $x^2 - y = 2$ at

A (0, 2) and $\left(\frac{2}{3}, 0\right)$ **B** (1, −1) and (−4, 14) **C** (0, −2) only

D (−3, 2) only **E** no points of intersection

10 The area of the triangle formed by the line $5y - 6x - 8 = 0$ and the axes is

A $\frac{32}{15}$ **B** $\frac{16}{3}$ **C** $\frac{16}{15}$ **D** $\frac{15}{64}$ **E** $\frac{32}{3}$

Key points

Coordinate geometry

- For the points $A(x_1, y_1)$ and $B(x_2, y_2)$

  $AB = \sqrt{(x_2 - x_1)^2 + (y_2 - y_1)^2}$

  Mid-point of AB is $\left(\frac{x_1 + x_2}{2}, \frac{y_1 + y_2}{2}\right)$

  Gradient of AB $= \frac{y_2 - y_1}{x_2 - x_1}$

  Equation of line through A with gradient m: $y - y_1 = m(x - x_1)$

  Equation of AB: $\frac{y - y_1}{y_2 - y_1} = \frac{x - x_1}{x_2 - x_1}$

- The equation of a line with gradient m and intercept c on the y-axis is $y = mx + c$.
- Forms of equations of straight lines

$y = mx + c$	Line gradient m; intercept on y-axis, c
$y = mx$	Line gradient m, passes through the origin
$y = x + c$	Line gradient 1, makes an angle of 45° with the x-axis; intercept on y-axis, c
$y = k$	Line parallel to the x-axis through $(0, k)$
$y = 0$	x-axis
$x = k$	Line parallel to the y-axis through $(k, 0)$
$x = 0$	y-axis
$ax + by + c = 0$	General form of the equation of a straight line

- For lines with gradients m, m'

  $m = m' \Leftrightarrow$ the lines are parallel

  $mm' = -1 \Leftrightarrow$ the lines are perpendicular

Revision Exercise 1

1 $f(x) = 2 - \sqrt{x}$. Find the simplest form of

a $f(2)$ **b** $\sqrt{2}f(2)$

2 $f(x) = \dfrac{1 + 2\sqrt{x}}{1 - \sqrt{x}}$, $x \neq 1$.

Find these expressions in the form $a + b\sqrt{2}$ where a and b are rational numbers:

a $f(2)$ **b** $\sqrt{2}f(2)$

3 **a** Find $\sqrt{1152}$ as the simplest possible surd.

b Express $(3 - 2\sqrt{2})^2$ in the form $a + b\sqrt{2}$.

c Hence express $\sqrt{34 - \sqrt{1152}}$ in the form $a + b\sqrt{2}$.

4 Find both the square and the reciprocal of $2 - \sqrt{3}$, writing your answers in the form $a + b\sqrt{3}$ where a and b are rational numbers.

5 Write these expressions in the form x^n:

a $\dfrac{x}{x^{-8}}$ **b** $\dfrac{(\sqrt{x})^3}{x}$ **c** $\dfrac{x^{\frac{1}{2}} \times x^{\frac{1}{3}}}{x^{\frac{1}{4}}}$

6 Solve these equations:

a $3^{2x-1} = 9^{-x}$ **b** $4(2^{x^2}) = 16^x$ **c** $2^{2x-1} = \frac{1}{8}$

7 Factorise these expressions.

a $x^2 - 1$ **b** $2x^2 - 2$ **c** $3x^3 - 12x$ **d** $x^4 - 1$

e $ab^2 - ac^2$ **f** $pq^2 - p$ **g** $x^2y + 2xy^2 + y^3$

8 Factorise fully the expression $x^2(x + 1) - 2x(x^2 - 1)$.

9 Given that $a = \dfrac{1}{\sqrt{2}}$ and $b = \sqrt{2} - 1$, express each of these in the form $m + n\sqrt{2}$:

a $b + 2a$ **b** $\dfrac{b}{a}$ **c** $\dfrac{1 + a}{b}$

10 Factorise these expressions.

a $x^2 + x - 12$ **b** $x^4 + x^2 - 12$ **c** $x + \sqrt{x} - 12$

d $\dfrac{1}{x^2} + \dfrac{1}{x} - 12$ **e** $(x + 1)^2 + (x + 1) - 12$ **f** $3x^3 + 3x^2 - 36x$

11 Factorise these expressions.

a $x^2 - x - 2$ **b** $\frac{1}{2}x^2 - \frac{1}{2}x - 1$ **c** $x^{\frac{5}{2}} - x^{\frac{3}{2}} - 2x^{\frac{1}{2}}$

12 Some of these statements are identities and the rest are equations. Identify the category to which each statement belongs. Prove all the identities, and attempt to solve all the equations.

a $(x + 1)^2 = x^2 + 1$ **b** $(x - 2)^2 = x^2 - 4$ **c** $\dfrac{x^3 + 2x}{x^2} = x + \dfrac{2}{x}$

d $\dfrac{1}{2 + x} = \dfrac{1}{2} + \dfrac{1}{x}$ **e** $\dfrac{6x - 1}{2x + 3} = 3 - \dfrac{10}{2x + 3}$

13 Rearrange the formula $y = \dfrac{1 + x}{2 - x}$ to make x the subject.

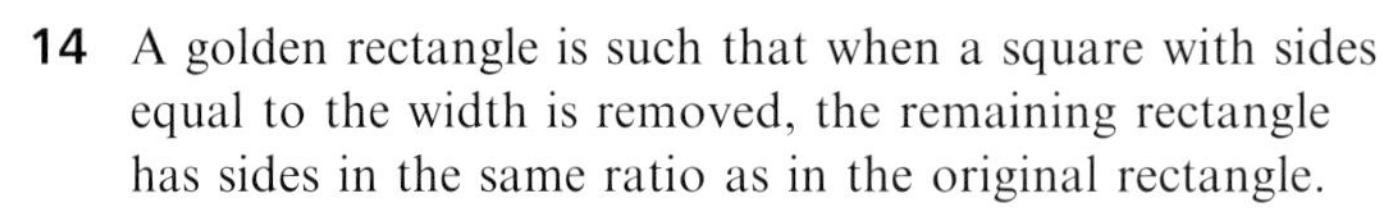

14 A golden rectangle is such that when a square with sides equal to the width is removed, the remaining rectangle has sides in the same ratio as in the original rectangle.

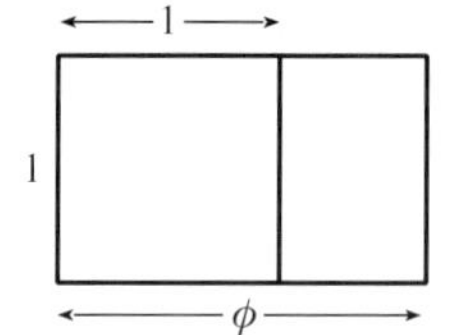

a Show that ϕ satisfies the equation $\phi(\phi - 1) = 1$.

b Hence find the exact value of ϕ.

15 Solve each of these equations.

a $(x - 3)^2 - (x - 1)^2 = 0$ **b** $4(x - 3)^2 - (x - 1)^2 = 0$

c $9(2x - 1)^2 - 16 = 0$

16 **a** Express $x^2 + px + q$ in completed square form.

b Hence prove that the equation $x^2 + px + q = 0$ has roots given by

$$x = \frac{-p \pm \sqrt{p^2 - 4q}}{2}$$

c By rearranging the general quadratic equation $ax^2 + bx + c = 0$ into the form

$$x^2 + \left(\frac{b}{a}\right)x + \frac{c}{a} = 0$$

use the result in **b** to prove the standard formula for the roots

$$x = \frac{-b \pm \sqrt{b^2 - 4ac}}{2a}$$

17 Determine how many distinct real roots each of these quadratic equations has. Do not solve the equations.

a $x^2 + x + 2 = 0$ **b** $x^2 + x - 2 = 0$ **c** $x^2 - x + 2 = 0$

d $x - 2 - x^2 = 0$ **e** $2 - x - x^2 = 0$ **f** $1 + 2x + x^2 = 0$

18 To which sets of numbers do the solutions to these equations belong? Select from the sets of $\mathbb{N}$ (natural numbers), $\mathbb{Z}$ (integers), $\mathbb{Q}$ (rational numbers) and $\mathbb{R}$ (real numbers), or possibly none of these sets. Note that some numbers will belong to *more* than one set.

a $x^2 + x - 1 = 0$ **b** $x^2 + x + 1 = 0$ **c** $x^2 - 3x + 2 = 0$

d $x^2 - x - 2 = 0$ **e** $2x^2 + x - 1 = 0$

19 The function f is given by $f(x) = \dfrac{4 + 5x - x^2}{5x - 4 - x^2}$. Find the exact values of x for which

a $f(x) = 0$ **b** the function f is undefined

20 Find the range of values of x for which $6x^2 \leqslant 11x + 2$.

21 One root of the equation $ax^2 - 8x + 4 = 0$ is $x = \frac{2}{3}$.
Find the value of a and the other root.

22 Find the solutions, correct to 2 decimal places, of the equation $ax^2 + bx + c = 0$ where $a = 10^2$, $b = 3 \times 10^5$ and $c = 2 \times 10^6$.

23 The simultaneous equations $ax - 3by = 11$ and $4ax + by = 31$ have the solution $x = 2$, $y = -1$. Find the values of a and b.

24 Find the coordinates of the point where these two lines intersect: $y = 2(x - 2)$ and $3x = 2y + 5$.

25 Given that $g(x) = |x| + 1$ and that $h(x) = |x + 1|$, evaluate

a $g(3)$ **b** $g(-3)$ **c** $h(3)$ **d** $h(-3)$

26 **a** Write down the exact solutions of the equation $x^2 = 5$.

b Rewrite the inequality $|x|^2 \leqslant 5$ in an algebraic form without a modulus sign.

c Show on a number line the solution set of the inequality $|x - 1|^2 < 5$.

27 The volume of a cylinder is $50\pi\,\text{cm}^3$ and the curved surface area is $20\pi\,\text{cm}^2$. Find the radius and height of the cylinder.

28 In statistics, the values of n and p are sometimes required when only the values of np and $np(1 - p)$ are known.
Find the values of n and p in the case when $np = 5$ and $np(1 - p) = 4\frac{7}{12}$.

29 Suppose that the graph of the function $y = \text{f}(x)$ is known. Explain in words how the graph of these functions may be obtained from the known graph. Describe fully all the transformations required and the order in which they are to be applied.

a $y = \text{f}(x + 2) - 3$ **b** $y = 3\text{f}(x - 1)$ **c** $y = \frac{1}{2}\text{f}\left(\frac{x}{3}\right)$ **d** $y = 1 - \text{f}(2x)$

30 The function f is given by $\text{f}(x) = \dfrac{1}{x - 1} + 2,\ x \neq 1$.
Sketch these graphs, showing clearly any intercepts and asymptotes.

a $y = \text{f}(x)$ **b** $y = \text{f}(x - 3) + 1$

31 The function f is given by $\text{f}(x) = x^2 - 4x + 3$.

a Evaluate $\text{f}(0)$ and solve the equation $\text{f}(x) = 0$.

b Express $\text{f}(x)$ in completed square form.

c Hence sketch the graph of $y = \text{f}(x)$, showing clearly the intercepts and the minimum point.

d Solve the inequality $x^2 + 3 < 4x$.

32 The diagram shows the graph of $y = \text{f}(x)$.
Sketch on separate diagrams the graphs of

a $y = |\text{f}(x)|$ **b** $y = \text{f}(|x|)$

c $y = \text{f}(-x)$ **d** $y = -\text{f}(x)$

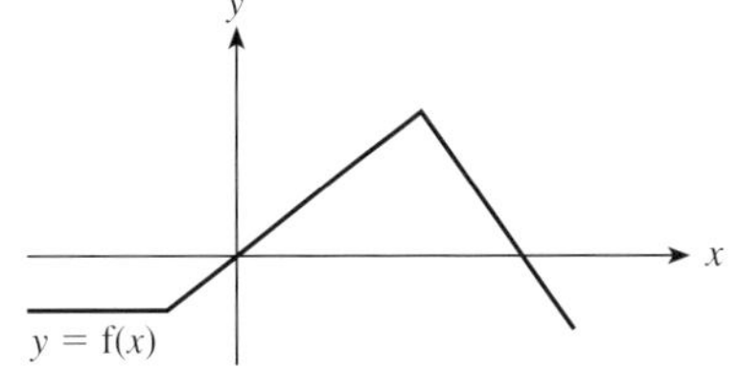

33 Find the points of intersection of the graphs of $y = x^5$ and $y = 16x$.
Sketch both curves on one diagram, showing clearly the coordinates of all the points where the curves cut the axes or each other.

34 $\text{f}(x) = (x - 2)^3$ and $\text{g}(x) = -x^2$.
Show that the curves representing $y = \text{f}(x)$ and $y = \text{g}(x)$ have only one point of intersection. Sketch on the same diagram the graphs of $y = \text{f}(x)$ and $y = \text{g}(x)$, showing clearly the intercepts and the point of intersection.

35 The points P and Q on the curve $y = x^2 - 4x$ have x coordinates 1 and 3 respectively. Find the equation of the perpendicular bisector of PQ.

36 A and B are the points on the curve $y = x^2 - 5x - 3$ whose y coordinates are -9. A has the smaller x coordinate. C and D are the points on the curve $y = x^2 - 5x - 3$ whose y coordinates are 3. C has the smaller x coordinate. Show that AD = BC.

Examination Questions 1

Algebra

1 **i** Write down the exact value of 7^{-2}.

ii Simplify $\dfrac{(x\sqrt{x})^3}{2x^4}$. *OCR*

2 **i** Solve the simultaneous equations $y = x^2 - 3x + 2$, $y = 3x - 7$.

ii Interpret your solution to part **i** geometrically. *OCR*

3 Express each of the following in the form $p + q\sqrt{7}$ where p and q are rational numbers

a $(2 + 3\sqrt{7})(5 - 2\sqrt{7})$; **b** $\dfrac{(5 + \sqrt{7})}{(3 - \sqrt{7})}$. *AEB*

4 Express the equation $(x - 5)(x - 3) = 6$ in the form $(x - m)^2 = n$ where m and n are positive integers.

Hence write down the exact values of the two irrational roots of this equation. *AEB*

5 **a** Find the range of values of x for which $6x^2 - 11x \geqslant 7$.

b Find the coordinates of the turning point of the curve $y = (2x - 3)^2 + 6$ and sketch the curve. *UCLES*

6 Show that the elimination of x from the simultaneous equations

$$x - 2y = 1,$$
$$3xy - y^2 = 8,$$

produces the equation

$$5y^2 + 3y - 8 = 0.$$

Solve this quadratic equation and hence find the pairs (x, y) for which the simultaneous equations are satisfied. *LONDON*

7 **a** Expand $(1 + x^2)(1 + x^3)$, arranging your answer in ascending powers of x.

b Find, as a decimal number, the exact value of $(1 + x^2)(1 + x^3)$ for $x = 10^{-3}$. *LONDON*

8 The specification for a new rectangular car park states that the length x m is to be 5 m more than the breadth. The perimeter of the car park is to be greater than 32 m.

a Form a linear inequality in x.

The area of the car park is to be less than 104 m^2.

b Form a quadratic inequality in x.

c By solving your inequalities, determine the set of possible values of x. *EDEXCEL*

9 **a** On the same axes, sketch the graphs of $y = 2 - x$ and $y = 2|x + 1|$.

b Hence, or otherwise, find the values of x for which $2 - x = 2|x + 1|$. *LONDON*

10 By substituting $t = x^{\frac{1}{2}}$, or otherwise, find the values of x for which $4x + 8 = 33x^{\frac{1}{2}}$.
LONDON

11 **a** Find, as surds, the roots of the equation $2(x+1)(x-4) - (x-2)^2 = 0$.
b Hence find the set of values of x for which $2(x+1)(x-4) - (x-2)^2 > 0$.
LONDON

12 **a** Use algebra to solve $(x-1)(x+2) = 18$.
b Hence, or otherwise, find the set of values of x for which $(x-1)(x+2) > 18$.
LONDON

13 Solve the equation $|x-3| = |x+10|$. *UCLES*

14 A quadratic function is defined by $f(x) = x^2 + kx + 9$, where k is a constant. It is given that the equation $f(x) = 0$ has two distinct real roots. Find the set of values that k can take.

For the case where $k = -4\sqrt{3}$,

i express $f(x)$ in the form $(x+a)^2 + b$, stating the values of a and b, and hence write down the least value taken by $f(x)$,
ii solve the equation $f(x) = 0$, expressing your answer in terms of surds, simplified as far as possible.
OCR

15 Express $(9a^4)^{-\frac{1}{2}}$ as an algebraic fraction in simplified form. *UCLES*

16 Given that a is a positive constant, sketch the graph of $y = |3x - a|$, indicating clearly in terms of a where the graph crosses or touches the coordinate axes.

Solve the inequality $|3x - a| < x$. *AEB*

17 The quadratic equation $x^2 + kx + 36 = 0$ has two different real roots. Find the set of possible values of k.
UCLES

18 Tickets for the zoo are of two types: A for adults, and C for children and senior citizens. The cost of 7 type A and 4 type C tickets is £46, whereas the cost of 8 type A and 6 type C tickets is £57. Calculate the cost of 5 type A and 3 type C tickets.
AEB

19 **a** Write down
i a rational number which lies between 4 and 5;
ii an irrational number which lies between 4 and 5.

b A student says: 'When you multiply two irrational numbers together the answer is always an irrational number.'

Simplify $(2+\sqrt{3})(2-\sqrt{3})$ and comment on the student's statement. *AEB*

20 Solve the simultaneous equations

$$x + y = 5$$
$$\frac{1}{x} - \frac{1}{y} = \frac{1}{6}$$

LONDON

21 Sketch the graph of $y = |x - 2a|$, where a is a positive constant. (You should indicate the coordinates of the points where the graph meets the axes.)

Find, in terms of a, the two values of x satisfying $|x - 2a| = \frac{1}{2}a$. *UCLES*

22 **i** Solve the equation $\frac{x+2}{3} - \frac{2x-1}{4} = \frac{1}{2}$.

ii Given that $ax + by + c = 0$, find an expression for y in terms of a, b, c and x.

LONDON

23 Solve $19 < 3(x + 2) < 35$. *C*

24 Sketch the graph of $y = |x + 2|$ and hence, or otherwise, solve the inequality $|x + 2| > 2x + 1$, $x \in \mathbb{R}$. *UCLES*

25 Find the set of values of a for which the equation $ax^2 - 6x + a = 0$ has two distinct real roots. *UCLES*

26 Factorise $(x + 3)^2 - 16$. *UCLES*

27 Solve the simultaneous equations

$$x + y = 1$$
$$x^2 - xy + y^2 = 7$$

UCLES

28 Solve the equation $|x + 3| = |x|$. *UCLES*

Factor theorem

1 The cubic polynomial $3x^3 - 7x^2 - 18x - 8$ is denoted by $f(x)$. Use the factor theorem to show that $(x + 1)$ is a factor of $f(x)$. Hence factorise $f(x)$ completely.

OCR

2 Given that $x - 1$ and $x + 2$ are factors of the polynomial $3x^3 + ax^2 + bx - 2$,

a find the values of the constants a and b

b determine the other factor of the polynomial. *WJEC*

3 The cubic polynomial $x^3 + ax^2 - 3x - 2$, where a is a constant, is denoted by $f(x)$. Given that $(x + 1)$ is a factor of $f(x)$,

a find the value of a **b** factorise $f(x)$ completely *UCLES*

4 $f(x) \equiv 2x^3 + x^2 - 8x - 4$.

a Show that $(2x + 1)$ is a factor of $f(x)$.

b Factorise $f(x)$ completely.

c Hence find the values of x for which $f(x) = 0$. *LONDON*

5 One root of the equation $x^3 + kx + 11 = 0$, where k is a constant, is 1. Find the value of k. Hence find the other two roots of the equation, giving your answers in an exact form. *UCLES*

6 $f(x) \equiv 2x^3 + 5x^2 - 8x - 15$.

a Show that $(x + 3)$ is a factor of $f(x)$.

b Hence factorise $f(x)$ as the product of a linear factor and a quadratic factor.

c Find, to 2 decimal places, the two other values of x for which $f(x) = 0$.

EDEXCEL

Remainder theorem

1 The polynomial $\text{p}(x) = x^3 + cx^2 + 7x + d$ has a factor of $x + 2$, and leaves a remainder of 3 when divided by $x - 1$.

a Determine the value of each of the constants c and d.

b Find the exact values of the three roots of the equation $\text{p}(x) = 0$. *AEB*

2 a Find the remainder when $x^3 + 3x - 2$ is divided by $x + 2$.

b Find the value of a for which $(1 - 2a)x^2 + 5ax + (a - 1)(a - 8)$ is divisible by $x - 2$ but not by $x - 1$.

c Given that $16x^4 - 4x^3 - 4b^2x^2 + 7bx + 18$ is divisible by $2x + b$,
i show that $b^3 - 7b^2 + 36 = 0$, **ii** find the possible values of b. *UCLES*

3 a Given that $3x^2 - 7x + 4 = A(x - 2)^2 + B(x - 2) + C$ for all values of x, find the value of A, of B and of C.

b When the expression $x^4 + 3ax^3 - 5a^2x^2 - 10a^3x + 24a^4$ is divided by $x + 2a$ the remainder is 625. Find the possible values of a. *UCLES*

4 a Given that $\text{f}(x) = x^3 - 7x + 6$,
i calculate the remainder when $\text{f}(x)$ is divided by $x + 2$,
ii solve the equation $\text{f}(x) = 0$.

b The expression $2x^3 + ax^2 + bx - 2$ is exactly divisible by $x - 1$ and by $x + 2$.
Calculate the value of a and of b, and find the third factor of the expression.

c Given that $x - p$ is a factor of the expression $x^2 + (p - 5)x - p^2 + 7p - 3$, calculate the possible values of p. *UCLES*

5 a The expression $2x^3 + ax^2 - 72x - 18$ leaves a remainder of 17 when divided by $x + 5$. Determine the value of a.

b Solve the equation $2x^3 = x^2 + 5x + 2$.

c Given that the expression $x^2 - 5x + 7$ leaves the same remainder whether divided by $x - b$ or $x - c$, where $b \neq c$, show that $b + c = 5$.
Given further that $4bc = 21$ and that $b > c$, find the value of b and of c.
UCLES

Coordinate geometry

1 The equations of two straight lines are $3x + 4y = 2$ and $4x + y = 1$. Calculate the coordinates of the point of intersection, giving your answers as exact fractions.
UCLES

2 The points A and B have coordinates (1, 5) and (3, 1) respectively. Find the equation of the perpendicular bisector of the line AB. *UCLES*

3 The points $A(0, 2)$, $B(-2, 8)$, $C(20, 12)$ are the vertices of triangle ABC. The point D is the mid-point of AB.

a Show that CD is perpendicular to AB.

b Find the area of triangle ABC. *WJEC*

4 A, B, C are the points (4, 3), (2, 2) and (5, −4) respectively.

a Show that the lines AB and BC are perpendicular.

b A point D is such that $ABCD$ is a rectangle. Find the equation of the line AD and the equation of the line CD. Hence, or otherwise, find the coordinates of D.

c Find the area of rectangle $ABCD$. *WJEC*

5 The line L passes through the points $A(1, 3)$ and $B(-19, -19)$.

a Calculate the distance between A and B.

b Find an equation of L in the form $ax + by + c = 0$, where a, b and c are integers. *LONDON*

6 The points (1, 0), (0, 2), (2, −1) are denoted by A, B and C, respectively.

a Show that the equation of the line L through C perpendicular to AB is $2y - x + 4 = 0$.

b The line BA produced meets the line L at the point D and the line DC produced meets the x-axis at the point E. Find the area of triangle BDE. *WJEC*

7 The points $A(-2, 4)$, $B(6, -2)$ and $C(5, 5)$ are the vertices of $\triangle ABC$ and D is the mid-point of AB.

a Find an equation of the line passing through A and B in the form $ax + by + c = 0$, where a, b, and c are integers to be found.

b Show that CD is perpendicular to AB. *EDEXCEL*

8 The straight lines with cartesian equations $3x + 2y = 1$ and $2x + 5y = 19$ intersect at the point P.

a Calculate the coordinates of P.

b Determine a cartesian equation for the line through the point $Q(7, 3)$ which is perpendicular to the line with equation $2x + 5y = 19$. *AEB*

9 The points A, B and C have coordinates (5, −3), (7, 8) and (−3, 4) respectively. The mid-point of BC is M.

a Write down the coordinates of M.

b Find the equation of the straight line which passes through the points A and M. *AEB*

10 **a** Find an equation of the straight line passing through the points with coordinates (−1, 5) and (4, −2), giving your answer in the form $ax + by + c = 0$, where a, b and c are integers.

The line crosses the x-axis at the point A and the y-axis at the point B, and O is the origin.

b Find the area of $\triangle OAB$. *LONDON*

11 **a** Find an equation of the line l which passes through the points $A(1, 0)$ and $B(5, 6)$.

The line m with equation $2x + 3y = 15$ meets l at the point C.

b Determine the coordinates of C.

The point P lies on m and has x-coordinate -3.

c Show, by calculation, that $PA = PB$. *LONDON*

12 The curve $y = \frac{1}{4}x^2 - 1$ and the line $2y = x + 10$ intersect at the points A and B, and O is the origin. Calculate the coordinates of A and B, and hence show that OA and OB are perpendicular. *UCLES*

13 The line $2x + 3y = 1$ intersects the curve $x(x + y) = 10$ at A and B. Calculate the coordinates of A and of B. *UCLES*

14 The equation of the straight line l_1 is $x + 3y - 33 = 0$. The point P is $(3, 0)$ and the point Q is $(6, 9)$. The straight line l_2 is parallel to l_1 and passes through P.

i Find the equation of l_2, giving your answer in the form $ax + by + c = 0$.
ii Verify that Q lies on l_1.
iii Show that the line joining P and Q is perpendicular to l_1.
iv Find the perpendicular distance between l_1 and l_2. *UCLES*

15 The point A has coordinates $(7, 4)$. The straight lines with equations $x + 3y + 1 = 0$ and $2x + 5y = 0$ intersect at the point B. Show that one of these two lines is perpendicular to AB. *OCR*

16 The line $x - y - 6 = 0$ meets the curve $y^2 = 8x$ at the points A and B. Calculate the length of AB. *UCLES*

17 $ABCD$ is a parallelogram, lettered anticlockwise, such that A and C are the points $(-1, 5)$ and $(5, 1)$ respectively. Find the coordinates of the mid-point of AC.

Given that BD is parallel to the line whose equation is $y + 5x = 2$, find the equation of BD.

Given that BC is perpendicular to AC, find the equation of BC.
Calculate

i the coordinates of B,
ii the coordinates of D,
iii the area of $ABCD$. *UCLES*

18 **Solutions to this question by accurate drawing will not be accepted.**

Two points have coordinates $A(1, 3)$ and $C(7, 7)$. Find the equation of the perpendicular bisector of AC.

B is the point on the y-axis equidistant from A and C and $ABCD$ is a rhombus. Find the coordinates of B and of D.

Show that the area of the rhombus is 52 square units and hence, or otherwise, calculate the perpendicular distance of A from BC. *UCLES*

9 Calculus – Differentiation

Before starting this chapter you will need to know

- about indices (Chapter 1)
- about function notation (Chapter 2)
- about coordinate geometry (Chapter 8).

9.1 Introduction to calculus

Calculus is a powerful tool in mathematics and has wide-ranging applications in all branches of mathematics.
Physicists, economists, engineers, designers, chemists, statisticians and many others use calculus to solve problems in fields as varied as pricing in supermarkets, space flight and design.

Rate of change

Consider this distance–time graph.

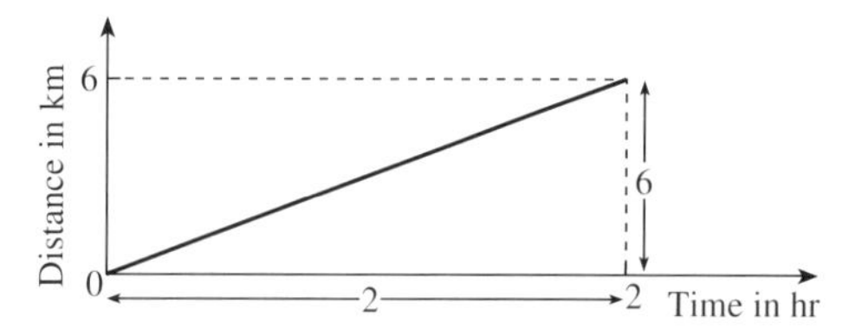

The gradient of a straight line measures how steep the line is. In this case, the gradient measures the rate at which distance varies with time.

Gradient $= \frac{6}{2} = 3$.

This corresponds to a speed of 3 km/hr.

Speed measures the rate of change of distance with respect to time.

There are numerous situations where the rate of change of one variable with respect to another is needed. In the above case, the relationship between the two variables is linear: the gradient is constant. In most cases, the variables are not related in a linear way.

The slope of this curve varies. From O to A the curve is not as steep as from A to B. From A to B the distance increases faster with respect to time than from O to A.

The speed would be greater during the motion from A to B than from O to A.

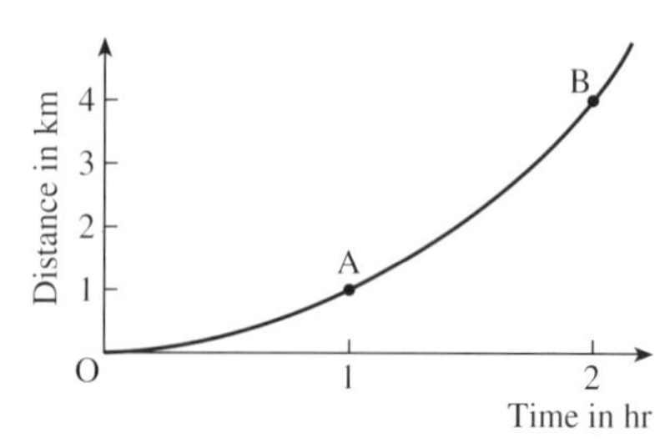

When a relationship is not linear the slope of the curve (and therefore the gradient and rate of change) varies.

Tangent to a curve

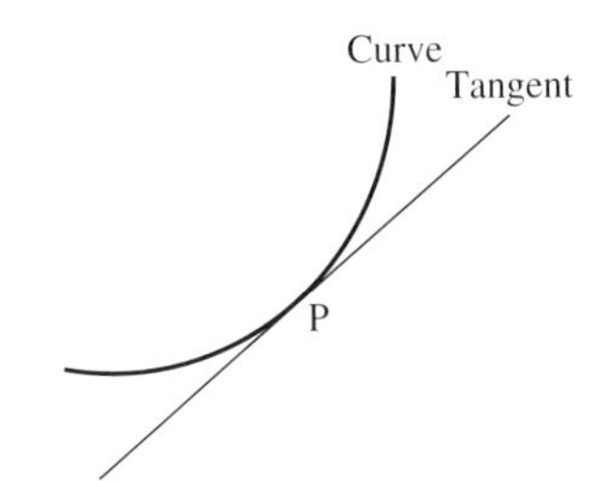

The tangent to a curve at any point is the straight line which touches the curve at that point.

At P the gradient of the curve is defined as the gradient of the tangent at P.

Gradient of a curve

The gradient of a curve at any point is the gradient of the tangent to the curve at that point.

To find an approximate value for the gradient of a curve at any point, the curve could be drawn, a tangent to the curve at the point drawn 'by eye' and its gradient calculated.

- Plot carefully the graph of $y = x^2$ for values of x from 0 to 4.
- Draw 'by eye' the tangents to the curve at $x = \frac{1}{2}, 1, 1\frac{1}{2}, 2, 3$.
- Find the gradient of each tangent.
- Compare the values of x and the gradient at each point.

This should have led to an interesting result. A more formal approach to find the gradient of a curve at any point is now given.

- To find the gradient of the tangent at P first choose a point, P_1, on the curve.
- Find the gradient of the line, PP_1.
  The gradient of PP_1 is clearly greater than the gradient of the tangent at P.
- Choose a point, P_2, on the curve nearer to P than P_1.
- Find the gradient of the line, PP_2.
  The gradient of PP_2 is still greater than the gradient of the tangent but is a better approximation.

Repeat this process. As the points P_3, P_4, ... approach closer and closer to P, so the gradients of PP_3, PP_4, ... approach closer and closer to the gradient of the tangent.

This approach is now used to find the gradient of $y = x^2$ at (1, 1).

Consider the points P_1, P_2, P_3, P_4, on the curve $y = x^2$.

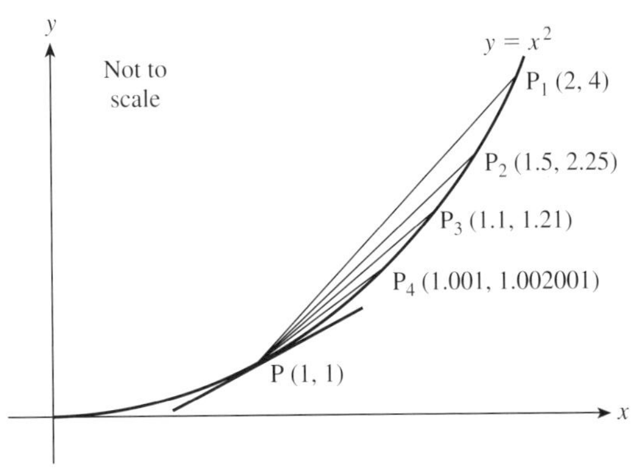

P_1 (2, 4) Gradient of $PP_1 = \dfrac{4-1}{2-1} = 3$

P_2 (1.5, 2.25) Gradient of $PP_2 = \dfrac{2.25-1}{1.5-1} = 2.5$

P_3 (1.1, 1.21) Gradient of $PP_3 = \dfrac{1.21-1}{1.1-1} = 2.1$

P_4 (1.001, 1.002001) Gradient of $PP_4 = \dfrac{1.002001-1}{1.001-1} = 2.001$

As the points P_1, P_2, P_3, P_4, approach closer and closer to P the gradients appear to approach closer and closer to 2.

To show that the gradients of the lines approach the limit 2, a series of points, P_k, can be taken closer and closer to P. A spreadsheet is an efficient way of carrying out the calculations.

The algebraic method given next illustrates a more general way of finding a gradient, in this case, at the point (1, 1).

Let P_k be the point $(1+h, (1+h)^2)$.

$$\begin{aligned}\text{Gradient of } PP_k &= \frac{(1+h)^2-1}{(1+h)-1}\\ &= \frac{1+2h+h^2-1}{h}\\ &= \frac{2h+h^2}{h}\\ &= \frac{h(2+h)}{h}\\ &= 2+h\end{aligned}$$

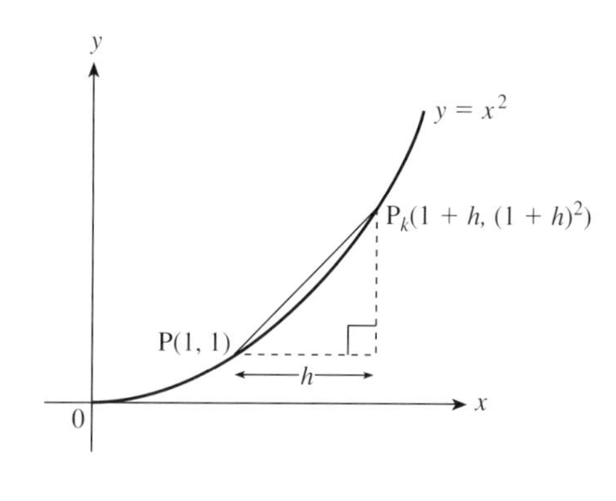

As P_k approaches closer and closer to P, h tends to 0, and so $2+h$ tends to 2.

By taking appropriate values of h one can get as close to the value, 2, as one wishes.

Expressed formally:

The limit of $2+h$ as $h \to 0$ is 2, or $\lim\limits_{h\to 0}(2+h) = 2$.

$\lim\limits_{h\to 0}(2+h)$ is read as 'limit as h tends to 0 of $2+h$'.

$$\begin{aligned}\text{So} \quad \text{Gradient at P(1, 1)} &= \lim_{h\to 0}(\text{Gradient of } PP_k)\\ &= \lim_{h\to 0}(2+h)\\ &= 2\end{aligned}$$

This corresponds to the result found numerically (above) and should correspond to those found graphically (page 177).

✓ ***Note*** Such a limit does not exist at all points for all functions. This chapter deals only with functions where the limit exists. For a fuller discussion on limits, see Chapter 18.

The method can now be applied to finding the gradient at any point on $y = x^2$.

To find the gradient at $P(x, x^2)$, take a point, $P_1(x+h, (x+h)^2)$, on the curve close to P.

$$\text{Gradient of } PP_1 = \frac{(x+h)^2 - x^2}{(x+h) - x} = \frac{x^2 + 2xh + h^2 - x^2}{h} = 2x + h$$

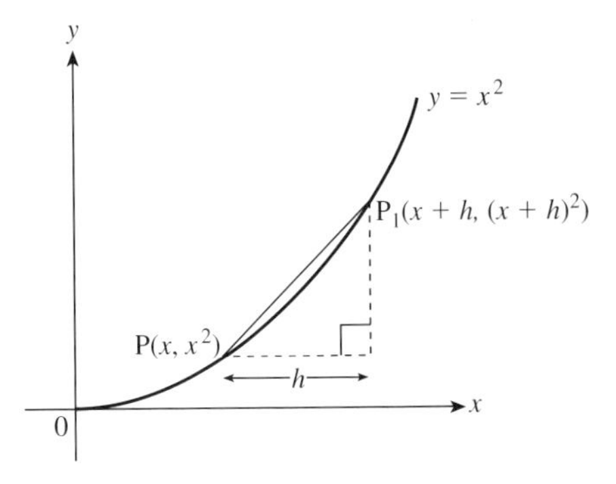

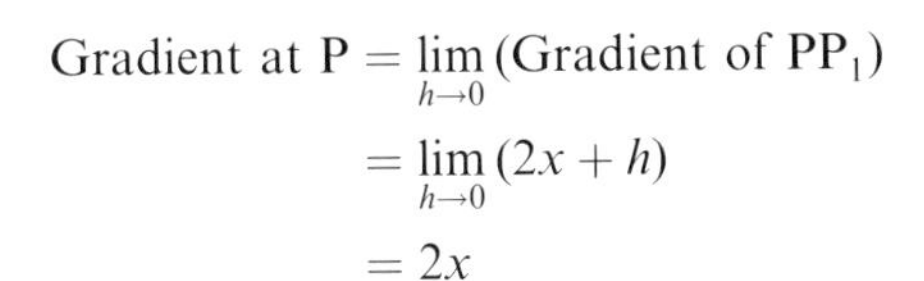

$$\text{Gradient at P} = \lim_{h \to 0}(\text{Gradient of } PP_1) = \lim_{h \to 0}(2x + h) = 2x$$

At any point on $y = x^2$ the gradient of the curve is $2x$.

So for $y = x^2$ the **gradient function** is $2x$.

This should have been the result suspected from drawing tangents by eye to the graph. See page 177.

This result enables the gradient at *any* point on $y = x^2$ to be found.

At the point (3, 9) $x = 3$, so the gradient is $2 \times 3 = 6$.

At the point (5, 25) $x = 5$, so the gradient is $2 \times 5 = 10$.

9.2 Differentiation

The process of finding the gradient function is called **differentiation**. There are many other terms used within calculus. This section introduces the notation and vocabulary of **differential calculus**.

The notation $\frac{dy}{dx}$

For any curve, $y = f(x)$, the gradient can be defined as follows.

Let $P(x, y)$ be any point on the curve and $P_1(x + \delta x, y + \delta y)$ be a point near P.

δx and δy are the small changes in x and y between P and P_1.

Read 'δx' as 'delta x'.

So gradient of $PP_1 = \dfrac{\delta y}{\delta x}$

$$\text{gradient at P} = \lim_{\delta x \to 0}(\text{Gradient of } PP_1) = \lim_{\delta x \to 0}\frac{\delta y}{\delta x} = \frac{dy}{dx}$$

Read as 'd y by d x'.

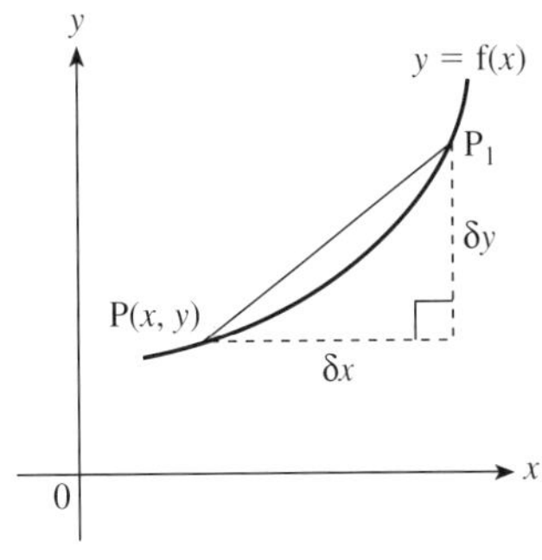

$\dfrac{dy}{dx}$ is the notation used for the gradient. It represents the limit of $\dfrac{\delta y}{\delta x}$ as $\delta x \to 0$.

$\frac{dy}{dx}$ is *not* a fraction. It must be considered as a single entity.

➤ $\frac{dy}{dx}$ is the gradient of the curve, i.e. the **rate of change** of y with respect to x.

Function notation

It is usually easier to work with h in place of δx.

Consider $y = f(x)$. Let $P(x, f(x))$ be any point on the curve and $P_1(x+h, f(x+h))$ be a point near P.

$$\text{Gradient of } PP_1 = \frac{f(x+h) - f(x)}{(x+h) - x}$$

$$\text{gradient at P} = \lim_{h \to 0}(\text{Gradient of } PP_1)$$

$$= \lim_{h \to 0} \frac{f(x+h) - f(x)}{h}$$

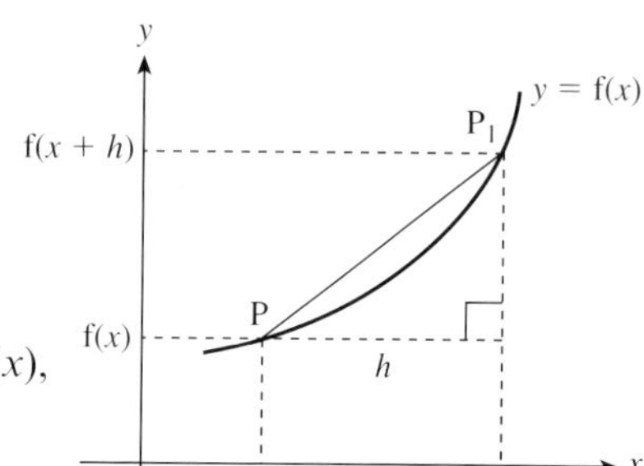

In function notation, the gradient is expressed as $f'(x)$,

➤ $$f'(x) = \lim_{h \to 0} \frac{f(x+h) - f(x)}{h}$$

Vocabulary

Consider $y = f(x) = x^2$.

The gradient function can be written as $\frac{dy}{dx}$ or $f'(x)$ or $\frac{d}{dx}(f(x))$ or $\frac{d}{dx}(x^2)$ or y'.

When a function of x, $y = f(x)$, is differentiated once, the result is called

- the (first) **derivative** with respect to x, or
- the (first) **differential coefficient** with respect to x, or
- the (first) **derived function** with respect to x, or
- the **gradient function**.

When a function of x, $y = f(x)$, is differentiated twice, the result is called the **second derivative** (or differential coefficient or derived function) with respect to x.

This is written as $\frac{d^2y}{dx^2}$ or $f''(x)$ or $\frac{d}{dx}\left(\frac{dy}{dx}\right)$ or y''.

✓ ***Note*** $\frac{d^2y}{dx^2} = \frac{d}{dx}\left(\frac{dy}{dx}\right)$ is the gradient of the gradient function.

➤ The **first derivative** (the gradient) is written as $\frac{dy}{dx}$, y' or $f'(x)$.

The **second derivative** (the gradient of the gradient function) is written as $\frac{d^2y}{dx^2}$, y'' or $f''(x)$.

Similarly, the third derivative is written as $\frac{d^3y}{dx^3}$, y''' or $f'''(x)$.

So far all differentiation has been with respect to x. One can differentiate with respect to any variable.
For example, if $s = t^2$, differentiating s with respect to t gives $\frac{ds}{dt} = 2t$.

Differentiating from first principles

The definition

$$f'(x) = \lim_{h \to 0} \frac{f(x+h) - f(x)}{h}$$

will now be used to differentiate x^3. This method is called 'differentiating from first principles'.

Example 1 Find, from first principles, the derivative of x^3.

$$f(x) = x^3$$

$$f'(x) = \lim_{h \to 0} \frac{f(x+h) - f(x)}{h}$$

To differentiate from first principles, use this formula.

$$= \lim_{h \to 0} \frac{(x+h)^3 - x^3}{h}$$

$$= \lim_{h \to 0} \frac{x^3 + 3x^2h + 3xh^2 + h^3 - x^3}{h}$$

The x^3 terms cancel.

$$= \lim_{h \to 0} (3x^2 + 3xh + h^2)$$

As h tends to 0, $3xh$ and h^2 also tend to 0.

$$= 3x^2$$

Example 2 Find, from first principles, the differential coefficient of $\frac{1}{x}$.

$$f(x) = \frac{1}{x}$$

$$f'(x) = \lim_{h \to 0} \frac{f(x+h) - f(x)}{h}$$

$$= \lim_{h \to 0} \frac{\frac{1}{x+h} - \frac{1}{x}}{h}$$

Multiply numerator and denominator by $x(x+h)$.

$$= \lim_{h \to 0} \frac{x - (x+h)}{hx(x+h)}$$

$$= \lim_{h \to 0} \frac{-h}{hx(x+h)}$$

$$= \lim_{h \to 0} \frac{-1}{x(x+h)}$$

As h tends to 0, $(x+h)$ in the denominator tends to x.

$$= -\frac{1}{x^2}$$

EXERCISE 9a

1 Find from first principles, the derived functions of these expressions.

a x^4 **b** x **c** $2x^2$ **d** $x^2 + 3$ **e** 5 **f** $\frac{1}{x^2}$ **g** $5x$

Summary of results obtained by differentiating from first principles

y	x	x^2	x^3	x^4	$2x^2$	$\frac{1}{x} = x^{-1}$	$\frac{1}{x^2} = x^{-2}$
$\frac{dy}{dx}$	1	$2x$	$3x^2$	$4x^2$	$4x^2$	$-\frac{1}{x^2} = -x^{-2}$	$-\frac{2}{x^3} = -2x^{-3}$

Differentiation of polynomials

The results in the table above lead to these two rules:

➤ $y = x^n \Rightarrow \frac{dy}{dx} = nx^{n-1} \quad n \in \mathbb{R}$

$y = kx^n \Rightarrow \frac{dy}{dx} = knx^{n-1}$

The result for $y = kx^n$ can be proved for positive integers using the binomial expansion. To prove it is true for all real values of n is beyond the scope of this book.

✓ ***Note*** To differentiate a power of x, multiply by the power and reduce the power by one.

Example 3 Find derivatives.

a $\frac{d}{dx}(7x^5) = 5 \times 7x^{5-1} = 35x^4$

b $\frac{d}{dx}\left(x^{\frac{1}{2}}\right) = \frac{1}{2}x^{\frac{1}{2}-1} = \frac{1}{2}x^{-\frac{1}{2}}$

c $\frac{d}{dx}(3x^{-4}) = -4 \times 3x^{-4-1} = -12x^{-5}$

Differentiation of $y = c$

$y = c$ represents a line parallel to the x-axis. This has gradient zero.

Differentiating confirms this result.

$$y = c = cx^0$$

Since $x^0 = 1$

$$\Rightarrow \frac{dy}{dx} = 0 \times cx^{-1} = 0$$

➤ $y = c \quad \Rightarrow \quad \frac{dy}{dx} = 0$

Differentiation of $y = kx$

$y = kx$ represents a line with gradient k. Differentiating confirms this result.

$$\begin{aligned} y &= kx^1 \\ \frac{dy}{dx} &= 1 \times kx^{1-1} \\ &= kx^0 \\ &= k \end{aligned}$$

➤ $y = kx \quad \Rightarrow \quad \frac{dy}{dx} = k$

Example 4 Find derivatives.

a $y = 3x \quad \Rightarrow \quad \frac{dy}{dx} = 3$

b $y = 7 \quad \Rightarrow \quad \frac{dy}{dx} = 0$

Differentiation of a number of terms

By differentiating from first principles it can be shown that, for the sum of a number of terms, such as

$$3x^3 - 2x^2 + \frac{4}{x} - \frac{1}{x^2}$$

the derived function is the sum of the derived functions of each term. For example

$$\begin{aligned} y &= 3x^3 - 2x^2 + \frac{4}{x} - \frac{1}{x^2} \\ \frac{dy}{dx} &= 9x^2 - 4x - \frac{4}{x^2} + \frac{2}{x^3} \end{aligned}$$

The proofs of the next two general results are beyond the scope of this book, but the results are included for completeness.

➤ $y = f(x) \pm g(x) \quad \Rightarrow \quad \frac{dy}{dx} = f'(x) \pm g'(x)$

$y = kf(x) \quad \Rightarrow \quad \frac{dy}{dx} = kf'(x)$

Example 5 Differentiate with respect to x.

a

$$\begin{aligned} y &= ax^2 + bx + c \\ \frac{dy}{dx} &= 2ax + b \end{aligned}$$

b

$$\begin{aligned} y &= \frac{6x + 2x^4}{x^2} \\ &= 6x^{-1} + 2x^2 \\ \frac{dy}{dx} &= -6x^{-2} + 4x \end{aligned}$$

Divide by x^2 before differentiating.

c
$$y = \frac{3}{x}$$
$$= 3x^{-1}$$
$$\frac{dy}{dx} = -3x^{-2}$$
$$= -\frac{3}{x^2}$$

Write in index notation.

The power is reduced by 1.

d
$$y = \frac{1}{4\sqrt{x}}$$
$$= \frac{1}{4} \times \frac{1}{\sqrt{x}}$$
$$= \frac{1}{4}x^{-\frac{1}{2}}$$
$$\frac{dy}{dx} = -\frac{1}{8}x^{-\frac{3}{2}}$$

Write $\frac{1}{\sqrt{x}}$ as $x^{-\frac{1}{2}}$. Note $\frac{1}{4}$ is unchanged.

The power is reduced by 1: $-\frac{1}{2} - 1 = -\frac{3}{2}$.

Alternatively, write $\frac{dy}{dx} = -\frac{1}{8\sqrt{x^3}}$.

e
$$y = \frac{2}{3x^{\frac{1}{3}}}$$
$$= \frac{2}{3} \times \frac{1}{x^{\frac{1}{3}}}$$
$$= \frac{2}{3}x^{-\frac{1}{3}}$$
$$\frac{dy}{dx} = -\frac{2}{9}x^{-\frac{4}{3}}$$

Write $\frac{1}{x^{\frac{1}{3}}}$ as $x^{-\frac{1}{3}}$. *Note*: $\frac{2}{3}$ is unchanged.

The power is reduced by 1: $-\frac{1}{3} - 1 = -\frac{4}{3}$.

Alternatively, write $\frac{dy}{dx} = -\frac{2}{9\sqrt[3]{x^4}}$.

f
$$y = 2x^2 - 3x + 4 - \frac{5}{x}$$
$$\frac{dy}{dx} = 4x - 3 + \frac{5}{x^2}$$

Example 6 Find $\frac{d^2y}{dx^2}$ given $y = 10x^3 - 3x^2 + 4x - 1$.

$$y = 10x^3 - 3x^2 + 4x - 1$$
$$\frac{dy}{dx} = 30x^2 - 6x + 4$$
$$\frac{d^2y}{dx^2} = 60x - 6$$

Differentiating y once gives $\frac{dy}{dx}$.

Differentiating again gives $\frac{d^2y}{dx^2}$.

Example 7 Find the y-coordinate and the gradient of $y = (3x + 1)^2$ when $x = 2$.

When $x = 2$ $\quad y = (3 \times 2 + 1)^2 = 49$

$$y = (3x + 1)^2$$
$$= 9x^2 + 6x + 1$$
$$\frac{dy}{dx} = 18x + 6$$

Multiply out the brackets before differentiating.

When $x = 2$ $\quad \frac{dy}{dx} = 18 \times 2 + 6 = 42$

So when $x = 2$, the y-coordinate is 49 and the gradient is 42.

Example 8 Find the points on $y = x + \frac{1}{x}$ where the gradient is $\frac{3}{4}$.

$$y = x + \frac{1}{x}$$

$$\frac{dy}{dx} = 1 - \frac{1}{x^2}$$

When gradient $= \frac{3}{4}$ $\quad 1 - \frac{1}{x^2} = \frac{3}{4}$

$$\frac{1}{x^2} = 1 - \frac{3}{4} = \frac{1}{4}$$

$\therefore \quad x = \pm 2$

When $x = 2$, $y = 2 + \frac{1}{2} = \frac{5}{2}$.

And when $x = -2$, $y = -2 - \frac{1}{2} = -\frac{5}{2}$.

So the gradient is $\frac{3}{4}$ at $(2, \frac{5}{2})$ and at $(-2, -\frac{5}{2})$

➤ Rewrite expressions as sums of terms with powers of x before differentiating, i.e. write

$y = (x + 1)(3x - 1)$ as $y = 3x^2 + 2x - 1$

or $y = \dfrac{x^5 - x^2}{\sqrt{x}}$ as $y = x^{\frac{9}{2}} - x^{\frac{3}{2}}$

EXERCISE 9b

1 Find $\dfrac{dy}{dx}$ for each of these.

a $y = x^{12}$ **b** $y = 3x^7$ **c** $y = 5x$ **d** $y = 5x + 3$ **e** $y = 5x^2 - 3x$

f $y = 5$ **g** $y = x^{-5}$ **h** $y = 4x^{-3}$ **i** $y = \dfrac{1}{x^2}$ **j** $y = \dfrac{2}{x}$

k $y = -\dfrac{3}{x^2}$ **l** $y = \dfrac{1}{3x^3}$ **m** $y = -\dfrac{1}{x^4}$ **n** $y = \dfrac{3}{4x^5}$ **o** $y = x^{\frac{1}{3}}$

p $y = 3x^{-\frac{1}{2}}$ **q** $y = \sqrt{x}$ **r** $y = \sqrt[4]{x}$ **s** $y = \dfrac{1}{\sqrt{x}}$ **t** $y = -\dfrac{3}{\sqrt[3]{x}}$

u $y = 4\sqrt{x^3}$ **v** $y = \dfrac{3}{2\sqrt{x}}$

2 Find the derived function, $f'(x)$, for these functions.

a $f(x) = 3x^4 - 2x^3 + x^2 - x + 10$ **b** $f(x) = 2x^4 + \frac{1}{3}x^3 - \frac{1}{4}x^2 + 2$

c $f(x) = x^6 + \dfrac{1}{x} - \dfrac{3}{\sqrt{x}}$ **d** $f(x) = ax^3 + bx^2 + cx$

e $f(x) = 2x(3x^2 - 4)$ **f** $f(x) = \dfrac{10x^5 + 3x^4}{2x^2}$

g $f(x) = \dfrac{6x + 3 + \sqrt{x}}{x^2}$ **h** $f(x) = \left(\sqrt{x} + \dfrac{1}{\sqrt{x}}\right)^2$

EXERCISE 9b
(continued)

3 Differentiate these expressions with respect to x.

a $-x$ **b** $+10$ **c** $4x^3 - 3x + 2$ **d** $\frac{1}{2}ax^2 - 2bx + c$

e $2(x^2 + x)$ **f** $\dfrac{3x(x+1)}{x^4}$ **g** $x^{\frac{1}{2}} + x^{\frac{1}{3}} + x^{\frac{1}{4}}$ **h** $3\sqrt{x} + \dfrac{4}{\sqrt{x}} + \dfrac{5}{x}$

i $\frac{1}{3}(x^3 - 3x + 6)$ **j** $(x+1)(x+2)$

4 Find $\dfrac{\mathrm{d}^2y}{\mathrm{d}x^2}$ in these cases.

a $y = 6x^3 + 3x^2 - 4x$ **b** $\dfrac{\mathrm{d}y}{\mathrm{d}x} = 5x^{\frac{1}{3}}$ **c** $y = 10x - 7$ **d** $\dfrac{\mathrm{d}y}{\mathrm{d}x} = \dfrac{4x-3}{\sqrt{x}}$

5 Find $\dfrac{\mathrm{d}s}{\mathrm{d}t}$ and $\dfrac{\mathrm{d}^2s}{\mathrm{d}t^2}$ when

a $s = 5t - 10t^2$ **b** $s = 3t^3 - 4t^2 + 7t$

c $s = 3t - \dfrac{5}{t^2}$ **d** $s = ut + \frac{1}{2}at^2$ (a and u constant)

6 Find the y-coordinate, and the gradient, at the points on these curves corresponding to the given values of x.

a $y = x^2 - 2x + 1,\ x = 2$ **b** $y = x^2 + x + 1,\ x = 0$

c $y = x^2 - 2x,\ x = -1$ **d** $y = (x+2)(x-4),\ x = 3$

e $y = \sqrt{x}(3 + x^2),\ x = 1$ **f** $y = (4x - 5)^2,\ x = \frac{1}{2}$

g $y = x + \dfrac{1}{x},\ x = 1$ **h** $y = \sqrt{x} + x^2,\ x = 4$

7 Find the coordinates of the points on these curves at which the gradient has the given values.

a $y = x^2$, gradient $= 8$ **b** $y = x^3$, gradient $= 12$

c $y = x(2 - x)$, gradient $= 2$ **d** $y = x^2 - 3x + 1$, gradient $= 0$

e $y = x^3 - 2x + 7$, gradient $= 1$ **f** $y = x^{\frac{1}{3}}$, gradient $= \frac{1}{12}$

g $y = x^2 - x^3$, gradient $= -1$ **h** $y = x(x-3)^2$, gradient $= 0$

i $y = x - \dfrac{1}{x}$, gradient $= 5$ **j** $y = \frac{1}{3}x^{\frac{3}{2}} - x^{\frac{1}{2}}$, gradient $= \frac{3}{4}$

8 The curve $y = ax^2 + bx$ passes through the point $(2, 4)$ with gradient 8. Find a and b.

9 The curve $y = cx + \dfrac{d}{x}$ has gradient 6 at the point $(\frac{1}{2}, 1)$. Find c and d.

10 Given that $f(x) = 2x^3 - x + \dfrac{1}{x}$, find the value of

a $f'(1)$ **b** $f''(1)$ **c** $\dfrac{1}{f(1)}$

11 Show that if $y = 2x - x^2$ then

$$y\frac{\mathrm{d}^2y}{\mathrm{d}x^2} - 2\frac{\mathrm{d}y}{\mathrm{d}x} + 2y = 4(x - 1)$$

12 If $y = x^3 + x^{\frac{5}{2}}$ find the value of y' and of y'', when $x = 4$.

13 A child's height h cm at age a years can be modelled by the equation

$$h = -\frac{a^4}{500} + (a - \tfrac{1}{2})^2 + 55$$

for ages $11 \leqslant a \leqslant 16$. Find the child's annual growth rate at age 12, and at age 15.

14 The temperature θ°C measured at a distance x cm from a candle flame is given by

$$\theta = 16 + \frac{450}{x^{\frac{3}{2}}}$$

for distances $x \geqslant 1$.

a Find the temperature gradient (i.e. the rate at which temperature decreases with distance) 10 cm from the flame.

b Find the rate of change of temperature gradient with respect to distance, 5 cm from the flame.

15 Some sugar is put into a cup of coffee, which is then stirred. The sugar concentration, c, measured in grams/litre, is given by

$$c = \frac{t^2}{200}(200 - t^2)$$

where t is the time in seconds after the sugar is added, for $0 \leqslant t \leqslant 10$.

a Find the rate at which the concentration is increasing after 8 seconds.

b Show that, after 10 seconds, the rate of change of concentration is zero.

9.3 Tangents and normals

The **tangent** to a curve at a given point is the straight line which touches the curve at that point.

The **normal** to a curve at a given point is a straight line through the point perpendicular to the tangent at the point.

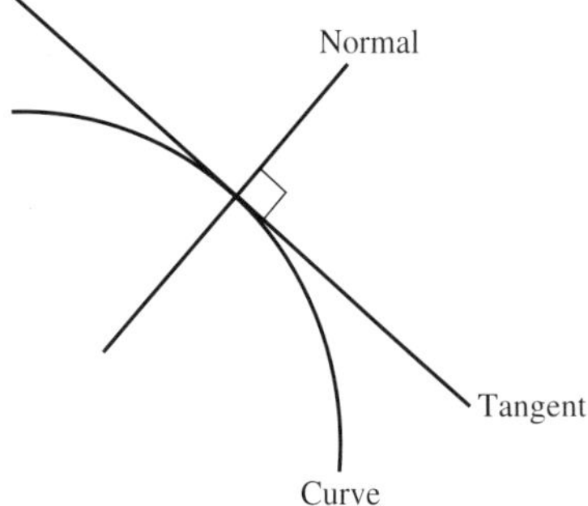

✓ ***Remember*** If two lines have gradients m and m' then $mm' = -1 \Leftrightarrow$ the lines are perpendicular.

Example 9 Find the equations of the tangent and the normal to $y = 2x^3 - 3x$ at the point where $x = 1$.

$$y = 2x^3 - 3x$$

$$\frac{dy}{dx} = 6x^2 - 3$$

When $x = 1$ $\quad y = 2 \times 1^3 - 3 \times 1 \quad$ and $\quad \frac{dy}{dx} = 6 \times 1^2 - 3$

$\quad = 2 - 3 = -1 \qquad\qquad = 6 - 3 = 3$

So the tangent is the line through $(1, -1)$ with gradient 3.

Using $y - y_1 = m(x - x_1)$

$$y - (-1) = 3(x - 1)$$
$$y + 1 = 3x - 3$$
$$y - 3x = -4$$

This is the equation of the tangent.

Gradient of the tangent is 3.

So gradient of the normal is $-\frac{1}{3}$.

$mm' = -1$
$3 \times -\frac{1}{3} = -1$

So the normal is the line through $(1, -1)$ with gradient $-\frac{1}{3}$.

$$y + 1 = -\tfrac{1}{3}(x - 1)$$

Multiply both sides by 3.

$$3y + 3 = -x + 1$$
$$3y + x = -2$$

So the tangent is $y - 3x = -4$ and the normal $3y + x = -2$.

The equation of the lines can be given in different forms. For good style, use the same form for both answers.

✓ ***Note*** A sketch is not necessary but can be helpful. On a graphics calculator, the tangent and normal will *not* look perpendicular if the scales on the axes are different.

Example 10 Find the equation of the tangent to the curve $y = 4x - x^3$ at the point, P(1, 3). Find also the coordinates of the point Q, where the tangent meets the curve again.

$$y = 4x - x^3$$
$$y' = 4 - 3x^2$$

At P(1, 3) $\quad y' = 4 - 3 = 1$

So the tangent passes through (1, 3) with gradient 1.

Using $y - y_1 = m(x - x_1)$

$$y - 3 = 1(x - 1)$$
$$y = x + 2$$

So the equation of the tangent is $y = x + 2$.

To find the point, Q, where this tangent meets the curve again, $y = x + 2$ and $y = 4x - x^3$ must be solved simultaneously.

$$y = x + 2 \quad ①$$
$$y = 4x - x^3 \quad ②$$

So $\quad x + 2 = 4x - x^3$

$$x^3 - 3x + 2 = 0$$

This can be factorised using the factor theorem.

$$(x - 1)(x^2 + x - 2) = 0$$

Or, since the tangent meets the curve when $x = 1$, $x - 1$ must be a factor.

$$(x - 1)(x - 1)(x + 2) = 0$$

There are two coincident points, so $x = 1$ is a double root.

$x = 1$ gives the point P.
$x = -2$ will be the x-coordinate of Q, the other point where the tangent meets the curve.

When $x = -2$, $y = -8 - (-8) = 0$.

$\therefore$ Q is the point $(-2, 0)$.

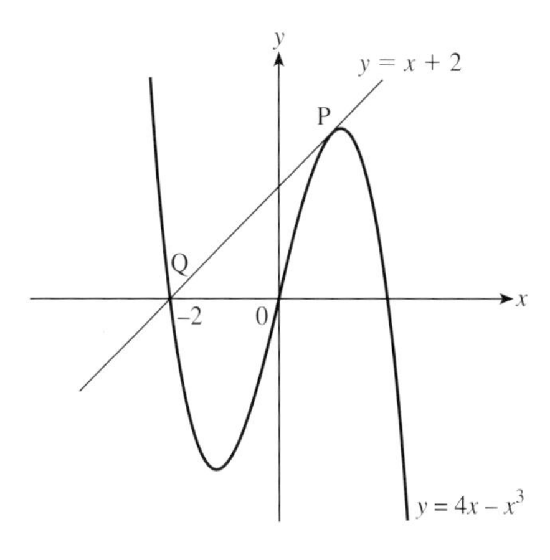

EXERCISE 9c

1 Find the equations of the tangents to these curves at the points corresponding to the given values of x.

a $y = x^2$, $x = 2$

b $y = 3x^2 + 2$, $x = 4$

c $y = \dfrac{2}{x^2}$, $x = 2$

d $y = 3x^2 - x + 1$, $x = 0$

e $y = \dfrac{x+3}{\sqrt{x}}$, $x = 4$

f $y = 2x + \dfrac{1}{x}$, $x = \frac{1}{2}$

2 Find the equations of the normals to the curves in Question 1 at the points corresponding to the given values of x.

3 Find the equation of the tangent to $y = 3x^3 - 4x^2 + 2x - 10$ at the point where the curve meets the y-axis.

4 The tangent to $y = ax^2 + bx$ has gradient 3 at the point (2, 10). Find a and b.

5 a Find the values of x for which the gradient of the curve $y = 2x^3 + 3x^2 - 12x + 3$ is zero.

b Hence find the equations of the tangents to the curve which are parallel to the x-axis.

6 a Find the gradient of the curve $y = 9x - x^3$ at the point where $x = 1$.

b Find the equation of the tangent to the curve at this point.

c Find the coordinates of the point where this tangent meets the line $y = x$.

7 a Find the coordinates of the points of intersection, O, A and B with the x-axis of the curve $y = x^3 - 3x^2 + 2x$.

b Find the equation of the tangents to the curve at O, A and B.

8 a Find the points of intersection of $y = 4 - x^2$ and $y = 3x$.

b Find the equations of the tangents to $y = 4 - x^2$ at the points of intersection.

c The tangents intersect at P. Find the coordinates of P.

9 a Show that there is only one point on the curve $y = 6x^3 + 6x^2 + 2x - 1$ where the gradient is zero. Find the coordinates of this point.

b State the equations of the tangent, and the normal, to the curve at the point.

EXERCISE 9c *(continued)*

10 The normal to the curve $y = x^{\frac{1}{2}} + x^{\frac{1}{3}}$ at the point (1, 2) meets the axes at $(h, 0)$ and $(0, k)$. Find h and k.

11 Tangents and normals are drawn to the curve $y = \dfrac{1}{x^2}$ at the points A(−1, 1) and B(1, 1).

Given that the tangents and normals meet the y-axis at the points C and D, find

a the length of CD

b the area of the quadrilateral ACBD

12 The normals to the curve $y = \sqrt{x}$ at the points where $x = 1$ and $x = 4$ meet at P. Find the coordinates of P.

13 The tangent to the curve $y = ax^2 + bx$ at the point where $x = 1$ has gradient 1 and passes through the point (4, 5). Find a and b.

14 The normal to the curve $y = ax^{\frac{1}{2}} + bx$ at the point where $x = 1$ has gradient 1 and intercepts the y-axis at (0, −4). Find a and b.

15 **a** Find the coordinates of the points on the curve $8y = 4 - x^2$ at which the gradients are $\frac{1}{2}$ and $-\frac{1}{2}$.

b Find the equations of the tangents to the curve at these points.

c Show that the tangents intersect at the point (0, 1).

16 **a** Find the equations of the normals to the parabola $4y = x^2$ at the points (−2, 1) and (−4, 4).

b Show that the point of intersection of these two normals lies on the parabola.

9.4 Increasing and decreasing functions

Consider $y = x^2$.

- For $x < 0$, y decreases as x increases. The gradient is negative. For $x < 0$, y is a **decreasing function** of x.
- For $x > 0$, y increases as x increases. The gradient is positive. For $x > 0$, y is an **increasing function** of x.

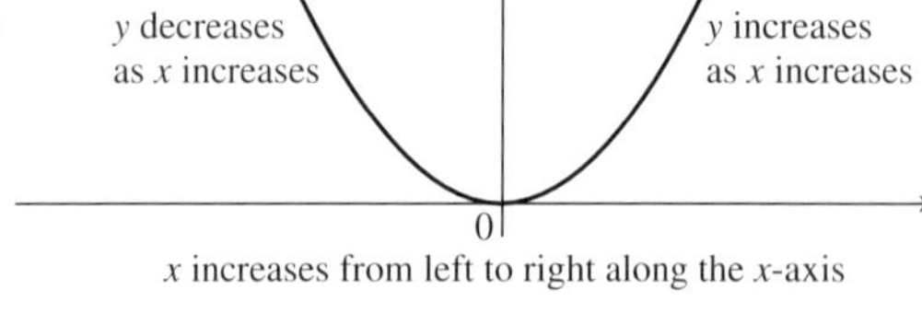

- At $x = 0$, y is neither increasing nor decreasing. At $x = 0$, y has a **stationary value**. The origin (0, 0) is a **stationary point**.

➤

A function f which increases as x increases for a set of values is called an **increasing function** for that set of values.

A function, $f(x)$ is *increasing* for $a < x < b$ if $f'(x) > 0$ for $a < x < b$.

A function f which decreases as x increases for a set of values is called a **decreasing function** for that set of values.

A function, $f(x)$, is *decreasing* for $a < x < b$ if $f'(x) < 0$, for $a < x < b$.

9.5 Stationary points

➤ At a stationary point on a curve, the gradient is zero.

There are three types of stationary points: **maxima**, **minima** and **points of inflexion**.

Maximum and minimum points are called **turning points** because the graph turns at these points.

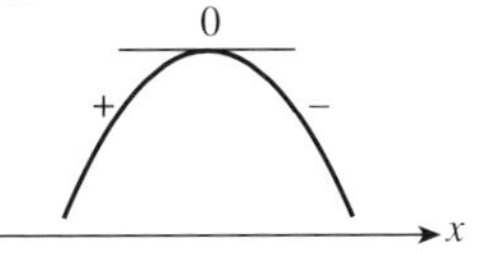

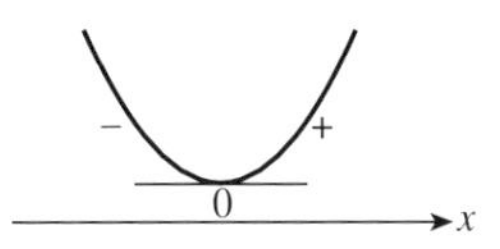

Maximum points – 'humps' As x increases, the gradient goes +ve → 0 → −ve.

Minimum points – 'troughs' As x increases, the gradient goes −ve → 0 → +ve.

a

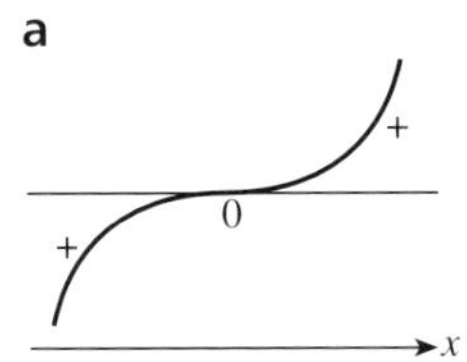

b

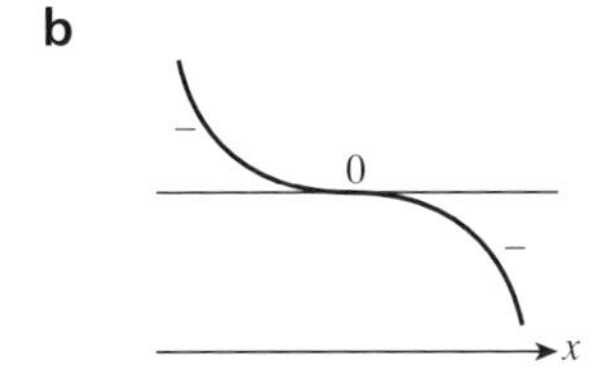

Points of inflexion As x increases, the gradient goes
a +ve → 0 → +ve or **b** −ve → 0 → −ve

Consider the gradient of the parts of this curve.

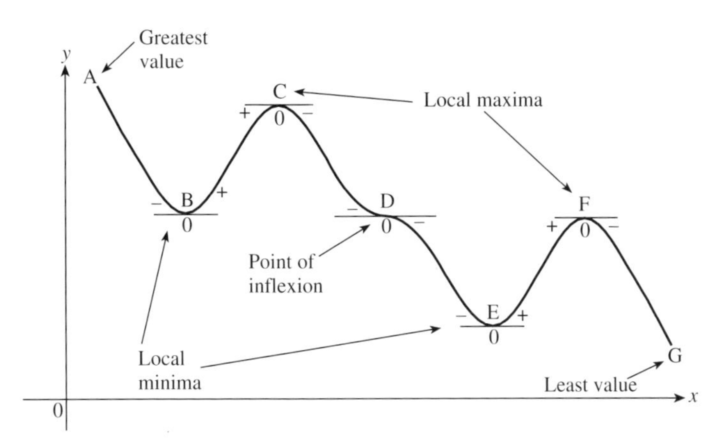

C and F are *maximum points* on the curve. The y-coordinates at C and F are the *maximum values* of the function in the region of those points, so these maximum values are called **local maxima**: they give the maximum value in the immediate vicinity of the point. Similarly B and E are **local minima**. D is also a stationary point: a *point of inflexion*.*

Notice that the value of the function at F (a local maximum) is less than the value at B (a local minimum).

The *greatest value* of the function (for the range of values shown) is its value at A and the *least value* is its value at G.

*Another type of point of inflexion (not a stationary point) is introduced in Book 2. Note that a common feature of all points of inflexion is that the tangent to the curve at the point of inflexion *passes through* the curve.

Identifying the type of a stationary point

To investigate the stationary values of a function, first find the stationary points (where $\frac{dy}{dx} = 0$) and then use either of two methods.

Method 1: Work out the sign of the gradient on either side of the stationary point(s).

L (left of point)	At point	R (right of point)	
+	0	−	⇒ a maximum point
−	0	+	⇒ a minimum point
+	0	+	⇒ a point of inflexion
−	0	−	⇒ a point of inflexion

- For a maximum point, the gradient goes +ve → 0 → −ve, i.e. it decreases as x increases.
- For a minimum point, the gradient goes −ve → 0 → +ve, i.e. it increases as x increases.

Method 2: Find $\frac{d^2y}{dx^2}$, the gradient of the gradient function.

- If $\frac{d^2y}{dx^2} < 0$, i.e. the gradient is decreasing as x increases, the point is a maximum point.
- If $\frac{d^2y}{dx^2} > 0$ i.e. the gradient is increasing as x increases, the point is a minimum point.
- If $\frac{d^2y}{dx^2} = 0$ use method 1.*

➤

$\frac{dy}{dx} = 0$ and $\frac{d^2y}{dx^2} < 0 \Rightarrow$ maximum point

$\frac{dy}{dx} = 0$ and $\frac{d^2y}{dx^2} > 0 \Rightarrow$ minimum point

$\frac{dy}{dx} = 0$ and $\frac{d^2y}{dx^2} = 0 \Rightarrow$ point of inflexion or maximum or minimum point.

So the nature of a stationary point can be determined by the above or by considering the gradient of the curve on either side of the stationary point.

*There are other methods available for dealing with this situation at a higher level.

Example 11 Find the coordinates of any stationary points of the curve $y = 4x^3 - x^4$.
Sketch the curve and state the range of values for which the function is increasing.

$$y = 4x^3 - x^4 \quad (1)$$

Differentiate y with respect to x.

$$\frac{dy}{dx} = 12x^2 - 4x^3$$

At a stationary point, $\frac{dy}{dx} = 0$

so $\quad 12x^2 - 4x^3 = 0$

Divide all terms by 4.

$$3x^2 - x^3 = 0$$

$$x^2(3 - x) = 0$$

$\therefore \quad x = 0$ or $x = 3$

When $x = 0$, $y = 0$, and when $x = 3$, $y = 4 \times 3^3 - 3^4 = 27$.

Substitute for x in (1)

So the stationary points are (0, 0) and (3, 27).

To decide on the type of stationary points both methods will be used.

Using Method 2

$$\frac{d^2y}{dx^2} = 24x - 12x^2$$

When $x = 0$, $\frac{d^2y}{dx^2} = 0$

Since $\frac{d^2y}{dx^2} = 0$, the point could be a maximum, or minimum or a point of inflexion.

So now use method 1: work out the sign of $\frac{dy}{dx}$ on either side of $x = 0$.

When $x = 3$, $\frac{d^2y}{dx^2} = -36 < 0$

$\therefore$ at $x = 3$, there is a maximum point.

Using Method 1

Value of x	L e.g. $x = -1$	0	R e.g. $x = 1$	L e.g. $x = 2$	3	R e.g. $x = 4$
Sign of $\frac{dy}{dx}$ (i.e. sign of $12x^2 - 4x^3$)	+	0	+	+	0	–
		Point of inflexion			Maximum point	

✓ ***Note*** In Method 1, $\frac{dy}{dx} = 4x^2(3 - x)$.

For $x \neq 0$, x^2 is always +ve and so only the sign of $3 - x$ need be considered.

The stationary points are (0, 0) point of inflexion, and (3, 27) maximum point.

The curve cuts the y-axis where $x = 0$.

To sketch the curve, the intersections of the curve with the axes should be found.

When $x = 0$, $y = 0$.

$\therefore$ the curve cuts the y-axis at (0, 0).

The curve cuts the x-axis where $y = 0$.

When $y = 0$ $\quad 4x^3 - x^4 = 0$

$x^3(4 - x) = 0$

$x = 0$ is a triple root.*

So $\quad x = 0$ or $x = 4$

(0, 0) is the point of inflexion already found.

(4, 0) is the other point where the curve cuts the x-axis.

When the stationary points and intercepts on the axes are known the sketch can be drawn.

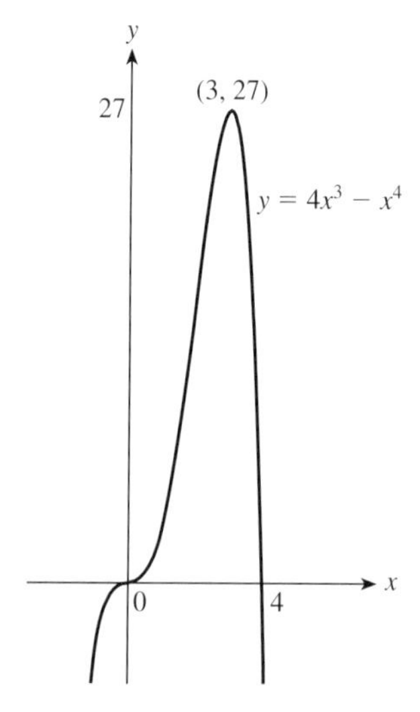

The graph shows that the function $f(x) = 4x^3 - x^4$ is increasing for $x < 0$ and $0 < x < 3$.

EXERCISE 9d

1 Find the coordinates of the points on these curves where the gradient is zero.

a $y = x^2 - 4x - 2$ **b** $y = x^2 + 6x + 7$ **c** $y = x(3x - 2)$

d $y = \dfrac{x^2 + 3x + 4}{x}$ **e** $y = (x + 8)(x - 3)$ **f** $y = x^4 - 2x^2 + 5$

g $y = 9 + 24x - 2x^3$ **h** $y = \sqrt{x} + \dfrac{1}{\sqrt{x}}$

2 $y = x^2 - 3x + 3$.

a Show that $\dfrac{dy}{dx} = 0$ when $x = \frac{3}{2}$.

b By considering the sign of $\dfrac{dy}{dx}$ for two values of x, one less than $\frac{3}{2}$ and one greater than $\frac{3}{2}$, or otherwise, show that $x = \frac{3}{2}$ gives a minimum value of y.

c Find the coordinates of the minimum point on the curve $y = x^2 - 3x + 3$.

*A triple root: curve cuts the x-axis with a point of inflexion. A double root: curve touches the x-axis. A single root: curve cuts the x-axis.

3 Find the coordinates of any stationary points on these curves, and state, giving reasons, whether each point is a maximum or a minimum.

a $y = x^4$ **b** $y = 2x^3 - 15x^2 + 36x - 20$

c $y = (x + 2)^2$ **d** $y = 5 - 9x + 6x^2 - x^3$

e $y = x^4 + 3x^2$ **f** $y = 25x + \dfrac{4}{x}$

g $y = 2x^{\frac{1}{2}} + 4x^{-\frac{1}{2}}$

4 Find the value(s) of x for which these *derived* functions are zero.

a $f'(x) = (x - 3)(x + 7)$ **b** $f'(x) = x - \dfrac{1}{x}$ **c** $f'(x) = \sqrt{2x} - \dfrac{1}{\sqrt{2x}}$

d $f'(x) = x + \dfrac{1}{x^2}$ **e** $f'(x) = \pi x - \dfrac{10}{x^2}$

5 Find the coordinates of any stationary points on these curves, and state, giving reasons, whether the points are maxima or minima or points of inflexion.

a $y = x^3$ **b** $y = x^5 - 15x^3$ **c** $y = x^4 + 3x^3$

d $y = 20 + 15x - x^2 - \dfrac{x^3}{3}$ **e** $y = \dfrac{1 - 27x^2}{x^3}$ **f** $y = x^3 + 6x^2 + 12x - 4$

6 $f(x) = 3x^2 - 2x^3$.

a Find $f'(x)$.

b Show that the function $f(x)$ is stationary (i.e. $f'(x) = 0$) when $x = 0$ and $x = 1$ and find $f(0)$ and $f(1)$.

c Show that $f(0)$ is a minimum value of the function and that $f(1)$ is a maximum value.

d Solve $f'(x) > 0$ to find the range of values of x for which the function is increasing.

e Solve $f'(x) < 0$ to find the range of values of x for which the function is decreasing.

f Sketch $y = f(x)$.

g Using the sketch, find the number of distinct real roots of $f(x) = 0$.

7 $f(x) = x^2 - x - 2$.

a Find $f'(x)$.

b Find the value(s) of x and $f(x)$ for which the function is stationary and the nature of the stationary value(s).

c Find the range of values of x for which the function is increasing, and the range for which it is decreasing.

d Sketch the curve $y = f(x)$.

e Use the sketch to state the number of distinct real roots of the equation $f(x) = 0$.

8 Repeat Question 7 for these functions.

i $f(x) = x^3 - 12x$

ii $f(x) = 3 - 2x - x^2$

iii $f(x) = 3x^2 - x^3$

iv $f(x) = 3 - x^3$

v $f(x) = x^3 - 5x^2 + 3x + 2$

EXERCISE 9d *(continued)*

9 Investigate the stationary points on these curves, stating the coordinates and the type of each stationary point.

a $y = x + \frac{1}{x}$ **b** $y = \frac{3x^{\frac{1}{2}}}{4} - x^{\frac{3}{2}}$ **c** $y = 4x^2 + \frac{1}{x}$ **d** $y = x^2 + \frac{16}{x}$

10 Given that $y = 5x^2 + ax + b$ has a turning point at (b, a) where $a \neq 0$, find a and b.

11 Given that $y = ax^3 + bx^2 + 3x + 4$ and that $y = 5$ and $\frac{dy}{dx} = 2$ when $x = 1$

a find a and b

b show that the curve has no stationary point.

12 A ball is thrown in the air. At time t in seconds, its height h in metres above ground is given by $h = 2 + 9t - 5t^2$.

a The formula given is valid only until the ball hits the ground. Find the time at which this happens.

b Find the time at which the ball's height reaches a maximum and find this maximum height.

9.6 Maximum and minimum problems

As the examples in Exercises 9e and 9f will show, finding maximum and minimum points has many useful applications.

To tackle each problem follow these steps.

- Draw a diagram, if relevant.
- Choose letters to represent unknown quantities.
- Express the quantity (e.g. y) to be maximised or minimised in terms of just *one* variable (e.g. x). (This may require some algebraic manipulation.)
- Differentiate y with respect to x.
- Solve $\frac{dy}{dx} = 0$ to find the value(s) of x at the maximum or minimum point(s).
- Substitute the value(s) of x in the expression for y, checking that the value(s) give possible answers.
- Check, if necessary, that the value gives a maximum or minimum.

Example 12

An open box is to be made from a rectangular sheet of card measuring 16 cm by 10 cm. Four equal squares are to be cut from each corner and the flaps folded up. Find the length of the side of a square which makes the volume of the box as large as possible. Find this largest volume.

As a practical exercise, take a sheet of paper 16 cm by 10 cm and cut off four equal squares from the corners. Fold up the flaps. Use intuition to cut off the corners which you think will give the largest volume box.

Let the side of each square be x cm.

Draw a diagram.

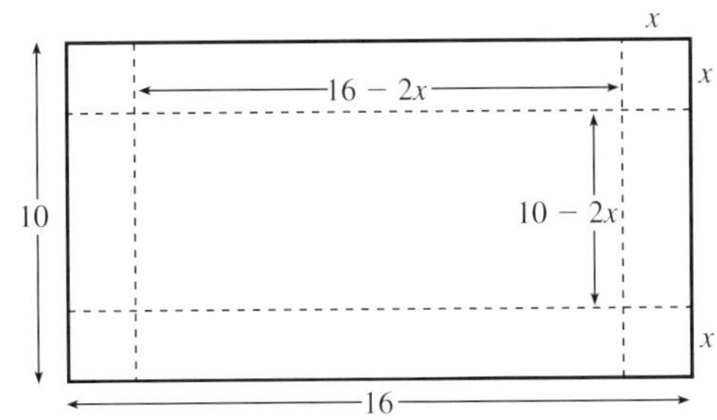

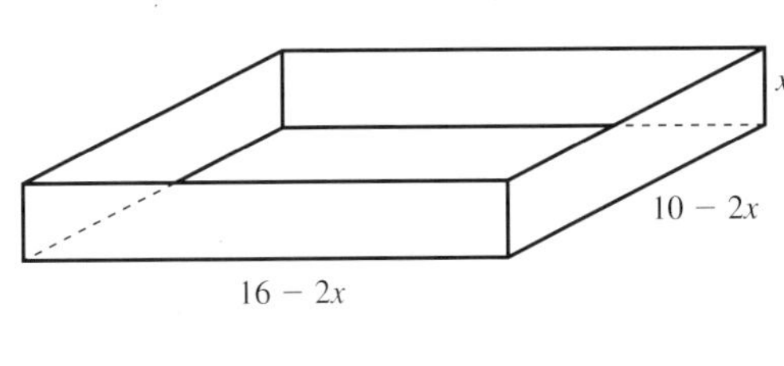

Let V be the volume of the box in cm^3.

Volume V is to be maximised.

Then $V = x(10 - 2x)(16 - 2x)$

Express V in terms of x.

$$= x(160 - 52x + 4x^2)$$

$$= 160x - 52x^2 + 4x^3$$

$$\frac{dV}{dx} = 160 - 104x + 12x^2$$

Differentiate V with respect to x.

At a maximum point, $\frac{dV}{dx} = 0$.

So $160 - 104x + 12x^2 = 0$

Divide all terms by 4.

$$3x^2 - 26x + 40 = 0$$

$$(3x - 20)(x - 2) = 0$$

Solve by the formula if the factors cannot be found.

$$x = \tfrac{20}{3} \text{ or } x = 2$$

$$x = 6\tfrac{2}{3} \text{ or } x = 2$$

The length of the side of the square must be less than half the side of the rectangle.
$\therefore\ x = 6\frac{2}{3}$ is *not* a possible solution.

So $x = 2$ is the solution.

When $x = 2$ $\quad V = 2 \times (10 - 4) \times (16 - 4)$

Substitute $x = 2$ in the expression for V.

$$= 2 \times 6 \times 12$$

$$= 144$$

To check that this is a maximum value,

$$\frac{d^2V}{dx^2} = -104 + 24x$$

When $x = 2$ $\quad \frac{d^2V}{dx^2} = -104 + 48 < 0$

Alternatively, to check $x = 2$ gives a maximum value:

x	L	2	R
$\frac{dV}{dx}$	+	0	−
	/	—	\

Maximum point

$\therefore\ x = 2$ gives a maximum value.

So the largest volume is $144\,cm^3$ and this is obtained by cutting off squares of size 2 cm.

Compare your paper 'box' with the solution. Also try drawing $V = 160x - 52x^2 + 4x^3$ on a graphics calculator and interpreting the graph.

Example 13 A sports area is to be designed in the form of a rectangular field with a semicircular area at each end. The perimeter of the sports area is to be 1400 metres. What should be the dimensions of the sports area if the rectangular field is to have as large an area as possible? Give answers in metres correct to 1 decimal place.

Let length be l m and radius of semicircle be r m. Draw a diagram.

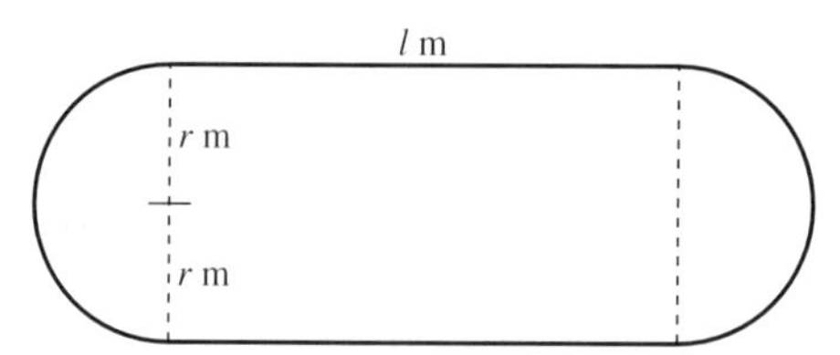

Let A m^2 be the area of the rectangular field. A is the quantity to be maximised.

$$A = 2r \times l$$
$$= 2lr \quad ①$$

A is expressed here in terms of two variables, r and l. A must be expressed in terms of one variable only so another equation connecting the variables is needed.

$$\text{Perimeter} = (2\pi r + 2l)\text{ m}$$

But perimeter is 1400 m

The perimeter is known; this gives the second equation.

so $$2\pi r + 2l = 1400$$

Divide all terms by 2.

$$\pi r + l = 700$$

Rearrange.

$$l = 700 - \pi r \quad ②$$

Substituting in ①

$$A = 2(700 - \pi r)r$$

A is now expressed in terms of only one variable, r.

$$= 1400r - 2\pi r^2$$

so $$\frac{dA}{dr} = 1400 - 4\pi r$$

Differentiate A with respect to r.

At a maximum point, $\frac{dA}{dr} = 0$.

So $1400 - 4\pi r = 0$

$$r = \frac{1400}{4\pi}$$
$$= \frac{350}{\pi}$$
$$= 111.4 \text{ (correct to 1 d.p.)}$$

The side of the rectangular area is $2r$.

$$2r = \frac{700}{\pi}$$
$$= 222.8 \text{ (correct to 1 d.p.)}$$

Substitute $r = \frac{350}{\pi}$ in ②.

> Use the exact value for r. This makes the calculation easier as π cancels.

$$l = 700 - \pi r$$
$$= 700 - \pi \times \frac{350}{\pi}$$
$$= 350$$

$A = 1400r - 2\pi r^2$ is a quadratic expression. The coefficient of r^2 is $-$ve.

$\therefore$ A has a maximum value.

So the dimensions of the rectangular field for maximum area are 350 m by 222.8 m, giving semi-circular ends of radius 111.4 m.

✓ ***Note*** To solve maximum and minimum problems express the quantity (e.g. y) to be maximised or minimised in terms of one variable (e.g. x) and find where $\frac{dy}{dx} = 0$.

EXERCISE 9e

1 A farmer has 100 m of metal railing with which to form two adjacent sides of a rectangular enclosure, the other two sides being two existing walls, meeting at right angles. Let the length of one side of the enclosure be x m.

a Draw a diagram and write down an expression for the length of the other side of the enclosure.

b Obtain an expression for the area, $A\,\text{m}^2$, of the enclosure in terms of x.

c Find $\frac{dA}{dx}$ and solve $\frac{dA}{dx} = 0$.

d Hence find the dimensions of the enclosure which gives the maximum area and find the maximum area.
(Remember to include proof that the answer does give a *maximum* area.)

2 A rectangular sheep pen is to be made out of 1000 m of fencing, using an existing straight hedge for one of the sides. Find the maximum area possible, and the dimensions necessary to achieve this.

3 An aeroplane flying level at 250 m above the ground suddenly swoops down to drop supplies, and then regains its former altitude. It is h m above the ground t s after beginning its dive, where $h = 8t^2 - 80t + 250$. Find

a its least altitude during this operation

b the interval of time during which it was losing height.

4 An open tank is to be constructed with a square base and vertical sides so as to contain 500 m^3 of water.

a Given that the length of the side of the square base is x m, find expressions, in terms of x, for the height of the tank, and for the external surface area of the tank.

b Find the value of x required so that the area of sheet metal used in constructing the tank is a minimum. (Remember to show that the value of x found gives a *minimum* value.)

c Find the minimum area of metal.

EXERCISE 9e
(continued)

5 An open cylinder has radius r cm and volume $27\pi\,\text{cm}^3$.

a Find an expression for the external surface area, $S\,\text{cm}^2$, in terms of r.

b Find the value of r which makes $\frac{dS}{dr} = 0$ and prove that this value of r gives a minimum value of S.

c Hence find the minimum surface area, leaving π in the answer.

6 An open rectangular box is to be made with an external area of $1620\,\text{cm}^2$. The ratio of the lengths of the sides of the base of the box is 3:5.

Let the length of the shorter side of the base be $3x$ cm, the height of the box h cm and its volume $V\,\text{cm}^3$.

a Draw a sketch of the box and write down an expression for the longer side of the base of the box in terms of x.

b Show that $V = 15hx^2$.

c Show that the external area of the box is given by $(16hx + 15x^2)\,\text{cm}^2$.

d Show that $h = \frac{1620 - 15x^2}{16x}$ and hence express V in terms of x only.

e Use differentiation to find the value of x which makes the volume of the box a maximum.

f Hence find the maximum volume.

7 This diagram represents the end view of the outer cover of a match box, AB and EF being gummed together, and assumed to be the same length.

If the total length of edge (ABCDEF) is 12 cm, calculate the lengths of AB and BC which will give the maximum possible cross-section area.

8 This diagram represents a rectangular sheet of metal 8 cm by 5 cm.

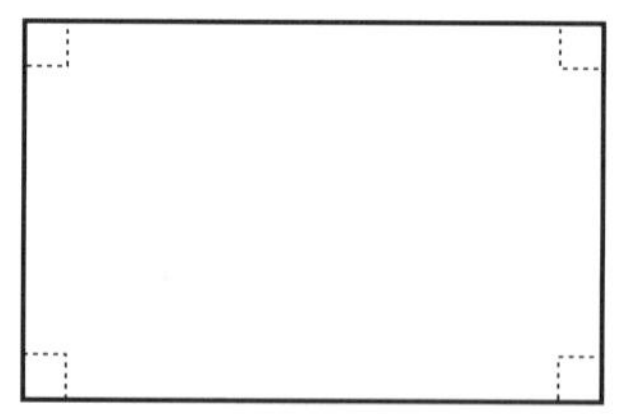

Equal squares of side x cm are removed from each corner, and the edges are then turned up to make an open box of volume $V\,\text{cm}^3$.

Show that $V = 40x - 26x^2 + 4x^3$.

Hence find the maximum possible volume, and the corresponding value of x.

9 Repeat Question 8 when the dimensions of the sheet of metal are 8 cm by 3 cm, showing that, in this case, $V = 24x - 22x^2 + 4x^3$.

10 A chemical factory wishes to make a closed cylindrical container, of thin metal, to hold $10\,\text{m}^3$, using the least possible area of metal.
Let the outside surface area be $S\,\text{m}^2$, the radius $r\,\text{m}$ and the height $h\,\text{m}$.

a Find a formula for h in terms of r.

b Show that $S = 2\pi r^2 + \dfrac{20}{r}$.

c Show that S has a minimum value when $r = \sqrt[3]{\dfrac{5}{\pi}}$.

d Hence find the required radius, height and surface area for the container, correct to 2 significant figures.

11 Using the data of Question 10 show that the surface area is a minimum when $h = 2\sqrt[3]{\dfrac{5}{\pi}}$ and $S = 6\sqrt[3]{25\pi}$.

12 A sealed cylindrical tin is of height $h\,\text{cm}$ and radius $r\,\text{cm}$.
The area of its total outer surface is $A\,\text{cm}^2$ and its volume is $V\,\text{cm}^3$.

a Find expressions for A and V in terms of r and h.

b Taking $A = 24\pi$, find an expression for h in terms of r, and hence an expression for V in terms of r.

c Find the value of r which will make V a maximum.

13 A sweet manufacturer estimates that if it sets the price of a box of speciality chocolates at £p it will sell n thousand boxes per year, where $n = 84 + 12p - p^2$, for $2.5 \leqslant p \leqslant 15$.

a Find the price that will maximise the number of boxes sold.

b Write down the revenue received by selling n boxes at price £p.

c Hence show that the price that will maximise the manufacturer's revenue is £10.50, to the nearest 50 pence.

14 Prove that, if the sum of the radii of two circles remains constant, the sum of the areas of the circles is least when the circles have equal radius.

15 A cylinder is such than the sum of its height and the circumference of its base is 5 m. Express the volume ($V\,\text{m}^3$) in terms of the radius of the base ($r\,\text{m}$).
What is the greatest volume of the cylinder?

16 A piece of wire of length l is cut into two parts of lengths x and $l - x$.
The former is bent into the shape of a square, and the latter into a rectangle of which the base is double the height.

a Find an expression for the sum of the areas of these two figures.

b Prove that the only value of x for which this sum is a maximum or a minimum is $x = \dfrac{8l}{17}$, and find which it is.

EXERCISE 9f
(Extension)

1 **a** Investigate the stationary values of $y = 3x^4 + 16x^3 + 24x^2 + 3$.

b Find the range of values of x for which y is an increasing function.

c Find the range of values of x for which y is a decreasing function.

2 The normal to the curve $y = \frac{p}{x}$ at the point P, where $x = 1$, meets the curve again at Q. Find the coordinates of Q.

3 The tangent to the curve $y = ax^2 + bx + c$ at the point where $x = 2$ is parallel to the line $y = 4x$. Given that y has a minimum value of -3 where $x = 1$ find the values of a, b and c.

4 Find the equation of the tangent to the curve $xy = 4$ at the point P whose coordinates are $(2t, \frac{2}{t})$. If O is the origin, and the tangent at P meets the x-axis at A and the y-axis at B, prove that

a P is the mid-point of AB

b the area of triangle OAB is the same for all positions of P.

5 Find the coordinates of any stationary points on $y = 4x^{\frac{1}{4}}(1 - x)$.

6 **a** Find the equation of the normal to the curve $y = 4x^3 + 5x^2 - 3x - 2$ at the point $P(-1, 2)$.

b The normal meets the curve again at A and B where $AP < AB$. Find the coordinates of A and B and show that P divides AB in the ratio 1:8.

7 An amateur gardener's annual yield y of currants, in kg, is $14 + 7a + 4b^{\frac{3}{4}}$, where a and b are the quantities of fertiliser and pesticide applied, also measured in kg. Pollution regulations allow the gardener to use up to 0.1 kg of chemicals altogether. Find the quantities of fertiliser and pesticide, correct to the nearest 10 g, that maximise the fruit yield, and find the yield to the nearest kg.

8 The probability that a baby will survive a certain necessary operation is

$$1 - 0.1\left(\sqrt{a^3} - 4\sqrt{a} + \frac{4}{\sqrt{a}} + 1\right)$$

where a is the baby's age in years and $a > 0.2$.

a Find an expression for the rate of change of probability of survival with respect to age.

b By putting the expression in part **a** over a common denominator, or otherwise, find the age at which the operation should be carried out to maximise the probability of survival.

9 An aeroplane's height h km is given in terms of the distance x km it has flown since take-off by the equation $h = 2x^{\frac{3}{5}} - 0.6x^{\frac{4}{5}}$ where $10 \leqslant x \leqslant 110$.

a Find an expression for the rate at which the aeroplane gains height with respect to distance flown since take-off.

b Find the aeroplane's maximum height and how far it has travelled when it reaches this height.

10 A point P, whose x-coordinate is a, is taken on the line $y = 3x - 7$.

If Q is the point (4, 1) show that $PQ^2 = 10a^2 - 56a + 80$.

Find the value of a which will make this expression a minimum.

Hence show that the coordinates of N, the foot of the perpendicular from Q to the line, are $(2\frac{4}{5}, 1\frac{2}{5})$.

Find the equation of QN.

11 The angle C of triangle ABC is always a right angle.

a If the sum of CA and CB is 6 cm, find the maximum area of the triangle.

b If on the other hand, the hypotenuse AB is kept equal to 4 cm, and the sides CA, CB allowed to vary, find the maximum area of the triangle.

12 A circular cylinder, open at the top, is to be made so as to have a volume of $1\,\text{m}^3$. If r m is the radius of the base, prove that the total outside surface area is

$$\left(\pi r^2 + \frac{2}{r}\right)\text{m}^2$$

Hence prove that this surface area is a minimum when the height equals the radius of the base.

13 A match box consists of an outer cover, open at both ends, into which slides a rectangular box without a top. The length of the box is one and a half times its breadth, the thickness of the material is negligible, and the volume of the box is $25\,\text{cm}^3$.

If the breadth of the box is x cm, find, in terms of x, the area of material used.

Hence show that, if the least area of material is to be used to make the box, the length should be 3.7 cm approximately.

14 Two opposite ends of a closed rectangular tank are squares of side x m and the total area of sheet metal forming the tank is $S\,\text{m}^2$.

Show that the volume of the tank is $\frac{1}{4}x(S - 2x^2)\,\text{m}^3$.

If the value of S is 2400, find the value of x for which the volume is a maximum.

15 The point P(x, y) lies on the curve $y = x^2$, the point A has coordinates (0, 1). Express AP^2 in terms of x.

Hence find the positions of P for which AP^2 is least and verify that, for each of these positions, the line AP is perpendicular to the tangent to the curve at P.

16 Find the equations of the tangents and normals to these curves at the points where $x = \pm 1$.

a $y = x^5 + \dfrac{1}{x^5}$ **b** $y = x^6 + \dfrac{1}{x^6}$ **c** $y = x^n + \dfrac{1}{x^n}$ where $n \in \mathbb{Z}$, $n \geqslant 1$

EXERCISE 9g
(Miscellaneous)

1 Differentiate the following with respect to x.

a $\dfrac{3}{x^2}$ **b** $\dfrac{1}{2\sqrt{x}}$ **c** $-\dfrac{3}{2x^{\frac{2}{3}}}$

2 Given that $y = 3x^3 + 2 - \dfrac{4}{x}$ find

a $\dfrac{dy}{dx}$ **b** the gradient when $x = -1$.

3 Find the coordinates of the points on these curves where the gradient is 12.

a $y = x^3$ **b** $y = x - \dfrac{11}{x}$ **c** $y = 48\sqrt{x}$ **d** $y = 2x^3 - 3x^2 + 4$

4 Find the coordinates of the points on these curves at which the gradient is zero, and determine whether the points are local maxima or local minima, giving reasons.

a $y = x^3 - 3x$ **b** $y = x^2(x^2 - 8)$ **c** $y = 6\sqrt{x} - 3x$ **d** $y = \dfrac{x^2 + 3}{\sqrt{x}}$

5 Find the range of values of a for which $y = x - \dfrac{a}{x}$ has no stationary points.

6 **a** Find the equations of the tangent and normal to the curve $xy = 4$ at the point where $x = 2$.

b Show that the tangent does not meet the curve again.

c Show that the normal does intersect the curve again and find the coordinates of the point of intersection.

7 For each of these functions decide whether the function is always decreasing, the function is always increasing, or the function is sometimes increasing and sometimes decreasing:

a $y = x^3 - 3x + 1$

b $y = x^3 + 3x + 1$

c $y = 1 - 3x - x^3$

8 The diagram shows the graphs of $y = f(x)$ and, below it, $y = f'(x)$, the gradient function of $y = f(x)$.

Note that at a maximum or minimum value of $y = f(x)$, $f'(x) = 0$ and that a positive gradient for $y = f(x)$ corresponds to $f'(x) > 0$ and a negative gradient for $y = f(x)$ corresponds to $f'(x) < 0$.

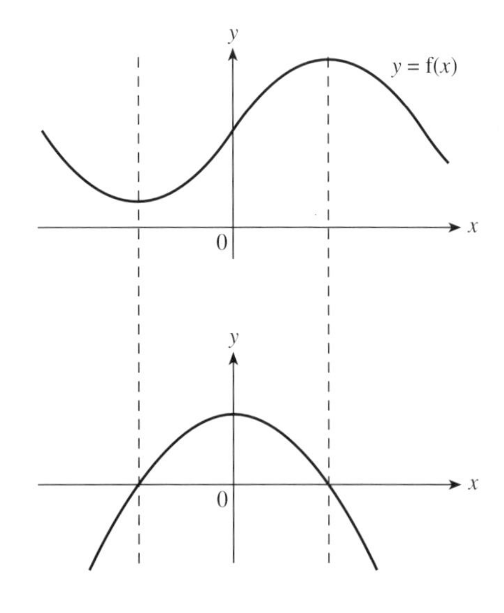

Draw similar sketches for $y = f'(x)$, given these sketches for $y = f(x)$.

a

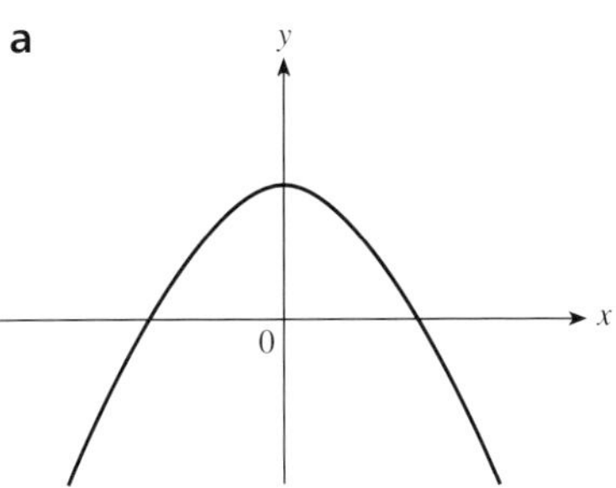

b

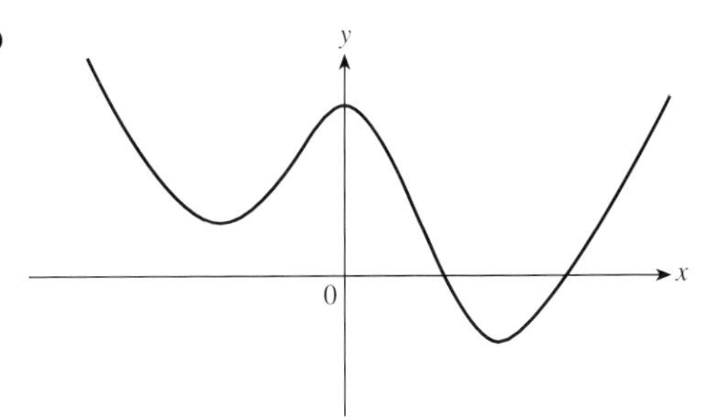

c

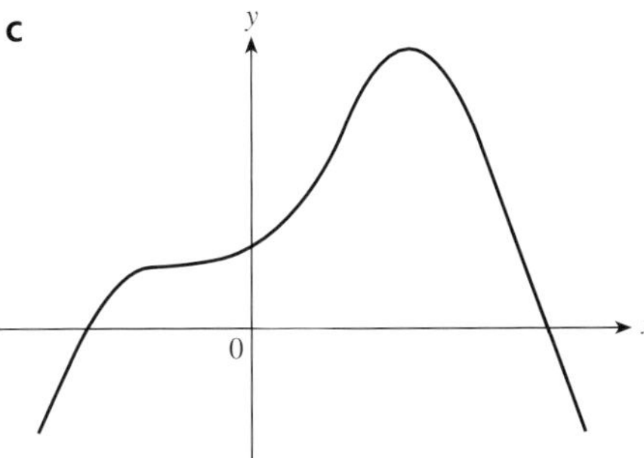

d

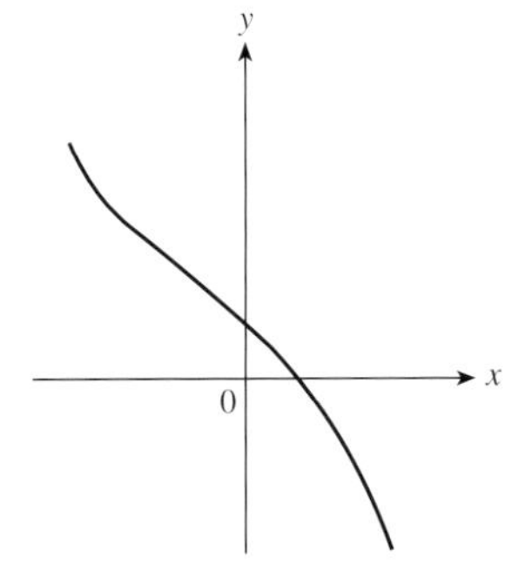

9 Find the maximum or minimum values of these functions first by completing the square and then by differentiation.

a $y = x^2 - 2x + 7$ **b** $y = 3 + 4x - x^2$

c $y = 2x^2 + x + 1$ **d** $y = 4 + 6x - 2x^2$

10 A circular pipe has outer diameter 4 cm and thickness t cm.

a Show that the area of cross-section, $A\,\text{cm}^2$, is given by $A = \pi(4t - t^2)$.

b Find the rate of increase of A with respect to t when $t = \frac{1}{4}$ and when $t = \frac{1}{2}$ leaving π in the answer.

11 Given that $y = ax^2 + bx - a^2$ has gradient -4 at $(-2, -13)$, find possible values for a and b.

12 The radius, r cm, of a circle at time t s is given by $r = \dfrac{t^4}{4} + \dfrac{4}{t}$.

Find the rate at which the radius is changing with respect to time when $t = 1$ and when $t = 2$. State whether the radius is increasing or decreasing in each case.

13 Given that $y = 2x^3 - 15x^2 + 36x - 7$, find the range of values of x for which y is

a an increasing function **b** a decreasing function.

14 Prove that there are two points on the curve $y = 2x^2 - x^4$ at which y has a maximum value, and one point at which y has a minimum value.
Give the equations of the tangents to the curve at these three points.

15 Find the equations of the normals of the curve $xy = 3$ which are parallel to the line $3x - y - 2 = 0$.

16 A solid rectangular block has a square base. Find its maximum volume if the sum of the height and any one side of the base is 12 cm.

17 A man wishes to fence in a rectangular enclosure of area 128 m^2.
One side of the enclosure is formed by part of a brick wall already in position.
What is the least possible length of fencing required for the other three sides?

18 Some water is gradually evaporating from an open vessel, so that the volume V, measured in cm^3 after t days, is given by $V = 24(a - t^{\frac{2}{3}} - t^{\frac{1}{3}})$, where a is constant.

a Given that the water evaporates completely after exactly 27 days, find a and hence the initial volume of water in the vessel.

b Find the rate of evaporation after 8 days.

19 At time t hours after the beginning of a storm, r mm of rain have fallen, where $r = t^3 - 6t^2 + 12t$, for $0 \leqslant t \leqslant 4$.

a Find the rate of rainfall one and two hours after the beginning of the storm.

b Find the rate at which the rate of rainfall is changing after three hours.

20 The stamp counter at a village post office is open from 9 a.m. to 3 p.m. daily.
The average queuing time q, measured in minutes, at time x hours after opening time is modelled by the equation $q = \frac{1}{4}(-x^3 + 6x^2 + 20)$.

a Show that, using this model, the longest average queuing time occurs around 1 p.m. and find how long it is.

b Find when the average queuing time is rising at its maximum rate, and show that this maximum rate of increase is 3 minutes/hour.

21 The mass m of a caterpillar, measured in milligrams, is

$$-\frac{t^3}{6} + \frac{9t^2}{4} + 5t + 10$$

where t is the time since hatching, measured in days. After n days, the caterpillar reaches its maximum mass, stops eating and pupates.

a Find the value of n and the caterpillar's maximum mass to the nearest mg.

b Find the caterpillar's maximum growth rate, in mg per day correct to the nearest mg, and when it occurs.

22 A region of low pressure is centred at a point C.
The pressure P in millibars, a distance x km from C, obeys the equation

$$P = 1008 - \frac{x^{1.2}}{24} - \frac{x^{1.1}}{11}$$

a Find the pressure 20 km from C correct to the nearest millibar.

b Find the pressure gradient (the rate of change of pressure with respect to position), correct to 2 significant figures, 40 km from C.

c Find the rate of change of pressure gradient with respect to position 60 km from C, giving the answer correct to 2 significant figures.

Test yourself

1 The gradient of the curve $y = \frac{x^2}{4} - \sqrt{x} + 4$ at the point where $x = 4$ is

A 6 **B** $\frac{7}{4}$ **C** $\frac{23}{4}$ **D** 1 **E** $\frac{29}{4}$

2 The maximum value of $y = 2x^3 - 3x^2 - 12x$ is

A 21 **B** 2 **C** 7 **D** 0 **E** -20

3 At the point $(-\frac{1}{2}, p)$ on the curve $y = \frac{1}{x^2} - x^2$ the gradient is m. The values of m and p respectively are

A $7, 3\frac{3}{4}$ **B** $17, 3\frac{3}{4}$ **C** $3\frac{3}{4}, 17$ **D** $-\frac{3}{2}, 0$ **E** $15, 3\frac{3}{4}$

4 If $g(x) = ax^4 + b - \frac{c}{x^3}$, where a, b and c are constants, then $g'(x)$ equals

A $ax^3 + \frac{b}{x} - \frac{c}{x^2}$ **B** $4ax^3 - \frac{3c}{x^2}$ **C** $4\left(ax^4 + b - \frac{c}{x^3}\right)^3$

D $\frac{ax^5}{5} + bx + \frac{c}{2x^2} + d$ **E** $4ax^3 + \frac{3c}{x^4}$

5 The curve $y = x^2 + 6x - 7$ has

A a maximum at $(3, -16)$

B a minimum at $(-7, 0)$ and a maximum at $(1, 0)$

C a minimum at $(-3, -16)$

D a maximum at $(7, 0)$ and a minimum at $(-1, 0)$

E a minimum at $(-6, -43)$

6 If the curve $y = 2ax^3 + 5ax^2 + 20x$, where a is a constant, has gradient zero when $x = -1$, then a is equal to

A 5 **B** $2\frac{1}{2}$ **C** $\frac{20}{3}$ **D** $-2\frac{1}{2}$ **E** 0

7 The number of stationary points on the curve $y = x^3 - 3x^2 + 9x + 5$ is

A 0 **B** 1 **C** 2 **D** 3 **E** 4

8 The function $f(x) = x^3 - 3x$ is increasing when x lies in the range

A $x < 1$ **B** $0 < x < 1$ **C** $x > 0$

D $x < -1$ or $x > 1$ **E** none of these

9 The tangent to $y = (2x + 1)^2$ at the point where $x = 2$ is the line

A $y = 6x + 13$ **B** $2y = 25x$ **C** $x + 6y - 152 = 0$

D $y = 2x + 21$ **E** $y = 20x - 15$

10 The normal to $y = x^{\frac{3}{2}}$ at the point where $x = 1$ has equation

A $3y - 2x - 1 = 0$ **B** $2y + 3x - 5 = 0$ **C** $3y + 2x - 5 = 0$

D $2y - 3x + 1 = 0$ **E** none of these

Key points

Differentiation

$\frac{dy}{dx}$ is the **rate of change** of y with respect to x.

$$f'(x) = \lim_{h \to 0} \frac{f(x+h) - f(x)}{h}$$

The **first derivative** (the gradient) can be written $\frac{dy}{dx}$, y' or $f'(x)$.

The **second derivative** (the gradient of the gradient) can be written $\frac{d^2y}{dx^2}$, y'' or $f''(x)$.

$$y = c \quad \Rightarrow \quad \frac{dy}{dx} = 0$$

$$y = kx \quad \Rightarrow \quad \frac{dy}{dx} = k \qquad y = kx^n \Rightarrow \frac{dy}{dx} = nkx^{n-1}$$

Rewrite expressions as sums of terms with powers of x before differentiating, i.e. write

$y = (x+1)(3x-1)$ as $y = 3x^2 + 2x - 1$ or $y = \frac{x^5 - x^2}{\sqrt{x}}$ as $y = x^{\frac{9}{2}} - x^{\frac{3}{2}}$

Stationary points

At a stationary point $\frac{dy}{dx} = 0$, i.e. the gradient is zero.

$\frac{dy}{dx} = 0$ and $\frac{d^2y}{dx^2} < 0 \Rightarrow$ the point is a local **maximum**.

$\frac{dy}{dx} = 0$ and $\frac{d^2y}{dx^2} > 0 \Rightarrow$ the point is a local **minimum**.

$\frac{dy}{dx} = 0$ and $\frac{d^2y}{dx^2} = 0 \Rightarrow$ the point could be a **point of inflexion** *or* a local maximum *or* minimum.

The nature of a stationary point can be determined by the above or by considering the gradient of the curve on either side of the stationary point.

To solve maximum and minimum problems express the quantity (e.g. y) to be maximised or minimised in term of one variable (e.g. x) and find where $\frac{dy}{dx} = 0$.

Increasing and decreasing functions

A function, $f(x)$ is **increasing** for $a < x < b$ if $f'(x) > 0$ for $a < x < b$.

A function, $f(x)$ is **decreasing** for $a < x < b$ if $f'(x) < 0$, for $a < x < b$.

10 Functions

Before starting this chapter you will need to know

- how to sketch a curve (Chapter 7)
- about function notation (Chapter 2)
- how to rearrange and solve equations (Chapter 3).

10.1 Mappings and relationships

Chapters 3 and 4 dealt with the relationship between two algebraic expressions. This chapter looks at the relationship between two sets of numbers.

Such a relationship or **mapping** can be expressed as a rule or by an equation or in a table. The relationship or mapping can be illustrated by a diagram, such as a graph, or, by ordered pairs.

Consider the mapping between the elements of set $A\{1, 2, 3, 4, 5\}$ and of set $B\{3, 5, 7, 9, 11\}$.

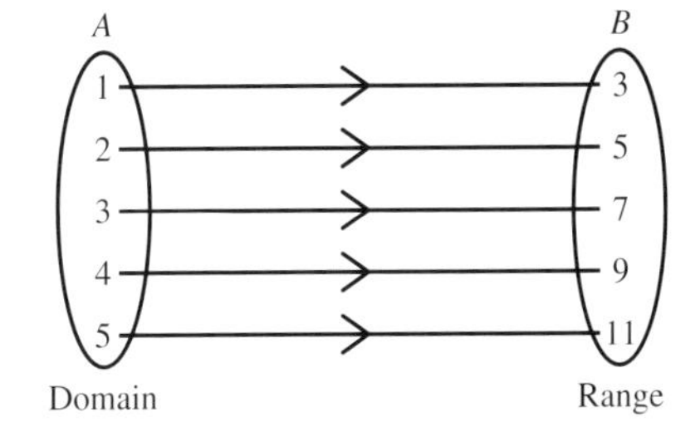

The set A (the 'input' set) is called the **domain**.

The set B (the 'output' set) is called the **range**.

Each member of the domain maps to a member of the range.

Each member of A is doubled and one is added to obtain the corresponding member of B.

If the elements of the domain are represented by x and of the range by y, the relationship is $y = 2x + 1$.

This can be expressed in function notation as

$$f(x) = 2x + 1$$

Read as 'f of x equals $2x + 1$'.

or $f: x \to 2x + 1$

Read as 'f maps x to $2x + 1$'.

Domain $= \{1, 2, 3, 4, 5\}$

Range $= \{3, 5, 7, 9, 11\}$

Each element of the domain has an **image** in the range. For example, the image of 2 is 5. This can be expressed as

$$f(2) = 5$$

Read as 'f of 2 equals 5'.

or $f: 2 \to 5$

Read as 'f maps 2 to 5'.

The mapping can be expressed as a set of ordered pairs.

(1, 3) (2, 5) (3, 7) (4, 9) (5, 11)

Member of domain ↗ ↖ Member of range

The mapping can be illustrated by plotting these ordered pairs as points.

Points on the x-axis represent the domain.

Points on the y-axis represent the range.

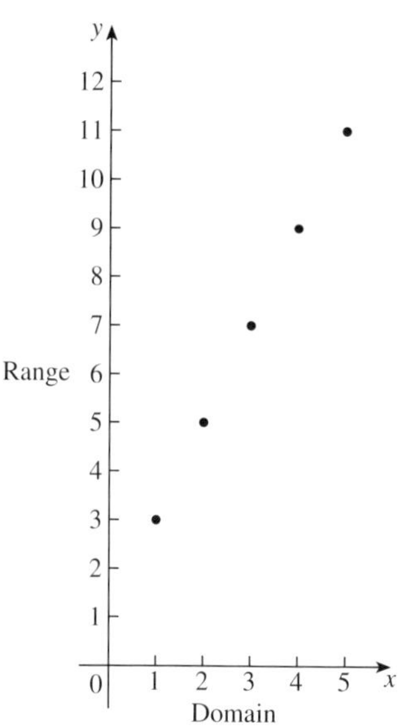

The value of y depends on the value of x so y is called the **dependent variable** and x the **independent variable**.

There are several ways in which sets, such as the domain or range, can be defined. Always use x for the domain and y or f(x) for the range.

Notation	Contents
$x \in \mathbb{R}$	x belongs to the set of real numbers $\mathbb{R}$.
$\{x : x \in \mathbb{R},\ x \neq 0\}$	The set of values x such that x belongs to $\mathbb{R}$ and $x \neq 0$. NB read : as 'such that'
$x \neq 5$	Assume x is a real number. This would imply $x \in \mathbb{R},\ x \neq 5$.
$y \in \mathbb{R},\ 1 < y \leqslant 2$	y is a real number greater than 1 and less than or equal to 2.

Relations between x and y can be illustrated as graphs and divided into four types: **one-to-one**, **many-to-one**, **one-to-many** and **many-to-many**.

Only the first two types – one-to-one and many-to-one – are called **functions**. The others are included for completeness.

The essential feature of a function is that, for each member of the domain, there is one and *only* one member of the range.

Relationships like $f(x) = \pm\sqrt{x}$, where for a given value of x there is more than one value of $f(x)$ are not functions.

➤ To be a function, a relationship must be one-to-one or many-to-one; it must be uniquely defined for all values of the domain.

The possible values of x (the domain if dealing with a function) and the possible values of y (the range if dealing with a function) can be determined from the graph of the function.

One-to-one relationships

For each value of x, there is a unique value of y, and vice-versa.

A horizontal line cuts the graph, at most, once.

A vertical line cuts the graph, at most, once.

The relationship is **one-to-one**.

This is a function.

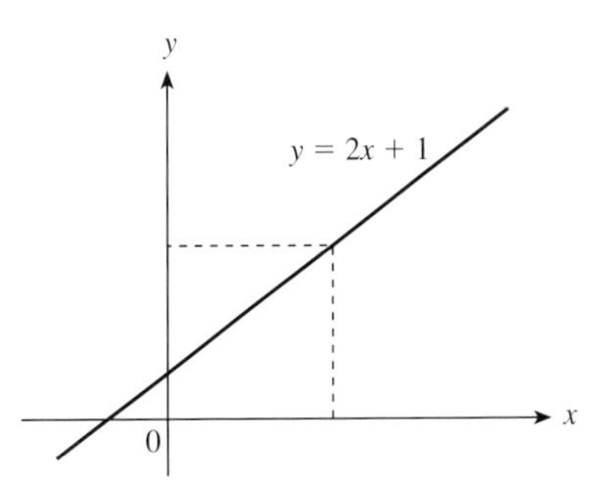

Many-to-one relationships

Many values of x (i.e. more than one) map to one value of y.

A horizontal line may cut the graph more than once.

A vertical line cuts the graph, at most, once.

The relationship is **many-to-one**.

This is a function.

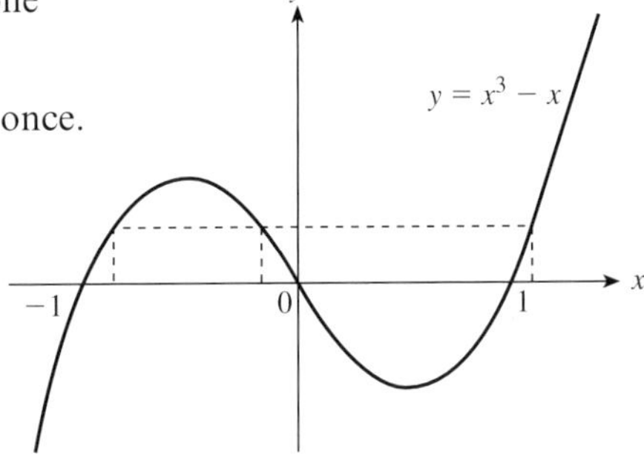

One-to-many relationships

One value of x maps to many (i.e. more than one) values of y.

A horizontal line cuts the graph, at most, once.

A vertical line may cut the graph more than once.

The relationship is **one-to-many**.

This is *not* a function.

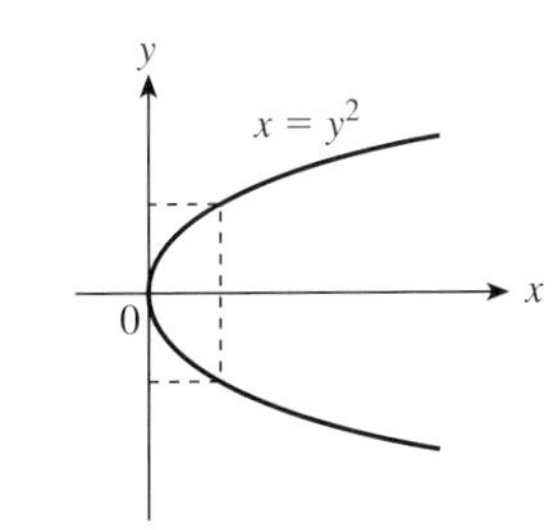

Many-to-many relationships

Many (i.e. more than one) values of x map to many (i.e. more than one) values of y.

For example, on $x^2 + y^2 = 9$, when $x = 1$, $y = \pm\sqrt{8}$, and when $y = 2$, $x = \pm\sqrt{5}$.

A horizontal line may cut the graph more than once.

A vertical line may cut the graph more than once.

The relationship is **many-to-many**.

This is *not* a function.

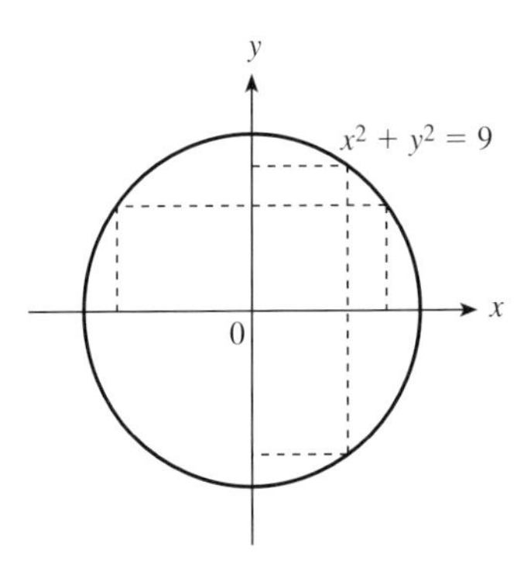

✓ ***Remember*** Only one-to-one and many-to-one relationships are functions.

Example 1 Find the range of given functions, and determine whether the functions are one-to-one or many-to-one.

When the elements of the domain are *listed*, substitute each in turn to find the elements of the range. In other cases, a sketch of the graph can be helpful in finding the range.

a $f(x) = 1 - 3x$. Domain: $\{0, 1, 2, 3, 4\}$.

The domain has five members 0, 1, 2, 3, 4.

$f(0) = 1$; $f(1) = -2$; $f(2) = -5$

$f(3) = -8$; $f(4) = -11$

Substituting each in turn gives the members of the range.

So, range is $\{-11, -8, -5, -2, 1\}$.

The order in the curly brackets need not relate to the order of the members of the domain. However, they should be in some order. Here they are given in ascending order.

Each member of the domain maps to a different member of the range.

$\therefore$ the function is one-to-one.

b $f(x) = 2x^2 - 1$. Domain: $x \in \mathbb{R}$.

Sketch the graph of $y = 2x^2 - 1$.

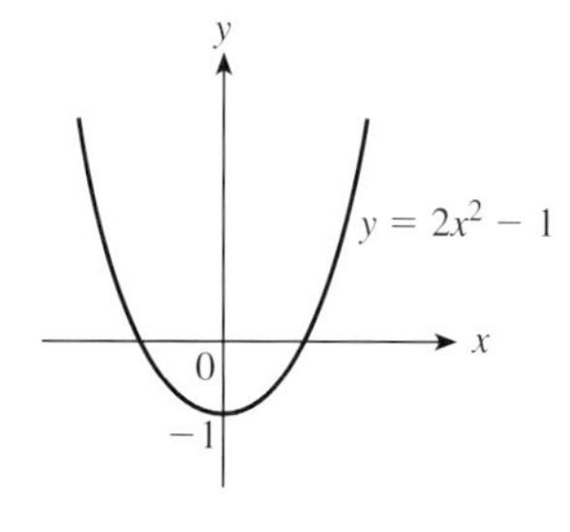

The domain (x-values) is all the real numbers.

From the sketch, the range is $y \in \mathbb{R}$, $y \geqslant -1$.

More than one value of x maps to a value of y.

For example, $f(1) = 1$ and $f(-1) = 1$.

$\therefore$ the function is many-to-one.

Note: a horizontal line can cut more than once.

c $f(x) = x^2 - 4$. Domain: $-1 \leqslant x \leqslant 3$.

Sketch the graph of $y = x^2 - 4$.

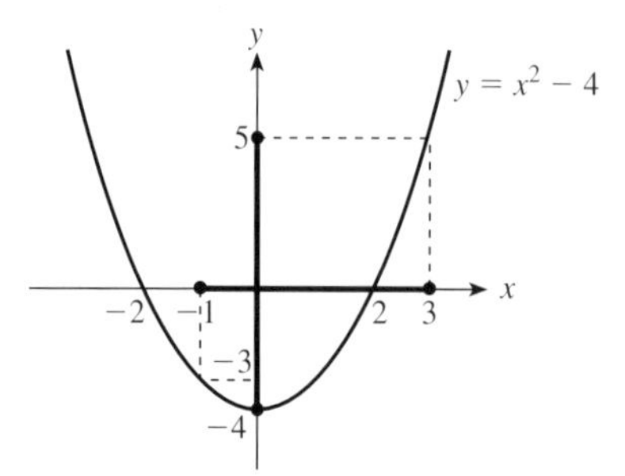

Note: Considering only the end values of the domain does not give the correct range. $f(-1) = -3$ and $f(3) = 5$. The range is not between -3 and 5 because, for example, $f(0) = -4$.

From the sketch, for $-1 \leqslant x \leqslant 3$, y can take values between -4 and 5.

So the range is $-4 \leqslant y \leqslant 5$.

The function is many-to-one.

d $f(x) = \frac{3}{x}$. Domain: $x \in \mathbb{R}, x \neq 0$.

The function is not defined for $x = 0$ because division by zero is not defined.

Sketch the graph.

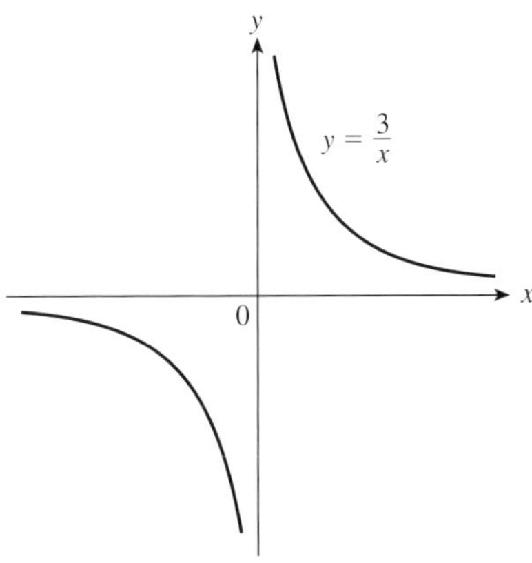

The domain (x values) is all the real numbers excluding zero. The range (y values) is also all the real numbers excluding zero.

From the sketch, range is $y \in \mathbb{R}, y \neq 0$.

The function is one-to-one.

A horizontal line can cut at most once.

e $f(x) = x^4$. Domain: $1 < x \leqslant 2$.

Assume $x \in \mathbb{R}$.

$x = 1$ is excluded from the domain so $y = f(1) = 1$ cannot be included in the range. $x = 2$ is included in the domain so $y = f(2) = 16$ is included in the range.

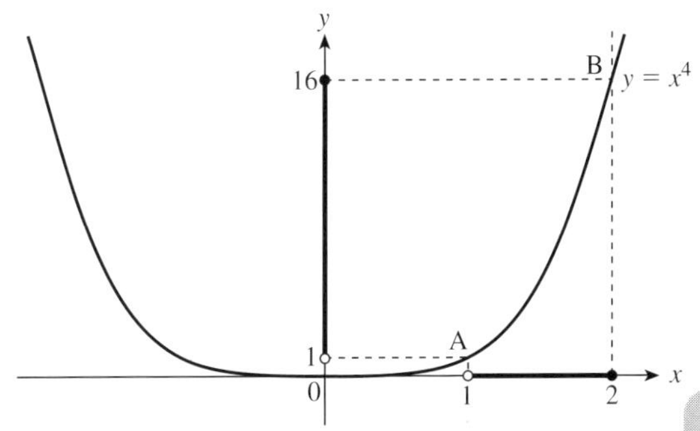

Range is $y \in \mathbb{R}, 1 < y \leqslant 16$.

For $1 < x \leqslant 2$, the function is one-to-one.

Although $f(x) = x^4$ is a many-to-one function, for the domain given, the function is one-to-one. Between A and B a horizontal line cuts only once.

f $f(x) = \begin{cases} 3x & 0 < x < 2 \\ x + 4 & 2 \leqslant x < 6 \end{cases}$. Domain: $0 < x < 6$.

Sketch the graph.

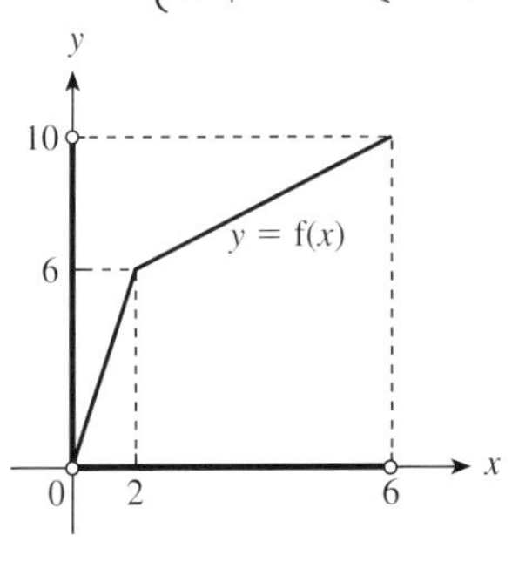

$0 < x < 6 \Rightarrow 0 < y < 10$

Range is $0 < y < 10$.

The function is one-to-one.

A horizontal line cuts at most once so the function is one-to-one.

Example 2

In this example, the range is given and is used working backwards, to find the domain.

Find the largest possible domain of given functions and determine whether the functions are one-to-one or many-to-one.

a $f(x) = x^2$. Range: $\{9, 16, 25\}$.

The range has three members: 9, 16, 25. Putting x^2 equal to each in turn and solving for x will give the corresponding values of the domain.

$x^2 = 9 \Rightarrow x = \pm 3$

$x^2 = 16 \Rightarrow x = \pm 4$

$x^2 = 25 \Rightarrow x = \pm 5$

Domain is $\{\pm 3,\ \pm 4,\ \pm 5\}$.

When the members of the range are listed, use this method to find the corresponding members of the domain.

Since more than one member of the domain maps to one member of the range the function is many-to-one.

b $f(x) = x^3$. Range: $-8 < y < 1$.

Calculate the values at the end of the range.

$x^3 = -8 \Rightarrow x = -2$
$x^3 = 1 \Rightarrow x = 1$

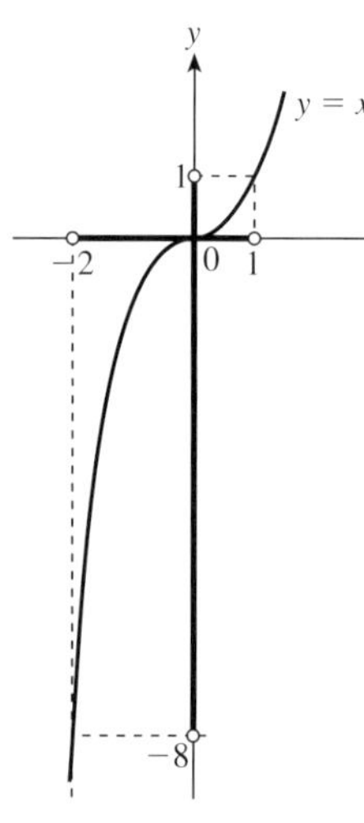

Sketch the graph.

The range (y-values) is $-8 < y < 1$.
-8 and 1 are excluded from the range, so -2 and 1 will be excluded from the domain.
$\therefore$ The domain (x-values) is $-2 < x < 1$

From the sketch, the domain is $-2 < x < 1$.

The function is one-to-one.

A horizontal line cuts at most once $\therefore$ one-to-one.

c $f(x) = 7x - 1$. Range: $6 \leqslant f(x) \leqslant 20$.

Find the values of x corresponding to $f(x) = 6$ and $f(x) = 20$.

$7x - 1 = 6 \Rightarrow x = 1$
$7x - 1 = 20 \Rightarrow x = 3$

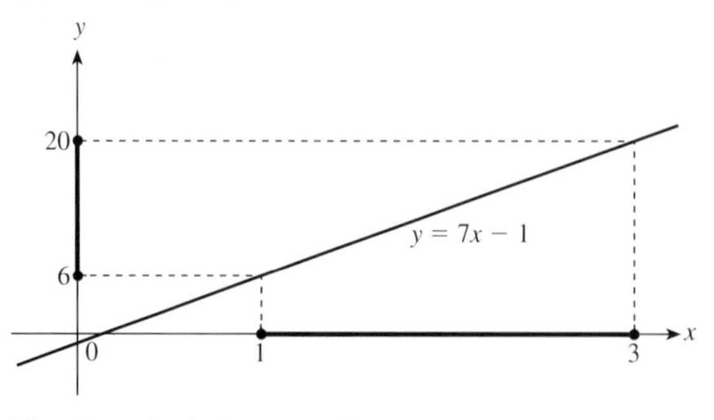

Sketch the graph.

The range is $6 \leqslant f(x) \leqslant 20$. The domain ($x$-values) is $1 \leqslant x \leqslant 3$.

The domain is $1 \leqslant x \leqslant 3$.

The function is one-to-one.

A horizontal line cuts at most once $\therefore$ one-to-one.

d $f(x) = \dfrac{7}{(x-1)^2}$. Range: $f(x) > 7$.

$f(x) = 7 \Rightarrow \dfrac{7}{(x-1)^2} = 7$

Find the values of x for which $f(x) = 7$.

That is, $(x-1)^2 = 1$

$x - 1 = \pm 1$

Take square root of both sides remembering $\pm$ sign.

$\therefore \quad x = 0$ or $x = 2$.

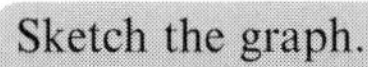

Sketch the graph.
For $x = 1$, the function is not defined
$\therefore \quad x = 1$ must be excluded from the domain.

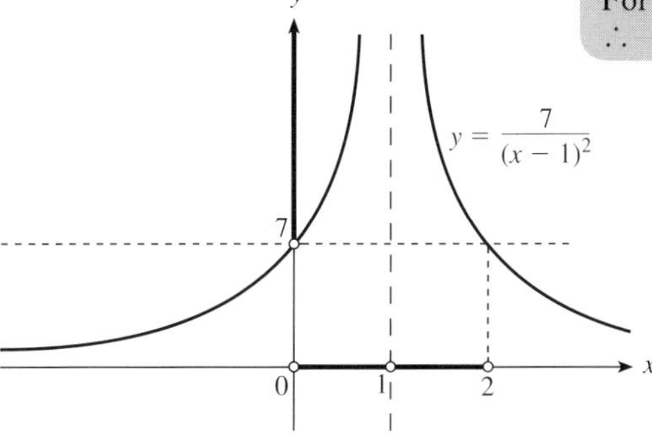

From the sketch the domain is $0 < x < 2$, $x \neq 1$.

The domain could be written $0 < x < 1$ and $1 < x < 2$.

The function is many-to-one.

A horizontal line cuts more than once $\therefore$ many-to-one.

Example 3 The function $f(x)$ is defined by $f(x) = x^2 - 2x - 8$, $x \in \mathbb{R}$.

a Find $f(-2)$.

b Solve $f(x) = 5x$.

c By completing the square, find the range of $f(x)$.

Solution

a $f(-2) = (-2)^2 - 2 \times (-2) - 8$

$= 4 + 4 - 8$

$= 0$

b $f(x) = 5x \Rightarrow x^2 - 2x - 8 = 5x$

$x^2 - 7x - 8 = 0$

$(x-8)(x+1) = 0$

$\Rightarrow \quad x = 8$ or $x = -1$

c $f(x) = x^2 - 2x - 8$

$= (x-1)^2 - 9$

Complete the square.

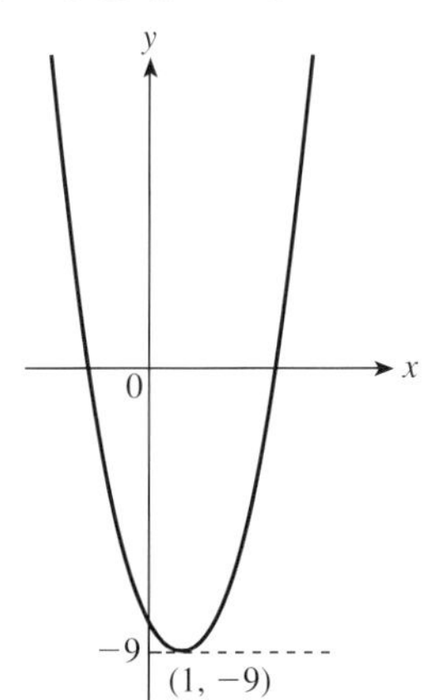

To find the range, either sketch the graph, or notice that $(x-1)^2 \geqslant 0$
$\therefore \quad (x-1)^2 - 9 \geqslant -9$.
For the sketch, $f(x) = x^2$ has been translated $\binom{1}{-9}$.
Only values of $y \geqslant -9$ are in the range.

The range is $y \geqslant -9$.

EXERCISE 10a

1 By sketching their graphs, or otherwise, find the range of these functions, and state whether each function is one-to-one or many-to-one.

a $f: x \to 2x$ Domain: $\{0, 2, 4, 8\}$

b $f: x \to x^2 + 1$ Domain: $x \in \mathbb{R}$

c $f: x \to 3x - 1$ Domain: $x \in \mathbb{R}, -2 < x < 2$

d $f: x \to \dfrac{1}{x}$ Domain: $x \in \mathbb{R}, x \neq 0$

e $f: x \to 2x^3$ Domain: $x \in \mathbb{R}, -1 \leqslant x \leqslant 4$

f $f: x \to \begin{cases} \sqrt{x} & 0 \leqslant x < 1 \\ 2 - x & 1 \leqslant x \leqslant 4 \end{cases}$ Domain: $x \in \mathbb{R}, 0 \leqslant x \leqslant 4$

g $f: x \to \dfrac{1}{(1+x)^2}$ Domain: $x \in \mathbb{R}, x \neq -1$

2 Find the largest possible domains of these functions, and state whether each function is one-to-one or many-to-one.

a $f(x) = 2x - 1$ Range: $\{5, 10, 15, 20\}$

b $f(x) = \sqrt{x}$ Range: $y \in \mathbb{R}, 2 < y < 7$

c $f(x) = 4 - x^2$ Range: $y \in \mathbb{R}, y < 0$

d $f(x) = \dfrac{1}{x - 6}$ Range: $\frac{1}{6} \leqslant y \leqslant 1$

e $f(x) = x^4$ Range: $1 < y \leqslant 81$

3 The function $f(x)$ is given by $f(x) = x^2 - 2x + 9$, $x \in \mathbb{R}$.

a Express $f(x)$ in the form $f(x) = (x - a)^2 + b$.

b Hence, or otherwise, sketch $y = f(x)$ and state the range of the function.

4 Given that $f(x) = x^2 + 3x - 4$, $x \in \mathbb{R}$, sketch $y = f(x)$ and hence

a find the range of f

b state the solution of $f(x) = 0$

5 **a** Given that $6 + 2x - x^2 \equiv p - (q - x)^2$, find p and q.

b Hence, or otherwise, find the range of the function, f, where $f: x \to 6 + 2x - x^2$, $x \in \mathbb{R}$.

6 These functions have domain $x \in \mathbb{R}$. Find, by completing the square, or otherwise, the range of each function.

a $f(x) = x^2 + 4x - 7$

b $f(x) = 2x^2 - 6x + 1$

c $f(x) = x^2 - 5x + 5$

d $f(x) = 6 - 3x - x^2$

7 **a** Given $f(x) = (x - 2)^2 + 5$ for the domain $1 \leqslant x \leqslant 5$, sketch $f(x)$ marking the vertex of the parabola.

b Show, with reference to the sketch or otherwise, that the range of $f(x)$ for the given domain is $5 \leqslant y \leqslant 14$.

c Solve $f(x) = 9$.

8 The function f is defined for $x > 0$ as $f: x \to 4 + \frac{5}{x}$

a Sketch the function for $x > 0$.

b State the range of the function.

c Solve $f(x) = x$.

9 **a** Sketch $f(x) = |5 - 2x|$ for the domain $0 \leqslant x \leqslant 7$.

b State the range of $f(x)$.

c Explain why $f(x)$ is not a one-to-one function.

d Solve $f(x) = 4$.

10 The function $f(x)$ is defined as $f(x) = \frac{2x + 3}{x - 1}$ with $x \neq 1$.

a Express $f(x)$ in the form

$$f(x) = a + \frac{b}{x - 1}$$

where a and b are constants.

b The diagram shows a sketch of $y = f(x)$. State the coordinates of the points A, B and C and the equations of the asymptotes.

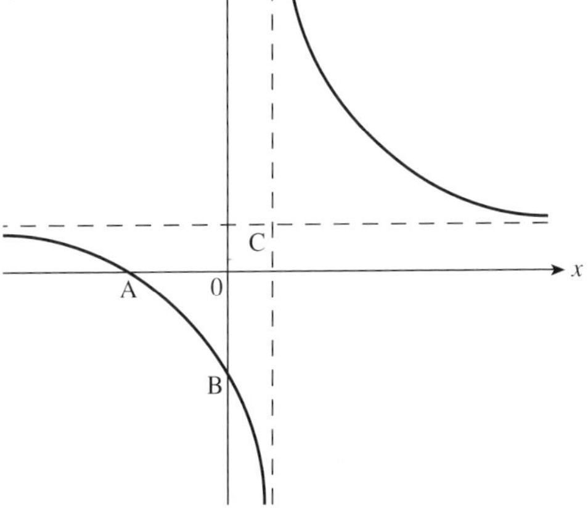

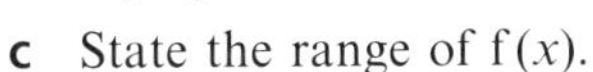

c State the range of $f(x)$.

d Solve $f(x) = x + 1$, leaving surds in the answer.

11 To be a function, a relationship must be one-to-one or many-to-one, and it must be uniquely defined for all values of the domain. Explain why these are *not* functions.

a $f(x) = \begin{cases} 3 + x & 0 \leqslant x \leqslant 2 \\ 2x & 2 \leqslant x \leqslant 4 \end{cases}$

b $f(x) = \pm\sqrt{x}$ for $x > 0$

c $y = f(x)$ for the graph of y shown here.

d $f(x) = \frac{3}{x - 2}$ for $x \in \mathbb{R}$.

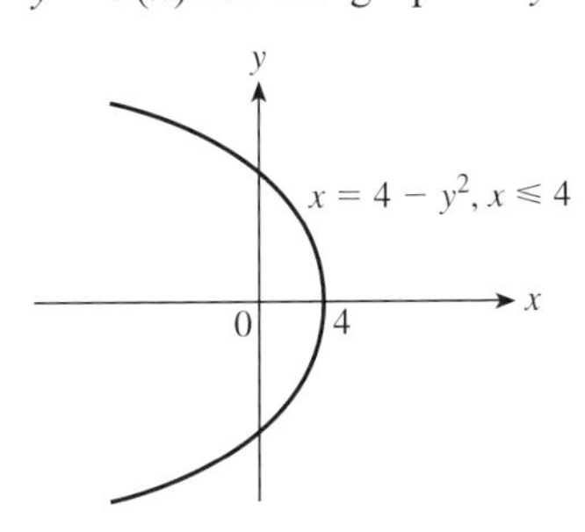

10.2 Composite functions

When two or more functions are combined, so that the output from the first function becomes the input to the second function, the result is called a **composite function.**

Consider $f(x) = 2x + 1$ with domain $\{1, 2, 3, 4, 5\}$ and $g(x) = x^2$ with domain the range of f.

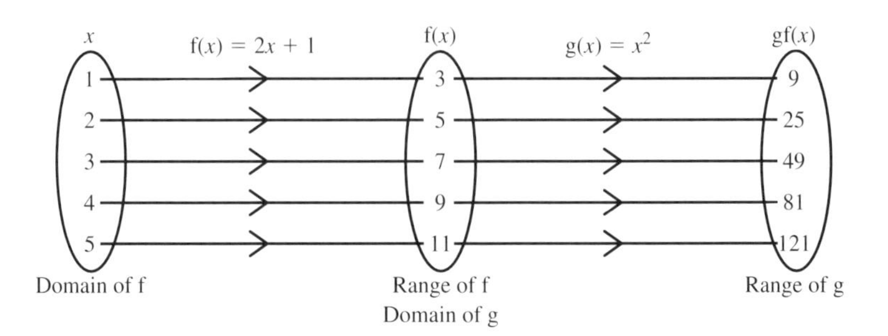

Here f is applied first, followed by g.
The function f is applied to x, and g is applied to $f(x)$. This is written

$$gf(x)$$

2nd function applied (g) ↑ ↑ 1st function applied (f)

The effect of f is to double the number and add 1.

The effect of g is to square the number.

The effect of f then g is to double the number, add 1 and then square.

The combined function of gf can be written $gf(x) = (2x + 1)^2$

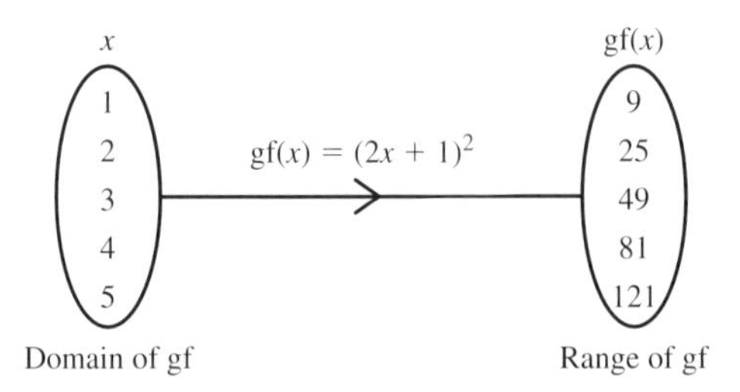

The following diagrams illustrate the process of finding composite functions. Once the process is understood it can be carried out mentally. The final algebraic expression may need to be simplified. If several functions are combined they are applied from the right.

$$fgh(x)$$

↑ ↑ ↑
3rd 2nd 1st

Consider the functions $f(x) = 2x + 1$, $g(x) = x^2$ and $h(x) = \frac{1}{x}$.

To find fg. Do g first, then f.

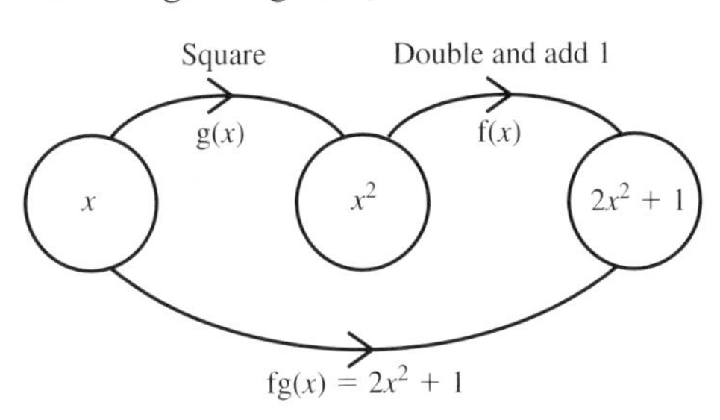

To find gh. Do h first, then g.

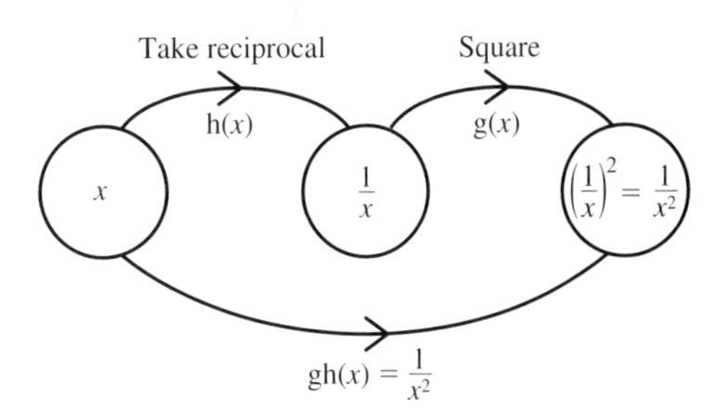

To find gfh. Do h, then f, then g.

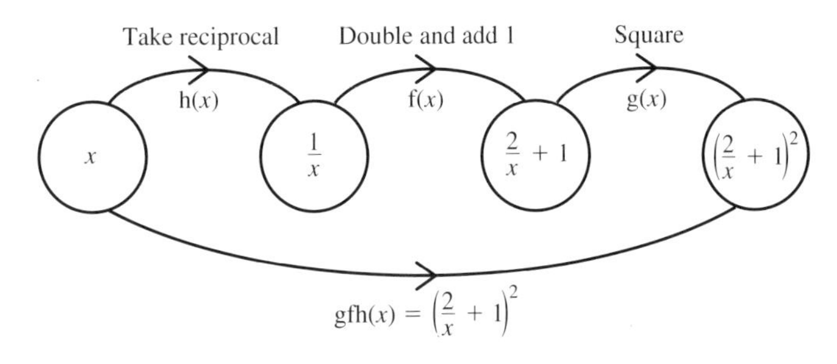

Example 4 For $f(x) = 2x + 1$, $g(x) = x^2$ and $h(x) = \frac{1}{x}$ find composite functions: fg, gh, f^2, h^2 and fgh.

a $fg(x) = 2x^2 + 1$

Do g first so x becomes x^2. Substitute x^2 in f.

Or $fg(x) = f(g(x)) = f(x^2) = 2x^2 + 1$

b $gh(x) = \left(\frac{1}{x}\right)^2 = \frac{1}{x^2}$

Do h first so x becomes $\frac{1}{x}$. Substitute $\frac{1}{x}$ in g.

Or $gh(x) = g(h(x)) = g\left(\frac{1}{x}\right) = \left(\frac{1}{x}\right)^2$

c $f^2(x) = 2(2x + 1) + 1 = 4x + 3$

$f^2(x)$ means $ff(x)$. f changes x to $2x + 1$
Substitute $2x + 1$ in f.

d $h^2(x) = \frac{1}{\frac{1}{x}} = x$

h changes x to $\frac{1}{x}$. Substitute $\frac{1}{x}$ in h.

e $fgh(x) = 2 \times \frac{1}{x^2} + 1 = \frac{2}{x^2} + 1$

h changes x to $\frac{1}{x}$. Substitute $\frac{1}{x}$ in g giving $\left(\frac{1}{x}\right)^2$.

Then substitute $\frac{1}{x^2}$ in f giving $2 \times \frac{1}{x^2} + 1$.

Example 5 $f(x) = x^2 \quad g(x) = 3x + 1$

a Show that, in general, $fg(x) \neq gf(x)$.

b Find the values of x such that $fg(x) = gf(x)$.

Solution

a

$$fg(x) = (3x + 1)^2$$

Do g first so x becomes $(3x + 1)$. Substitute $(3x + 1)$ in f.

$$= 9x^2 + 6x + 1$$

$$gf(x) = 3x^2 + 1$$

Do f first so x becomes x^2. Substitute x^2 in g.

$$\therefore \quad fg(x) \neq gf(x)$$

b

$$fg(x) = gf(x)$$

Put the two expressions equal to each other.

So $9x^2 + 6x + 1 = 3x^2 + 1$

Tidy up.

$$6x^2 + 6x = 0$$

Divide both sides by 6 and factorise.

$$x(x + 1) = 0$$

Solve the quadratic equation.

$$\Rightarrow \quad x = 0 \quad \text{or} \quad x = -1$$

So, the values of x such that $fg(x) = gf(x)$ are $x = -1$ and $x = 0$.

➤ The composite function, fg, can be formed only if the range of g is a subset of (i.e. is contained within) the domain of f.

Example 6

This example illustrates problems which may arise from incompatible domains and ranges.

Given that $f: x \rightarrow 2x + 1$, domain $0 < x < 10$, and $g: x \rightarrow x^2$, domain $0 < x < 3$, can fg and gf be formed?

$f: x \rightarrow 2x + 1, \; 0 < x < 10$

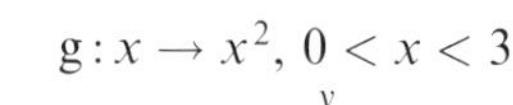

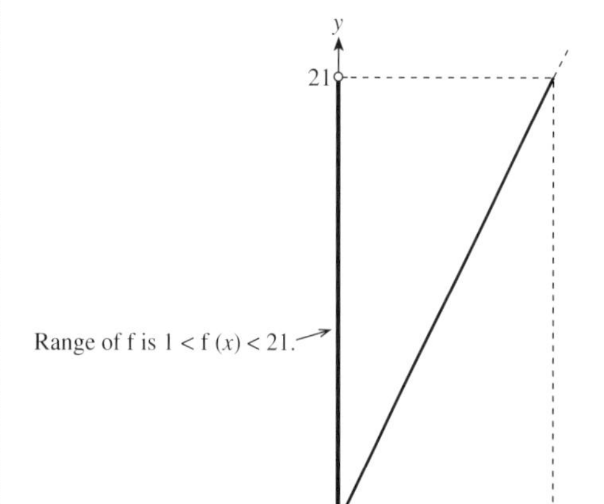

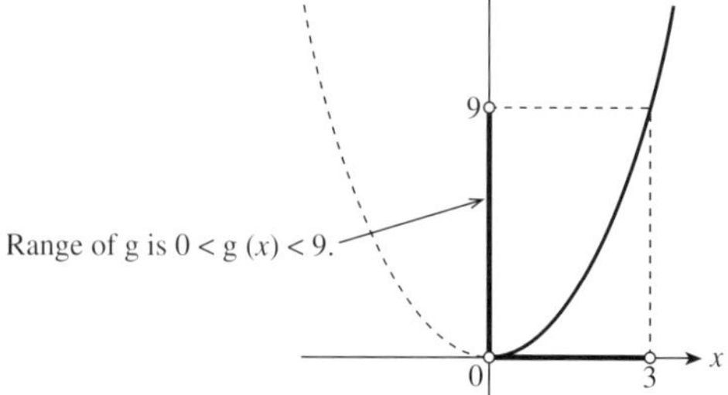

Consider fg. Applying g first will give the range $0 < g(x) < 9$.
This range falls within domain of f so f can be applied. Hence fg can be formed.

Consider gf. Applying f first will give range $1 < f(x) < 21$.
The domain of g is $0 < x < 3$ so g can only be applied to the range of f which falls between 0 and 3, i.e. $1 < x < 3$.

So gf can only be formed if the domain of f is restricted to $0 < x < 1$.

EXERCISE 10b

In this exercise, the domain is $x \in \mathbb{R}$, unless stated otherwise.

1 Given that $f(x) = 3x + 4$ and $g(x) = x^2$ find

a $g(2)$ **b** $f(g(2))$ **c** $fg(x)$ **d** $fg(2)$

2 For each of these pairs of functions, find $fg(x)$ and $gf(x)$.

a $f(x) = x + 1$, $g(x) = x + 2$
b $f(x) = 2x - 1$, $g(x) = 3x + 2$
c $f(x) = x + 2$, $g(x) = x - 2$
d $f(x) = 2x + 1$, $g(x) = 4 - 3x$
e $f(x) = x + 1$, $g(x) = x^2$
f $f(x) = \frac{1}{x}$, $x \neq 0$, $g(x) = 2x$
g $f(x) = \frac{1}{x}$, $x \neq 0$, $g(x) = x + 1$
h $f(x) = (x + 1)(x - 2)$, $g(x) = 2x$

(Notice how rarely fg and gf are the same.)

3 Given that $f : x \rightarrow x^2$, $g : x \rightarrow \frac{1}{x}$ and $h : x \rightarrow 3x - 1$

find expressions for these functions, expressing them in the form $fg : x \rightarrow \ldots$

(Note $hgf(x) = h(gf(x))$ so the answer to part **b** can be used in part **g** for example).

a fg **b** gf **c** gh **d** ff
e gg **f** hh **g** hgf **h** fgh
i fhg **j** hfg **k** ghf **l** gfh

4 **a** Given that $f(x) = 3x + 1$ and $g(x) = 5x + k$, find k if $fg(x) = gf(x)$.

b Check the answer to part **a** by showing that $fg(3) = gf(3)$.

5 Given that

$f(x) = x^2 - 1$, $g(x) = 3x + 2$ and $h(x) = \frac{1}{x}$

solve these equations.

a $fg(x) = 15$ **b** $gh(x) = -4$ **c** $hg(x) = x$ **d** $gg(x) = h(x)$

6 Given $f(x) = 2x + 7$, $g(x) = x^2$ and $h(x) = x^3$, find, stating the range, an expression for

a $fg(x)$ **b** $fh(x)$ **c** $gf(x)$ **d** $hf(x)$

7 Suppose $f : x \rightarrow x^2 - 3$ and $g : x \rightarrow x + 4$.

a Express fg and gf in the form $fg : x \rightarrow \ldots$ and $gf : x \rightarrow \ldots$

b State the ranges of fg and of gf.

c Find k such that $fg(k) = gf(k)$.

d Find l leaving surds in the answer, such that $fg(l) = gf(3l)$.

8 **a** Given that $f(x) = x + 5$ find $ff(x)$, $fff(x)$ and $f^n(x)$, where $f^n(x)$ indicates that the function f is applied n times.

b Find the function $g(x)$ such that $g^n(x) = 2^n x$

c Find the function $h(x)$ such that $h^n(x) = \frac{x}{a^n}$

EXERCISE 10b *(continued)*

9 Suppose $f: x \to 2x - 1$, $g: x \to 3x^2 + 2$ and $h: x \to ax + b$ where a and b are positive constants.

a Show that $fg: x \to 6x^2 + 3$ and find the function gf.

b Find a and b such that $fgh: x \to 6x^2 + 12x + 9$.

c Find the values of x for which $fgh(x) = 57$.

10 Given that $f: x \to x + 2$, $g: x \to 2x^2 + 3$ and $h(x) \to \frac{1}{x}$, $x \neq 0$, find these functions.

a ff **b** gg **c** hh **d** hgf

e hfg **f** fgh **g** fhg **h** hgh

11 **a** Given that $f(x) = |x| + 1$ and $g(x) = x^2 + 4$, state the range of f and the range of g.

b Find the functions, ff, gg and fg, stating their ranges.

12 The composite function, fg, can be formed only if the range of g is a subset of (i.e. is contained within) the domain of f.

In the following examples this is not the case. Suggest the largest possible restricted domain of g which allows fg to be formed.

a $f(x) = \sqrt{x}$, $x \geqslant 0$
$g(x) = x + 2$, $x \in \mathbb{R}$

b $f(x) = 2x + 1$, $x \leqslant 20$
$g(x) = 5x$, $x \in \mathbb{R}$

c $f(x) = \frac{1}{x+2}$, $x \geqslant 0$
$g(x) = 4 - x^2$, $x \in \mathbb{R}$

d $f(x) = \sqrt{x - 3}$, $x \geqslant 3$
$g(x) = \frac{2}{x}$, $x \in \mathbb{R}$, $x \neq 0$

10.3 Inverse functions

Consider again the example $f(x) = 2x + 1$ with domain $\{1, 2, 3, 4, 5\}$, and range $\{3, 5, 7, 9, 11\}$ (page 209).

The **inverse function** of f maps from the range of f back to the domain. The arrows would go in the opposite direction.

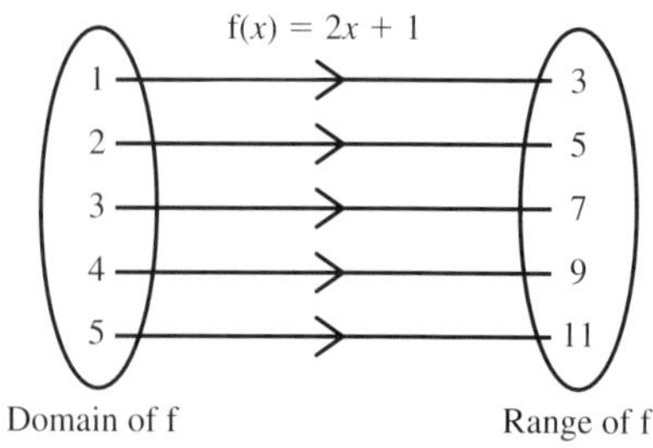

Since f has the effect of 'double and add one', the inverse function would be 'subtract one and halve'.

The inverse function is written $f^{-1}(x)$.

In this case,

$$f^{-1}(x) = \frac{x-1}{2}$$

or

$$f^{-1}: x \to \frac{x-1}{2}$$

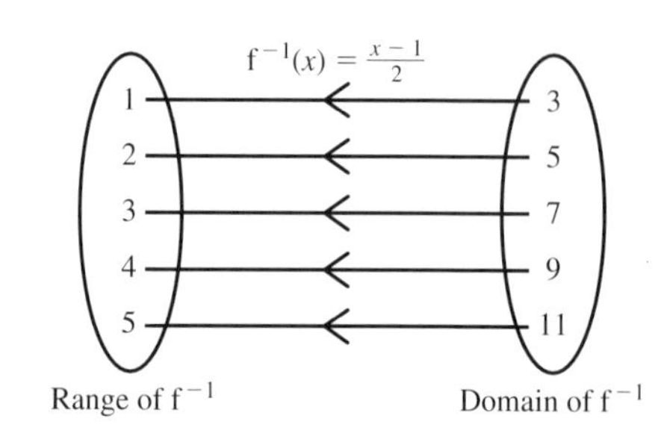

✓ ***Note*** The notation for inverse functions is unfortunate as it can be confused with reciprocals. Take care!

These are examples using $^{-1}$ for a reciprocal

$$x^{-1} = \frac{1}{x} \quad (\mathrm{f}(x))^{-1} = \frac{1}{\mathrm{f}(x)} \quad (\sin x)^{-1} = \frac{1}{\sin x}$$

whereas $\mathrm{f}^{-1}(x)$ is the inverse of $\mathrm{f}(x)$ and $\sin^{-1} x$ is inverse of $\sin x$.

For a unique inverse to exist the function must be one-to-one for the given domain.

Consider $\mathrm{f}(x) = x^2$, $x \in \mathbb{R}$, a many-to-one function.

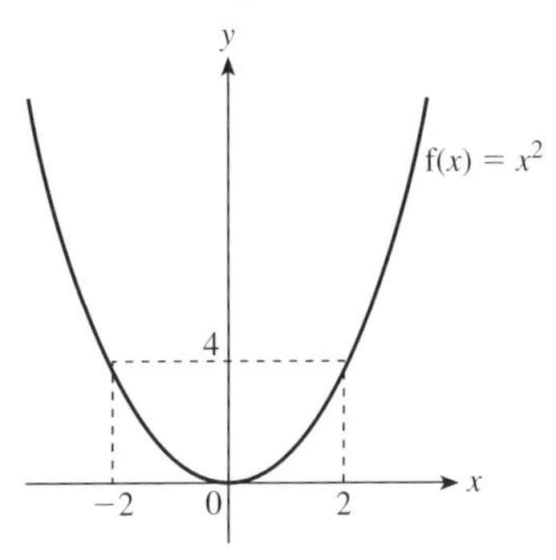

$\mathrm{f}(2) = 4$

$\mathrm{f}(-2) = 4$

Two values of x, $+2$ and -2, have an image 4. Working backwards $\mathrm{f}^{-1}(4)$ does not have a unique answer and hence $\mathrm{f}(x) = x^2$ does not have an inverse function. However, if the domain of f is restricted to exclude negative numbers the inverse function $\mathrm{f}^{-1}(x) = \sqrt{x}$ can then be defined.

✓ ***Remember*** $\sqrt{}$ means take the +ve square root.

✓ ***Note*** One-to-one functions have inverses.

For many-to-one functions, an inverse can be defined by restricting the domain so that, for that part of the domain, the function is one-to-one.

Graphs of functions and their inverse functions

Consider $\mathrm{f}(x) = 2x + 1$ and its inverse function $\mathrm{f}^{-1}(x) = \dfrac{x-1}{2}$

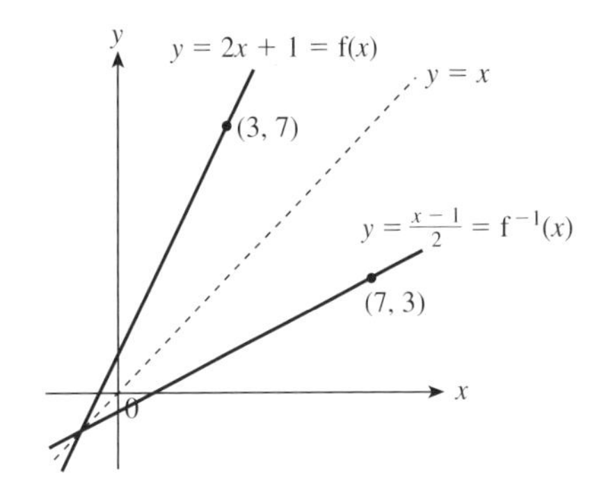

$\mathrm{f}(3) = 7$

$\mathrm{f}^{-1}(7) = 3$

A point on the graph of $y = \mathrm{f}(x)$ will be (3, 7) and a point on the graph of $y = \mathrm{f}^{-1}(x)$ will be (7, 3).

In general if (a, b) lies on $y = \mathrm{f}(x)$ then (b, a) lies on $y = \mathrm{f}^{-1}(x)$.

For a function and its inverse, the roles of x and y are interchanged, so the two graphs are reflections of each other in the line $y = x$.

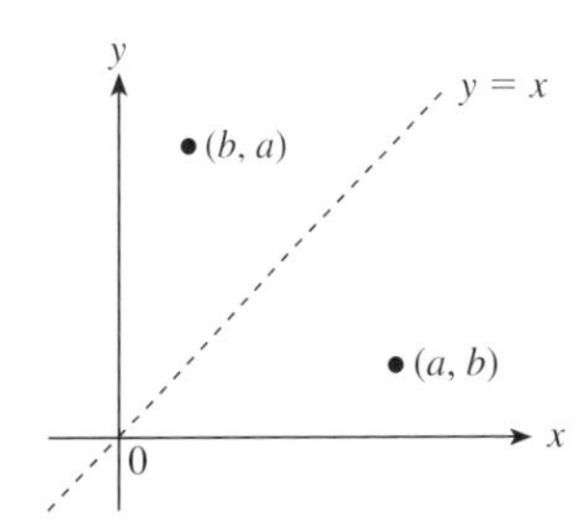

The graphs of a function and its inverse are reflections of each other in $y = x$, provided the scales on the axes are the same.

To see what the graph of an inverse function looks like, turn over a page that has the graph of the function on it and rotate the page through 90° (clockwise). Hold the page to the light; the graph of the inverse function is seen.

Finding an inverse, i.e. working backwards, requires the same process as rearranging a formula or solving an equation.

For simple examples no formal method is needed.

Function $f(x)$	Process	Inverse process	Inverse function $f^{-1}(x)$
kx	Multiply by k	Divide by k	$\frac{x}{k}$ 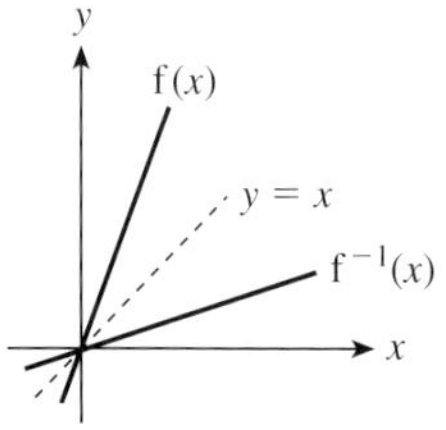
$2x$	Double	Halve	$\frac{x}{2}$
$x + c$	Add c	Subtract c	$x - c$ 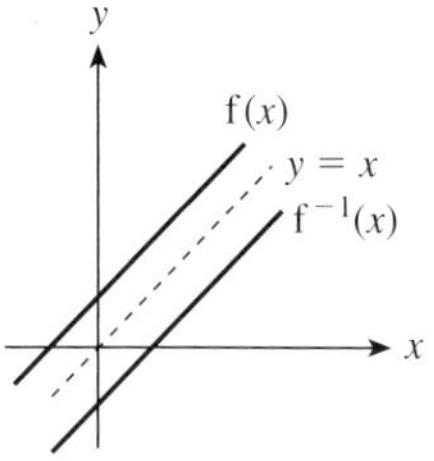
$x + 1$	Add 1	Subtract 1	$x - 1$
$ax + b$	Multiply by a and add b	Subtract b and divide by a	$\frac{x - b}{a}$ 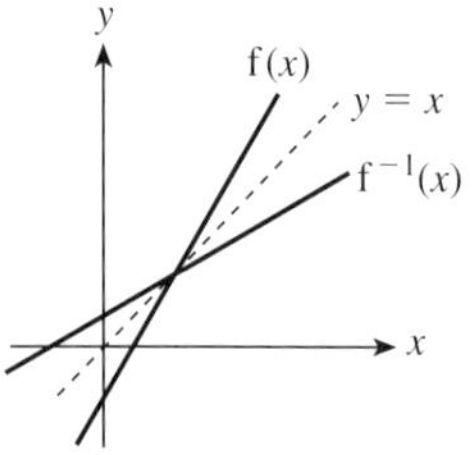
$3x - 4$	Multiply by 3 and subtract 4	Add four and divide by 3	$\frac{x + 4}{3}$
$x^2, x \geqslant 0$	Square	Find square root	$\sqrt{x} \quad x \geqslant 0$ 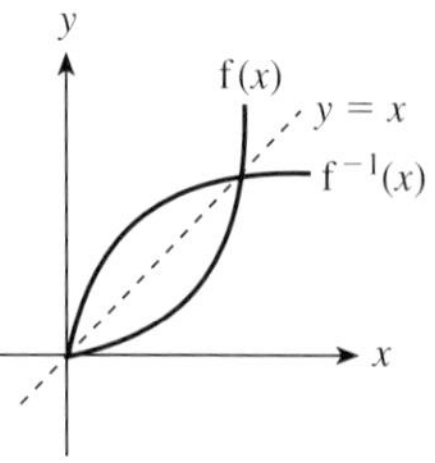

For more complicated examples, the following method of finding an inverse is suggested. A simple example is used to illustrate the method.

Example 7 Given $f(x) = 3x - 4$, find the inverse function, $f^{-1}(x)$.

Let $3x - 4 = y$

Let the image of x be y. That is, the result of applying the function to x is y.

$3x = y + 4$

To find how to go backwards, rearrange to give x in terms of y.

$\therefore \quad x = \dfrac{y+4}{3}$

So $f^{-1}(x) = \dfrac{x+4}{3}$.

So given the image, y, $\frac{y+4}{3}$ must be worked out to get back to x. That is, add 4 to the number and divide by 3. *Note*: y in $\frac{y+4}{3}$ has been replaced by x.

➤ To find the inverse function, $f^{-1}(x)$ of $f(x)$

- Put the function equal to y.
- Rearrange to give x in terms of y.
- Rewrite as $f^{-1}(x)$ replacing y by x.

Example 8 Given $f(x) = \dfrac{1}{2-x}$ for $x \neq 2$, find the inverse function, $f^{-1}(x)$.

Let $\dfrac{1}{2-x} = y$

Put the function equal to y. Rearrange to give x in terms of y.

so $1 = y(2 - x)$

Multiply both sides by $2 - x$.

$= 2y - xy$

$xy = 2y - 1$

Isolate the term with x on one side and the rest of the terms on the other.

$x = \dfrac{2y-1}{y}$

Divide by y.

$\therefore \quad f^{-1}(x) = \dfrac{2x-1}{x}$

Rewrite as $f^{-1}(x)$ replacing y by x.

From the graph, for $f(x)$, the domain is $x \in \mathbb{R}$, $x \neq 2$, and the range is $y \in \mathbb{R}$, $y \neq 0$.

For the inverse function, $f^{-1}(x)$, the domain and range are reversed.

For $f^{-1}(x)$, the domain is $x \in \mathbb{R}$, $x \neq 0$, and the range is $y \in \mathbb{R}$, $y \neq 2$.

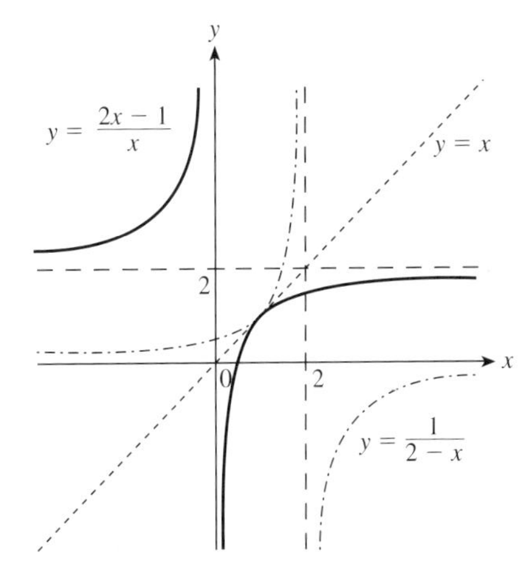

➤ For a function and its inverse, the roles of x and y are interchanged, so the range of $f(x)$ is the domain of $f^{-1}(x)$, and the range of $f^{-1}(x)$ is the domain of $f(x)$.

Example 9 Given $f(x) = \frac{13 - 6x}{7}$

a find the inverse function, $f^{-1}(x)$

b check the result using $x = 2$

c show that $ff^{-1}(x) = f^{-1}f(x) = x$.

Solution

a Let $\frac{13 - 6x}{7} = y$

Put the function equal to y.

$$13 - 6x = 7y$$

Rearrange to give x in terms of y.

$$6x = 13 - 7y$$

So $x = \frac{13 - 7y}{6}$

Rewrite as $f^{-1}(x)$ replacing y by x.

And $f^{-1}(x) = \frac{13 - 7x}{6}$

b $f(2) = \frac{13 - 6 \times 2}{7} = \frac{1}{7}$

Applying the function to 2 gives $\frac{1}{7}$; applying the inverse function to $\frac{1}{7}$ gives 2.

$f^{-1}\left(\frac{1}{7}\right) = \frac{13 - 7 \times \frac{1}{7}}{6} = \frac{13 - 1}{6} = 2$

$f(2) = \frac{1}{7}$ and $f^{-1}\left(\frac{1}{7}\right) = 2$. The inverse function 'undoes' the function.

c $f^{-1}(x) = \frac{13 - 7x}{6}$

From part **a**.

$$ff^{-1}(x) = \frac{13 - \frac{6 \times (13 - 7x)}{6}}{7}$$

Substitute $\frac{13 - 7x}{6}$ in f.

$$= \frac{13 - (13 - 7x)}{7}$$

Note: $13 - (13 - 7x) = 13 - 13 + 7x$

$$= x$$

$$f(x) = \frac{13 - 6x}{7}$$

$$f^{-1}f(x) = \frac{13 - \frac{7 \times (13 - 6x)}{7}}{6}$$

Substitute $\frac{13 - 6x}{7}$ in f.

$$= \frac{13 - (13 - 6x)}{6}$$

$$= x$$

So $ff^{-1}(x) = f^{-1}f(x) = x$.

Self-inverse functions

When $f(x) = f^{-1}(x)$ the function is said to be **self-inverse**.

Example 10

Show that $f(x) = \dfrac{x}{x-1}$ is self-inverse.

Let $\dfrac{x}{x-1} = y$

Put the function equal to y, and rearrange to give x in terms of y, by multiplying both sides by $x - 1$.

$$x = y(x-1)$$
$$= xy - y$$
$$y = xy - x$$
$$= x(y-1)$$

Take x outside the bracket.

So $x = \dfrac{y}{y-1}$

Rewrite as $f^{-1}(x)$ replacing y by x.

And $f^{-1}(x) = \dfrac{x}{x-1}$

Since $f(x) = f^{-1}(x)$ the function is self-inverse.

> Since a function, $f(x)$, and its inverse, $f^{-1}(x)$, undo each other $ff^{-1}(x) = f^{-1}f(x) = x$.
> If $f(x) = f^{-1}(x)$, then $f(x)$ is self-inverse.
> If $ff(x) = x$, then $f(x)$ is self-inverse.

EXERCISE 10c

For this exercise, the domain is $\mathbb{R}$ unless stated otherwise.

1 Find the inverse functions, $f^{-1}(x)$, of these functions, and state which of them have the property $f(x) = f^{-1}(x)$ (i.e. are self-inverse).

a $f(x) = 3x$ **b** $f(x) = x + 4$ **c** $f(x) = x - 5$

d $f(x) = \dfrac{x}{6}$ **e** $f(x) = \dfrac{1}{x}, \quad x \neq 0$ **f** $f(x) = x^2, \quad x \geqslant 0$

g $f(x) = 3x - 4$ **h** $f(x) = 3 - 2x$ **i** $f(x) = 4 - x$

j $f(x) = \dfrac{x+6}{5}$ **k** $f(x) = \dfrac{5}{x}$ **l** $f(x) = \dfrac{1}{1-x}$

2 Find the inverse of each of these functions, stating which functions are self-inverse.

a $f: x \to \dfrac{2x+5}{3}$ **b** $f: x \to \dfrac{2x}{3} + 5$ **c** $f: x \to 2\left(\dfrac{x}{3} + 5\right)$

d $f: x \to 2x + \frac{5}{3}$ **e** $f: x \to \frac{2}{3}(x + 5)$ **f** $f: x \to \sqrt{x+4}, x \geqslant -4$

g $f: x \to 7(x - 4)$ **h** $f: x \to 4 - 7x$ **i** $f: x \to 3x^2 + 2, x \geqslant 0$

j $f: x \to \dfrac{4}{7x}, x \neq 0$ **k** $f: x \to \dfrac{1}{x+1}, x \neq -1$ **l** $f: x \to \dfrac{1}{1-\frac{1}{x}}, x \neq 0, -1$

m $f: x \to \dfrac{1}{x} + 1, x \neq 0$ **n** $f: x \to \dfrac{3}{5x}, x \neq 0$ **o** $f: x \to \dfrac{a}{bx}, x \neq 0$

p $f: x \to \frac{1}{2}\sqrt{x}, x > 0$ **q** $f: x \to \sqrt{2-x}, x \leqslant 2$ **r** $f: x \to x^3 - 1$

s $f: x \to (3x+1)^2 - 4, x \geqslant -\frac{1}{3}$ **t** $f: x \to \sqrt{2x-1} + 5, x \geqslant \frac{1}{2}$

EXERCISE 10c
(continued)

3 For each of these functions, by completing the square, or otherwise, find the range and the inverse function $f^{-1}(x)$. State the domain and range of $f^{-1}(x)$ and sketch, on the same axes, $y = f(x)$, $y = f^{-1}(x)$ and $y = x$.

a $f(x) = x^2 + 6x,\ x > -3$ **b** $f(x) = x^2 - 4x + 7,\ x > 2$

c $f(x) = 2 - 2x - x^2,\ x \geqslant -1$

4 **a** For $f(x) = 3x + 1$:

i Find $f^{-1}(x)$ and state its domain.

ii Sketch the graphs $y = f(x)$, $y = f^{-1}(x)$ and $y = x$ on the same axes, showing where the lines intersect.

iii Show that $ff^{-1}(x) = f^{-1}f(x) = x$.

iv Solve $f(x) = f^{-1}(x)$ and hence state the coordinates of the point of intersection in **ii**.

b Repeat part **a** for $f(x) = 2 - 4x$.

5 $f(x) = 3x + 2$ and $g(x) = \dfrac{1}{x}$ with $x \neq 0$.

a Find $f^{-1}(x)$, $g^{-1}(x)$ and $gf(x)$

b Show that $(gf)^{-1}(x) = f^{-1}g^{-1}(x) = \dfrac{1}{3}\left(\dfrac{1}{x} - 2\right)$.

6 Given that $f(x) = 2x - 5$ and $g(x) = 1 - x$ show that $(fg)^{-1}(x) = g^{-1}f^{-1}(x)$.

7 These functions are many-to-one and, therefore, do not have inverses. However, by restricting the domain, an inverse function can be found. Find a largest possible domain such that the functions are one-to-one, the corresponding ranges, and the inverse functions for the domains found. Assume $x \in \mathbb{R}$ and $x > -6$.

a $f(x) = x^2$

b $f(x) = (x + 2)^4$

c $f(x) = 4 - (x + 1)^2$

8 **a** Show that the function $g(x) = \dfrac{x}{x - 1}$ is self-inverse.

b Sketch $y = \dfrac{x}{x - 1}$ and $y = x$ on the same axes and comment on the graphs.

9 **a** Copy the graph and, on the same axes, sketch $y = f^{-1}(x)$ and $y = f(x - 2)$.

b State the points at which the curves of $y = f^{-1}(x)$ and $y = f(x - 2)$ cut the axes.

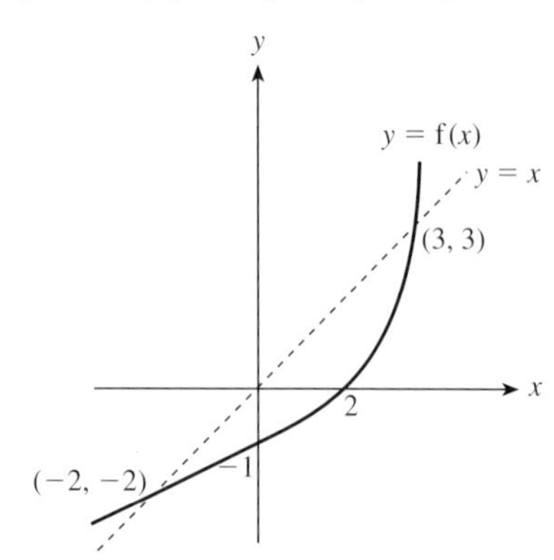

10 **a** Given that $f(x) = \dfrac{4}{x-1}$ with $x > 1$, find the inverse function $f^{-1}(x)$ and state its domain.

b Sketch the graphs of $y = f(x)$, $y = f^{-1}(x)$ and $y = x$ on the same axes.

c Solve $f(x) = f^{-1}(x)$, giving the answer correct to 3 significant figures.

11 For a function to have an inverse, it must be a one-to-one function. Find, giving reasons, which of these have inverses.

a $f: x \to 4 - x^2 \quad x \in \mathbb{R}$

b $f: x \to 4 - x^2 \quad x \in \mathbb{R} \quad x \leqslant 0$

c $f: x \to \dfrac{1}{x} \quad x \in \mathbb{R} \quad x \neq 0$

d $f: x \to \dfrac{1}{x-1} \quad x \in \mathbb{R}$

12 A function is defined as $f(x) = \dfrac{10-x}{x+2}$ with $x \neq -2$. Find

a $f(6)$ **b** $f^{-1}(2)$ **c** k such that $f(k) = k$

13 **a** Given that $g(x) = \dfrac{2x+1}{x+2}$ with $x \neq -2$, find $g^{-1}(x)$ stating its domain.

b Solve $g(x) = g^{-1}(x)$.

14 **a** Given that $h(x) = -\dfrac{1}{x+1}$ with $x \neq -1$, find $h^{-1}(x)$ stating its domain.

b Show that $h(x) = h^{-1}(x)$ has no real solution.

15 Given $f(x) = \dfrac{2x+1}{a-x} \quad x \neq a$

a Find $f^{-1}(x)$ and state its domain

b Find the value of a such that $f^{-1}(3) = 4$.

c Find the value of a, $a \neq 0$, such that $f(x+a) = f(x)$ and explain the answer.

10.4 Even and odd functions

An **even function** is one where $f(x) = f(-x)$ for all values of x.

The graph is symmetrical about the y-axis.

Examples of even functions are $f(x) = x^2$, $f(x) = x^4$ and $f(x) = \cos x$.

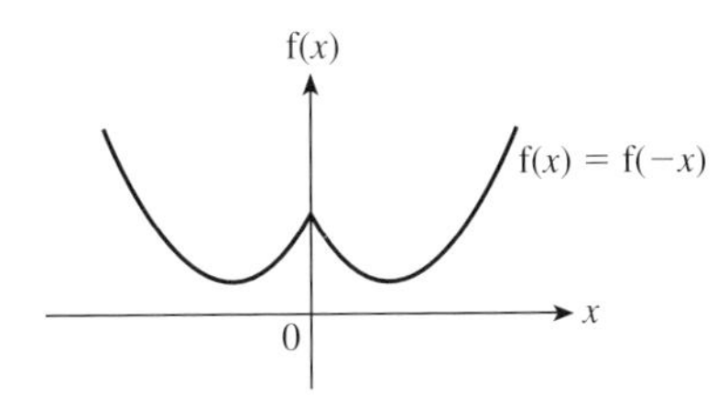

An **odd function** is one where $f(x) = -f(-x)$ for all values of x.

The graph has 180° rotational symmetry about the origin, (0, 0).

Examples of odd functions are $f(x) = x$, $f(x) = x^3$ and $f(x) = \sin x$.

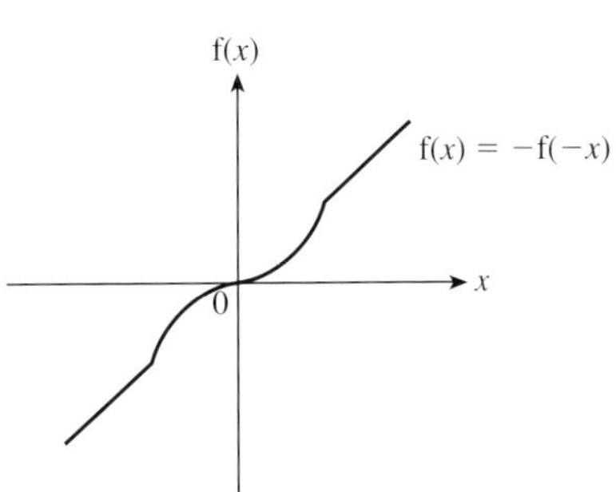

Most functions are neither even nor odd.

For example, $f(x) = x^2 + \dfrac{1}{x}$.

10.5 Periodic functions

Functions which repeat at regular intervals are called **periodic functions**.

Formally, if there is some value of h such that $f(x) = f(x + h)$ for all values of x then $f(x)$ is said to be **periodic**.

If h is the smallest value for which $f(x) = f(x + h)$ then $f(x)$ has period h.

For example, a function may be defined for $x \in \mathbb{R}$ as $f(x) = 2x$, with $0 \leqslant x < 2$ and $f(x) = f(x + 2)$. This function is periodic of period 2.

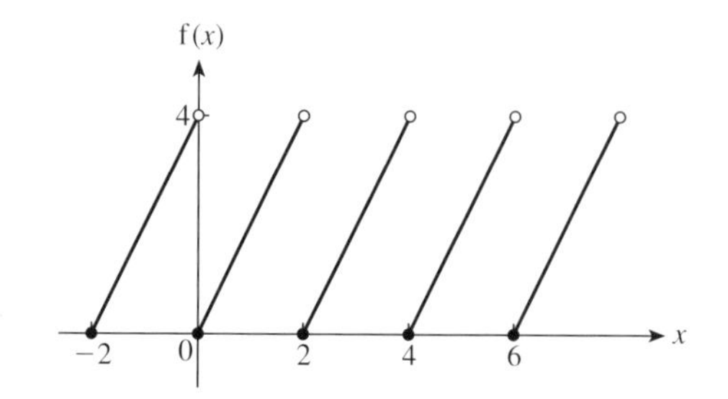

Consider $f(x) = \sin x$ where x is measured in degrees. $\sin x = \sin(x + 360°)$ so $\sin x$ is periodic of period 360°.

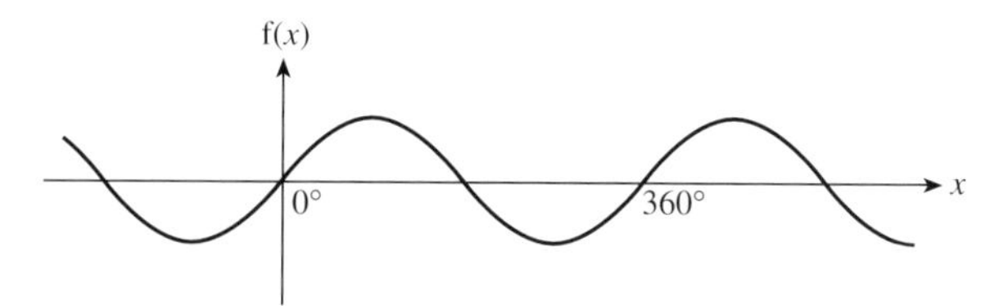

10.6 Curve sketching 2

In Chapter 7, curve sketching was approached by transformation of curves. In this section, further techniques are introduced. Ask these questions when sketching a graph.

- Is the graph a standard function or the transformation of one?
- Where does the graph cross the axes?

  Putting $x = 0$ will give the intercept(s) on the y-axis.
  Putting $y = 0$ will give the intercept(s) on the x-axis.
- Does the graph have symmetry?

  Is it symmetrical about the y-axis?
  This applies to all *even* functions: $f(x) = f(-x)$.

  > *Note*: If all powers of x are even, the graph will be symmetrical about the y-axis.

  Does it have 180° rotational symmetry about the origin?
  This applies to all *odd* functions: $f(x) = -f(-x)$.

  > *Note*: If all powers of x are odd, the graph will have 180° rotational symmetry about the origin.

- Does the graph have discontinuities? Are there values of x for which the function is not defined (values which make the denominator zero)? These values will give rise to asymptotes.
- What happens for large positive and negative values of x?

  If $f(x)$ is a polynomial in x then the highest power of x will determine its behaviour as $x \to \pm\infty$.

  (Read $x \to \pm\infty$ as 'x tends to plus or minus infinity'.

  If the highest power term is ax^n then

  n even, $a > 0$ $\quad f(x) \to +\infty$ as $x \to +\infty$

  $\qquad\qquad\qquad f(x) \to +\infty$ as $x \to -\infty$

  n odd, $a > 0$ $\quad f(x) \to +\infty$ as $x \to +\infty$

  $\qquad\qquad\qquad f(x) \to -\infty$ as $x \to -\infty$

  If $a < 0$ the results are reversed. The term ax^n is the dominant term.
- Does the function have stationary values, i.e. points where the gradient is zero?

Example 11

$f(x) = 2x^3 - 9x^2 + 12x - 4$

a Show that $2x - 1$ is a factor of $f(x)$.

b Find where the curve $y = f(x)$ crosses the axes.

c State the behaviour of $f(x)$ as $x \to \pm\infty$.

d Find any stationary points of $y = f(x)$.

e Sketch the curve.

f Using the sketch, or otherwise, determine the range of values of k for which $f(x) = k$ has three distinct real roots.

Solution

a $f\left(\frac{1}{2}\right) = 2 \times \left(\frac{1}{2}\right)^3 - 9 \times \left(\frac{1}{2}\right)^2 + 12 \times \frac{1}{2} - 4$

$2x - 1 = 0 \Rightarrow x = \frac{1}{2}$

$= \frac{1}{4} - \frac{9}{4} + 6 - 4 = 0$

$f\left(\frac{1}{2}\right) = 0 \Rightarrow 2x - 1$ is a factor of $f(x)$

$\therefore\ 2x - 1$ is a factor of $f(x)$.

b $y = 2x^3 - 9x^2 + 12x - 4$

When $x = 0$, $y = -4$, so the curve crosses the y-axis at $(0, -4)$.
The curve crosses the x-axis when $y = 0$.

$$\begin{aligned} y &= 2x^3 - 9x^2 + 12x - 4 \\ &= (2x - 1)(x^2 - 4x + 4) \\ &= (2x - 1)(x - 2)^2 \end{aligned}$$

When $(2x - 1)(x - 2)^2 = 0$

$x = \frac{1}{2}$ or $x = 2$ (double root)

$x = 2$ is a *double* root so the curve will meet the x-axis in *two* coincident points, i.e. will touch the x-axis, at $x = 2$.

$\therefore\ y = f(x)$ crosses the x-axis at $\left(\frac{1}{2}, 0\right)$ and touches the x-axis at $(2, 0)$.

So the curve crosses the axes at $(0, -4)$ and $\left(\frac{1}{2}, 0\right)$ and touches the x-axis at $(2, 0)$.

c As $x \to +\infty$, $y \to +\infty$
and as $x \to -\infty$, $y \to -\infty$

$2x^3$ is the dominant term and since the power is odd $y \to +\infty$ for large +ve values of x and $y \to -\infty$ for large −ve values of x.

d $f'(x) = 6x^2 - 18x + 12$

At a stationary value, $f'(x) = 0$

$$6x^2 - 18x + 12 = 0$$
$$x^2 - 3x + 2 = 0$$
$$(x - 1)(x - 2) = 0$$
$$\Rightarrow \quad x = 1 \text{ or } x = 2$$

Differentiate $f(x)$ to find stationary points where gradient $f'(x) = 0$ $\left(\text{use } f'(x) \text{ or } \frac{dy}{dx}\right)$.

Stationary points occur when $x = 1$ and $x = 2$.

$$f'(x) = 6x^2 - 18x + 12$$
$$\Rightarrow \quad f''(x) = 12x - 18$$

Consider the value of $f''(x)$ to determine the nature of the stationary points.

When $x = 1$ $\quad f(x) = 2 - 9 + 12 - 4$
$$= 1$$
and $\quad f''(x) = -6 < 0$

$\therefore$ (1, 1) is a maximum point.

$f''(x) < 0 \Rightarrow$ maximum point

When $x = 2$ $\quad f(x) = 2 \times 2^3 - 9 \times 2^2 + 12 \times 2 - 4$
$$= 16 - 36 + 24 - 4$$
$$= 0$$
and $\quad f''(x) = 6 > 0$

$\therefore$ (2, 0) is a minimum point.

$f''(x) > 0 \Rightarrow$ minimum point

e

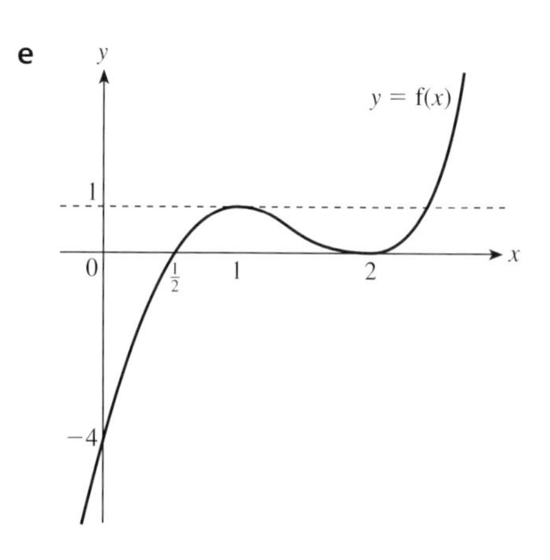

Assemble the information for the sketch.

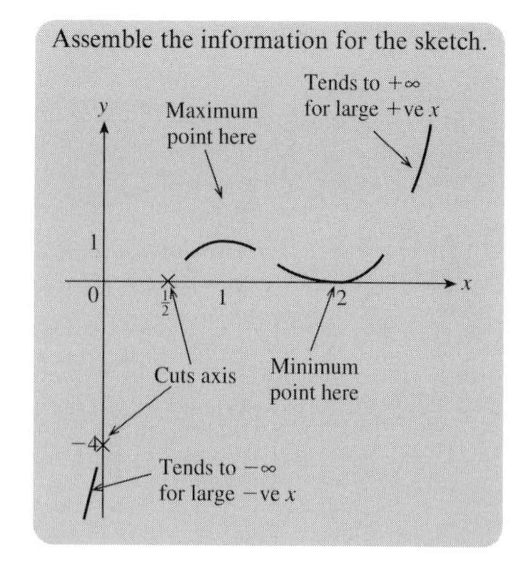

f $f(x) = k$ has three distinct real roots if $y = k$ cuts $y = f(x)$ in three distinct points.

From the sketch, it can be seen that, for $0 < k < 1$, there are three distinct real roots.

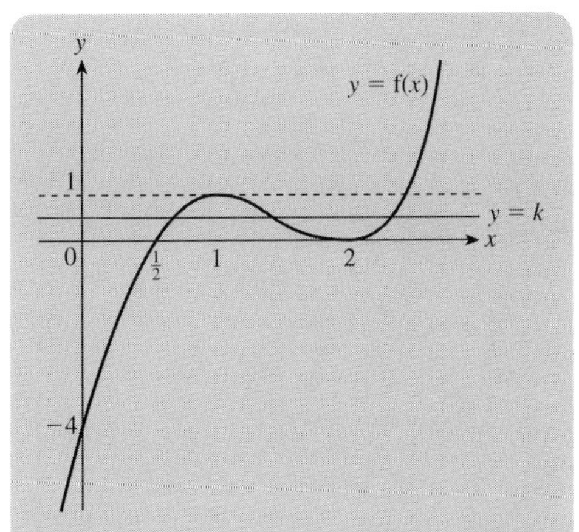

For $0 < k < 1$ the line $y = k$ cuts $y = f(x)$ in 3 points.

✓ *Note* In Example 11:

$k = 0$ or $k = 1$ will give two distinct real roots

$k < 0$ or $k > 1$ will give one real root.

Example 12 $f(x) = \dfrac{x+4}{x-1}$

a Express $f(x)$ in the form $f(x) = A + \dfrac{B}{x-1}$ where A and B are constants.

b State the behaviour of $f(x)$ as $x \to \pm\infty$.

c State any value(s) of x for which the curve $y = f(x)$ is discontinuous and the equation of any associated asymptote(s).

d Find where the curve cuts the axes.

e Sketch the curve.

f Show that $f(x)$ is self-inverse.

Solution

a $f(x) = \dfrac{x+4}{x-1}$

$= \dfrac{(x-1)+5}{x-1}$

$= 1 + \dfrac{5}{x-1}$

$\dfrac{(x-1)+5}{x-1} = \dfrac{x-1}{x-1} + \dfrac{5}{x-1} = 1 + \dfrac{5}{x-1}$

b As $x \to \pm\infty$, $f(x) \to 1$

So $y = 1$ is an asymptote to the curve $y = f(x)$.

As $x \to \pm\infty$, $\dfrac{5}{x-1} \to 0$

c $y = \dfrac{x+4}{x-1}$

At $x = 1$ the curve is discontinuous.

So $x = 1$ is an asymptote.

When $x = 1$ the denominator, $x - 1$, is zero and there is a break in the curve.

d When $x = 0$, $y = -4$.

The y-axis is $x = 0$.

When $y = 0$ $\quad \dfrac{x+4}{x-1} = 0$

The x-axis is $y = 0$.

$$x + 4 = 0$$

Remember: If a fraction is zero, its numerator must be zero.

$$\therefore \quad x = -4$$

So the curve cuts the x-axis at $(-4, 0)$ and the y-axis at $(0, -4)$.

e

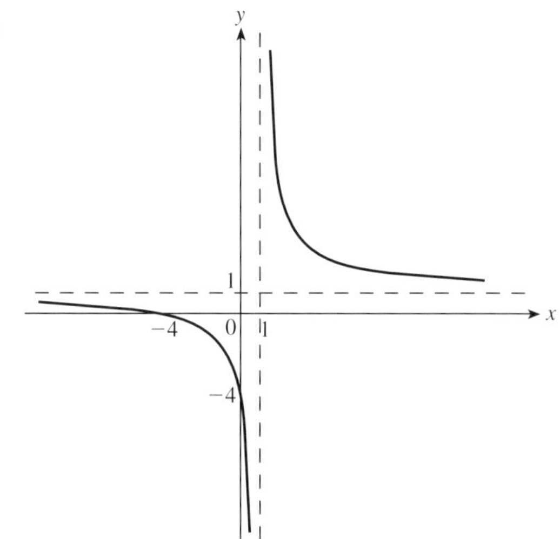

Assemble the information for the sketch.

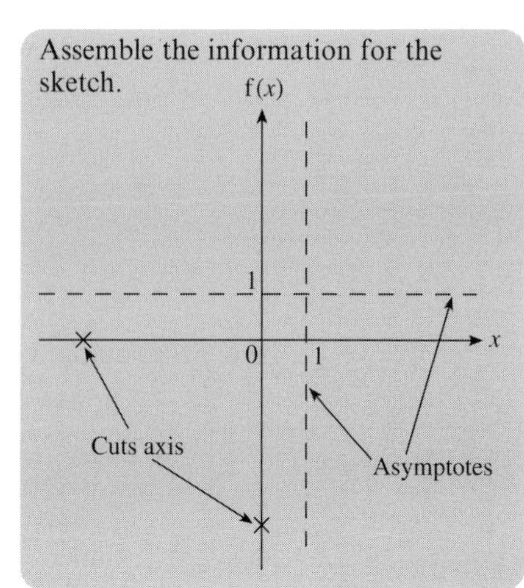

Note To obtain $y = 1 + \frac{5}{x-1}$ by transforming standard curves, $y = \frac{1}{x}$ is moved 1 unit to the right and stretched parallel to the y-axis scale factor 5, giving $y = \frac{5}{x-1}$.
To obtain $y = 1 + \frac{5}{x-1}$ the curve is moved up 1 unit.

f $\mathrm{f}(x) = \dfrac{x+4}{x-1}$

Put the function equal to y.

Let $\dfrac{x+4}{x-1} = y$

Rearrange to give x in terms of y.

$$x + 4 = yx - y$$

$$x(y - 1) = y + 4$$

Isolate the terms with x on one side, the rest of the terms on the other.

$$\therefore \quad x = \frac{y+4}{y-1}$$

So $\mathrm{f}^{-1}(x) = \dfrac{x+4}{x-1}$

Rewrite as $\mathrm{f}^{-1}(x)$ replacing y by x.

$$= \mathrm{f}(x)$$

$\mathrm{f}^{-1}(x) = \mathrm{f}(x) \Rightarrow \mathrm{f}(x)$ is self-inverse.

So $\mathrm{f}(x)$ is self-inverse.

Note: The sketch of $y = \mathrm{f}(x)$ is symmetrical about $y = x$.

Example 13 $y = x^4 - 2x^2$

a State any symmetry of the curve.

b State the behaviour of y for large values of x.

c Find where the curve meets the axes.

d Find any stationary points of the curve.

e Sketch the curve.

f Find the range of values of k for which $x^4 - 2x^2 - k = 0$ has no real roots.

Solution

a Let $f(x) = x^4 - 2x^2$
$f(x)$ is an even function so the curve $y = f(x)$ is symmetrical about the y-axis.

All powers of x are even. $\therefore \; f(x) = f(-x)$

b For large x, both +ve and −ve, y is large and +ve.

x^4 is the dominant term and this is always +ve.

c When $x = 0$, $y = 0$.

When $y = 0$, $x^4 - 2x^2 = 0$

$x^2(x^2 - 2) = 0$

So $x = 0$ (double root) or $x = \pm\sqrt{2}$.

So the curve cuts the x-axis at $(-\sqrt{2}, 0)$ and $(\sqrt{2}, 0)$, touches the x-axis at $(0, 0)$ and cuts the y-axis at $(0, 0)$.

$x = 0$ is a double root so the curve will meet the x-axis in two coincident points, i.e. will touch the x-axis, at $x = 0$.

d
$$y = x^4 - 2x^2$$
$$y' = 4x^3 - 4x$$

Differentiate to find stationary points where gradient $y' = 0$

$y' = 0$ when $4x^3 - 4x = 0$

$$x(x^2 - 1) = 0$$

$\therefore \quad x = 0$ or $x = \pm 1$

$$y'' = 12x^2 - 4$$

Consider the value of y'' to determine the nature of the stationary points.

When $x = 0$, $y = 0$, and $y'' = -4 < 0$.

$\therefore$ (0, 0) is a maximum point.

When $x = \pm 1$, $y = -1$, and $y'' = 8 > 0$

$\therefore$ (1, −1) and (−1, −1) are both minimum points.

Since y and y'' contain only even powers of x the same value will be obtained when $x = +1$ or $x = -1$ is substituted.

e

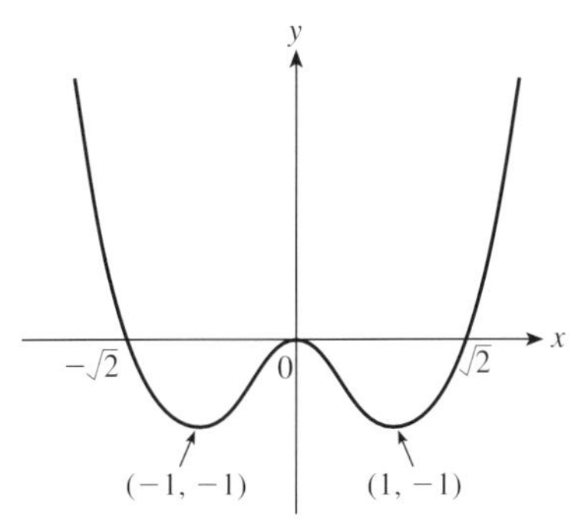

Assemble data for the sketch.

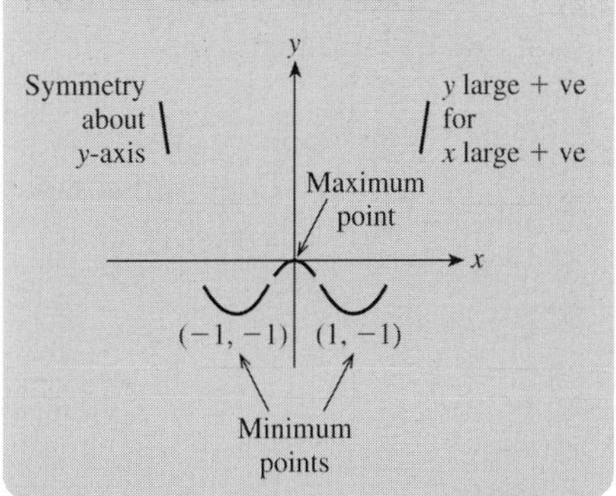

f For $k < -1$, the line $y = k$ will not intersect the curve $y = x^4 - 2x^2$

The intersection of $y = k$ and $y = x^4 - 2x^2$ gives the roots of $x^4 - 2x^2 = k$, i.e. $x^4 - 2x^2 - k = 0$.

$\therefore$ for $k < -1$, $x^4 - 2x^2 - k = 0$ will have no real roots.

EXERCISE 10d

1 For these curves, find where the curve meets the axes, state any symmetry, and the behaviour as $x \to \pm\infty$. Find the coordinates of any stationary points, determine whether they are maximum or minimum points or points of inflexion, and then sketch each curve.

a $y = 3x^2 - x^3$ **b** $y = x^3 - 6x^2$

c $y = x^4 - 10x^2 + 9$ **d** $y = 3x^5 - 5x^3$

2 For these curves find where the curve meets the axes, and the coordinates of any stationary points and determine their nature. State the behaviour of y as $x \to \pm\infty$ and then sketch each curve.

a $y = (x - 3)(x^2 + 3x + 6)$ **b** $y = 12x - x^3$

c $y = (2 - x)^3$ **d** $y = (x - 1)(x^2 + 4)$

3 **a** Given that $y = 4x^4 - x^2$ sketch the curve.

b Find the value(s) of k for which $4x^4 - x^2 = k$ has four, three, two, one and no distinct real roots.

4 **a** Given that $y = 8x^3 - x^4$ sketch the curve.

b Find the value(s) of c for which $8x^3 - x^4 - c = 0$ has three, two, one, and no distinct real roots.

5 $y = \dfrac{x - 3}{x + 1}$

a Express y in the form $y = A + \dfrac{B}{x + 1}$.

b State the behaviour of y as $x \to \pm\infty$.

c State the value of x for which the curve has an asymptote and the equation of the asymptote.

d Find where the curve cuts the axes.

e Sketch the curve.

6 Copy and complete these two graphs assuming the function is **a** even and **b** odd.

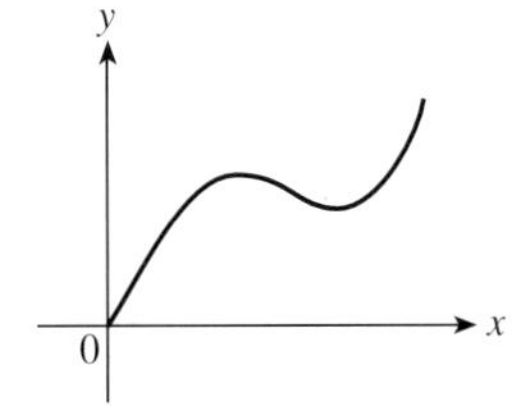

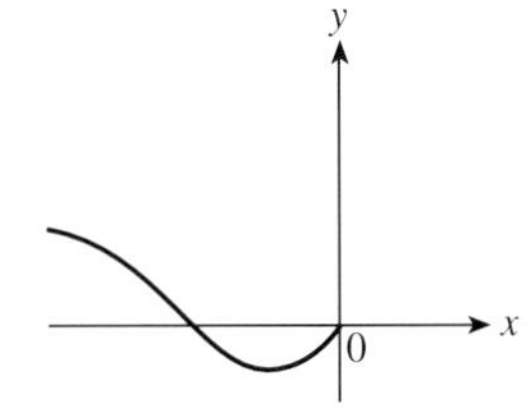

7 Copy and complete these graphs for $-6 \leqslant x \leqslant 6$, assuming the function is periodic.

a Period 3

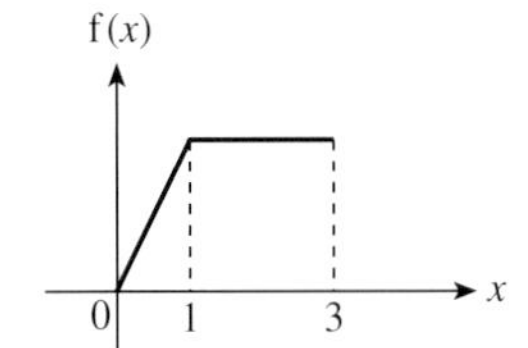

b Period 2

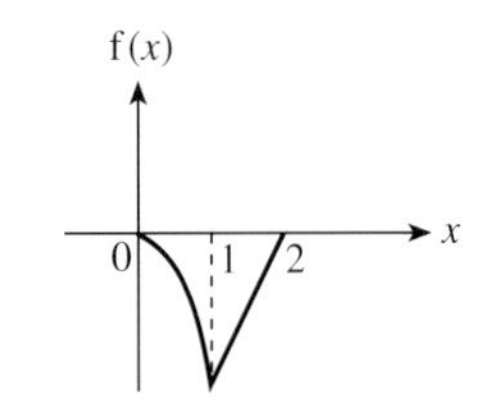

8 State which of these functions are even, odd, or neither.

a $f(x) = 3x^4 + 2x^2$ **b** $f(x) = x(x-2)(x+2)$ **c** $f(x) = 4$

d $f(x) = 3x$ **e** $f(x) = 3x + 4$

9 Sketch these periodic functions for $-6 \leqslant x \leqslant 6$.

a $f(x) = \begin{cases} \sqrt{x} & 0 \leqslant x < 1 \\ 2x - 1 & 1 \leqslant x < 2 \end{cases}$ where $f(x)$ has period 2.

b $f(x) = \begin{cases} \dfrac{x}{2} & 0 \leqslant x \leqslant 2 \\ 1 - (x-2)^2 & 2 < x \leqslant 3 \end{cases}$ and $f(x) = f(x+3)$.

10 Copy and complete these two graphs for $-8 \leqslant x \leqslant 8$.

a An odd function with period 4

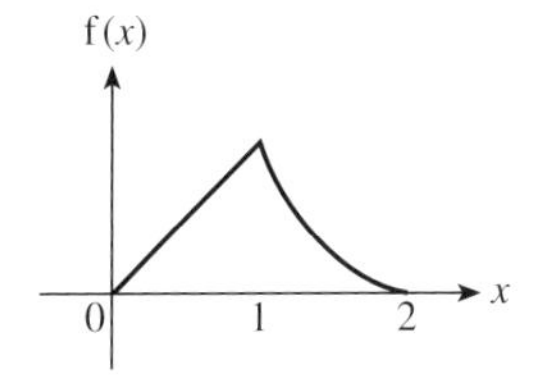

b An even function with period 4

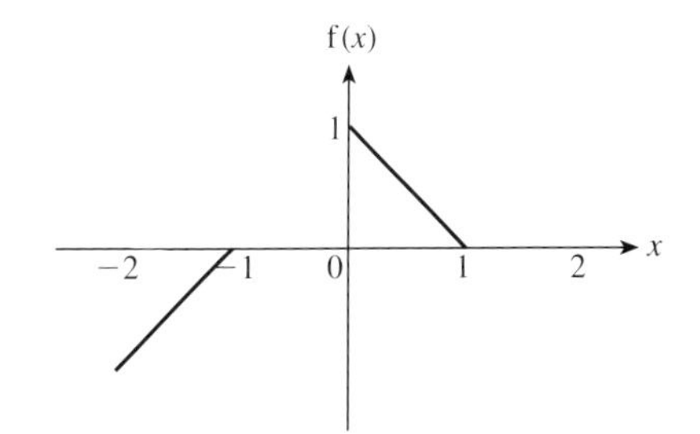

EXERCISE 10e (Extension)

For this exercise, the domain is ℝ unless otherwise stated.

1 $f(x) = \dfrac{1}{x+3}$ with $x \neq -3$ and $g(x) = \dfrac{x+2}{x-4}$ with $x \neq 4$.

a Find fg, gf and g^{-1}. **b** Solve $f(x) + g(x) = 1$.

2 The function $f(x) = |x-1| + |x| + |x+1|$ is defined for $-3 \leqslant x \leqslant 3$.

a Sketch $f(x)$. **b** State the range.

3 $f(x) = x + 2 - \dfrac{15}{x}$ and $g(x) = \dfrac{1}{x}$, $x \neq 0$.

a Find $gf(x)$ and $fg(x)$. **b** Solve $gf(x) = 0$, and $fg(x) = 0$.

4 **a** Sketch the graph of the function $f{:}x \rightarrow ||x+2| - |x||$.

b State the range of f.

5 Given that $f(x) = \dfrac{ax+b}{cx+d}$ with $x \neq -\dfrac{d}{c}$, show that

a if $f(x)$ is an even function, then $ad = bc$ and hence $f(x) = k$, where k is constant

b if $f(x)$ is an odd function, then either $a = d = 0$ or $b = c = 0$ and hence $f(x) = kx$ or $f(x) = \dfrac{k}{x}$ where k is a constant

c if $f(x)$ is self-inverse, then $a + d = 0$.

EXERCISE 10e *(continued)*

6 Given that $f(x) = 2x - 1$, find an expression for $f^n(x)$. (*Note*: $f^n(x)$ means $ff\dots f(x)$ where f is applied n times.

7 **a** Show that for any function, $f(x)$, for which $f(-x)$ is defined

- $g(x) = f(x) + f(-x)$ is an even function
- $h(x) = f(x) - f(-x)$ is an odd function

b Hence show that any function can be expressed as the sum of an even and an odd function.

c Express $f(x) = \dfrac{x+3}{x-2}$ as the sum of an even and an odd function.

8 The description 'even or odd' can be applied to integers or functions. (Functions may also be neither even nor odd.)

Complete these four tables with E (for even) or O (for odd) or N (for neither).

Multiplication of integers

$\times$	E	O
E		
O		

Addition of integers

$+$	E	O
E		
O		

Multiplication of functions

$\times$	E	O
E		
O		

Addition of functions

$+$	E	O
E		
O		

9 A quadratic equation has two, one or no distinct real roots.
A cubic equation has three, two or one distinct real roots.
A quartic equation has four, three, two, one or no distinct real roots.

a Explain, with the help of sketches, why the above statements are true.

b Find a general rule for the possible numbers of distinct real roots of an equation $f(x) = 0$ where $f(x)$ is a polynomial of degree n.

10 A quadratic curve always has one stationary point.
A cubic curve may have two, one or no stationary point(s).
A quartic curve may have three, two or one stationary point(s).

a Explain why the above statements are true.

b Find a general rule for the possible number of stationary points of a function $y = f(x)$, where $f(x)$ is a polynomial of degree n.

11 A periodic function $f(x)$ is defined for $x \in \mathbb{R}$ such that $f(x) = 2x$ with $0 \leqslant x < 2$ and $f(x) = f(x+2)$ for all values of x.

a Find a general solution for $f(x) = 2$.

b Find the number of solutions of $f(x) = 4 - \dfrac{x}{4}$.

c Find a general solution for $f(x) = 4 - \dfrac{x}{4}$.

EXERCISE 10f (Miscellaneous)

For this exercise, the domain is $\mathbb{R}$, unless otherwise stated.

1 Given that $f(x) = x^3 + 2$ and $g(x) = x - 3$ find

a $gf(2)$ **b** $gf(x)$ **c** $fg(x)$ **d** $(fg)^{-1}(-6)$

2 Given that $f(x) = 3x^2 + 2,\ x \geqslant 0$ find

a $f(5)$ **b** $f'(5)$ **c** $f^{-1}(5)$ **d** $(f(5))^{-1}$

3 $f(x) = \dfrac{x}{5}$ and $g(x) = 7 - x$.

a Find $f^{-1}(x)$, $g^{-1}(x)$, $fg(x)$ and $(fg)^{-1}(x)$. **b** Solve $fg(x) = (fg)^{-1}x$.

4 **a** Given $f(x) = 6 - 5x$ find $f^{-1}(x)$. **b** Solve $f(x) = f^{-1}(x)$.

c Sketch, on the same axes, $y = f(x)$, $y = f^{-1}(x)$ and $y = x$, marking the points where the lines intersect and where they cut the axes.

5 Given that $f(x) = 2x$, $g(x) = x^2$ and $h(x) = x - 1$ match these expressions to the composite functions fgh, fhg, gfh, ghf, hfg and hgf.

a $4x^2 - 1$ **b** $(2x - 1)^2$ **c** $4(x - 1)^2$

d $2(x - 1)^2$ **e** $2(x^2 - 1)$ **f** $2x^2 - 1$

6 For these curves, find where the curves meet the axes, state the behaviour as $x \to \pm\infty$, find the coordinates and type of any stationary points, and then sketch the curve.

a $y = x^3 - 2x^2 + x$ **b** $y = x^2(x - 2)^2$

c $y = (x + 1)^2(2 - x)$ **d** $y = x^4 + 4x$

7 The sketch shows part of a function $y = f(x)$.

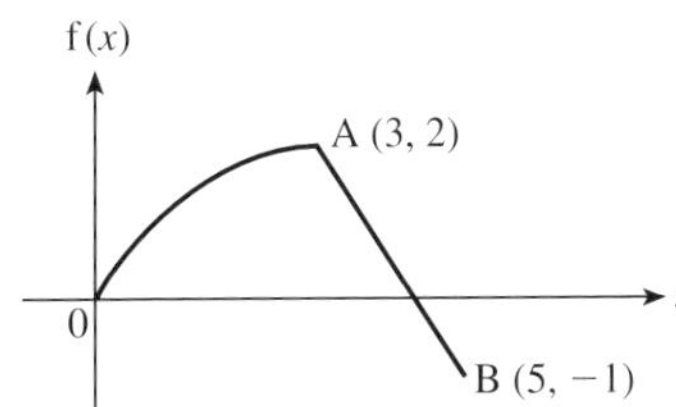

Sketch each of these curves, on separate diagrams, stating and marking the coordinates of two points (other than (0, 0)) on each curve.

a $y = f(x)$ for $-5 \leqslant x \leqslant 5$, given that $f(x)$ is an even function of x

b $y = f(x)$ for $-5 \leqslant x \leqslant 5$, given that $f(x)$ is an odd function of x

c $y = f(x)$ for $-10 \leqslant x \leqslant 10$, given that $f(x)$ is a periodic function of period 5

d $y = -f(x)$ for $0 \leqslant x \leqslant 5$

e $y = 2f(x)$ for $0 \leqslant x \leqslant 5$

8 $f: x \to 10x + 2$, $g: x \to \dfrac{1}{x + 4}$, $x \neq -4$ and $h: x \to x^2 + 1$.

a State, with reasons, whether the above functions are one-to-one or many-to-one.

b Express fgh, in its simplest form, using the notation $fgh: x \to \ldots$.

c State if $\mathbb{R}$ is a suitable domain for fgh.

d Find the range of fgh and sketch the graph of $y = fgh(x)$.

e Solve $fgh(x) = 3$.

EXERCISE 10f
(continued)

9 **a** Show that $g(x) = \dfrac{2x-1}{x-3}$ can be expressed in the form $g(x) = \dfrac{a}{x-3} + b$, where a and $b \in \mathbb{R}$ and $x \neq 3$.

b The graph of $y = g(x)$ can be obtained by translating the graph of $y = \dfrac{a}{x}$.
State the translation and hence sketch $y = g(x)$, showing the intercepts with the axes.

c Solve $g(x) = x + 3$.

10 The function f is defined as $f(x) = \dfrac{|x|}{x}$ for $x \neq 0$.

a Sketch $f(x)$ **b** State the range of f.

11 **a** Sketch the curve $y = 4x^5 - 5x^4$.

b Given that $4x^5 - 5x^4 = c$ has only one real root, find the range of values of c.

12 The function $f(x)$ is defined as $f(x) = 3x^2 - 4$, $x \geqslant 0$.

a Explain why, without the restriction $x \geqslant 0$, $f(x)$ would not be a one-to-one function.

b Find $f^{-1}(x)$, stating its domain.

c Sketch, on the same axes, the graphs of $y = f(x)$, $y = f^{-1}(x)$ and $y = x$.

13 The function $f(x)$ is defined for the domain $0 \leqslant x \leqslant 3$ as

$$f(x) = \begin{cases} x & 0 \leqslant x \leqslant 1 \\ -1 + 3x - x^2 & 1 \leqslant x \leqslant 2 \\ 3 - x & 2 \leqslant x \leqslant 3 \end{cases}$$

a Show that $f(1)$ and $f(2)$ have unique values and that the curve $y = f(x)$ is continuous.

b Find the function $f'(x)$.

c By showing that $f'(1)$ and $f'(2)$ have unique values, show that the gradient does not change abruptly at $x = 1$ and $x = 2$.

d Sketch $y = f(x)$ and $y = f'(x)$ for $0 \leqslant x \leqslant 3$.

Test yourself

1 If $h(x) = 2x + 5$, then $h^2(1)$ is equal to

A 55 **B** 29 **C** 19 **D** −2 **E** 49

2 Given a suitable choice of domain, one of these functions is many-to-one. Which one?

A $f: x \to \sqrt{x}$ **B** $f: x \to 3x - 1$ **C** $f: x \to x^3 + 4$

D $f: x \to (x+1)^2$ **E** $f: x \to \dfrac{2}{x}$

3 The range of $f(x) = \dfrac{1}{x+1}$ for $x \in \mathbb{R}$, $x \geqslant 0$ is

A $-\infty$ to ∞ **B** $0 < f(x) \leqslant \frac{1}{2}$ **C** $0 < f(x) \leqslant 1$

D $f(x)$ positive **E** undefined

4 If $f(x) = 3x + 1$ and $g(x) = x^2$ then $fg(x)$ is equal to

A $3x^2 + 1$ **B** $(3x+1)^2$ **C** $\frac{x^2-1}{3}$ **D** $\sqrt{3x+1}$ **E** $\sqrt{\frac{x-1}{3}}$

5 If $f(t) = t^3 + 4t^2 - 1$ then $f(-2)$ is equal to

A 7 **B** -25 **C** 23 **D** -23 **E** 9

6 The function $f(x)$ illustrated in the diagram is

A even and one-to-one

B even and many-to-one

C odd and one-to-one

D odd and many-to-one

E neither even nor odd

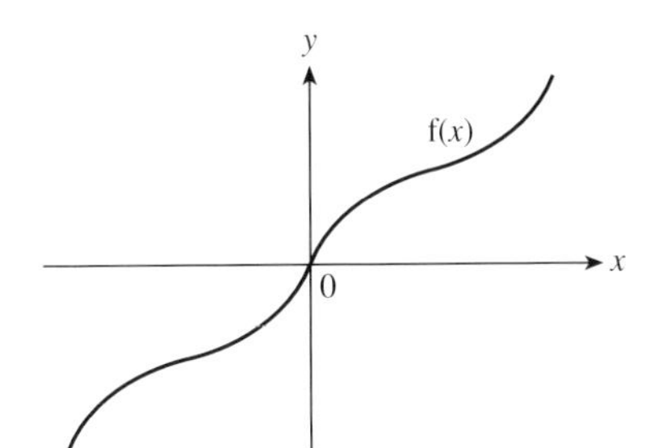

7 If the range of $f(x) = \frac{2}{x} + 1$ is $\{\frac{3}{2}, 2, 3, 5,\}$, the domain is

A $\{1\frac{2}{5}, 1\frac{2}{3}, 2, 2\frac{1}{3}\}$ **B** $\{\frac{1}{4}, \frac{1}{2}, 1, 2\}$ **C** $\{2, 3, 5, 9\}$

D $\{\frac{1}{2}, 1, 2, 4\}$ **E** $\{1\frac{1}{2}, 2, 3, 5\}$

8 The inverse of $f: t \to \sqrt{t} + 2$ is

A $f^{-1}: t \to t^2 + 2$ **B** $f^{-1}: t \to t^2 - 2$ **C** $f^{-1}: t \to \frac{1}{\sqrt{t}+2}$

D $f^{-1}: t \to \sqrt{t-2}$ **E** none of these

9 The range of $f(x) = x^2 - 6x + 4$ for $0 \leqslant x \leqslant 5$ is

A $-1 \leqslant f(x) \leqslant 4$ **B** $f(x) \geqslant -26$ **C** $f(x) \leqslant 4$

D $-5 \leqslant f(x) \leqslant 4$ **E** $-5 \leqslant f(x) \leqslant -3$

10 $f(x) = \sqrt{25 - x^2}$, $x \leqslant 5$, $g(t) = \frac{1}{t+1}$, $t \neq -1$ and $h(s) = -\frac{3}{s}$, $s \neq 0$.

Which of these function(s) are self-inverse?

A f only **B** g only **C** f and g only

D f and h only **E** all three

11 If $f(x) = x^2 - 1$ and $g(x) = \frac{1}{x-1}$ then $gf(x)$ is equal to

A $\frac{1}{x^2-1} - 1$ **B** $\left(\frac{1}{x-1}\right)^2 - 1$ **C** $x + 1$

D $\frac{1}{x^2-2}$ **E** $x^2 - \frac{1}{x-1}$

12 If the range of $f: x \to \frac{2}{(x-3)^2}$ is $y < \frac{1}{2}$, the domain is

A $1 < x < 5$ **B** $x < 1$ and $x > 5$ **C** $x \neq -3$

D $x > \frac{8}{25}$ **E** $0 < x < \frac{1}{2}$

➤➤➤ Key points

Functions

A **function** is a relationship between two sets: the **domain** (the set of 'inputs') and the **range** (the set of 'outputs').

A function is defined by
- a rule connecting the domain and range sets and
- the domain set.

The essential feature of a function is that, for each member of the domain, there is one and only one member of the range.

A function $y = f(x)$ is:
- **one-to-one** if $a = b \Leftrightarrow f(a) = f(b)$
  i.e. for each value of x there is a unique value of y and vice-versa
- **many-to-one** if for some values of a and b, $(a \neq b)$, $f(a) = f(b)$
  i.e. more than one value of x maps to the same value of y.

The composite function, fg, can be formed only if the range of g is a subset of (i.e. is contained within) the domain of f.

The **composite function** $fg(x)$ means apply g first then f. $fg(x) = f(g(x))$.
The output from g becomes the input for f.

The **inverse function** $f^{-1}(x)$ 'undoes' $f(x)$. So $ff^{-1}(x) = f^{-1}f(x) = x$.
- If $f(x) = f^{-1}(x)$ the function $f(x)$ is **self-inverse**.
- The range of $f(x)$ is the domain of $f^{-1}(x)$ and vice-versa.
- The graphs of $y = f(x)$ and $y = f^{-1}(x)$ are reflections of each other in $y = x$, since for a function and its inverse function the roles of x and y are interchanged.
- To obtain the inverse function, rearrange $y = f(x)$ to give x in terms of y, then replace y by x.
- Only one-to-one functions have inverses. For many-to-one functions, an inverse only exists over a domain restricted so that the function is one-to-one for that domain.

Even functions: $f(x) = f(-x)$, symmetrical about y-axis.

Odd functions: $f(x) = -f(-x)$, 180° rotational symmetry about the origin.

Periodic functions follow a repeating pattern. If h is the smallest value for which $f(x) = f(x + h)$, for all values of x, then $f(x)$ has period h.

Curve sketching

Points to consider
- Standard function (or transformation of one)
- Where does the curve cross the axes?
- Symmetry (even or odd functions)
- Discontinuities (denominator zero and therefore an asymptote)
- Behaviour as $x \to \pm\infty$
- Stationary values, $\dfrac{dy}{dx} = 0$

11 Exponential and Logarithmic Functions

Before starting this chapter you will need to know

- the rules for indices (Chapter 1)
- about functions and their inverses (Chapter 10).

Exponential functions have the variable x not in the base ($y = x^a$) but in the exponent or index ($y = a^x$). Exponential functions and their inverses, logarithmic functions, occur frequently in the physical world. They can be found in such varied fields as: measuring the strength of an earthquake, wave propagation, measuring intensity of sound, and the rate of cooling of a body.

By the beginning of the seventeenth century, there was a pressing need for easier methods of computation, especially in astronomy and navigation. The concept of, for example, multiplying numbers simply by adding (as is the case with logarithms) was important and exciting.
The idea was developed by John Napier, a Scotsman, and independently, but at the same time, by Joost Bürgi, a Swiss. For the following 300 years, logarithms were the main method of computation.
Logarithms have now been superseded by calculators and computers. The concept of logarithms led, however, to the development of new functions which play an important role in higher mathematics.

11.1 Definition of a logarithm

The **logarithm (log)** of a positive number to a given **base** is the **power** to which the base must be raised to equal the given number.

$$a^b = c \Leftrightarrow \log_a c = b$$

(log: b; base: a)

Say 'log to the base a of c is b'.

Assume $a > 0$ and $a \neq 1$.

Example 1

a As $2^5 = 32$, the log of 32 to the base 2 is 5

or $2^5 = 32 \Leftrightarrow \log_2 32 = 5$

b As $10^4 = 10\,000$, the log of 10 000 to the base 10 is 4

or $10^4 = 10\,000 \Leftrightarrow \log_{10} 10\,000 = 4$.

The index form ($10^4 = 10\,000$) and the log form ($\log_{10} 10\,000 = 4$) are equivalent.
The two forms say the same thing in two different ways.
It is important to be able to convert readily from one form to other.

EXERCISE 11a

This exercise may be done orally.

1 What are the bases and logarithms in these statements?

a $10^2 = 100$ **b** $10^{1.6021} \approx 40$ **c** $9 = 3^2$ **d** $4^3 = 64$

e $1 = 2^0$ **f** $8 = (\frac{1}{2})^{-3}$ **g** $a^b = c$

2 Express these statements in logarithmic notation.

a $2^4 = 16$ **b** $27 = 3^3$ **c** $125 = 5^3$

d $10^6 = 1000\,000$ **e** $1728 = 12^3$ **f** $64 = 16^{\frac{3}{2}}$

g $10^4 = 10\,000$ **h** $4^0 = 1$ **i** $0.01 = 10^{-2}$

j $\frac{1}{2} = 2^{-1}$ **k** $9^{\frac{3}{2}} = 27$ **l** $8^{-\frac{2}{3}} = \frac{1}{4}$

m $81 = (\frac{1}{3})^{-4}$ **n** $e^0 = 1$ **o** $16^{-\frac{1}{4}} = \frac{1}{2}$

p $(\frac{1}{8})^0 = 1$ **q** $27 = 81^{\frac{3}{4}}$ **r** $4 = (\frac{1}{16})^{-\frac{1}{2}}$

s $c = a^5$ **t** $a^3 = b$ **u** $p^q = r$

3 Express these in index notation.

a $\log_2 32 = 5$ **b** $\log_3 9 = 2$ **c** $2 = \log_5 25$

d $\log_{10} 100\,000 = 5$ **e** $7 = \log_2 128$ **f** $\log_9 1 = 0$

g $-2 = \log_3 \frac{1}{9}$ **h** $\log_4 2 = \frac{1}{2}$ **i** $\log_e 1 = 0$

j $\log_{27} 3 = \frac{1}{3}$ **k** $2 = \log_a x$ **l** $\log_3 a = b$

m $\log_a 8 = c$ **n** $y = \log_x z$ **o** $\log_q r = p$

4 Evaluate these.

a $\log_2 64$ **b** $\log_{10} 100$ **c** $\log_{10} 10^7$

d $\log_a a^2$ **e** $\log_8 2$ **f** $\log_4 1$

g $\log_{27} 3$ **h** $\log_5 125$ **i** $\log_e e^3$

j $\log_e \frac{1}{e}$ **k** $\log_a \sqrt{a}$ **l** $\log_{2a} 4a^2$

11.2 Combining logs

As a log is a power (or index) the rules for combining powers (or indices) apply.

➤ For any base, the rules are

- $\log ab = \log a + \log b$
- $\log \dfrac{a}{b} = \log a - \log b$
- $\log a^n = n \log a$

When the same base is used throughout a piece of work, the base is usually omitted, as here.

Note: $\log a^n = \log (a^n)$.

To prove these rules, let c be any base and let $x = \log_c a$ and $y = \log_c b$

$\log_c a = x \Leftrightarrow a = c^x$ ①

$\log_c b = y \Leftrightarrow b = c^y$ ②

To prove $\log ab = \log a + \log b$

From ① and ② $ab = c^x c^y$

$= c^{x+y}$

Note: To *multiply* numbers *add* indices or logs.

So $\log_c ab = x + y$

$= \log_c a + \log_c b$

To prove $\log \frac{a}{b} = \log a - \log b$

From ① and ② $\frac{a}{b} = \frac{c^x}{c^y}$

$= c^{x-y}$

Note: To *divide* numbers *subtract* indices or logs.

So $\log_c \frac{a}{b} = x - y$

$= \log_c a - \log_c b$

To prove $\log a^n = n \log a$

From ① $a^n = (c^x)^n$

$= c^{nx}$

Note: To *raise to a power multiply* by the index or log.

So $\log_c a^n = nx$

$= n \log_c a$

Considering -1, 0 and 1 as powers of a, gives three important results, which are useful when simplifying logs.

➤

For any base a

- $a^1 = a \Rightarrow \log_a a = 1$
- $a^0 = 1 \Rightarrow \log_a 1 = 0$
- $a^{-1} = \frac{1}{a} \Rightarrow \log_a\left(\frac{1}{a}\right) = -1$

Example 2 Express in terms of a single logarithm $\log 45 - 2\log 3$.

$\log 45 - 2\log 3 = \log 45 - \log 3^2$

$= \log 45 - \log 9$

$= \log \frac{45}{9}$

$= \log 5$

$\log a^n = n\log a \Rightarrow 2\log 3 = \log 3^2$

$\log \frac{a}{b} = \log a - \log b \Rightarrow \log 45 - \log 9 = \log \frac{45}{9}$

Example 3 Express $3\log_{10} a + \frac{1}{2}\log_{10} b - 2$ as the logarithm of a single term.

$3\log_{10} a = \log_{10} a^3$ — Using $\log a^n = n\log a$

$\frac{1}{2}\log_{10} b = \log_{10} b^{\frac{1}{2}} = \log_{10} \sqrt{b}$

$2 = \log_{10} 10^2 = \log_{10} 100$

So $3\log_{10} a + \frac{1}{2}\log_{10} b - 2 = \log_{10} a^3 + \log_{10} \sqrt{b} - \log_{10} 100$

$= \log_{10}(a^3\sqrt{b}) - \log_{10} 100$ — Using $\log ab = \log a + \log b$

$= \log_{10}\left(\frac{a^3\sqrt{b}}{100}\right)$ — Using $\log\frac{a}{b} = \log a - \log b$

Example 4 Express $\log\sqrt{\frac{a^4 b}{3c^3}}$ in terms of $\log a$, $\log b$ and $\log c$.

$\log\sqrt{\frac{a^4 b}{3c^3}} = \log\left(\frac{a^4 b}{3c^3}\right)^{\frac{1}{2}}$ — Use index form.

$= \frac{1}{2}\log\left(\frac{a^4 b}{3c^3}\right)$ — Using $\log a^n = n\log a$

$= \frac{1}{2}(\log a^4 b - \log 3c^3)$ — Using $\log\frac{a}{b} = \log a - \log b$

$= \frac{1}{2}(\log a^4 + \log b - \log 3 - \log c^3)$ — Using $\log ab = \log a + \log b$

$= \frac{1}{2}(4\log a + \log b - \log 3 - 3\log c)$ — Using $\log a^n = n\log a$

Example 5 Simplify $\frac{\log 64}{\log 32}$.

$\frac{\log 64}{\log 32} = \frac{\log 2^6}{\log 2^5}$

$= \frac{6\log 2}{5\log 2}$

$= \frac{6}{5}$

64 and 32 are powers of the same number, 2. By expressing them both as powers of 2 and using the log rules the expression can be simplified.

EXERCISE 11b

In this exercise, the base of the logarithms is omitted unless it has a special bearing on the question. Note: $\lg x$ means $\log_{10} x$.

1 Express in terms of $\log a$, $\log b$ and $\log c$

a $\log ab$ **b** $\log\frac{a}{c}$ **c** $\log\frac{1}{b}$ **d** $\log a^2 b^{\frac{3}{2}}$

e $\log\frac{1}{b^4}$ **f** $\log\frac{a^{\frac{1}{3}}b^4}{c^3}$ **g** $\log\sqrt{a}$ **h** $\log\sqrt[3]{b}$

i $\log\sqrt{(ab)}$ **j** $\lg(10a)$ **k** $\lg\frac{1}{100b^2}$ **l** $\log\sqrt{\left(\frac{a}{b}\right)}$

2 Express these as single logarithms.

a $\log 2 + \log 3$ **b** $\log 18 - \log 9$ **c** $\log 4 + 2\log 3 - \log 6$
d $3\log 2 + 2\log 3 - 2\log 6$ **e** $\log c + \log a$ **f** $\log x + \log y - \log z$
g $2\log a - \log b$ **h** $2\log a + 3\log b - \log c$ **i** $\frac{1}{2}\log x - \frac{1}{2}\log y$
j $\log p - \frac{1}{3}\log q$ **k** $2 + 3\lg a$ **l** $1 + \lg a - \frac{1}{2}\lg b$
m $2\lg a - 3 - \lg 2c$ **n** $3\lg x - \frac{1}{2}\lg y + 1$ **o** $a\log b - b\log a$

3 Simplify

a $\lg 1000$ **b** $\frac{1}{2}\log_3 81$ **c** $\frac{1}{3}\log_2 64$ **d** $-\log_2 \frac{1}{2}$
e $\frac{1}{3}\log 8$ **f** $\frac{1}{2}\log 49$ **g** $-\frac{1}{2}\log 4$ **h** $3\log 3 - \log 27$
i $5\log 2 - \log 32$ **j** $\dfrac{\log 8}{\log 2}$ **k** $\dfrac{\log 81}{\log 9}$ **l** $\dfrac{\log 49}{\log 343}$

11.3 Exponential functions and their inverses

Consider $f(x) = x^2$ and $g(x) = 2^x$.

For $f(x) = x^2$ the base, x, is the variable; the power (or exponent), 2, is constant.

For $g(x) = 2^x$ the base, 2, is constant; the power (or exponent), x, is the variable.

$f(x) = x^2$ is a quadratic function.

$g(x) = 2^x$ is an exponential function.

An **exponential function** has the form $f(x) = a^x$ where a is a constant. Its inverse function, the function that reverses the process of 'raising to a power' is 'taking the log'.

So $f^{-1}(x) = \log_a x$.

The function $f(x) = a^x$ has domain $\mathbb{R}$ and range $\mathbb{R}^+$.

The inverse function $f^{-1}(x) = \log_a x$ has domain $\mathbb{R}^+$ and range $\mathbb{R}$.

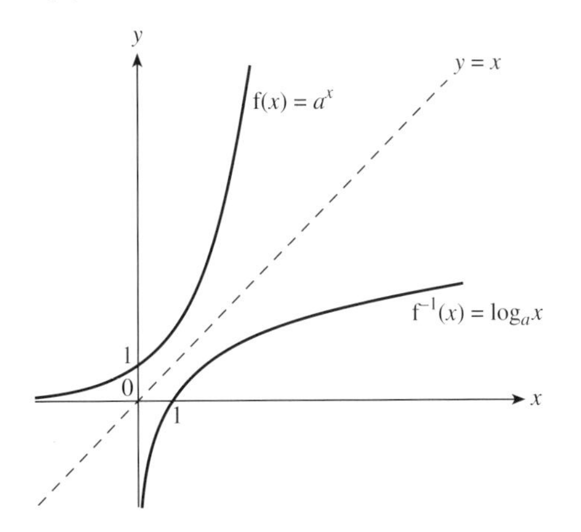

$0 < a < 1$

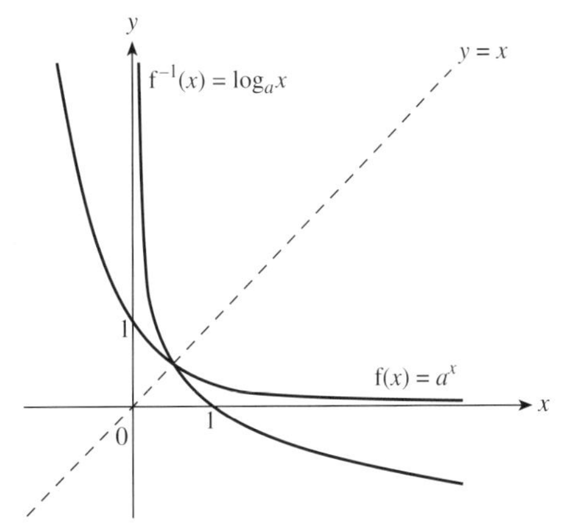

✓ ***Note*** Exponential functions and log functions are one-to-one functions.
The graphs of $y = a^x$ and $y = \log_a x$ are reflections of each other in the line $y = x$.

Notice also that

$a^x = N \Leftrightarrow x = \log_a N$

So $\quad N = a^{\log_a N}$

or $\quad x = \log_a a^x$

This gives two more important results:

➤ Log functions and exponential functions are inverses of each other. One 'undoes' the other.

For any base a

- $\log_a a^x = x$
- $a^{\log_a N} = N$

Example 6 Simplify **a** $3^{\log_3 4}$ **b** $\log_2 2^7$

a $3^{\log_3 4} = 4$ — Using $a^{\log_a N} = N$

b $\log_2 2^7 = 7$ — Using $\log_a a^x = x$

The most important bases for logarithms are 10 and e, a number which is introduced in detail in Chapter 17. The integer powers of 10 are convenient in the decimal system, while e arises naturally in many areas of mathematics and science. Logs to base e, abbreviated to ln, are called natural or Napierian logarithms (after John Napier).

To change the base of a log

Calculators only evaluate $\log_{10}$ (lg or log) and $\log_e$ (ln), but it is possible to change the base of a logarithm so that any log can be expressed in one of these two bases (or in any other base).

$\log_a b = x \Leftrightarrow a^x = b$

Taking logs to base c of both sides of $a^x = b$

Doing the same to both sides does not affect the equality, because the log function is one-to-one.

$$\log_c a^x = \log_c b$$

$$x \log_c a = \log_c b$$

$$x = \frac{\log_c b}{\log_c a}$$

So $\quad \log_a b = \dfrac{\log_c b}{\log_c a}$

➤ To change the base of a log use $\log_a b = \dfrac{\log_c b}{\log_c a}$

Example 7 Find $\log_2 7$ by changing the base of the log.

$$\log_2 7 = \frac{\log_{10} 7}{\log_{10} 2}$$

$$= 2.81 \text{ (3 s.f.)}$$

On a calculator, $\log_2$ cannot be evaluated directly, but $\log_{10}$ (lg) or $\log_e$ (ln) can. Here, base 10 has been used and the two logs have been divided on the calculator. Check mentally: $2^2 = 4$, $2^3 = 8$, so the answer should lie between 2 and 3.

EXERCISE 11c

Note: ln means $\log_e$

1 Evaluate or simplify

a $\log_a a^2$ **b** $x^{\log_x y}$ **c** $\log_3 3^5$

d $\log_2 2^n$ **e** $x^{\log_x 7}$ **f** $\log_a a^n$

g $3^{\log_3 5}$ **h** $\ln e^5$ **i** $\ln e^x$

j $\log_7 1$ **k** $\log_5 5^{2x+1}$ **l** $\ln e^e$

m $\log_3(\log_4 4^3)$ **n** $\log_x(\log_y y^x)$

2 Evaluate, correct to 3 decimal places, by changing the base of the log

a $\log_6 7$ **b** $\log_3 \frac{1}{2}$ **c** $\log_{0.5} 9$

d $\log_2 3$ **e** $\log_{0.25} 6$ **f** $\log_8 72.4$

g $\log_5 4$ **h** $\log_{0.7} 0.1$

Solving equations involving indices and logs

One way of solving equations of the type $a^x = b$ is by taking logs of both sides. This is not always necessary as Example 8 shows.

Example 8 Solve $3^{2x+1} = 81$.

No need to use logs. Recognise 81 as a power of 3.

$$3^{2x+1} = 81$$

$$3^{2x+1} = 3^4$$

$81 = 3^4$

So $\quad 2x + 1 = 4$

$$2x = 3$$

$\therefore \quad x = \frac{3}{2}$

Example 9 Solve $3^{2x+1} = 80$.

$$3^{2x+1} = 80$$

Need to take logs.

Taking logs to base 10 of both sides

$$(2x+1)\log_{10} 3 = \log_{10} 80$$

$$2x + 1 = \frac{\log_{10} 80}{\log_{10} 3}$$

$$2x = \frac{\log_{10} 80}{\log_{10} 3} - 1$$

$$x = \frac{1}{2}\left(\frac{\log_{10} 80}{\log_{10} 3} - 1\right)$$

$$= 1.49 \text{ (3 s.f.)}$$

Example 10 Solve $3^{2x+1} - 3^x - 24 = 0$.

$$3^{2x+1} - 3^x - 24 = 0$$

$3^{2x+1} = 3^{2x} \times 3^1 = (3^x)^2 \times 3$

Let $y = 3^x$

Then $\quad 3y^2 - y - 24 = 0$

$$(3y+8)(y-3) = 0$$

If the substitution $y = 3^x$ is not used, the equation factorises as $(3^{x+1} + 8)(3^x - 3) = 0$.

$\Rightarrow \quad y = -\frac{8}{3}$ or $y = 3$

Substituting for y

$$3^x = -\tfrac{8}{3} \text{ or } 3^x = 3$$

There is no solution for $3^x < 0$ but $3^x = 3$ gives $x = 1$.

Example 11 Solve the simultaneous equations $\log_2 x + \log_2 y = 3$ and $\log_4 x - \log_4 y = -\frac{1}{2}$.

$\log_2 x + \log_2 y = 3 \quad$ ①

$\log_4 x - \log_4 y = -\frac{1}{2} \quad$ ②

From ① $\quad \log_2 xy = 3$

$$2^3 = xy$$

So $\quad xy = 8 \quad$ ③

From ② $\quad \log_4 \frac{x}{y} = -\frac{1}{2}$

$$4^{-\frac{1}{2}} = \frac{x}{y}$$

So $\quad \frac{x}{y} = \frac{1}{2} \quad$ ④

③ × ④ gives $\quad x^2 = 4$

Simultaneous equations are usually solved by addition or subtraction. Here the equations are multiplied.

x must be positive for its log to exist.

$\therefore \quad x = 2$ and $y = 4$.

EXERCISE 11d

In this exercise, use logs only when necessary.

1 Solve for x.

a $2^x = 64$ **b** $2^x = \frac{1}{32}$ **c** $3^x = 64$

d $(0.2)^x = 125$ **e** $3^{4x} = 2$ **f** $3^{x-2} = 27$

g $3^{x-2} = 28$ **h** $5^{3x} = 7$ **i** $7^{-x} = 1$

2 Solve for x.

a $2^{x+1} = 5^x$ **b** $7^{x-3} = 4^{2x}$ **c** $2^x \times 2^{x+1} = 10$

d $\dfrac{1}{2^x} = 6$ **e** $\left(\dfrac{2}{3}\right)^x = \dfrac{1}{16}$ **f** $7^x = 6^{-x}$

3 Solve for x.

a $2^{2x} - 2^x - 6 = 0$ **b** $2^{2x} - 6 \times 2^x + 8 = 0$

c $3^{2x} - 10 \times 3^x + 9 = 0$ **d** $3^{2x+1} - 26 \times 3^x - 9 = 0$

e $2(2^{2x}) - 5(2^x) + 2 = 0$ **f** $3^{2x+1} - 4(3^x) + 1 = 0$

g $5^{2x} - 7 \times 5^x = 0$ **h** $4^{2x} - 9 = 0$

i $9^x - 2 \times 3^{x+1} + 8 = 0$ **j** $4^x - 6(2^x) + 5 = 0$

4 Given that $a^s = b^t$ find t in terms of a, b and s.

EXERCISE 11e (Extension)

1 Solve for x.

a $\log_2 x = \log_4 (x + 6)$ **b** $9 \log_x 5 = \log_5 x$

c $\log_2 x + \log_x 2 = 2$ **d** $2^x \times 6^{x-2} = 5^{2x} \times 7^{1-x}$

e $\log_{10} (x^2 - 2x + 8) = 2 \log_{10} x$ **f** $\log x + \log (3 + x) = \log 4$

2 Solve for x and y ($x > 0$, $y > 0$).

a $\log_3 x = y = \log_9 (2x - 1)$ **b** $\log_x y = 2$, $xy = 8$

c $\log_a xy = 8$, $\log_a \dfrac{x}{y} = 2$ **d** $\log_3 x + \log_3 y^2 = 2$, $\log_{27} y^2 - \log_{27} x = \frac{2}{3}$

3 Simplify these expressions.

a $\log_a a\sqrt{a}$ **b** $\log_4 1.6 + \log_4 40$

4 Express, without use of logs.

a $\lg x + \lg y = 3$ **b** $x \log 5 = \log 6$

c $3 \lg x - 2 \lg y = 1$ **d** $\log x - 3 \log y = \log 5$

5 Find a if $\log_a 45 + 4 \log_a 2 - \frac{1}{2} \log_a 81 - \log_a 10 = \frac{3}{2}$.

6 $\log_{10} 875^{12} = 12 \log_{10} 875 = 35.3$ so $875^{12} \approx 10^{35.3}$. So 875^{12} would be a number of 36 digits. Use this method to find

a the number of digits in 421^{15}

b the number of digits in 421^{15} if it were expressed in base 2 (binary).

EXERCISE 11f (Miscellaneous)

In this exercise, for Question 6, remember that lg stands for $\log_{10}$.

1 Express in logarithmic notation

a $2^5 = 32$ **b** $10^2 = 100$ **c** $a^b = c$

d $p^3 = q$ **e** $3 = 27^{\frac{1}{3}}$ **f** $\frac{1}{3} = 3^{-1}$

2 Express in index notation

a $\log_2 8 = 3$ **b** $\log_6 36 = 2$ **c** $\log_a b = c$

d $\log_d c^4 = e$ **e** $\log_p 8 = 4$ **f** $q = \log_c 3$

3 Evaluate

a $\log_2 128$ **b** $\log_{10} 1000$ **c** $\log_p p^4$

d $\log_2 16$ **e** $\log_{16} 2$ **f** $\log_e \dfrac{1}{e^2}$

4 Express in terms of $\log a$, $\log b$ and $\log c$

a $\log \dfrac{ab^2}{c}$ **b** $\log \sqrt{ab}$ **c** $\log \dfrac{a^4}{b^2c}$ **d** $\log a^2b^3c^4$

5 Express each of these as a single logarithm.

a $\log(a^2b) - \log(b^2a)$ **b** $\frac{1}{2}\log x + 3\log y$

c $\log 5 + 2\log 10 - 3\log 2$ **d** $a\log x + a\log x^2$

6 Simplify

a $\lg 75 + 2\lg 2 - \lg 3$ **b** $\lg 1000\,000$ **c** $\frac{1}{2}\log 64$

d $5\log 3 - \log 81$ **e** $\dfrac{\log 16}{\log 2}$ **f** $\dfrac{\log 5}{\log 125}$

7 Solve these.

a $\log_{10}(n^2 - 90n) = 3$ **b** $9^x = 27^{\frac{3}{4}}$ **c** $3^x = 4$

d $5^{2x+1} = 25$ **e** $5^{2x+1} = 8$ **f** $\log_2(y^2 + 7y) = 3$

g $5^{2x} - 6 \times 5^x + 5 = 0$ **h** $4^{2x+1} - 7(4^x) + 3 = 0$ **i** $2^{2x} - 5(2^x) = 14$

j $2^{x^2+x} = 4$

8 Many phenomena – from stock market prices to census data to heat capacities of chemicals – obey Benford's Law. This states that for a set of numerical data, the proportion of numbers starting with the digit D is approximately

$$\log_{10}\left(1 + \frac{1}{D}\right)$$

a Show that Benford's Law predicts that around 30% of numbers will start with a 1, and around 18% with a 2. What proportion of numbers does the law predict will start with a 9?

b Show that $\displaystyle\sum_{D=1}^{9} \log_{10}\left(1 + \frac{1}{D}\right) = 1$.

Test yourself

1 $\log_{64} 4$ is equal to

A 3 **B** −3 **C** −16 **D** $\frac{1}{3}$ **E** $\frac{1}{16}$

2 $4^{3x-1} = 40$. Correct to 3 significant figures, x is equal to

A 3.67 **B** 1.22 **C** 1.10 **D** 0.73 **E** 0.64

3 $\log_{12} 18 + 3\log_{12} 2$ is equal to

A 1.88 **B** 1.31 **C** 1 **D** 2 **E** 4.33

4 Correct to 2 decimal places, $\log_4 5^3$ is equal to

A 1.16 **B** 2.58 **C** 3.48 **D** 0.86 **E** 2.10

5 $\log \dfrac{a\sqrt{b^3}}{c^2}$ is equal to

A $\frac{3}{4}\log a \log b \log c$ **B** $\log(a + \frac{3}{2}b - 2c)$ **C** $\log a + \frac{3}{2}\log b - 2\log c$

D $\frac{1}{2}\log a \log b^3 - \log c^2$ **E** $\frac{3}{2}\log ab - 2\log c$

6 Given that $3^{t+1} = 6^{t-1}$, correct to 3 significant figures, t is equal to

A 3.00 **B** 4.17 **C** −3.82 **D** −6.52 **E** 1.86

7 $\log(a+b)$ is equivalent to

A $(\log a)^b$ **B** $(\log a)(\log b)$ **C** $\log a + \log b$

D $\log a^b$ **E** none of these

8 If $2\log_p q = r$, then

A $(q^p)^2 = r$ **B** $p^{2q} = r$ **C** $q^p = r^2$ **D** $p^r = q^2$ **E** $q^{2r} = p$

9 If $3^{2y} - 2(3^{y+1}) = 27$, then y is equal to

A 2 **B** $\pm\sqrt{28}$ **C** 0 **D** 9 **E** −6

10 $2\log 10 + \log 12 - 2\log 4$ is equal to

A $\log 30$ **B** $\log 75$ **C** $\log 52$ **D** $\log 96$ **E** $\log 60$

Key points

Log functions

- For *any* base

  $\log ab = \log a + \log b$ $\log \frac{a}{b} = \log a - \log b$ $\log a^n = n\log a$

  $\log_a a = 1$ $\log_a 1 = 0$ $\log_a\left(\frac{1}{a}\right) = -1$

- To change the base of a log use $\log_a b = \dfrac{\log_c b}{\log_c a}$

- Log functions and exponential functions are inverses of each other. One 'undoes' the other.

  $N = a^{\log_a N}$ $x = \log_a a^x$

- To solve an equation of the type $a^x = b$, take logs of both sides.

  $\lg x = \log_{10} x$ $\ln x = \log_e x$

Revision Exercise 2

1 For each of these expressions, remove the brackets, simplify and then differentiate.

a $4x(x-2)^2$ **b** $\dfrac{(2x+1)^3}{2x^2}$ **c** $2\sqrt{x}(x-1)$

2 Find the tangents to the curve at each of the points where the curve $y = x^2 + 2x - 3$ cuts the x-axis.
Also find the coordinates of the point where these two tangents intersect.

3 a $f(x) = x^3 - 2x^2 - 9$. Evaluate $f(3)$ and hence factorise $f(x)$.

b Find the tangent and normal to the curve $y = x^3 - 2x^2 - 4$ at the point whose y-coordinate is 5.

4 Find the equation of the normals at each of the points where the curve $y = 2x^2 - x + 2$ meets the straight line $y = 2x + 1$.

5 One of these three functions has two stationary points.
One has one stationary point, the other has no stationary points.
Determine which is which.
(There is no need to find the coordinates of these points.)

a $f(x) = x^3 + 6x^2 + 12x + 5$

b $f(x) = x^3 + 6x^2 + 15x + 5$

c $f(x) = x^3 + 6x^2 + 9x + 5$

6 A function is defined for all real values by $f(x) = x^9(9x - 10)$.

a Find the coordinates of the points where the gradient is zero.
Determine the nature of these points.

b Find the coordinates of the points where the curve crosses the x-axis.

c Use the information in parts **a** and **b** to sketch the curve.

d State the range of the function.

e Write down the range of values of x for which $9x^{10} < 10x^9$.

7 For three adjacent rectangular enclosures, 40 metres of fencing is to be used, which includes the internal boundaries.
Find the values of x and y for which the total area is a maximum.

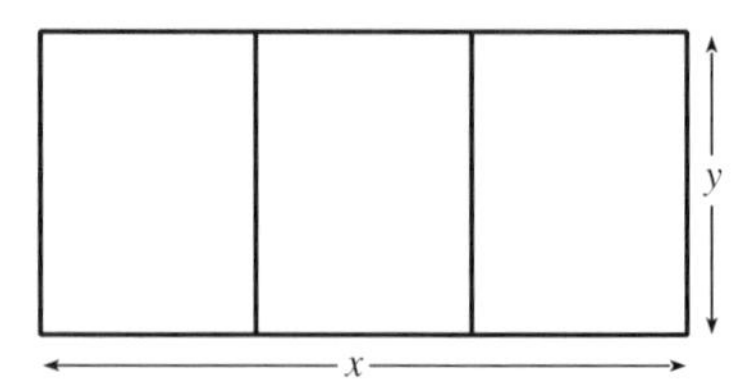

8 A wire of total length 100 cm is bent into the shape shown: three sides of a rectangle and a semicircle standing on the fourth side.
Find the exact value of x for which the area enclosed by the shape is a maximum. Also find the corresponding area, correct to 3 significant figures.

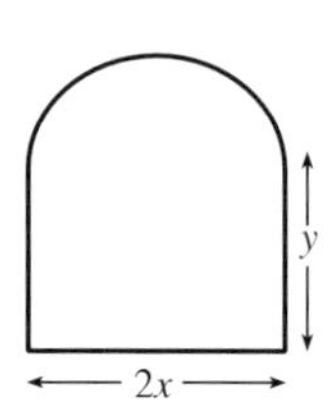

9 The functions f, g and h are defined for all real values of x by

$f(x) = x + 2 \quad g(x) = 2x \quad h(x) = x^2$

a By combining two functions at a time, it is possible to form six composite functions: fg, gf, fh, hf, gh and hg.

Match each of the composite functions to the correct function **i–vi**.

i $(x+2)^2$	**ii** $2x+4$	**iii** $2x^2$
iv $2x+2$	**v** $4x^2$	**vi** x^2+2

b By combining three different functions at a time, it is possible to form six composite functions: fgh, fhg, gfh, ghf, hfg and hgf.

Match each of these composite functions with the correct function **i–vi**.

i $4x^2+2$	**ii** $2x^2+4$	**iii** $4(x+2)^2$
iv $2(x+2)^2$	**v** $(2x+2)^2$	**vi** $2x^2+2$

10 The functions f, g and h are defined by

$f(x) = \frac{1}{x} \quad (x \neq 0) \qquad g(x) = \sqrt{x} \quad (x \geqslant 0) \qquad h(x) = x - 1$

Express these composite functions in terms of f, g and h.

a $\sqrt{x} - 1$	**b** $\dfrac{1}{\sqrt{x} - 1}$	**c** $\dfrac{1}{x-1}$
d $\dfrac{1}{\sqrt{x}} - 1$	**e** $\dfrac{1}{x} - 1$	**f** $\sqrt{x-1}$

11 The function f is defined for the domain $x \geqslant 2$ by $f(x) = x^2 - 4x + 3$.

a Express $f(x)$ in the completed square form $(x - a)^2 - b$.

b Find the coordinates of the point where $f(x) = 0$.

c Sketch the graph of $y = f(x)$.

d State the range of f.

e Obtain the inverse function $f^{-1}(x)$, and state the domain and range of f^{-1}.

f Add the graph of $y = f^{-1}(x)$ to your sketch.

g Obtain the exact coordinates of the point where the curve $y = f(x)$ meets the straight line $y = x$.

12 The function f is defined for the domain $-4 \leqslant x \leqslant 1$ by $f(x) = 4 - (x + 3)^2$.

a Write down the coordinates of the maximum point.

b Obtain the coordinates of the points where the curve crosses the axes.

c Sketch the graph of $y = f(x)$, showing clearly the information obtained above.

d State the range of f.

13 The function f is defined for the domain $x > -3$ by $f(x) = \dfrac{2x - 1}{x + 3}$.

a Obtain the inverse function $f^{-1}(x)$.

b Show that the equation $f(x) = f^{-1}(x)$ has no solution.

14 Classify each of these functions into one of the categories: even, odd, or neither.

a $f(x) = 2x^3 + 4$ **b** $f(x) = x^4 - 2x^3$ **c** $f(x) = x^4 - 3x^2$

d $f(x) = x^2(x^3 + 5x)$ **e** $f(x) = \dfrac{3x^4}{x^3 + 2x}$ **f** $f(x) = \dfrac{2x^3}{1 - x}$

15 Sketch the graph of $y = f(x)$ for the domain $-3 \leqslant x \leqslant 9$ given that

- $f(x) = \begin{cases} x - 1 & 0 \leqslant x \leqslant 2 \\ 1 & 2 < x \leqslant 3 \end{cases}$
- f is an even function, and
- f is a periodic function with period 6.

16 **a** Express $\log 10 - \log 4 - \log 3 + \log 24 - \log 1$ in the form $\log n$.

b Express $\frac{1}{2}\log 4 + 3\log 2 - \log 32$ in the form $-\log m$.

17 Solve these equations correct to 3 significant figures:

a $\log_2 x = 3$ **b** $\log_x 2 = 3$ **c** $2\log_4 x = 5$ **d** $2\log_x 4 = 5$

18 $f(x) = 2(5 - 3\log_2 x)$. Solve the equation $f(x) = -8$.

19 Solve the equation $4^x - 2^{x+1} - 3 = 0$ correct to 2 decimal places.

20 $f(x) = \log_{10} x$ and $g(x) = 3x + 1$. Find the exact solutions to these equations.

a $fg(x) = 2$ **b** $gf(x) = 2$

21 The function f is defined for $x > 0$ by $f(x) = 2\log_{10} x - 1$. Find the inverse function $f^{-1}(x)$, and state the domain and range of f^{-1}.

22 Solve the equation $3^{2x+1} = 5^x$ correct to 3 decimal places.

23 $f(x) = 2^{x-1}$ and $g(x) = 4^x$

a Find the coordinates of the point of intersection of the curves $y = f(x)$ and $y = g(x)$

b State the equation of the asymptote to each curve.

c Obtain the coordinates of the points where each of the curves crosses the y-axis.

d Sketch on the same diagram the graphs of $y = f(x)$ and $y = g(x)$.

24 **a** Factorise completely $t^3 - 15t^2 + 71t - 105$

b Hence find the solutions, correct to 3 significant figures, of the equation $8^x - 15(4^x) + 71(2^x) - 105 = 0$.

25 The function f is defined for all real values of x by $f(x) = \frac{1}{2}(3^{x+1})$.
Find the inverse function $f^{-1}(x)$, expressing the answer in terms of logarithms to base three. State the domain and range of $f^{-1}(x)$.

Examination Questions 2

Differentiation

1 The equation of a curve is $y = 6x^2 - x^3$. Find the coordinates of the two stationary points on the curve, and determine the nature of each of these stationary points. State the set of values of x for which $6x^2 - x^3$ is a decreasing function of x. The gradient at the point M on the curve is 12. Find the equation of the tangent to the curve at M. *OCR*

2 A rectangular field $ABCD$ has area 1600 square metres and is fenced on all sides. The field is divided into two parts by another fence parallel to BC. Denoting the length of AB by x metres and the total length of fencing by L metres, show that

$$L = 2x + \frac{4800}{x}$$

Show that the minimum length of fencing required is approximately 196 metres. *WJEC*

3 The equation of the curve C is

$$y = 4 + 12x - 3x^2 - 2x^3$$

a Find, showing your working, the stationary points of C and determine their nature.

b Sketch the curve C. *WJEC*

4 The diagram shows a closed cardboard box in the shape of a cuboid with base $3x$ cm by x cm and height h cm. The total surface area of the cardboard (i.e. the outside of the box) is 1152 cm^2.

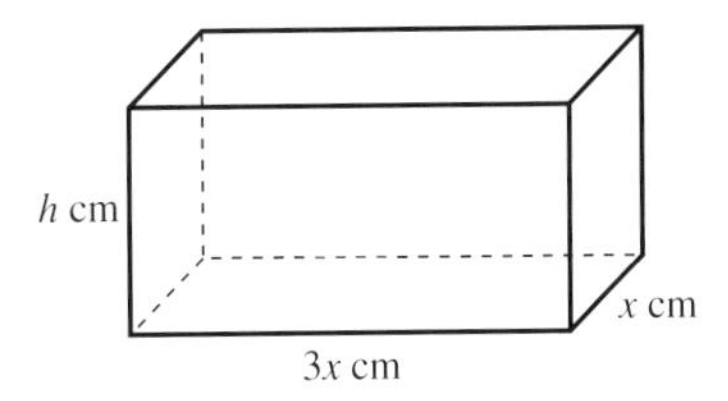

i By first expressing h in terms of x, show that the volume of the box, $V\text{ cm}^3$, is given by

$$V = 9x\left(48 - \tfrac{1}{4}x^2\right)$$

ii Given that x can vary, find the maximum value of V, explaining why it is a maximum and not a minimum. *UCLES*

5 The equation of the curve C is

$$y = 2x^3 - 6x^2 - 48x + 1$$

Showing your working, find the coordinates of the stationary points of C and determine their nature. *WJEC*

6 The diagram shows the graph of $y = f(x)$, for a certain cubic polynomial $f(x)$.

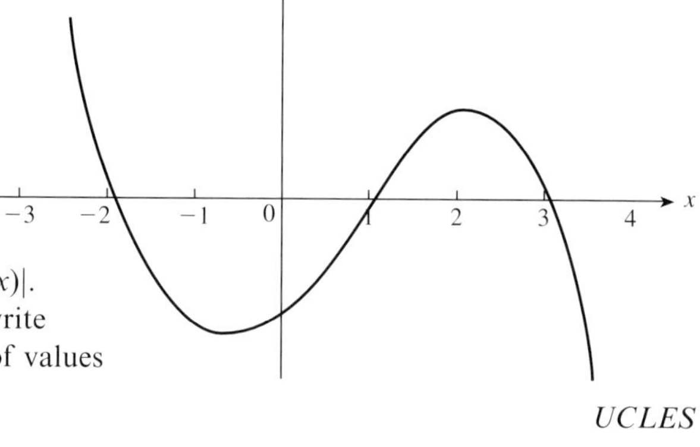

i Write down values, to the nearest integer, for all the roots of

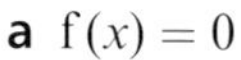

a $f(x) = 0$
b $f'(x) = 0$.

ii Sketch the graph of $y = |f(x)|$.

iii Using your answer to **i b**, write down the approximate set of values of x for which $f'(x) < 0$.

UCLES

7 The diagram shows the part of the curve with equation $y = 5 - \frac{1}{2}x^2$ for which $y \geqslant 0$. The point $P(x, y)$ lies on the curve and O is the origin.

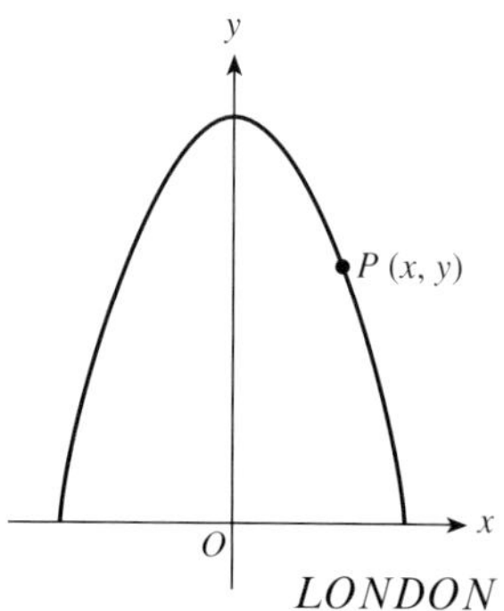

a Show that $OP^2 = \frac{1}{4}x^4 - 4x^2 + 25$.

Taking $f(x) \equiv \frac{1}{4}x^4 - 4x^2 + 25$,

b find the values of x for which $f'(x) = 0$.

c Hence, or otherwise, find the minimum distance from O to the curve, showing that your answer is a minimum.

LONDON

8 Find the equation of the normal to the curve $y = x^2 - 4x + 5$ at (3, 2). This normal meets the curve again at Q. Find the co-ordinates of Q. *UCLES*

9 Find the co-ordinates of the stationary points of the curve

$$y = \frac{(x-3)^2}{x}$$

and determine the nature of each point.

UCLES

10 An architect is drawing up plans for a mini-theatre. The diagram shows the plan of the base which consists of a rectangle of length $2y$ metres and width $2x$ metres and a semicircle of radius x metres which is placed with one side of the rectangle as diameter.

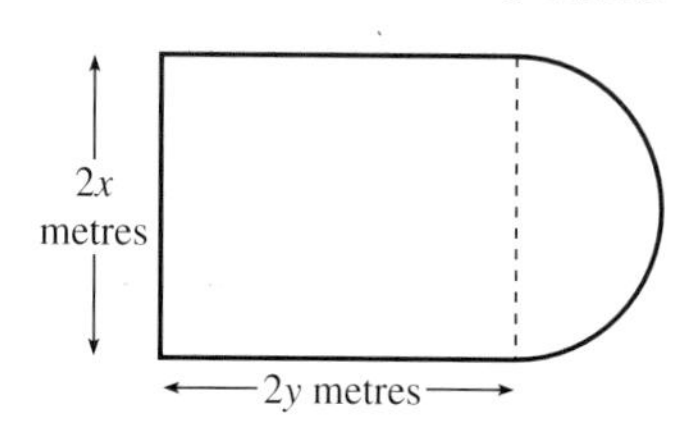

Find in terms of x and y, expressions for

a the perimeter of the base, **b** the area of the base.

The architect decides the base should have a perimeter of 100 metres.

c Show that the area A square metres of the base is given by
$A = 100x - 2x^2 - \frac{1}{2}\pi x^2$.

d Given that x can vary, find the value of x for which $\frac{dA}{dx} = 0$ and determine the corresponding value of y, giving your answers to 2 significant figures.

e Find the maximum value of A and explain why this value is a maximum.

EDEXCEL

11 A cuboid has a total surface area of $150\,\text{cm}^2$ and is such that its base is a square of side x cm.

Show that the height, h cm, of the cuboid is given by $h = \dfrac{75 - x^2}{2x}$.

Express the volume of the cuboid in terms of x. Hence determine, as x varies, its maximum volume and show that this volume is a maximum. *UCLES*

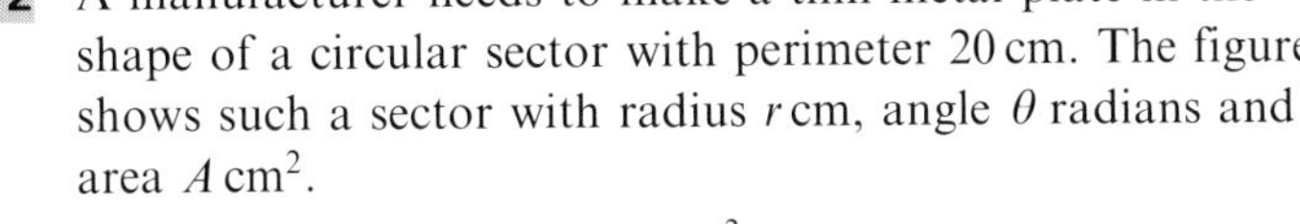

12 A manufacturer needs to make a thin metal plate in the shape of a circular sector with perimeter 20 cm. The figure shows such a sector with radius r cm, angle θ radians and area $A\,\text{cm}^2$.

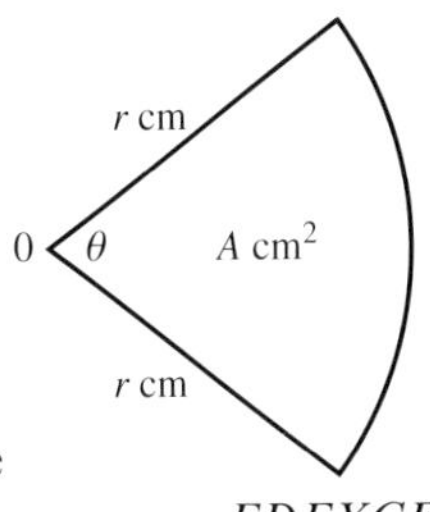

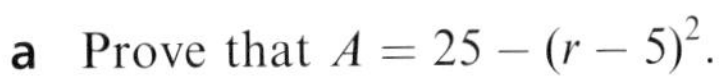

a Prove that $A = 25 - (r - 5)^2$.

Given that r can vary,

b deduce the value of r for which A is a maximum and state the maximum value of A. *EDEXCEL*

13 The diagram shows an open tank for storing water, $ABCDEF$. The sides $ABFE$ and $CDEF$ are rectangles. The triangular ends, ADE and BCF are isosceles and $\angle AED = \angle BFC = 90°$. The ends ADE and BCF are vertical and EF is horizontal. Given that $AD = x$ metres,

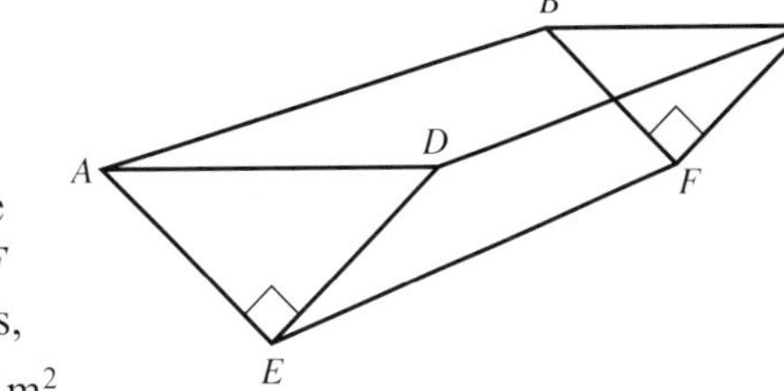

a show that the area of $\triangle ADE$ is $\frac{1}{4}x^2\,\text{m}^2$.

Given also that the capacity of the container is $4000\,\text{m}^3$ and that the total area of the two triangular and two rectangular sides of the container is $S\,\text{m}^2$,

b show that $S = \dfrac{x^2}{2} + \dfrac{16\,000\sqrt{2}}{x}$.

Given that x can vary,

c use calculus to find the minimum value of S,

d justify that the value of S you have found is a minimum. *LONDON*

Functions

1 The functions f and g are defined by

$\text{f}: x \rightarrow 1 + x^{\frac{1}{2}} \quad x \geqslant 0$

$\text{g}: x \rightarrow x^2 \quad x \in \mathbb{R}$

a Find the domain of the inverse function f^{-1}.

b Find an expression for $\text{f}^{-1}(x)$.

c Find and simplify an expression for $\text{fg}(x)$ for the case where $x \geqslant 0$.

d Explain clearly why the value of $\text{fg}(-2)$ is 3.

e Sketch the graph of $y = \text{fg}(x)$, for both positive and negative values of x, and give the equation of this graph in a simplified form. *OCR*

2 The functions f and g are defined by $f(x) = 2x - 5$ for all x and $g(x) = \sqrt{x-3}$ for $x \geqslant 3$.

The composite function fg is denoted by h.

a Find an expression for $h(x)$.

b State the domain and range of h. *WJEC*

3 The function f has domain $(-1, \infty)$ and is defined by $f(x) = x^2 + 2x + 2$.

a Show that f is an increasing function.

b Write down the range of f.

c Find an expression for $f^{-1}(x)$.

d Write down the range and domain of f^{-1}.

e **Sketch** the graphs of f and f^{-1} on the same diagram. *WJEC*

4 Functions f and g are defined by $\text{f}: x \to 4 - x$, $x \in \mathbb{R}$, and $\text{g}: x \to 3x^2$, $x \in \mathbb{R}$.

a Find the range of g.

b Solve $\text{gf}(x) = 48$.

c Sketch the graph of $y = |\text{f}(x)|$ and hence find the values of x for which $|\text{f}(x)| = 2$. *LONDON*

5 The functions f and g are defined for all real numbers by

$\text{f}: x \to x^2 + 4x + 1$

$\text{g}: x \to ax + b$

where a and b are constants.

i Given that $\text{fg}(2) = -2$, show that

$4a^2 + 4ab + b^2 + 8a + 4b + 3 = 0$.

ii Given that $\text{gf}(0) = -3$, obtain a second equation involving a and b.

iii Solve the pair of simultaneous equations from **i** and **ii** to find a and b. *UCLES*

6 Given that $\text{f}(x) = \dfrac{2}{x}$, write down simplified expressions for

a $\text{f}(x^{-1})$ **b** $\text{f}^{-1}(x)$ *UCLES*

7 The function f is an odd function defined on the interval $[-2, 2]$. Given that

$\text{f}(x) = -x, \quad 0 \leqslant x < 1$

$\text{f}(x) = x - 2, \ 1 \leqslant x \leqslant 2$

a sketch the graph of f for $-2 \leqslant x \leqslant 2$

b find the values of x for which $\text{f}(x) = -\frac{1}{2}$. *LONDON*

8 The functions f and g are defined by

$\text{f}: x \to 4x - 1, \ x \in \mathbb{R}$

$\text{g}: x \to \dfrac{3}{2x-1}, \ x \in \mathbb{R}, \ x \neq \frac{1}{2}$

Find in its simplest form

a the inverse function f^{-1}

b the composite function gf, stating its domain.

c Find the values of x for which $2\text{f}(x) = \text{g}(x)$, giving your answers to 3 decimal places. *LONDON*

9 The functions f and g are defined by

$f(x) = \dfrac{1}{\sqrt{x-5}}$ for $x > 5$

$g(x) = x^2 - 4$ for $x \geqslant 0$

a Derive an expression for $gf(x)$.

b State the domain and range of gf. *WJEC*

10 **a** Functions f and g are defined by

$\mathrm{f}: x \to 3x - 2$

$\mathrm{g}: x \to \dfrac{12}{x} - 4, \quad x \neq 0.$

Find an expression for the function
i ff **ii** fg **iii** g^{-1}

b The function $\mathrm{h}: x \to x^3 + ax + b$ is such that the equation $\mathrm{h}(x) = x$ has solutions of $x = 2$ and $x = 3$.

Find the value of a and of b. *UCLES*

11 Express $x^2 + 4x$ in the form $(x + a)^2 + b$, stating the numerical values of a and b.

The functions f and g are defined as follows:

$\mathrm{f}: x \to x^2 + 4x, \quad x \geqslant -2$

$\mathrm{g}: x \to x + 6, \quad x \in \mathbb{R}$

a Show that the equation $\mathrm{gf}(x) = 0$ has no real roots.

b State the domain of f^{-1}.

c Find an expression in terms of x for $\mathrm{f}^{-1}(x)$.

d Sketch, on a single diagram, the graphs of $y = \mathrm{f}(x)$ and $y = \mathrm{f}^{-1}(x)$. *UCLES*

12 Given that $\mathrm{f}: x \to ax + b$, $(a > 0)$ and $\mathrm{f}^2: x \to 4x - 9$, find

a an expression for f^4

b the value of a and of b

c $\mathrm{f}^{-1}(7)$ *UCLES*

13 Functions f and g are defined by

$\mathrm{f}: x \to \dfrac{3}{x+3}, \quad x \in \mathbb{R}, x \geqslant 0$

$\mathrm{g}: x \to x + 1, \quad x \in \mathbb{R}, x \geqslant 0$

Show that

$\mathrm{gf}: x \to \dfrac{x+6}{x+3}, \quad x \in \mathbb{R}, x \geqslant 0.$

Express fg in a similar form.

Find $(\mathrm{gf})^{-1}(x)$. *UCLES*

14 The function f is defined by $f(x) = \dfrac{2}{\sqrt{x^2 - 4}}$ for $x > 2$.

a Write down the range of f.

b Derive an expression for $f^{-1}(x)$ and verify that $ff^{-1}(x) = x$.

c Write down the domain of ff^{-1}. *WJEC*

15 **a** Given that $f{:}x \to ax + b$ and that $f(2) = 8$ and $f^{-1}(3) = 1$, find the value of a and of b.

b Given the functions $f{:}x \to 2x - 3$ and $g{:}x \to \dfrac{8}{x}$ (for $x \neq 0$), find in similar form

i f^{-1} **ii** ff **iii** gg **iv** fg

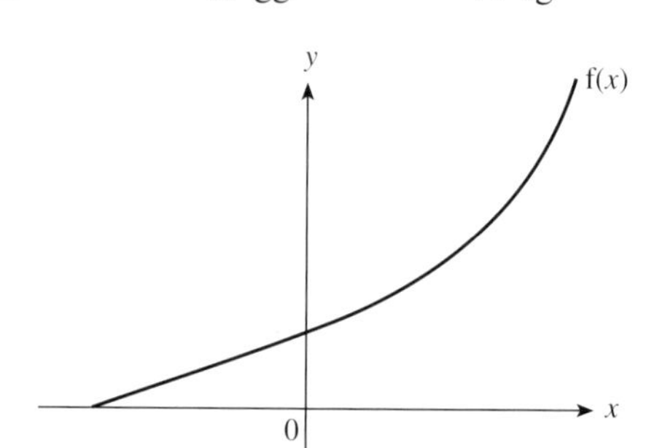

c The diagram shows part of the graph of $y = f(x)$. Copy the diagram and on it sketch the corresponding part of the graph of $y = f(-x)$. *UCLES*

Exponential and logarithmic functions

1 Solve the equation $2^x = 3$, giving your answer correct to two decimal places. *UCLES*

2 **a** Solve the equation $5^{x+1} = 6$.

b Solve the equation, $\log_2 x + \log_2(6x + 1) = 1$.

c Given that $\lg x = a$ and $\lg y = b$, express $\lg\sqrt{\dfrac{1000x^3}{y}}$ in terms of a and b. *UCLES*

3 **a** Solve the equations

i $2 \times 4^{x+1} = 16^{2x}$ **ii** $\log_2 y^2 = 4 + \log_2(y + 5)$.

b Given that $y = ax^n + 3$, that $y = 4.4$ when $x = 10$ and $y = 12.8$ when $x = 100$, find the value of n and of a. *UCLES*

4 Given that $t^{\frac{1}{3}} = y$, $y \neq 0$,

a express $6t^{-\frac{1}{3}}$ in terms of y.

b Hence, or otherwise, find the values of t for which $6t^{-\frac{1}{3}} - t^{\frac{1}{3}} = 5$. *LONDON*

5 Given that $y = 10^x$, show that

a $y^2 = 100^x$

b $\dfrac{y}{10} = 10^{x-1}$

c Using the results from **a** and **b** write the equation

$100^x - 10\,001(10^{x-1}) + 100 = 0$

as an equation in y.

d By first solving the equation in y, find the values of x which satisfy the given equation in x. *LONDON*

6 Given that $27^{3x+1} = 9^y$,

a obtain an expression for y in the form $y = ax + b$, where a and b are constants,

b solve the equation $27^{3x+1} = 9$, giving your answer as an exact fraction.

LONDON

7 Express in the form 2^y

a 4^{5x} **b** 8^{x-1}

Solve exactly the equation

$$\frac{4^{5x}}{2^4} = 8^{x-1}$$

giving your answer as a fraction in its lowest terms. *UCLES*

8 Use the substitution $y = 5^x$ in the equation

$5^{-x} - 18 \times 5^x = 3$

to find the value of x, correct to two decimal places. *WJEC*

9 Using the substitution $y = 3^x$, solve the equation $9^x + 3^x = 56$. Give your answer correct to three significant figures. *WJEC*

10 Solve the equation $3^{2x} = 4^{2-x}$, giving your answer to three significant figures.

UCLES

11 Solve the inequality $|x - 100| < 10$.

Hence find the set of integers n that satisfy the inequality

$|1.01^n - 100| < 10$. *OCR*

12 Sequences and Series

Before starting this chapter you will need to know

- about logarithms for some of the later questions (Chapter 11).

12.1 Sequences

A **sequence** is a set of terms, in a definite order, where the terms are obtained by some rule.

A **finite sequence** ends after a certain number of terms.

An **infinite sequence** is one that continues indefinitely.

Consider the infinite sequence 1, 3, 5, 7, ..., the sequence of odd numbers:

$$\begin{aligned} \mathit{1st} \text{ term} &= 2 \times \mathit{1} - 1 = 1 \\ \mathit{2nd} \text{ term} &= 2 \times \mathit{2} - 1 = 3 \\ \mathit{3rd} \text{ term} &= 2 \times \mathit{3} - 1 = 5 \\ &\vdots \\ \mathit{nth} \text{ term} &= 2 \times n - 1 = 2n - 1 \end{aligned}$$

Notice there is a constant difference of 2 between the terms, leading to $2n$ in the formula.

Notation

The terms of a sequence can be expressed as $u_1, u_2, u_3, \ldots u_n, \ldots$ where u_1 = first term, u_2 = second term and so on.

Finding the formula for the terms of a sequence

The formula for the terms in a sequence can be given as a formula for the nth term and/or a recurrence relation. A **recurrence relation** defines the first term(s) in the sequence and the relation between successive terms.

For example the sequence 5, 8, 11, 14, ... can be defined as $u_n = 3n + 2$ and/or as $u_1 = 5$, $u_{n+1} = u_n + 3$, $n \geqslant 1$.

When looking for the rule defining a sequence, consider these points:

- Look at the difference between consecutive terms. Is it constant?
- Compare the sequence with sequences such as the squares (1, 4, 9, 16, ...; nth term $= n^2$) and the cubes (1, 8, 27, 64, ...; nth term $= n^3$).
- Look for powers of numbers, e.g. for the sequence 1, 2, 4, 8, ... the nth term is 2^{n-1}.
- Do the signs of the terms alternate, e.g. $-1, +2, -3, +4, \ldots$? If so, use the fact that
  $(-1)^k = -1$ when k is odd, and
  $(-1)^k = +1$ when k is even.

  Include in the expression for the nth term $(-1)^n$ if the first term is $-$ve; include $(-1)^{n+1}$ or $(-1)^{n-1}$ if the first term is $+$ve.

  This technique is illustrated in Example 3.

Example 1 Find the next three terms in the sequence 5, 8, 11, 14, ... and the formula for the nth term.

Look at the difference between the terms.

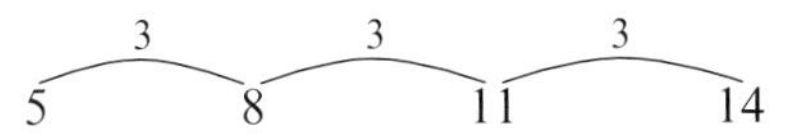

The constant difference of 3 will lead to a formula containing $3n$.

The sequence with nth term $3n$ has terms 3, 6, 9, 12, ...

The terms of the sequence 5, 8, 11, 14, ... are each 2 more, so its nth term is $3n + 2$.

✓ Check: $1st$ term $= 3 \times 1 + 2 = 5$

$2nd$ term $= 3 \times 2 + 2 = 8$

This sequence could also be defined by the **recurrence relation**:

$u_{n+1} = u_n + 3$, $n \geqslant 1$, $u_1 = 5$

The first term is 5 ($u_1 = 5$) and each term is 3 more than the previous one ($u_{n+1} = u_n + 3$).

Example 2 The nth term of a sequence is given by $u_n = \dfrac{1}{2^n}$.

a Find the first four terms of the sequence.

b Which term in the sequence is $\frac{1}{1024}$?

c Express the sequence as a recurrence relation.

Solution

a Putting $n = 1$ $u_1 = \dfrac{1}{2^1} = \dfrac{1}{2}$

$n = 2$ $u_2 = \dfrac{1}{2^2} = \dfrac{1}{4}$

$n = 3$ $u_3 = \dfrac{1}{2^3} = \dfrac{1}{8}$

$n = 4$ $u_4 = \dfrac{1}{2^4} = \dfrac{1}{16}$

The first four terms are $\frac{1}{2}$, $\frac{1}{4}$, $\frac{1}{8}$ and $\frac{1}{16}$.

b Let the rth term be $\frac{1}{1024}$.

So $\dfrac{1}{2^r} = \dfrac{1}{1024}$

$\therefore$ $2^r = 1024$

But $2^{10} = 1024$

$\therefore$ $r = 10$

So $\frac{1}{1024}$ is the 10th term.

To find which power of 2 is 1024, either

- express 1024 as the product of prime factors ($1024 = 2^{10}$) or
- use the calculator to find which power of 2 is 1024, or
- use logs: $r \log 2 = \log 1024$

$$r = \frac{\log 1024}{\log 2}$$

c $u_{n+1} = \frac{1}{2}u_n$ $n \geqslant 1$ $u_1 = \frac{1}{2}$

Each term is half the previous one. The first term is $\frac{1}{2}$.

Example 3 Find the nth term of the sequence +1, −4, +9, −16, +25, ...

The terms of the sequence are the square numbers 1, 4, 9, 16, 25, ... but with alternating signs.

For the sequence +1, −4, +9, −16, +25, ...

$u_n = (-1)^{n+1}n^2$

Check:
1st term $= (-1)^{1+1} \times 1^2$
$= (-1)^2 \times 1 = 1$
2nd term $= (-1)^{2+1} \times 2^2$
$= (-1)^3 \times 4 = -4$ ✓

12.2 Convergent, divergent, oscillating and periodic sequences

- A sequence is defined as **convergent** if its terms approach closer and closer to a **limit**.
- A sequence is defined as **divergent** if its terms grow larger and larger. The sequence can tend to $+\infty$ or $-\infty$.
- A sequence is **oscillating** if, however far along the sequence one goes, there are always terms larger and smaller than a particular value.
- In a **periodic** sequence the terms are repeated at regular intervals.

Illustrating the first few terms of the sequence on a graph helps to show how the sequence behaves. A point should be plotted for each term. The 'horizontal' axis gives the number, n, of the term, the 'vertical' axis the value, u_n, of the term.

Example 4 The sequence, $\frac{1}{2}, \frac{2}{3}, \frac{3}{4}, \frac{4}{5} \ldots$, is a convergent sequence.

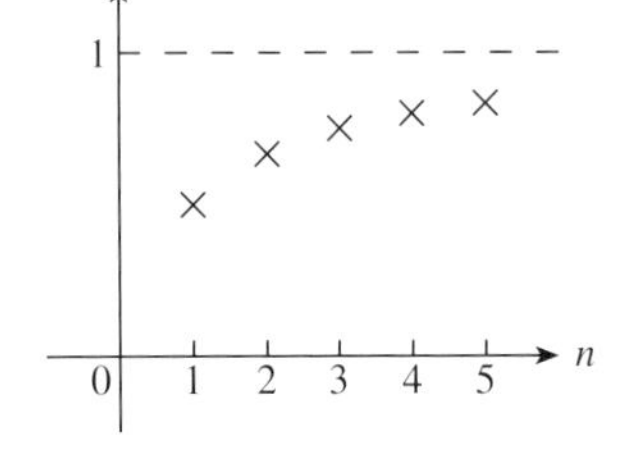

The terms approach closer and closer to 1.
1 is the **limiting value** and it is possible to choose a term as close to this limit as one wishes, providing one goes far enough along the sequence.

As the sequence progresses, the points approach closer and closer to the line $u_n = 1$.

$u_n \to 1$ as $n \to \infty$.

Example 5 The sequence 5, 8, 11, 14, ... is a divergent sequence.

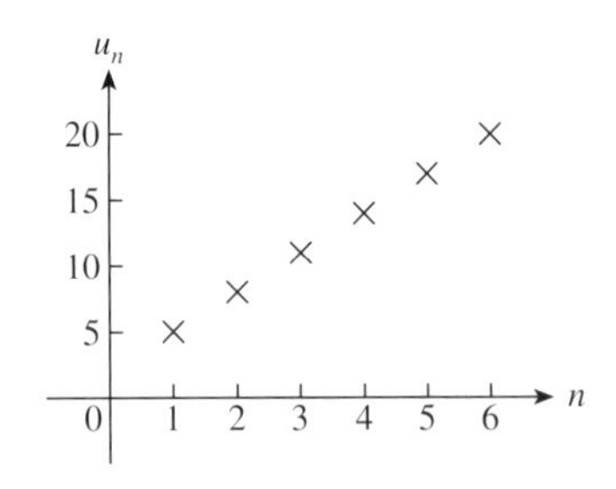

The further along the sequence one goes the larger the terms become.

The points are further and further from the n axis as the sequence progresses.

$u_n \to +\infty$ as $n \to \infty$.

Example 6 The sequence $+1, -2, +3, -4, +5, \ldots$ is an oscillating sequence.

The points neither converge nor diverge to $+\infty$ or $-\infty$ as the sequence progresses. However far along the sequence one goes, there will always be numbers larger and smaller than zero. This sequence oscillates about zero.

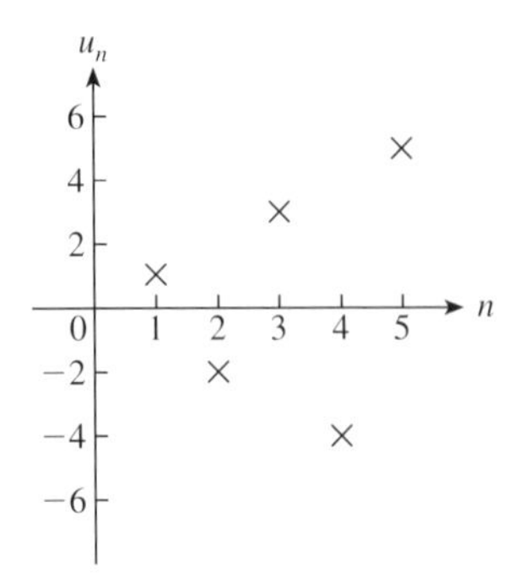

Example 7 The sequence $0, \frac{3}{2}, \frac{2}{3}, \frac{5}{4}, \frac{4}{5}, \frac{7}{6}, \frac{6}{7}, \ldots$ is an example of an oscillating convergent sequence. It oscillates about 1 and converges to 1.

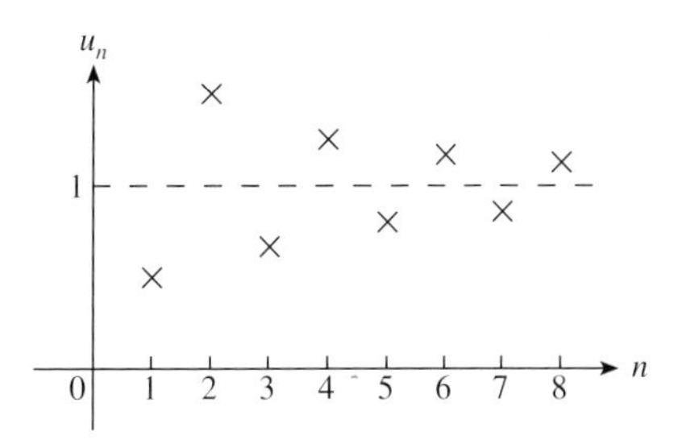

✓ *Note* A sequence which neither converges to a limit, nor diverges to $+\infty$ or $-\infty$ must be an oscillating sequence.

Example 8 Consider this periodic sequence: 2, 7, 12, 17, 2, 7, 12, 17, 2, 7, ...

$u_1 = u_5 = u_9 = u_{13} = \cdots = 2$

$u_2 = u_6 = u_{10} = u_{14} = \cdots = 7$

$u_3 = u_7 = u_{11} = u_{15} = \cdots = 12$

$u_4 = u_8 = u_{12} = u_{16} = \cdots = 17$

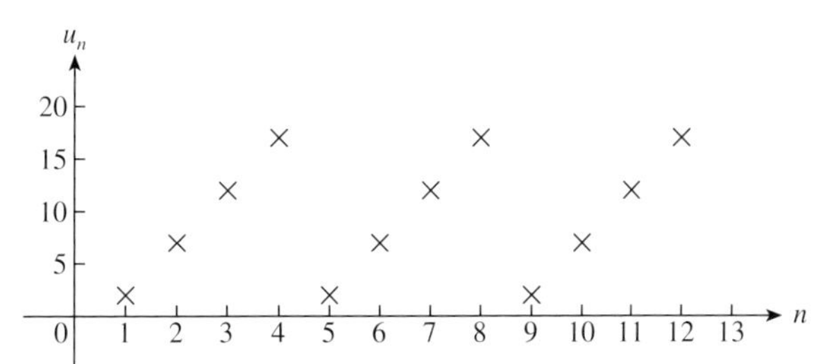

The terms are repeated in groups of 4.
The sequence is said to be periodic of period 4.
Expressed formally:

$u_r = 5r - 3$ for $1 \leqslant r \leqslant 4$

and

$u_{r+4} = u_r$ for all values of $r \geqslant 1$. ($5r - 3$ generates the sequence 2, 7, 12, 17.)

➤

Convergent sequence $u_r \to a$ as $r \to \infty$
Read 'u_r tends to a as r tends to infinity'. The terms approach closer and closer to the limiting value (or limit) a.

Divergent sequence $u_r \to +\infty$ as $r \to \infty$ or $u_r \to -\infty$ as $r \to \infty$
Read 'u_r tends to plus (or minus) infinity as r tends to infinity'.

Oscillating sequence However far along the sequence one goes, there are always terms larger and smaller than a particular value.
A sequence which neither converges nor diverges to $+\infty$ or $-\infty$ must necessarily be an oscillating sequence.

Periodic sequence A sequence for which there is some value of k such that $u_{r+k} = u_r$ for all values of $r \geqslant 1$ is called periodic. If k is the smallest value for which $u_{r+k} = u_r$ then the sequence has **period** k.

Example 9

Write out the first eight terms of the sequence defined by $u_r = 2r + 3$ for $1 \leqslant r \leqslant 3$ and $u_{r+3} = u_r$.

$u_1 = 2 \times 1 + 3 = 5 \quad u_2 = 2 \times 2 + 3 = 7 \quad u_3 = 2 \times 3 + 3 = 9$

$u_r = u_{r+3}$ so $u_1 = u_4 = u_7 = u_{10} = \cdots$, $u_2 = u_5 = u_8 = u_{11} = \cdots$, $u_3 = u_6 = u_9 = u_{12} = \cdots$

So the first eight terms of the sequence are 5, 7, 9, 5, 7, 9, 5, 7.

The sequence is periodic of period 3.

Example 10

Write down the first six terms of each sequence and state whether the sequence is convergent, divergent or oscillating. If the sequence is convergent state the limit to which the sequence converges. If the sequence is periodic, state the period.

a $u_1 = 2 \quad u_n = 2 - \dfrac{1}{u_{n-1}} \quad n > 1$

> To find u_2, put $n = 2$: $u_2 = 2 - \dfrac{1}{u_1}$.
> Substituting $u_1 = 2$ gives u_2.

$u_2 = 2 - \frac{1}{2} = 1\frac{1}{2}$

$u_3 = 2 - \frac{2}{3} = 1\frac{1}{3}$

$u_4 = 2 - \frac{3}{4} = 1\frac{1}{4}$

> Similarly $u_3 = 2 - \dfrac{1}{u_2} = 2 - \dfrac{1}{\frac{3}{2}}$. *Note:* $\dfrac{1}{\frac{3}{2}} = \frac{2}{3}$

and so on.

So the first six terms are 2, $1\frac{1}{2}$, $1\frac{1}{3}$, $1\frac{1}{4}$, $1\frac{1}{5}$, $1\frac{1}{6}$.

The sequence is convergent and converges to 1.

An algebraic approach to the convergence of sequences is given in Chapter 18. A spreadsheet or graphics calculator is a powerful tool for investigating the behaviour of sequences. The sequence in Example 10a can be seen to converge to 1.

b $u_1 = 1 \quad u_{n+1} = 3 + (-1)^{n+1} u_n \quad n \geqslant 1$

$u_2 = 3 + (-1)^2 \times 1 = 4$

> Putting $n = 1$ gives $u_2 = 3 + (-1)^2 u_1$.

$u_3 = 3 + (-1)^3 \times 4 = 3 - 4 = -1$

> Putting $n = 2$ gives $u_3 = 3 + (-1)^3 u_2$.

$u_4 = 3 + (-1)^4 \times (-1) = 3 - 1 = 2$

$u_5 = 3 + (-1)^5 \times 2 = 1$

> $u_5 = u_1 = 1$ so the sequence will repeat with period 4.

So the first six terms are 1, 4, −1, 2, 1, 4

The sequence is oscillating and periodic of period 4.

EXERCISE 12a

In this exercise, use of a spreadsheet or graphics calculator is recommended for Question 3.

1 For each of these sequences, find the first four terms of the sequence, and which term of the sequence equals X.

a	$u_n = 3n$	$X = 303$	**b**	$u_n = 3^n$	$X = 729$
c	$u_n = 4n - 3$	$X = 245$	**d**	$u_n = 8 - 2n$	$X = -32$
e	$u_n = n^4$	$X = 14641$	**f**	$u_n = n^2 - 1$	$X = 840$

2 For each of these sequences find the next three terms, and a formula for the nth term.

Illustrate the sequence graphically with a sketch and state whether each sequence is convergent, divergent or oscillating.

If convergent, state the limit to which the terms converge.
If oscillating, state whether periodic or not. If periodic, state the period.

a 11, 16, 21, 26, ... **b** $1, \frac{1}{4}, \frac{1}{16}, \frac{1}{64}, \ldots$ **c** 20, 17, 14, 11, ...

d 2, 4, 6, 8, ... **e** 2, 4, 8, 16, ... **f** $\frac{1}{2}, \frac{2}{3}, \frac{3}{4}, \frac{4}{5}, \ldots$

g 1, 4, 9, 16, ... **h** 1, 8, 27, 64, ... **i** 2, 16, 54, 128, ...

j 3, 6, 9, 3, 6, 9, 3, ... **k** $-3, 5, -7, 9, \ldots$ **l** 256, 128, 64, 32, ...

m 4, 7, 12, 19, ... **n** $1, -1, 1, -1, 1, \ldots$ **o** $10, 1, \frac{1}{10}, \frac{1}{100}, \ldots$

3 For each of these sequences, find the first six terms, and decide whether the sequence is convergent, divergent or oscillating.

If oscillating, state whether periodic. If periodic, state the period.

a $u_1 = 3 \quad u_{n+1} = u_n + 4 \quad n \geqslant 1$ **b** $u_1 = 64 \quad u_{n+1} = \dfrac{u_n}{2} \quad n \geqslant 1$

c $u_1 = 1 \quad u_{n+1} = u_n + 2n + 1 \quad n \geqslant 1$ **d** $u_1 = 6 \quad u_{n+1} = \dfrac{u_n + 1}{2} \quad n \geqslant 1$

e $u_1 = 1 \quad u_2 = 2 \quad u_{n+2} = \dfrac{u_{n+1}}{u_n} \quad n \geqslant 1$ **f** $u_1 = -4 \quad u_{n+1} = u_n + (-2)^n \quad n \geqslant 1$

g $u_1 = 4 \quad u_n = \dfrac{(u_{n-1})^2}{8} \quad n > 1$ **h** $u_1 = 3 \quad u_{n+1} = (u_n - 1)^2 \quad n \geqslant 1$

i $u_1 = 1 \quad u_{n+1} = 3 + (-1)^n u_n \quad n \geqslant 1$ **j** $u_1 = 3 \quad u_n = 1 - \dfrac{1}{u_{n-1}} \quad n > 1$

k $u_1 = 7 \quad u_2 = 19 \quad u_3 = -\frac{1}{2} \quad u_{n+3} = u_n \quad n \geqslant 1$

l $u_1 = \frac{1}{2} \quad u_2 = 2 \quad u_{n+1} = u_n u_{n-1} \quad n \geqslant 1$

m $u_1 = 3 \quad u_2 = 2 \quad u_{n+2} = 2(u_{n+1} - u_n) \quad n \geqslant 1$

4 a A Fibonacci sequence is defined by $u_1 = 1 \quad u_2 = 1 \quad u_n = u_{n-1} + u_{n-2}$ for $n \geqslant 3$.
Find the first ten terms of the sequence.

b A further sequence, a_n, is generated by forming the ratio of consecutive terms of the Fibonacci sequence. If

$$a_n = \frac{u_{n+1}}{u_n}$$

find the first nine terms of this sequence in decimal form.

Explore the convergence of the sequence a_n.

12.3 Series and Σ notation

When the terms of a sequence are added the sum of the terms is called a **series**. A finite series is one which ends after a finite number of terms. An infinite series continues indefinitely.

S_n is used to denote the sum of the first n terms. S_∞ is used to denote the sum of an infinite series, if it exists.

The greek capital letter, Σ, (pronounced 'sigma') is used to show that the terms of a sequence are to be added.

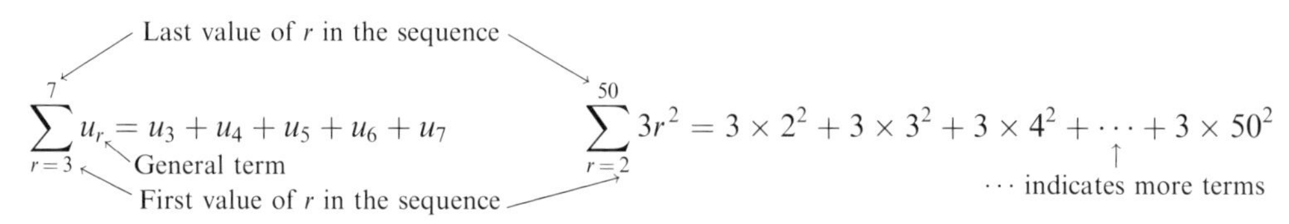

The values of r go up in steps of 1 from the first to the last.

When there is no possibility of confusion the notation can be simplified.

$$\sum_{1}^{10} r^3 = 1^3 + 2^3 + 3^3 + \cdots + 10^3$$

The notation can also be used for an infinite series.

$$\sum_{1}^{\infty} \frac{1}{r} = \tfrac{1}{1} + \tfrac{1}{2} + \tfrac{1}{3} + \cdots$$

Example 11 Write the series in full.

a $\sum_{2}^{5} m^2 = 2^2 + 3^2 + 4^2 + 5^2$

b $\sum_{1}^{k} m(m-1) = 1\times 0 + 2\times 1 + 3\times 2 + 4\times 3 + \cdots + k(k-1)$

Example 12 Write, using $\sum$ notation, $\frac{1\times 4}{3} + \frac{2\times 5}{5} + \frac{3\times 6}{7} + \cdots + \frac{10\times 13}{21}$

Notice that there are three sequences within the series, labelled •, ▪ and ▲, and that there are ten terms.▲

$$\frac{\overset{\bullet}{1}\times\overset{\blacksquare}{4}}{\underset{\blacktriangle}{3}} + \frac{\overset{\bullet}{2}\times\overset{\blacksquare}{5}}{\underset{\blacktriangle}{5}} + \frac{\overset{\bullet}{3}\times\overset{\blacksquare}{6}}{\underset{\blacktriangle}{7}} + \cdots + \frac{\overset{\bullet}{10}\times\overset{\blacksquare}{13}}{\underset{\blacktriangle}{21}}$$

- • 1, 2, 3, ..., 10, $\Rightarrow u_r = r$
- ▪ 4, 5, 6, ..., 13, $\Rightarrow u_r = r + 3$
- ▲ 3, 5, 7, ..., 21, $\Rightarrow u_r = 2r + 1$

So $\frac{1\times 4}{3} + \frac{2\times 5}{5} + \frac{3\times 6}{7} + \cdots + \frac{10\times 13}{21} = \sum_{1}^{10} \frac{r(r+3)}{2r+1}$.

Here are some useful results. (The proof of these is left to the reader.)

Summation results

$$\sum_{h}^{k}(a_r + b_r) = \sum_{h}^{k} a_r + \sum_{h}^{k} b_r$$

$$\sum_{h}^{j} a_r + \sum_{j+1}^{k} a_r = \sum_{h}^{k} a_r \quad h < j < k$$

$$\sum_{1}^{n} c = nc \text{ where } c \text{ is a constant}$$

$$\sum_{m}^{n} ka_r = k\sum_{m}^{n} a_r \text{ where } k \text{ is a constant}$$

These formulae can be quoted.

Summing integers, squares and cubes

Sum of first n integers $\quad \sum_{1}^{n} r = \dfrac{n(n+1)}{2}$

Sum of first n squares $\quad \sum_{1}^{n} r^2 = \dfrac{n(n+1)(2n+1)}{6}$

Sum of first n cubes $\quad \sum_{1}^{n} r^3 = \dfrac{n^2(n+1)^2}{4}$

Example 13 Use the formulae to find sums of terms.

a $S = 6^3 + 7^3 + 8^3 + \cdots + 30^3$

$$= \sum_{1}^{30} r^3 - \sum_{1}^{5} r^3$$

$$= \frac{30^2(30+1)^2}{4} - \frac{5^2(5+1)^2}{4}$$

$$= \frac{30^2 \times 31^2}{4} - \frac{5^2 \times 6^2}{4}$$

$$= 216\,000$$

$S = (1^3 + 2^3 + 3^3 + \cdots + 30^3) - (1^3 + 2^3 + 3^3 + 4^3 + 5^3)$
So S can be found by subtracting the sum of the first 5 cubes from the sum of the first 30.

b $S = 1^2 + 2^2 + 3^2 + \cdots + (2n)^2$

$$= \frac{2n(2n+1)(2 \times 2n + 1)}{6}$$

$$= \frac{n(2n+1)(4n+1)}{3}$$

Use the formula for the sum of the first n squares with n replaced by $2n$.

c $S = 2\times 3 + 3\times 4 + 4\times 5 + \cdots + 21\times 22$

The rth term is $(r+1)(r+2)$. There are 20 terms.

$$= \sum_1^{20}(r+1)(r+2)$$

$$= \sum_1^{20}(r^2+3r+2)$$

$$= \sum_1^{20} r^2 + \sum_1^{20} 3r + \sum_1^{20} 2$$

$\sum 3r = 3\sum r$

$$= \sum_1^{20} r^2 + 3\sum_1^{20} r + \sum_1^{20} 2$$

$\sum_1^n r^2 = \frac{n(n+1)(2n+1)}{6}$

$\sum_1^n r = \frac{n(n+1)}{2} \quad \sum_1^n c = nc$

$$= \frac{20\times 21\times 41}{6} + \frac{3\times 20\times 21}{2} + 20\times 2$$

$$= 3540$$

EXERCISE 12b

1 Write in full

a $\sum_1^4 m^3$ **b** $\sum_2^n m^2$ **c** $\sum_1^n (m^2+m)$ **d** $\sum_1^3 \frac{1}{m(m+1)}$ **e** $\sum_2^5 2^m$

f $\sum_1^4 (-1)^m m^2$ **g** $\sum_1^n m^m$ **h** $\sum_3^6 \frac{(-1)^m}{m}$ **i** $\sum_n^{n+2} m(m-1)$ **j** $\sum_{n-2}^n \frac{m}{m+1}$

2 Write in the Σ notation

a $1+2+3+\cdots+n$

b $1^4+2^4+\cdots+n^4+(n+1)^4$

c $1+\frac{1}{2}+\frac{1}{3}+\frac{1}{4}+\frac{1}{5}$

d $3^2+3^3+3^4+3^5$

e $1+\frac{2}{3}+\frac{3}{9}+\frac{4}{27}+\frac{5}{81}$

f $\frac{1\times 3}{4}+\frac{2\times 5}{6}+\frac{3\times 7}{8}+\frac{4\times 9}{10}+\frac{5\times 11}{12}$

g $-1+2-3+4-5+6$

h $1-2+4-8+16-32$

i $2\times 7+3\times 8+4\times 9+5\times 10+6\times 11$

j $1\times 3-2\times 5+3\times 7-4\times 9+5\times 11$

3 Write in full and evaluate

a $\sum_1^6 n$ **b** $\sum_1^5 (2r+3)$ **c** $\sum_1^4 (-1)^m m^3$ **d** $\sum_1^5 \frac{n}{n+1}$

e $\sum_1^6 \left(-\frac{2}{p}\right)$ **f** $\sum_5^9 n(n-3)$ **g** $\sum_4^7 (-2)^r$ **h** $\sum_2^7 \frac{(-1)^r}{3(r-1)}$

i $\sum_1^5 |5+(-2)^r|$ **j** $\sum_{n=1}^{2k} (-1)^n$ **k** $\sum_1^6 4$ **l** $\sum_4^{30}(2m-1)-\sum_8^{30}(2m-1)$

4 Write in full and simplify

a $\sum_{n=1}^5 k^2 n$ **b** $\sum_{k=1}^5 k^2 n$ **c** $\sum_{r=1}^6 \frac{ar(r+1)}{2}$

d $\sum_{n=1}^{2k} (-1)^{n+1} n$ **e** $\sum_{m=1}^4 \frac{a}{m}$ **f** $\sum_{r=1}^4 \frac{a}{m}$

5 Find these sums, using the formulae on page 271.

a $1^2 + 2^2 + 3^2 + \cdots + 10^2$

b $1^3 + 2^3 + 3^3 + \cdots + 13^3$

c $6 + 7 + 8 + \cdots + 40$

d $6 + 7 + 8 + \cdots + n$

e $18^3 + 17^3 + 16^3 + \cdots + 5^3$

f $2^2 + 4^2 + 6^2 + \cdots + 200^2$

g $\sum_{1}^{15} (r^2 + 2r^3)$

h $1^2 + 2^2 + 3^2 + \cdots + (n-1)^2$

i $1^3 + 2^3 + 3^3 + \cdots + (2n)^3$

j $1 \times 2 + 2 \times 3 + 3 \times 4 \cdots$, to n terms

6 How many squares are there on a chessboard? (The squares can be of any size.)

12.4 Arithmetic and geometric series

Consider the series $2 + 6 + 10 + 14 + \cdots$ and $2 + 6 + 18 + 54 + \cdots$

In the first case, each term has 4 *added* to it to obtain the next term.
The series is said to have a **common difference** of 4.
Such a series is called an *arithmetic* series or progression (often abbreviated to **AP**).

In the second case, each term is *multiplied* by 3 to obtain the next term.
The series is said to have a **common ratio** of 3.
Such a series is called a *geometric* series or progression (often abbreviated to **GP**).

Arithmetic progressions

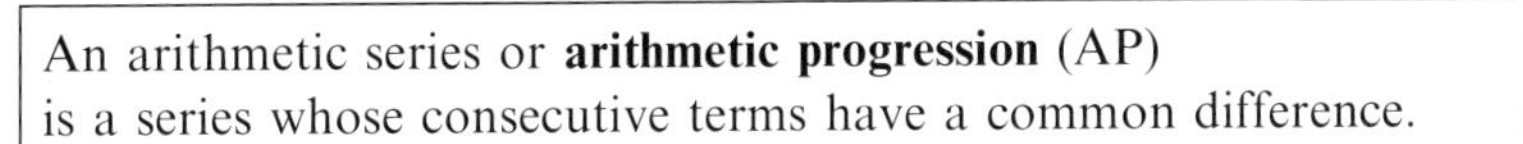

➤ An arithmetic series or **arithmetic progression** (AP) is a series whose consecutive terms have a common difference.

If the common difference is d, each term is obtained from the previous term by adding d. Expressed formally: $u_r = u_{r-1} + d$ or $u_r - u_{r-1} = d$.

Problems involving APs can be solved with or without using formulae.
It is often helpful to consider intuitive methods first.

Examples 14 to 16 are solved without using the formulae for APs.

Example 14 Find the tenth term of the AP: $2 + 6 + 10 + 14 + \cdots$

The common difference is the difference between consecutive terms.
In this case, the common difference is $6 - 2 = 4$.

For the tenth term nine lots of the common difference will have been added to the first term, 2.

So the tenth term is $2 + 9 \times 4 = 38$.

Example 15 Find the number of terms in the AP: $50 + 47 + 44 + 41 + \cdots - 34$

The common difference is $47 - 50 = -3$.

For the last term, -34, 84 will have been subtracted from the first term, 50. $(50 - (-34) = 84)$

Since 3 is subtracted for each new term and 84 is subtracted in all, there must be $84/3 = 28$ terms after the first.

So there are 29 terms in all.

Example 16 Find the sum of the AP: $2 + 5 + 8 + 11 + \cdots + 32$.

> The common difference is 3. 30 (= 32 − 2) is added to the first
> term to obtain the last term.

Let $S = 2 + 5 + 8 + 11 + \cdots + 29 + 32$ ①

Writing the terms in reverse order

$S = 32 + 29 + 26 + 23 + \cdots + 5 + 2$ ②

Adding ① and ②

$$2S = (2 + 32) + (5 + 29) + (8 + 26) + \cdots + (32 + 2)$$
$$= 34 + 34 + 34 + \cdots + 34$$
$$= 11 \times 34$$
$$S = \frac{11 \times 34}{2} = 187$$

> 30 is 10 lots of the common difference, 3. So there are $10 + 1 = 11$ terms in all.

When Carl Friedrich Gauss (1777–1855) was ten, he was told by his teacher to add up all the numbers from 1 to 100. The teacher, so the story goes, assumed the task would keep Gauss occupied for some time. In fact he gave the answer immediately, using, presumably, the method in Example 16.

$$\text{Sum of an AP} = \frac{\text{Number of terms} \times \text{Sum of first and last terms}}{2}$$

EXERCISE 12c

In this exercise, do not use the formulae for APs.

1 Which of these series are arithmetical progressions?
Write down the common differences of those that are APs.

a $7 + 8\frac{1}{2} + 10 + 11\frac{1}{2}$

b $-2 - 5 - 8 - 11$

c $1 + 1.1 + 1.2 + 1.3$

d $1 + 1.1 + 1.11 + 1.111$

e $\frac{1}{2} + \frac{5}{6} + \frac{7}{6} + \frac{3}{2}$

f $1^2 + 2^2 + 3^2 + 4^2$

g $n + 2n + 3n + 4n$

h $1 + \frac{1}{2} + \frac{1}{3} + \frac{1}{4}$

i $1\frac{1}{8} + 2\frac{1}{4} + 3\frac{3}{8} + 4\frac{1}{2}$

j $19 + 12 + 5 - 2 - 9$

k $1 - 2 + 3 - 4 + 5$

l $1 + 0.8 + 0.6 + 0.4$

2 Write down the terms indicated in each of these APs.

a $3+11+\cdots$, 10th, 19th

b $8+5+\cdots$, 15th, 31st

c $\frac{1}{4}+\frac{7}{8}+\cdots$, 12th, nth

d $50+48+\cdots$, 100th, nth

e $7+6\frac{1}{2}+\cdots$, 42nd, nth

f $3+7+\cdots$, 200th, $(n+1)$th

3 Find the number of terms in these APs.

a $2+4+6+\cdots+46$

b $50+47+44+\cdots+14$

c $2.7+3.2+\cdots+17.7$

d $6\frac{1}{4}+7\frac{1}{2}+\cdots+31\frac{1}{4}$

e $407+401+\cdots-133$

f $2-9-\cdots-130$

4 Find the sums of these APs.

a $1+3+5+\cdots+101$

b $-10-7-4-\cdots+50$

c $2.01+2.02+2.03+\cdots+3.00$

d $x+3x+5x+\cdots+21x$

e $a+(a+d)+\cdots+\{a+(n-1)d\}$

5 Find the sums of these APs as far as the terms indicated.

a $4+10+\cdots+$ 12th term

b $15+13+\cdots+$ 20th term

c $1+2+\cdots+$ 200th term

d $20+13+\cdots+$ 16th term

e $6+10+\cdots+$ nth term

f $1\frac{1}{4}+1+\cdots+$ nth term

Formulae for arithmetic progressions

Let the first term be a, last term l, common difference d and sum of the first n terms S_n.

Formula for the nth term

First term $= a$

Second term $= a + d$

Third term $= a + 2d$

Fourth term $= a + 3d$

and so on.

➤ nth term $= a + (n-1)d$

If there are n terms in all, the last term, l is given by

$$l = a + (n-1)d$$

Formula for the sum of an AP

$S_n = a + (a + d) + (a + 2d) + (a + 3d) + \cdots + (l - 2d) + (l - d) + l$ ①

Writing the terms in reverse order

$S_n = l + (l - d) + (l - 2d) + (l - 3d) + \cdots + (a + 2d) + (a + d) + a$ ②

Adding ① and ②

$$2S_n = (a + l) + (a + l) + (a + l) + (a + l) + \cdots + (a + l) + (a + l) + (a + l)$$

$$= n(a + l)$$

$$S_n = \frac{n}{2}(a + l) \quad ③$$

If the last term is not known but the number of terms, n, is known, then since the last term, l, is the nth term

$$l = a + (n - 1)d$$

Substituting this in ③

$$S_n = \frac{n}{2}\Big(a + a + (n - 1)d\Big)$$

$$= \frac{n}{2}\Big(2a + (n - 1)d\Big)$$

➤

$$S_n = \frac{n}{2}(a + l)$$

$$S_n = \frac{n}{2}\Big(2a + (n - 1)d\Big)$$

✓ ***Note*** For an AP, $u_{n+1} = u_n + d$

Examples 17 to 25 are solved using the formulae for arithmetic progressions.

Example 17

Find the fiftieth term of the AP: $\frac{1}{2} + 2 + 3\frac{1}{2} + 5 + \cdots$

$a = \frac{1}{2}, \quad d = 1\frac{1}{2}, \quad n = 50.$

Use $u_n = a + (n - 1)d$

$$u_{50} = \frac{1}{2} + 49 \times \frac{3}{2} = \frac{1 + 147}{2} = 74$$

The fiftieth term is 74.

Example 18

Find the number of terms in the AP: $67 + 62 + 57 + \cdots - 13$

$a = 67, \quad d = -5, \quad u_n = -13.$

Use $u_n = a + (n - 1)d$

$$-13 = 67 - 5(n - 1)$$

$$5(n - 1) = 80$$

$$n - 1 = 16$$

$$\therefore \quad n = 17$$

The AP has 17 terms.

Example 19

Examples 17 and 18 were quite simple. For more complex calculations, as in this example, assemble the data and then state which formula is used.

Find the sum of these APs:

a $k + 4k + 7k + 10k + \cdots + 91k$

b $\frac{1}{4} - \frac{1}{4} - \frac{3}{4} - \frac{5}{4} - \cdots$ as far as the sixteenth term

Solution

a $a = k, \quad d = 3k, \quad u_n = l = 91k$

Assemble the data.

$$u_n = a + (n-1)d$$

Quote the first formula to be used.

$$91k = k + 3k(n-1)$$

Substitute into the formula.

$$91 = 1 + 3n - 3$$

Divide through by k.

$$3n = 93$$

$$\therefore \quad n = 31$$

There are 31 terms.

$$S_n = \frac{n}{2}(a + l)$$

Quote the next formula to be used.

$$= \tfrac{31}{2} \times (k + 91k)$$
$$= \tfrac{31}{2} \times 92k$$
$$= 31 \times 46k$$
$$= 1426k$$

b $a = \frac{1}{4}, \quad d = -\frac{1}{2}, \quad n = 16$

Assemble the data.

$$S_n = \frac{n}{2}\left(2a + (n-1)d\right)$$

Quote the formula to be used.

$$S_{16} = \tfrac{16}{2}\left(2 \times \tfrac{1}{4} + 15 \times \left(-\tfrac{1}{2}\right)\right)$$
$$= 8\left(\tfrac{1}{2} - 7\tfrac{1}{2}\right)$$
$$= 8 \times (-7)$$
$$= -56$$

Example 20

Evaluate $\sum_{1}^{100}(3r + 1)$.

At first sight this may not look like an AP. Writing out the first few terms will show that it is one.

$$\sum_{1}^{100}(3r+1) = 4 + 7 + 10 + \cdots + 301$$

This is an AP with $a = 4$, $d = 3$ and $n = 100$.

$$S_n = \frac{n}{2}\left(2a + (n-1)d\right)$$

or use $S_n = \frac{n}{2}(a + l)$ with $l = 301$.

$$\sum_{1}^{100}(3r+1) = \tfrac{100}{2}(2 \times 4 + 99 \times 3)$$
$$= 50 \times 305$$
$$= 15\,250$$

Alternatively, use $\sum_{1}^{100}(3r+1) = 3\sum_{1}^{100} r + 100$.

Example 21 Find

a the sum of the integers 1 to 1000 inclusive

b the sum of the integers 1 to 1000 inclusive that are *not* divisible by 5.

Solution

a $a = 1, l = 1000, n = 1000.$

Assemble the data.

$$S_n = \frac{n}{2}(a + l)$$

Quote the formula to be used.

$$S_{1000} = \frac{1000(1 + 1000)}{2}$$

Substitute into the formula.

$$= 500 \times 1001$$

$$= 500\,500$$

The sum of the integers from 1 to 1000 is 500 500.

b Let S be required sum and S' be the sum of integers from 1 to 1000 divisible by 5.

The sum of the integers *not* divisible by 5 equals the sum of the integers which are divisible by 5 subtracted from the sum of all the integers.

Then $S = S_{1000} - S'$

But $S' = 5 + 10 + 15 + \cdots + 1000$

$$= \tfrac{200}{2} \times (5 + 1000)$$

$$= 100 \times 1005$$

$$= 100\,500$$

So $S = 500\,500 - 100\,500$

$$= 400\,000$$

The sum of the integers from 1 to 1000 not divisible by 5 is 400 000.

There are 200 multiples of 5. Find this either by dividing each term by 5 mentally; this would number the terms 1 to 200. Alternatively, use $a = 5$, $d = 5$, $u_n = 1000$ and $u_n = a + (n - 1)d$:

$$1000 = 5 + 5(n - 1)$$
$$= 5 + 5n - 5$$
$$5n = 1000$$
$$n = 200$$

Example 22 The third term of an AP is 13 and the sum of the first six terms is 96. Find the tenth term.

Let the first term be a and the common difference d.

There are two unknowns so two equations are needed to find their values.

3rd term = 13 so $a + 2d = 13$ ①

$S_6 = 96$ so $\tfrac{6}{2}(2a + 5d) = 96$

S_6 is the sum of 6 terms, so $n = 6$.

$$3(2a + 5d) = 96$$

Divide both sides by 3.

$2a + 5d = 32$ ②

① × 2 $\quad 2a + 4d = 26$ ③

② − ③ $\quad d = 6$

Substituting in ①

$$a + 12 = 13$$

$$a = 1$$

Check mentally by substituting $a = 1$ and $d = 6$ in ②.

$$10\text{th term} = a + 9d$$

$$= 1 + 9 \times 6$$

$$= 55$$

Example 23

The first, third and fifth terms of an AP are $2y$, $4y+2$ and $7y$. Find y.

First, third and fifth terms are $2y$, $4y+2$ and $7y$, so

nth term $= a + (n-1)d$

$$2y = a \quad ①$$

Three simultaneous equations with three unknowns. a and d must be eliminated to find y.

$$4y + 2 = a + 2d \quad ②$$

Note: There are many ways of solving these three simultaneous equations.

$$7y = a + 4d \quad ③$$

Substituting $a = 2y$ from ① in ②

$$4y + 2 = 2y + 2d$$

$$2d = 2y + 2$$

Divide through by 2.

$$\therefore \quad d = y + 1 \quad ④$$

Substituting ① and ④ in ③

$$7y = 2y + 4(y+1)$$

$$= 6y + 4$$

$$\therefore \quad y = 4$$

Check the solution by finding the terms.

Example 24

Three consecutive terms of an AP are $2x-2$, $x-3$ and $1-x$. Find the next term.

Since the terms are consecutive terms of an AP

$$d = x - 3 - (2x - 2) = -x - 1$$

The difference, d, between consecutive terms is constant. So for consecutive terms, a, b and c, $b - a = c - b$.

Also

$$d = 1 - x - (x - 3) = -2x + 4$$

So $\quad -x - 1 = -2x + 4$

$$\therefore \quad x = 5$$

and $\quad d = -6$

Substitute for x in one of the expressions to find d.

So the terms are 8, 2 and -4.

Substitute $x = 5$ in $2x-2$, $x-3$ and $1-x$.

Next term is $-4 - 6 = -10$.

Example 25

The sum of the first n terms of a series is $3n^2 + 6n$.

a Find the first three terms of the series.

b Prove algebraically that the series is an arithmetic progression.

Solution

$S_n = 3n^2 + 6n$

a

$$S_1 = u_1 = 3 + 6 = 9$$

Substitute $n = 1$ in S_n to find S_1

$$S_2 = 3 \times 2^2 + 6 \times 2 = 24$$

Substitute $n = 2$ in S_n for S_2
$S_2 = u_1 + u_2$

So $\quad u_1 + u_2 = 24$

$$u_2 = 24 - 9 = 15$$

$$S_3 = 27 + 18 = 45$$

$$\therefore \quad u_3 = 45 - 24 = 21$$

$S_3 - S_2 = u_3$

So the first three terms are 9, 15 and 21.

b $u_n = S_n - S_{n-1}$

$= 3n^2 + 6n - [3(n-1)^2 + 6(n-1)]$

$= 3n^2 + 6n - 3(n^2 - 2n + 1) - 6n + 6$

$= \cancel{3n^2} + 6n - \cancel{3n^2} + \cancel{6n} - 3 - \cancel{6n} + 6$

$= 6n + 3$

$S_n = u_1 + u_2 + \cdots + u_{n-1} + u_n$
$S_{n-1} = u_1 + u_2 + \cdots + u_{n-1}$
so $S_n - S_{n-1} = u_n$
Take care with the signs when removing the brackets.

$d = u_n - u_{n-1}$

$= 6n + 3 - [6(n-1) + 3]$

$= 6n + 3 - (6n - 6 + 3)$

$= 6$

The common difference, d, is the difference between consecutive terms.

6 is the common difference of the terms found in **a**.

The difference between consecutive terms is constant.

So the series is an AP.

EXERCISE 12d

For this exercise, use the formulae for APs.

1 Find the number of terms in these APs.

a $10 + 12 + 14 + \cdots + 80$ **b** $3 + 6 + 9 + \cdots + 51$

c $3 + 7 + \cdots + 87$ **d** $13 + 8 + \cdots - 32$

e $-7 - 5\frac{1}{2} - \cdots + 18\frac{1}{2}$ **f** $2 + 4 + \cdots + 4n$

g $x + 2x + \cdots + nx$ **h** $a + (a + d) + \cdots + (a + (n-1)d)$

2 Write down the forty-first term of each AP in Question 1.

3 Find the sums of these APs.

a $2 + 7 + 12 + \cdots + 77$ **b** $71 + 67 + 63 + \cdots -53$

c $1 + 1\frac{1}{6} + 1\frac{1}{3} + \cdots + 4\frac{1}{2}$ **d** $15 + 11 + \cdots -25$

e $a + (a+1) + \cdots + (a + n - 1)$ **f** $a + (a - d) + (a - 2d) + \cdots + (a - (n-1)d)$

4 Find the sums of these APs to the terms indicated.

a $3 + 6 + \cdots$ 10th term **b** $16 + 12 + \cdots$ 9th term

c $-3 - 2 - \cdots$ 14th term **d** $2 + 6 + \cdots$ nth term

e $3\frac{1}{2} + 3 + \cdots$ 12th term **f** $p + 3p + \cdots$ rth term

5 Evaluate

a $\sum_{3}^{12} r$ **b** $\sum_{1}^{6} (3r + 2)$ **c** $\sum_{1}^{8} (2r - 7)$

d $\sum_{1}^{11} (32 - 5r)$ **e** $\sum_{1}^{n} (2r + 1)$ **f** $\sum_{6}^{n} \left(4 - \frac{r}{2}\right)$

6 The third term of an AP is 5 and the fifth term is 9.
Find the first term and the common difference.

7 The second term of an AP is 16 and the fifth term is 37.
Find the first term and the sum of the first eight terms.

8 The first term of an AP is -12 and the last term is 40.
If the sum of the progression is 196, find the number of terms and the common difference.

9 Show that the sum of the integers from 1 to n is $\frac{1}{2}n(n+1)$.

10 The twenty-first term of an AP is 37 and the sum of the first twenty terms is 320.
What is the sum of the first ten terms?

11 The sum of the first n terms of an AP is $n(n+4)$.

a Find the first three terms

b Find the sum to six terms

12 The third term of an AP is 5 and the sixth term is 11.
Find the first term and the sum of the first eight terms.

13 The sixth term of an AP is 2 and the ninth term is 11.
Find the first term and the sum of the first twelve terms.

14 The first term of an AP is 14.
The common difference and the sum of the first n terms are both -6.
Find n.

15 The sum of an AP to four terms is 38.
The sum of the same AP to eight terms is 124.
Find the first term and the common difference.

16 Find the sum of the odd numbers between 100 and 200.

17 Find the sum of the even numbers, divisible by three, lying between 400 and 500.

18 The twenty-first term of an AP is $5\frac{1}{2}$, and the sum of the first twenty-one terms is $94\frac{1}{2}$.
Find the first term, the common difference and the sum of the first thirty terms.

19 The first two terms of an AP are -3.1 and -2.8.

a Which term is the first positive one, and what is its value?

b How many terms must be summed to give a positive total?

20 The first three terms of an AP are $2x+1$, $3x+2$ and $5x-1$. Find x.

21 The first three terms of an AP are $y-1$, $2y$ and $4y-2$.
Find the fourth and fifth terms. Do not include y in the answer.

22 Three consecutive terms of an AP are $z+4$, $2z+9$ and $6-z$.
Find z and hence find the sum of the three terms.

23 A shop assistant is arranging a display of a triangular array of tins so as to have one tin in the top row, two in the second, three in the third and so on. If there are 100 tins altogether, how many rows can be completed and how many tins will be left over?

24 A farmer has a triangular orchard in which trees are planted in rows. The row along the base of the triangle has 64 trees. Each row has three fewer trees than the previous one until the row at the top of the triangle contains a single tree.

a Find the total number of rows of trees.

b Find the number of trees in **i** the fifth, and **ii** the twelfth row.

c The seven shortest rows are removed to make way for a road.
Find the percentage of trees lost.

EXERCISE 12d *(continued)*

25 A lecture theatre has a trapezium-shaped floor plan, so that the number of chairs in successive rows are in AP. The back row of chairs contains eight chairs and the front row contains thirty. There are twelve rows altogether.

a Find the number of seats in the theatre.

b Find the percentage of the seats that are in the rear half of the theatre.

26 A teacher illustrates APs by cutting a length of string into pieces so that the lengths of the pieces are in arithmetic progression and the entire length of string is used up exactly.

a On one occasion a 1 m length is cut so that the first piece measures 30 cm and the fourth 15 cm. Find how many pieces there are altogether.

b On another occasion a 2 m length is cut so that the first piece measures 2 cm and there are eight pieces. Find the length of the longest piece.

Geometric progressions

➤ A geometric series or **geometric progression (GP)** is a series whose terms have a common ratio.

If the common ratio is r, each term is obtained from the previous term by multiplying by r.

Expressed formally:

➤ $$u_n = ru_{n-1} \quad \text{or} \quad \frac{u_n}{u_{n-1}} = r$$

Before introducing formulae for geometric progressions Examples 26 to 28 solve some problems without using formulae.

Example 26

For the GPs given

i find the next two terms

ii find the sum of n terms, S_n, for $n = 1, 2, 3, 4$

iii comment on the sequence $S_1, S_2, S_3, S_4, \ldots$

Solution

a $2 + 6 + 18 + 54 + \cdots$

i The common ratio, $r = \frac{6}{2} = \mathbf{3}$.

$\therefore$ 5th term $= 54 \times \mathbf{3} = 162$

and 6th term $= 162 \times \mathbf{3} = 486$

Any term divided by the previous term will give the common ratio.

ii $S_1 = 2$

$S_2 = 2 + 6 = 8$

$S_3 = 2 + 6 + 18 = 26$

$S_4 = 26 + 54 = 80$

iii The sequence $S_1, S_2, S_3, S_4, \ldots$ is divergent and, therefore, the series $2 + 6 + 18 + 54 + \cdots$ is said to be divergent.

b $1 + \frac{1}{2} + \frac{1}{4} + \frac{1}{8} + \cdots$

i The common ratio, $r = \frac{1}{2}$.

$\therefore$ 5th term $= \frac{1}{8} \times \frac{1}{2} = \frac{1}{16}$

and 6th term $= \frac{1}{16} \times \frac{1}{2} = \frac{1}{32}$

ii $S_1 = 1$
$S_2 = 1 + \frac{1}{2} = 1\frac{1}{2}$
$S_3 = 1 + \frac{1}{2} + \frac{1}{4} = 1\frac{3}{4}$
$S_4 = 1\frac{3}{4} + \frac{1}{8} = 1\frac{7}{8}$

iii By calculating further values of S_n it can be seen that as $n \to \infty$, $S_n \to 2$.

The sequence $S_1, S_2, S_3, S_4, \ldots$ is convergent and, therefore, the series $1 + \frac{1}{2} + \frac{1}{4} + \frac{1}{8} + \cdots$ is said to be convergent.

The series is said to have a sum to infinity, S_∞. In this case $S_\infty = 2$.

By taking enough terms of the series one can get as close to the limit, 2, as one wants.

c $2 - 4 + 8 - 16 + \cdots$

i The common ratio, $r = -\frac{4}{2} = \mathbf{-2}$.

$\therefore$ 5th term $= -16 \times \mathbf{-2} = 32$

and 6th term $= 32 \times \mathbf{-2} = -64$

ii $S_1 = 2$
$S_2 = 2 - 4 = -2$
$S_3 = 2 - 4 + 8 = 6$
$S_4 = 6 - 16 = -10$

iii The sequence $S_1, S_2, S_3, S_4, \ldots$ oscillates; it is neither convergent nor divergent.

Example 27 For the GP $4 + 12 + 36 + 108 + \cdots$, find

a the 8th term and

b the sum of the first eight terms.

Solution

a $r = \frac{12}{4} = 3$

To obtain the eighth term, the first term has to be multiplied by r seven times $(8 - 1 = 7)$.

1st term	2nd term	3rd term	4th term	...	8th term
4	4×3	4×3^2	4×3^3		4×3^7

$\therefore$ the 8th term is 4×3^7.

In general, to obtain the nth term, the first term is multiplied by r, $(n - 1)$ times.

b

To find the sum of the first eight terms: Multiply both sides by $r (= 3)$ and line up the terms.

$$S_8 = 4 + 4 \times 3 + 4 \times 3^2 + 4 \times 3^3 + \cdots + 4 \times 3^7 \quad ①$$

$$3S_8 = 4 \times 3 + 4 \times 3^2 + 4 \times 3^3 + \cdots + 4 \times 3^7 + 4 \times 3^8 \quad ②$$

② − ① $\Rightarrow 2S_8 = 4 \times 3^8 - 4$

Subtracting ① from ② eliminates all but the 1st term of S_8 and the last term of $3S_8$.

$$S_8 = \frac{4 \times 3^8 - 4}{2} = 2 \times 3^8 - 2 = 13\,120$$

Example 28

This example offers a proof without words!

Find the sum to infinity of the GP: $1 + \frac{1}{2} + \frac{1}{4} + \frac{1}{8} + \frac{1}{16} + \cdots$.

This diagram should be sufficient to demonstrate that $S_\infty = 2$.

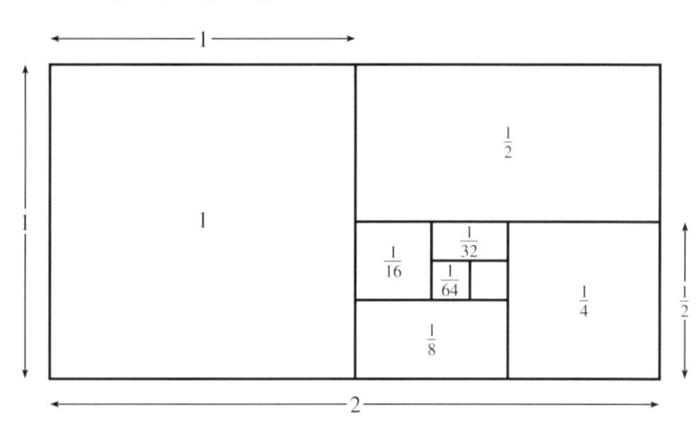

Formulae for geometric progressions

Let the first term be a, the common ratio r, the sum of the first n terms S_n, and the sum to infinity, S_∞.

Formula for the nth term

First term $= a$, second term $= ar$, third term $= ar^2$ and so on. So nth term $= ar^{n-1}$.

➤ $n\text{th term} = ar^{n-1}$

Formula for the sum of a GP

$$S_n = a + ar + ar^2 + \cdots + ar^{n-1} \quad ①$$

$$rS_n = ar + ar^2 + \cdots + ar^{n-1} + ar^n \quad ②$$

Multiply both sides by r and line up the terms.

② − ①

$$rS_n - S_n = ar^n - a$$

$$S_n(r-1) = a(r^n - 1)$$

$$S_n = \frac{a(r^n - 1)}{r - 1} \quad ③$$

Subtracting ① from ② eliminates all but two terms.

Multiplying numerator and denominator of ③ by -1 gives an alternative formula, which is useful when $|r| < 1$.

$$S_n = \frac{a(1 - r^n)}{1 - r}$$

Two versions of the formula are given to avoid dealing with negative quantities.

➤ When $|r| > 1$ use $S_n = \frac{a(r^n - 1)}{r - 1}$ When $|r| < 1$ use $S_n = \frac{a(1 - r^n)}{1 - r}$

✓ ***Note*** For a GP, $u_{n+1} = ru_n$.

Example 29 For the GP $3 + 6 + 12 + 24 + \ldots$, find

a the 12th term and
b the sum of the first 20 terms.

Solution

a $a = 3, \quad r = 2, \quad n = 12.$

12th term $= ar^{11} = 3 \times 2^{11} = 6144$

b $S_{20} = \dfrac{a(r^{20} - 1)}{r - 1}$

$= \dfrac{3(2^{20} - 1)}{2 - 1} = 3(2^{20} - 1) = 3\,145\,725$

Example 30 Find the value of

$$\sum_{i=10}^{20} 3 \times \left(-\tfrac{2}{3}\right)^i$$

correct to 3 significant figures.

At first sight this may not look like a GP. Writing out the first few terms will show that it is one.

$$\sum_{i=10}^{20} 3 \times \left(-\tfrac{2}{3}\right)^i = 3 \times \left(-\tfrac{2}{3}\right)^{10} + 3 \times \left(-\tfrac{2}{3}\right)^{11} + 3 \times \left(-\tfrac{2}{3}\right)^{12} + \cdots + 3 \times \left(-\tfrac{2}{3}\right)^{20}$$

This is a GP with $a = 3 \times \left(-\tfrac{2}{3}\right)^{10}$, $r = -\tfrac{2}{3}$ and $n = 11$.

Take care with signs. $\left(-\tfrac{2}{3}\right)^{10}$ is +ve. $\left(-\tfrac{2}{3}\right)^{11}$ is −ve.

Using $S_n = \dfrac{a(1 - r^n)}{1 - r}$

$$\sum_{i=10}^{20} 3 \times \left(-\tfrac{2}{3}\right)^i = 3 \times \left(-\tfrac{2}{3}\right)^{10} \frac{\left(1 - \left(-\tfrac{2}{3}\right)^{11}\right)}{1 - \left(-\tfrac{2}{3}\right)}$$

$1 - \left(-\tfrac{2}{3}\right) = 1 + \tfrac{2}{3} = \tfrac{5}{3}$

$$= 3 \times \left(\tfrac{2}{3}\right)^{10} \left(1 + \left(\tfrac{2}{3}\right)^{11}\right) \times \tfrac{3}{5}$$

Dividing by $\tfrac{5}{3}$ is the same as multiplying by $\tfrac{3}{5}$.

$$= 0.0316$$

Example 31 $(x - 3)$, $(x + 1)$ and $(3x - 5)$ are consecutive terms of a GP. Find possible values of x.

Since the terms are consecutive terms of a GP

$$r = \frac{x + 1}{x - 3}$$

The ratio, r, of consecutive terms is constant.
So for consecutive terms a, b and c
$\dfrac{b}{a} = \dfrac{c}{b}$

Also $$r = \frac{3x - 5}{x + 1}$$

So $$\frac{x + 1}{x - 3} = \frac{3x - 5}{x + 1}$$

Two equal fractions, so cross multiply.

$$(x + 1)(x + 1) = (x - 3)(3x - 5)$$

$$x^2 + 2x + 1 = 3x^2 - 14x + 15$$

$$2x^2 - 16x + 14 = 0$$

Divide through by 2.

$$x^2 - 8x + 7 = 0$$

$$(x - 7)(x - 1) = 0$$

$\Rightarrow \quad x = 7$ or $x = 1$

Note: When $x = 7$, terms are 4, 8, 16.
When $x = 1$, terms are −2, 2, −2.

Example 32 A machine depreciates in value by 5% every year. After how many years would a machine have lost more than half its value?

Let the original value of the machine be £x. *No value is given. Use algebra.*

After one year: value = £$x \times 0.95$ *To reduce by 5%, multiply by 1 – 0.05 = 0.95.*

After n years: value = £$x \times 0.95^n$

If the machine has lost more than half its value,

$$x \times 0.95^n < \frac{x}{2}$$

Divide through by x.

$$0.95^n < 0.5$$

Take logs of both sides.

$$n \log 0.95 < \log 0.5$$

$$n > \frac{\log 0.5}{\log 0.95}$$

Division is by a negative number (log 0.95), so inequality sign must be reversed.

$\therefore$ $n > 13.5$

So $n = 14$ *n, the number of years, must be an integer.*

So after 14 years the machine loses more than half its value.

Example 33 A building society pays 6% compound interest per annum.

Mr X deposits £1500 and asks for interest to be added to his account annually.

Mr Y decides to invest £2500 at the start of each year.

a How much will be in Mr X's account at the end of the first year, and at the end of five years?

b Find expressions for the amount in Mr Y's account at the end of the first year, the second year, and the third year.

Form a series to find the total value of Mr Y's account after 10 years.

Solution Let £A_n be the amount in an account after n years.

a For Mr X:

$A_1 = 1500 \times 1.06 = 1590$ *To increase by 6% multiply by 1.06.*

So, after one year, £1590 is in Mr X's account.

$A_5 = 1500 \times 1.06^5 = 2007.34$

So after five years, £2007.34 is in Mr X's account.

b For Mr Y:

$$A_1 = 2500 \times 1.06$$

$$A_2 = (2500 \times 1.06 + 2500) \times 1.06$$

Each year, £2500 is added to the total.

$$= 2500 \times 1.06^2 + 2500 \times 1.06$$

$$A_3 = 2500 \times 1.06^3 + 2500 \times 1.06^2 + 2500 \times 1.06$$

$$A_{10} = 2500 \times 1.06^{10} + 2500 \times 1.06^9 + \cdots + 2500 \times 1.06$$

A GP with $a = 2500 \times 1.06$, $r = 1.06$ and $n = 10$.

$$= \frac{2500 \times 1.06(1.06^{10} - 1)}{1.06 - 1}$$

$$= 34\,929.11$$

So after ten years, £34 929.11 is in Mr Y's account.

EXERCISE 12e

This exercise (and 12f) give practice in using the formula for GPs.

1 Which of these series are geometrical progressions?
Write down the common ratios of those that are.

a $3+9+27+81$
b $1+\frac{1}{4}+\frac{1}{16}+\frac{1}{64}$
c $-1+2-4+8$
d $1-1+1-1$
e $1+1\frac{1}{2}+1\frac{1}{4}+1\frac{1}{8}$
f $a+a^2+a^3+a^4$
g $1+1.1+1.21+1.331$
h $\frac{1}{2}+\frac{1}{6}+\frac{1}{12}+\frac{1}{36}$
i $2+4-8-16$
j $\frac{3}{4}+\frac{9}{2}+27+162$

2 Write down the terms indicated for each of these GPs. Do not simplify the answers.

a $5+10+\cdots$, 11th, 20th
b $10+25+\cdots$, 7th, 19th
c $\frac{2}{3}+\frac{3}{4}+\cdots$, 12th, nth
d $3-2+\cdots$, 8th, nth
e $\frac{2}{7}-\frac{3}{7}+\cdots$, 9th, nth
f $3+1\frac{1}{2}+\cdots$, 19th, $2n$th

3 Find, giving the answer as a fraction, the sum to n terms of these GPs with first term a and common ratio r.

a $a=2$, $r=\frac{1}{3}$ and $n=5$
b $a=4$, $r=-\frac{1}{2}$ and $n=7$
c $a=-2$, $r=-\frac{2}{3}$ and $n=6$
d $a=1$, $r=-2$ and $n=11$

4 Find the number of terms in these geometrical progressions:

a $2+4+8+\cdots+512$
b $81+27+9+\cdots+\frac{1}{27}$
c $0.03+0.06+0.12+\cdots+1.92$
d $\frac{8}{81}-\frac{4}{27}+\frac{2}{9}-\cdots-1\frac{11}{16}$
e $5+10+20+\cdots+5\times 2^n$
f $a+ar+ar^2+\cdots+ar^{n-1}$

5 Find the sums of the GPs in Question 4. Simplify, but do not evaluate the answers.

6 Evaluate

a $\sum_{1}^{6} 3^r$
b $\sum_{5}^{15} 4(1.5^r)$
c $\sum_{1}^{5} \frac{1}{2^r}$

7 The third term of a geometrical progression is 10, and the sixth is 80.
Find the common ratio, the first term and the sum of the first six terms.

8 The third term of a geometrical progression is 2, and the fifth is 18.
Find two possible values of the common ratio, and the second term in each case.

9 The three numbers, $n-2$, n, $n+3$, are consecutive terms of a geometrical progression. Find n, and the term after $n+3$.

10 A man starts saving on 1 April. He saves 1p the first day, 2p the second, 4p the third, and so on, doubling the amount every day.
If he kept on saving under this system until the end of the month (30 days), how much would he have saved?
Give your answer in pounds, correct to 3 significant figures.

11 The first term of a GP is 16 and the fifth term is 9.
What is the value of the seventh term?

EXERCISE 12e
(continued)

12 Find the sums of these GPs to ten terms.
Give the answers correct to 3 significant figures.

a $0.1 + 0.2 + \cdots$ **b** $50 + 49 + \cdots$ **c** $16 - 8 + \cdots$

d The GP whose second term is 110 and whose fourth term is 133.1

e The GP whose fourth term is a thousand and whose ninth term is 0.01

f The GP whose first term is 96 and whose fourth term is 40.5

13 The second term of a GP of positive terms is 100 and the fourth term is 64. Find the number of terms that must be added if the total is to exceed four times the first term.

14 Write down the terms indicated for both of these GPs. Simplify your answers.

a $\frac{1}{k^4} + \frac{1}{k^3} + \frac{1}{k^2} + \cdots$, 13th, nth **b** $2p^3 + 2p^2 + 2p + \cdots$, 4th, $(n-1)$th

15 The numbers $x - 4$, $x + 2$, $3x + 1$ are in geometric progression.
Find the two possible values of the common ratio.

16 Find the sum of the first n terms of the geometrical progression $5 + 15 + 45 + \cdots$.
What is the smallest number of terms whose total is more than 10^8?

17 Estimates are produced for the number of babies born worldwide each year. The estimates for 1996 and for 2000, given in thousands of births to the nearest thousand, were 130 350 and 137 804 respectively.
Assume that successive yearly estimates are in geometric progression.

a Find the annual percentage increase in the number of births.

b Find the estimates for 1998 and 2003 (to the nearest thousand).

c Find the estimated total number of births between 1996 and 2004 inclusive (to the nearest thousand).

18 The profit made by a supermarket chain in 2000 is £700 million. The managing director wishes to increase this by 2% per year for the next ten years. In fact, the profit increases annually in geometric progression to £765 million in 2005.

a Find the annual percentage increase in profit from 2000 to 2005, giving the answer correct to 2 significant figures.

b Find what the annual percentage increase will need to be from 2005 to 2010 if the profit in 2010 is to match the managing director's original target.

The chain again fails to meet the target between 2006 and 2010; instead profits continue to grow at the same annual rate as in 2000 to 2005.

c Using the answer to **a**, find the total profit (to the nearest million pounds) from 2000 to 2010 inclusive.

19 A finance company offers a high-interest account with these conditions:

- The client must deposit a fixed amount on 1 January each year.
- The client must not make any withdrawals for at least ten years.
- On 31 December each year, the finance company adds 8% to the value of the investment.

A client decides to invest £1500 each year.

a Write down a series whose sum is the total value of the investment on 31 December of the tenth year, after the addition of interest.

b Evaluate this series.

Infinite geometric series

Consider the GP $1 + \frac{1}{2} + \frac{1}{4} + \frac{1}{8} + \cdots$ of Example 28.

Using the formula $S_n = \dfrac{a(1 - r^n)}{1 - r}$ with $a = 1$ and $r = \frac{1}{2}$:

$$S_n = \frac{1 - \left(\frac{1}{2}\right)^n}{\frac{1}{2}}$$

Multiply numerator and denominator by 2.

$$= 2 - \left(\tfrac{1}{2}\right)^{n-1}$$

$$= 2 - \frac{1}{2^{n-1}}$$

As n increases, 2^{n-1} increases and so $\dfrac{1}{2^{n-1}}$ tends to zero.

By taking large enough values of n, S_n can be made as close to 2 as one wishes.

As $n \to \infty$, $S_n \to 2$.

The sum to infinity, $S_\infty = \lim\limits_{n \to \infty} S_n = 2$.

To obtain a general formula for S_∞, consider

$$S_n = \frac{a(1 - r^n)}{1 - r}$$

$$= \frac{a}{1 - r} - \frac{ar^n}{1 - r}.$$

For r^n to get smaller as n increases, r must be numerically less than 1.

Providing that $|r| < 1$ then, as $n \to \infty$, $r^n \to 0$ and so the term $\dfrac{ar^n}{1 - r} \to 0$.

➤ $$S_\infty = \frac{a}{1 - r} \quad \text{providing} \quad |r| < 1$$

✓ ***Note*** The sum to infinity of a GP exists if, and only if, $|r| < 1$, i.e. $-1 < r < 1$.

Example 34 Express $0.\dot{7}\dot{2}$ as a fraction by considering the recurring decimal as a GP.

$$0.\dot{7}\dot{2} = 0.727\,272\,72\ldots$$

$$= \tfrac{72}{100} + \tfrac{72}{10\,000} + \tfrac{72}{1\,000\,000} + \cdots$$

$$= \tfrac{72}{100}\left(1 + \tfrac{1}{100} + \tfrac{1}{10\,000} + \cdots\right)$$

The series in the bracket is an infinite GP with $a = 1$, $r = \frac{1}{100}$.

$$= \tfrac{72}{100} \times \frac{1}{1 - \frac{1}{100}}$$

Use $S_\infty = \dfrac{a}{1 - r}$.

$$= \tfrac{72}{100} \times \tfrac{100}{99}$$

$$= \tfrac{72}{99}$$

$$= \tfrac{8}{11}$$

Example 35

The second term of a GP is 16 and its sum to infinity is 100.
Find two possible values of the common ratio and the corresponding first terms.

2nd term $= 16 \Rightarrow \quad ar = 16$ ①

$S_\infty = 100 \Rightarrow \quad \dfrac{a}{1-r} = 100$ ②

The two equations in a and r have to be solved simultaneously.

Rearranging ② $\quad a = 100(1-r)$

Substituting in ①

$$100(1-r)r = 16$$

Divide both sides by 4.

$$25r - 25r^2 = 4$$

$$25r^2 - 25r + 4 = 0$$

Factorise or use the formula.

$$(5r-1)(5r-4) = 0$$

$\Rightarrow \quad r = \frac{1}{5}$ or $r = \frac{4}{5}$

Both values of r are such that $|r| < 1$ so S_∞ does exist.

When $r = \frac{1}{5}$, $a = \dfrac{16}{r} = 80$.

When $r = \frac{4}{5}$, $a = \dfrac{16}{r} = 20$.

So, either $a = 20$ and $r = \frac{4}{5}$, or $a = 80$ and $r = \frac{1}{5}$.

EXERCISE 12f

This exercise includes questions involving sums to infinity.

1 Find the sums of these series **i** to n terms and **ii** to infinity:

a $1 + \frac{1}{3} + \frac{1}{9} + \frac{1}{27} + \cdots$

b $12 + 6 + 3 + 1\frac{1}{2} + \cdots$

c $\frac{3}{10} + \frac{3}{100} + \frac{3}{1000} + \frac{3}{10000} + \cdots$

d $\frac{13}{100} + \frac{13}{10000} + \frac{13}{1000000} + \cdots$

e $0.5 + 0.05 + 0.005 + \cdots$

f $0.54 + 0.0054 + 0.000\,054 + \cdots$

g $1 - \frac{1}{2} + \frac{1}{4} - \frac{1}{8} + \cdots$

h $54 - 18 + 6 - 2 + \cdots$

2 Evaluate these sums to infinity.

a $\displaystyle\sum_{r=1}^{\infty} 0.8^r$

b $\displaystyle\sum_{r=1}^{\infty} \frac{5}{3^{r-1}}$

c $\displaystyle\sum_{r=4}^{\infty} \left(\tfrac{3}{4}\right)^r$

d $\displaystyle\sum_{r=6}^{\infty} \frac{3p}{2^{2r}}$

3 If the sum to infinity of a GP is three times the first term, what is the common ratio?

4 The sum to infinity of a GP is 4 and the second term is 1.
Find the first, third, and fourth terms.

5 The second term of a GP is 24 and its sum to infinity is 100.
Find the two possible values of the common ratio and the corresponding first terms.

6 The second term of a GP is 11 and the sum to infinity is twice as large as the first term. Find the sum of the first ten terms.

7 The sum to three terms of a GP is 61 and the common ratio is 0.8.
Find the sum to infinity.

8 The second term of a GP is 4 and the sum to infinity is 18.

a Show that one possible value of the common ratio is $\frac{1}{3}$ and find the sum of the first ten terms given this common ratio.

b Find the other possible value of the common ratio. Given this second value, find how many terms must be summed for the total to exceed 17.

Extension material: Arithmetic and geometric means

For two numbers, x and y:

Arithmetic mean $= \dfrac{x+y}{2}$ Geometric mean $= \sqrt{xy}$

EXERCISE 12g
(Extension)

1 The sum of the first n terms of a series is $n^2 + 5n$.

a Find the first three terms of the series.

b Prove algebraically that the series is an arithmetic progression.

2 Find the ratio of the sum of the first ten terms of this series to its first term.

$\log x + \log x^2 + \log x^4 + \log x^8 + \cdots$

3 The first two terms of a GP are $\sqrt{2} - 1$ and $3 - 2\sqrt{2}$.

a Find the common ratio.

b Find the third term of the progression.

4 A steeply rising stretch of roller coaster track is supported on seven vertical struts whose lengths are in geometric progression. The middle strut is $\sqrt{8}$ m long.
The struts immediately flanking it have a combined length of 6 m.

a Find the length of the shortest strut.

b Find the combined length of all seven struts. Express the answer using surds.

5 x and y have a geometric mean of 2 and an arithmetic mean of 3, and $x > y$.

a Find x and y.

b If y, 3 and x are the first, second and third terms of an AP, find the sum to ten terms.

c If x, 2 and y are the second, third and fourth terms of a GP, find the sum to infinity.

6 Evaluate

a $\sum_{1}^{7}(3[r-1] + 2^{r-1})$ **b** $\sum_{1}^{7}(40 - 2r + 3 \times 1.5^{r-1})$

7 Show that the sum of the first n odd numbers is a perfect square.
Hence show that $57^2 - 13^2$ is the sum of certain consecutive odd numbers, and find them.

EXERCISE 12g
(continued)

8 The sum of n terms of a certain series is $4^n - 1$ for all values of n.
Find the first three terms and the nth term, and show that the series is a geometrical progression.

9 If ab, b^2 and c^2 are in AP, prove that b, c and $2b - a$ are in GP.

10 A houseowner borrows £30 000 from the building society at the start of month 1. At the end of each month, 0.6% interest is charged and added to the debt. On the first day of month 2 and each subsequent month, the borrower pays back £250.

a Find an expression for the debt outstanding at the end of month n.

b Show that after a year the debt, to the nearest pound, is £29 113.

11 A bouncy ball is dropped on to a hard surface.
Its first bounce reaches a height h m and its second a height of 1m.
The heights of each bounce and the next are in a constant ratio.

Show that, in metres, the total distance travelled by the ball after its first contact with the ground is

$$\frac{2h^2}{h-1}$$

12 Prove that the sum to n terms of $\log a + \log ax + \log ax^2 + \cdots$ is $n \log a + \frac{1}{2}n(n-1)\log x$.

13 Show that if $\log a$, $\log b$, $\log c$ are in AP then a, b, c are in GP.

14 For the series $1 + 2x + 3x^2 + 4x^3 + \cdots$

a find the sum of the first n terms when $x = 1$

b find, by multiplying by $1 - x$, the sum of the first n terms when x is not equal to one.

15 Prove that the arithmetic mean of two positive numbers must be at least as large as their geometric mean.

16 An eccentric engineer decides it would be useful to produce an infinite set of weights whose masses are in geometric progression.
The second has a mass of 1.5 kg and the whole set has a mass of 8 kg.

a Find the two possible masses of the heaviest weight.

b Find the total mass of the seven heaviest weights in each case.

17 Prove that that sum to infinity of a GP, all of whose terms are positive, must be at least four times as great as the second term.

18 A square is drawn. The mid-points of its sides are joined to form a smaller square; the mid-points of the sides of this square are joined to form a yet smaller square and so on.

If the largest square has a perimeter of 24 cm, find the total perimeter of all the squares.

19 Prove that if j, k, l are in AP and j, $k - j$, $l - j$ are in GP, then $j{:}k{:}l = 1{:}3{:}5$.

20 A tree grows 12 cm on its first day.
On the second day, two new branches 6 cm long grow at right angles to each other.
On the third day, four new branches 3 cm long grow and so on.

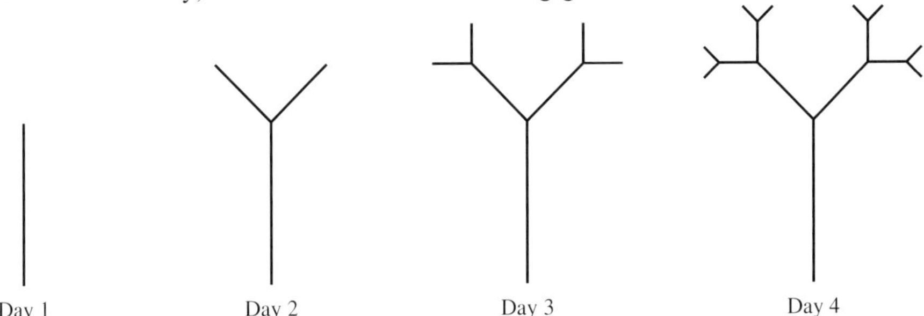

Prove that the tree has a limiting height of $4(4+\sqrt{2})$ cm and a limiting breadth of $8(\sqrt{2}+1)$ cm.

EXERCISE 12h (Miscellaneous)

1 Find the sum of the even numbers up to and including 100.

2 The fourth term of a GP is -6 and the seventh term is 48.
Find the first three terms of the progression.

3 What is the sum of the integers from 1 to 100 which are not divisible by 6?

4 The sum to infinity of a GP is four times its first term. Find the common ratio.

5 How many terms of the AP $15+13+11+\cdots$ are required to make a total of -36?

6 Determine whether each of these sequences is convergent, divergent or oscillating. If the sequence is oscillating, state whether it is periodic. If it is periodic, state the period.

a $u_n = (-2)^{n+1}$ **b** $u_n = 3 - \dfrac{1}{2^n}$ **c** $u_n = |5-n|$

d $u_1 = 3,\ u_2 = 4,\ u_{n+2} = \dfrac{u_{n+1}}{u_n}$ for $n \geqslant 1$ **e** $u_1 = 1,\ u_{n+1} = \dfrac{u_n}{u_n+1}$ for $n \geqslant 1$

f $u_1 = 2,\ u_2 = 4,\ u_n = u_{n-1} + u_{n-2}$ for $n \geqslant 3$ **g** $u_1 = 2,\ u_{n+1} = \dfrac{(-1)^n}{u_n}$ for $n \geqslant 1$

7 Evaluate these sums.

a $\displaystyle\sum_1^4 r^2$ **b** $\displaystyle\sum_1^5 (-1)^r r^2$

c $\displaystyle\sum_{r=1}^{\infty} \frac{3k}{6^r}$ **d** $\displaystyle\sum_4^8 (k+1)(k-6)$

e $\displaystyle\sum_3^7 \{(-2)^r + r - 2\}$ **f** $\displaystyle\sum_1^5 (k-1)(k-2)(k-3)(k-4)(k-5)$

8 Find the difference between the sums to ten terms of the AP and the GP whose first two terms are -2 and 4.

EXERCISE 12h
(continued)

9 Find x and y given that $x+3y$, 4 and $2x+2y$ are consecutive terms of a GP, and $x+4y$, 4 and $x-2y$ are consecutive terms of an AP.

10 Express these recurring decimals as rational numbers.

a $0.\dot{8}$ **b** $0.\dot{1}\dot{2}$ **c** $3.\dot{2}$

d $2.\dot{6}\dot{9}$ **e** $1.00\dot{4}$ **f** $2.9\dot{6}\dot{0}$

11 Find **i** a recurrence relation and **ii** the fifth term for each of these sequences.

a 2, 4, 8, 16, ... **b** 2, 4, 8, 14, ...

12 The sum of the first six terms of an AP is 21, and the seventh term is three times the sum of the third and the fourth.
Find the first term and the common difference.

13 The sum of the first five terms of an AP is 30, and the third term is equal to the sum of the first two.
Find the first five terms of the progression.

14 Show that if x, y and z are in arithmetic progression, then 10^x, 10^y and 10^z are in geometric progression.

15 The sum of the integers from 1 to $n-1$ is equal to the sum of the integers from $n+1$ to 49. Find n.

16 Show that the sums to infinity of the GPs $3+\frac{9}{4}+\frac{27}{16}+\cdots$ and $4+\frac{8}{3}+\frac{16}{9}+\cdots$ are equal.

17 Show that there are two possible geometrical progressions in each of which the first term is 8, and the sum of the first three terms is 14.
Find the second term and the sum of the first seven terms in each progression.

18 If a and b are the first and last terms of an arithmetical progression of $r+2$ terms, find the second and the $(r+1)$th term.

19 The third, fourth and fifth terms of an AP are $2x$, $x-3$ and $11-x$.

a Find the first term.

b Find the sum of the first fifteen terms.

20 A building society offers 6% interest per year on investments.
Someone deposits £4000 in an account and leaves the interest to accumulate.

a Find the total value of the investment (to the nearest pound) after six years.

b Find how many years have elapsed before the investment has at least doubled in value.

c Find how much interest is paid (to the nearest pound) at the end of the second and at the end of the seventh year.

Test yourself

1 The sum of the first ten terms of the series $2 - 4 + 8 - 16 + \cdots$ is

A 1366 **B** -682 **C** 110 **D** 682 **E** 2046

2 The sum of the series $c + 4c + 7c + 10c + \cdots + 31c$ is

A $320c$ **B** $160c$ **C** $176c^2$ **D** $352c$ **E** $176c$

3 The value of $\sum_{n=1}^{5} (3 \times 4^{n-1})$ is equal to

A 1023 **B** $2 \times (3^5 - 1)$ **C** 3×4^5 **D** $\dfrac{3069}{4}$ **E** $\dfrac{4^5 - 1}{3}$

4 The first term of an AP is 2 and the sum of the first thirteen terms is 143. The common difference is

A $1\frac{1}{2}$ **B** $11\frac{2}{13}$ **C** 1.389 **D** $1\frac{2}{3}$ **E** $10\frac{11}{13}$

5 The sum of the first n even numbers is

A $n(n+1)$ **B** $(n+1)(n-1)$ **C** $n^2 + 1$

D $n^2 - 1$ **E** none of these

6 The value of $\sum_{r=1}^{17} (1.5r - 12)$ is

A 217.5 **B** 12 **C** 24 **D** 25.5 **E** 0

7 The second and fifth terms of a geometric series are -2 and $4\sqrt{2}$ respectively. The common ratio r is

A $-2\sqrt{2}$ **B** $-\sqrt{2}$ **C** $-8\sqrt{2}$ **D** $-\dfrac{1}{2\sqrt{2}}$ **E** $\sqrt{2}$

8 The sum of all the negative integer powers of four is

A 4 **B** $\frac{1}{3}$ **C** 1 **D** ∞ **E** $\frac{3}{4}$

9 A GP whose first term is a and whose common ratio is r, $a \neq 0$, $r \neq 0$

A always converges

B never converges

C may converge, depending on the value of a only

D may converge, depending on the value of r only

E may converge, depending on the values of a and r

10 A GP has first term 8 and $S_\infty = 5$. The common ratio is

A $\frac{13}{5}$ **B** $-\frac{8}{5}$ **C** $\frac{3}{5}$ **D** $-\frac{3}{5}$

E undefined (no such GP can exist)

Key points

Sequences and series

A **convergent sequence** tends to a limit. It may oscillate about the limit.

A **divergent sequence** tends to $+\infty$ or $-\infty$

In an **oscillating sequence**, however for along the sequence one goes, there are always terms larger and smaller than a particular value. A sequence which neither converges nor diverges to $+\infty$ or $-\infty$ must necessarily be an oscillating sequence.

A periodic sequence repeats at regular intervals.

$$\sum_h^k (a_r + b_r) = \sum_h^k a_r + \sum_h^k b_r$$

$$\sum_h^j a_r + \sum_{j+1}^k a_r = \sum_h^k a_r \quad h < j < k$$

$$\sum_1^n c = nc \text{ where } c \text{ is a constant}$$

$$\sum_m^n ka_r = k\sum_m^n a_r \text{ where } k \text{ is a constant}$$

Sum of first n integers $\sum_1^n r = \dfrac{n(n+1)}{2}$

Sum of first n squares $\sum_1^n r^2 = \dfrac{n(n+1)(2n+1)}{6}$

Sum of first n cubes $\sum_1^n r^3 = \dfrac{n^2(n+1)^2}{4}$

Arithmetic series or progression (AP)

An **arithmetic progression** is a series whose consecutive terms have a common difference.

For first term, a, common difference, d

nth term $= a + (n-1)d$

For n terms with last term, l, and sum to n terms, S_n

$$l = a + (n-1)d$$

$$S_n = \frac{n}{2}(a + l)$$

$$S_n = \frac{n}{2}\Big(2a + (n-1)d\Big)$$

For an AP with terms $u_1, u_2, u_3, \ldots, u_r, \ldots$

$$d = u_r - u_{r-1}$$

Geometric series or progression (GP)

A **geometric progression** is a series whose consecutive terms have a common ratio.

For first term, a, and common ratio, r

nth term $= ar^{n-1}$

$$S_n = \frac{a(1-r^n)}{1-r} = \frac{a(r^n-1)}{r-1}$$

Use $S_n = \dfrac{a(1-r^n)}{1-r}$ for $r < 1$

Use $S_n = \dfrac{a(r^n-1)}{r-1}$ for $r > 1$

If $-1 < r < 1$, i.e. $|r| < 1$, the series converges.

$$S_\infty = \frac{a}{1-r} \qquad \text{for } |r| < 1$$

For a GP with terms $u_1, u_2, u_3, \ldots, u_n, \ldots$

$$r = \frac{u_n}{u_{n-1}}$$

13 Integration

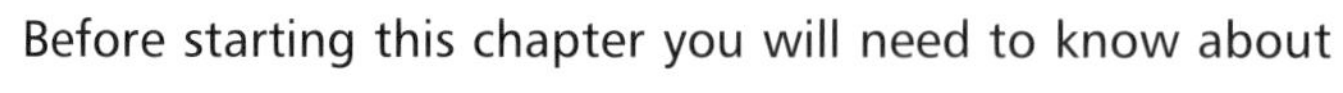

Before starting this chapter you will need to know about

- differentiation (Chapter 9)
- curve sketching (Chapters 7 and 10).

13.1 The reverse of differentiation, indefinite integrals

Chapter 9 dealt with **differentiation**. This chapter deals with the reverse process, called **integration**.

Integration was originally discovered, not as the reverse of differentiation, but as a process of summation (adding). This is covered in Book 2.

Consider $\frac{dy}{dx} = 2x$. This is a **differential equation**.

Any equation with terms in $\frac{dy}{dx}$ or $\frac{d^2y}{dx^2}$ etc. ... is a differential equation.

For example, the statement '*The rate at which bacteria multiply is proportional to the number of bacteria*' can be expressed as a differential equation. Using n for the number of bacteria at time t, the statement can be written as

$$\frac{dn}{dt} = kn$$

$\frac{dn}{dt}$ is the rate of change of n with respect to time t.

where k is the constant of proportionality.

Solving such differential equations, i.e. in this case, expressing n in terms of t, is an important branch of calculus.

So, given $\frac{dy}{dx} = 2x$, can an expression for y in terms of x be found?

$\frac{dy}{dx} = 2x$ is the result of differentiating, with respect to x, $y = x^2$ or $y = x^2 + 7$ or $y = x^2 - 2$ or .... In fact $y = x^2 +$ any constant will, when differentiated, give

$$\frac{dy}{dx} = 2x$$

So $\frac{dy}{dx} = 2x \Leftrightarrow y = x^2 + c$ where c is a constant.

$y = x^2 + c$ is the **general solution** of the differential equation.

The process of finding, for example, $y = x^2 + c$ given $\frac{dy}{dx} = 2x$ is called **integration**.

$\frac{dy}{dx} = 2x$ and $y = x^2 + c$ can be illustrated graphically by the family of parabolas.

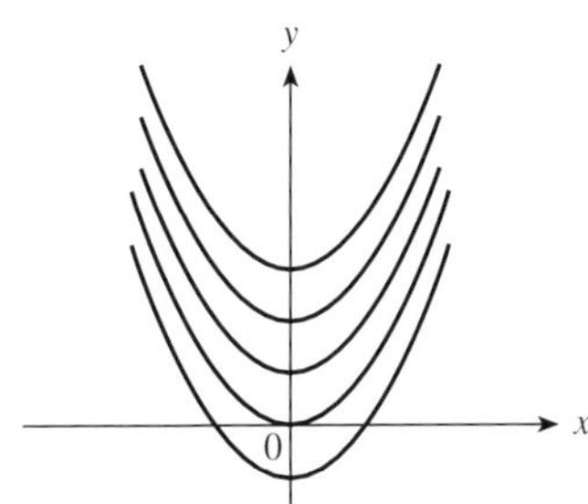

Finding the constant c

If a curve is known to pass through a given point then the constant c can be found.

Example 1 Given that $\frac{dy}{dx} = 2x$ find the equation of the curve that passes through the point (1, 2).

$\frac{dy}{dx} = 2x \Leftrightarrow y = x^2 + c$

This is the general solution of the differential equation.

When $x = 1$ $\quad y = 2$

Substituting $x = 1$ and $y = 2$ in $y = x^2 + c$ gives an equation which can be solved to find c.

$2 = 1 + c$

$\therefore \quad c = 1$

So $y = x^2 + 1$.

This is a particular solution of the differential equation.

✓ ***Note*** $y = x^2 + c$ is the **general solution** of the differential equation $\frac{dy}{dx} = 2x$.

$y = x^2 + 1$ is a **particular solution** of the differential equation $\frac{dy}{dx} = 2x$.

Using the integral sign

This notation for integration evolved from the summation approach. The sign for integration, the integral sign $\int$, is an elongated S.

$\frac{dy}{dx} = 2x \Rightarrow y = x^2 + c$ can be expressed, using the integral sign.

$$\int 2x\,dx = x^2 + c$$

$\int 2x\,dx$ is read as 'the integral of $2x\,dx$' or 'the integral of $2x$ with respect to x.

dx denotes 'integration with respect to x', i.e. x is the variable.

c is called the **constant of integration** or the **arbitrary constant**.

Before finding a rule for integrating x^n look at Example 2. Check the results by differentiating.

Example 2

a $\frac{dy}{dx} = x^2 \Leftrightarrow y = \frac{x^3}{3} + c$ i.e. $\int x^2\,dx = \frac{x^3}{3} + c$

b $\frac{dy}{dx} = 3x + \frac{1}{x^2} \Leftrightarrow y = \frac{3x^2}{2} - \frac{1}{x} + c$ i.e. $\int \left(3x + \frac{1}{x^2}\right) dx = \frac{3x^2}{2} - \frac{1}{x} + c$

c $\frac{dy}{dx} = k \Leftrightarrow y = kx + c$ i.e. $\int k\,dx = kx + c$

Rules for differentiating and integrating x^n

$y = x^n \Rightarrow \frac{dy}{dx} = nx^{n-1}$

The process for differentiating x^n is to multiply by the power and reduce the power by one.

The reverse process, for integrating, is to add one to the power and divide by the new power.

➤ $\int x^n\,dx = \frac{x^{n+1}}{n+1} + c \quad \text{for } n \neq -1$

Division by zero is not defined, so $n = -1$ is excluded.

✓ ***Remember*** Since any constant will disappear on differentiation, a constant must always be added on integration.

Example 3

Find $\int x^{-3}\,dx$.

$$\int x^{-3}\,dx = \frac{x^{-3+1}}{-3+1} + c$$
$$= -\frac{x^{-2}}{2} + c$$

To integrate x^n, add 1 to the power and divide by the new power. Remember the constant.

✓ ***Note*** All powers of x can be integrated using this rule except x^{-1}.

Imagine, historically, the frustration of finding one value of n which was excluded from the rule. When $n = -1$ the integral is $\int \frac{1}{x} dx$. A new function had to be discovered (or invented) to integrate $\frac{1}{x}$. This function is introduced in Chapter 17.

Integration of a polynomial

For a polynomial, the derived function is the sum of the derived functions of each term. Similarly, the integral of a polynomial is the sum of the integrals of each term.

Example 4

$$\int \left(3x^4 + \frac{x}{2}\right) dx = \frac{3x^5}{5} + \frac{x^2}{4} + c$$

$$\int \left(3x^4 + \frac{x}{2}\right) dx = \int 3x^4\,dx + \int \frac{x}{2}\,dx$$
$$= \frac{3x^5}{5} + \frac{x^2}{4} + c$$

Two general results for integrating follow from the results for differentiating on page 183.

$$\int\{f(x) \pm g(x)\}\,dx = \int f(x)\,dx \pm \int g(x)\,dx$$
$$\int kf(x)\,dx = k\int f(x)\,dx$$

Example 5 Find these integrals.

a $\displaystyle\int\left(\frac{5}{x^2} + 3\sqrt{x} - \frac{2}{7x^3}\right)dx$

Use index notation for each power of x.

$$= \int\left(5x^{-2} + 3x^{\frac{1}{2}} - \frac{2}{7}x^{-3}\right)dx$$

Add 1 to each power and divide by the new power. *Note*: dividing by $\frac{3}{2}$ is the same as multiplying by $\frac{2}{3}$.

$$= \frac{5x^{-1}}{-1} + 3x^{\frac{3}{2}} \times \frac{2}{3} - \frac{2}{7} \times \frac{x^{-2}}{-2} + c$$

Remember the constant.

$$= -\frac{5}{x} + 2x^{\frac{3}{2}} + \frac{1}{7x^2} + c$$

b $\displaystyle\int\left(t - \frac{3}{t}\right)^2 dt$

Multiply out the brackets before integrating.

$$= \int\left(t^2 - 6 + \frac{9}{t^2}\right)dt$$

$$= \int(t^2 - 6 + 9t^{-2})\,dt$$

Integrating a constant, 6, gives $6t$.

$$= \frac{t^3}{3} - 6t - 9t^{-1} + c$$

$\displaystyle\int 9t^{-2}\,dt = \frac{9t^{-2+1}}{-2+1} + c = -9t^{-1} + c$

$$= \frac{t^3}{3} - 6t - \frac{9}{t} + c$$

c $\displaystyle\int\frac{x^3 + \sqrt{x}}{x}\,dx$

Divide both terms in the numerator by the denominator, x, before integrating.

$$= \int\left(\frac{x^3}{x} + \frac{x^{\frac{1}{2}}}{x}\right)dx$$

$$= \int(x^2 + x^{-\frac{1}{2}})\,dx$$

$$= \frac{x^3}{3} + 2x^{\frac{1}{2}} + c$$

$-\frac{1}{2} + 1 = \frac{1}{2}$. Dividing by $\frac{1}{2}$ is the same as multiplying by 2.

$$= \frac{x^3}{3} + 2\sqrt{x} + c$$

d $\displaystyle\int dx = x + c$

$\displaystyle\int dx = \int 1 \times dx$ and $\displaystyle\int 1\,dx = x + c$. If $\dfrac{dy}{dx} = 1$, $y = \displaystyle\int 1dx = \int dx$.

Example 6 Find the equation of the curve whose gradient at (x, y) is given by $x^3 + \frac{3}{x^3}$ and which passes through the point $(1, -1)$.

$$\frac{dy}{dx} = x^3 + 3x^{-3}$$

$\frac{dy}{dx}$ is the gradient. Write $\frac{3}{x^3}$ as $3x^{-3}$.

$$\Rightarrow \quad y = \frac{x^4}{4} - \frac{3x^{-2}}{2} + c$$

Integrate term by term. Remember the constant.

When $x = 1$, $y = -1$

(1, −1) lies on the curve so $x = 1$, $y = -1$ satisfies the equation.

So $\quad -1 = \frac{1}{4} - \frac{3}{2} + c$

$\therefore \quad c = \frac{1}{4}$

Hence the value of c can be found.

So $\quad y = \frac{x^4}{4} - \frac{3}{2x^2} + \frac{1}{4}.$

This is the equation of the curve.

Example 7 Given that $f''(x) = 7$, $f'(2) = 8$ and $f(2) = -1$ find $f(x)$.

$$f''(x) = 7$$

Integrate $f''(x)$, the second derivative, to find $f'(x)$.

$$\Rightarrow \quad f'(x) = 7x + c$$

But $f'(2) = 8$.

Use $f'(2) = 8$ to find c.

So $\quad 7 \times 2 + c = 8$

$\therefore \quad c = -6$

So $\quad f'(x) = 7x - 6$

Integrate $f'(x)$ to find $f(x)$.

and $\quad f(x) = \frac{7x^2}{2} - 6x + k$

But $f(2) = -1$.

Use $f(2) = -1$ to find k.

So $\quad \frac{7 \times 2^2}{2} - 6 \times 2 + k = -1$

$\quad 14 - 12 + k = -1$

$\therefore \quad k = -3$

So $f(x) = \frac{7x^2}{2} - 6x - 3.$

State $f(x)$.

EXERCISE 13a

1 Find these integrals.

a $\int 3x^2\,dx$ **b** $\int 3x\,dx$ **c** $\int 3x^4\,dx$

d $\int (3 + 2x)\,dx$ **e** $\int (x - x^2)\,dx$ **f** $\int 2\,dx$

g $\int (ax + b)\,dx$ **h** $\int m\,dx$ **i** $\int x\,dx$

2 Use the integral sign, as in Question 1, to integrate these expressions, with respect to x.

a x^{-3} **b** $\frac{1}{x^2}$ **c** $2x^{-4}$ **d** $\frac{3}{x^2}$

e $-\frac{1}{4x^3}$ **f** $\frac{3}{2x^4}$ **g** $x^{\frac{1}{2}}$ **h** $x^{\frac{1}{3}}$

i $x^{-\frac{1}{3}}$ **j** $-\frac{1}{\sqrt{x}}$ **k** $\frac{2}{3x^{\frac{2}{3}}}$ **l** $-\frac{x^{-\frac{3}{4}}}{4}$

3 Find y in terms of x.

a $\dfrac{dy}{dx} = 4x^3$

b $\dfrac{dy}{dx} = 6 + x$

c $\dfrac{dy}{dx} = (2x+3)^2$

d $\dfrac{dy}{dx} = \left(x + \dfrac{1}{x}\right)^2$

e $\dfrac{dy}{dx} = \dfrac{x^2 + 3x}{\sqrt{x}}$

f $\dfrac{dy}{dx} = x(x+1)^2$

4 Find $\int y\,dx$.

a $y = 3 + 5x$

b $y = 6x^2$

c $y = \dfrac{1}{x^2}$

d $y = (\sqrt{x} + 1)^2$

e $y = \dfrac{x^5 + x^6}{x^4}$

f $y = \dfrac{5 + x}{x^{\frac{1}{4}}}$

g $y = \dfrac{3}{4\sqrt{x}}$

h $y = (x^2 + 2)^2$

5 Find A in terms of x.

a $\dfrac{dA}{dx} = 4x^5$

b $\dfrac{dA}{dx} = \dfrac{x^{-5}}{4}$

c $\dfrac{dA}{dx} = 4$

d $\dfrac{dA}{dx} = \dfrac{6 + \sqrt{x}}{\sqrt{x}}$

6 Find $\int f(t)\,dt$ for these functions.

a $f(t) = at$, a constant

b $f(t) = \frac{1}{3}t^3$

c $f(t) = (t+1)(t+3)$

d $f(t) = \dfrac{1}{t^{n+1}}$

e $f(t) = \dfrac{1}{t^2} + \dfrac{3+t}{t^4}$

f $f(t) = \sqrt{t}(t+1)$

7 Find

a $\int ax\,dx$, a constant

b $\int ay^2\,dy$, a constant

c $\int \dfrac{k}{x^2}\,dx$

d $\int \dfrac{(y^2+2)(y^2-3)}{y^2}\,dy$

e $\int x^2(\sqrt{x}+1)\,dx$

f $\int \sqrt[5]{y}\,dy$

g $\int \left(\dfrac{3}{\sqrt[4]{x}} - \dfrac{2}{\sqrt[3]{x}}\right)dx$

h $\int x^{\frac{1}{3}}\left(x^{\frac{1}{2}} + x^{-\frac{1}{2}}\right)dx$

i $\int \dfrac{3x^3 + x - 2\sqrt{x}}{x}\,dx$

8 If $f'(x) = 2x - \dfrac{1}{x^2}$ and $f(1) = 1$, find $f(x)$

9 If $f'(x) = 3x^2 - \sqrt{x}$ and $f(0) = 4$, find $f(x)$.

10 Find y in terms of x given that

$$\frac{d^2y}{dx^2} = 6x - 1$$

and that when $x = 2$, $\dfrac{dy}{dx} = 4$ and $y = 0$.

EXERCISE 13a *(continued)*

11 Express s as a function of t given that

$$\frac{d^2s}{dt^2} = a$$

where a is a constant and that when $t = 0$, $s = 0$ and $\frac{ds}{dt} = u$.

12 Find the equation of a curve whose gradient, $\frac{dy}{dx}$, is given by $2x + 5$ and which passes through the point $(3, -1)$.

13 A curve passes through the point $(2, 0)$ and its gradient is given by $3x^2 - \frac{1}{x^2}$. Find the equation of the curve.

14 The gradient of a curve at the point (x, y) is $3x^2 - 8x + 3$. Find

a the equation of the curve, given that it passes through the origin

b the other points of intersection of the curve with the x-axis.

15 The gradient of a curve is given by $\frac{dy}{dx} = 8x - 3x^2$.

Given that the curve passes through the origin, find

a the equation of the curve

b where the curve cuts the x-axis

c the equation of the tangent to the curve parallel to the x-axis.

16 a Find y in terms of x if $\frac{dy}{dx} = 6x^2 - \frac{1}{x^3}$, given that $y = 3$ when $x = 1$.

b Find s in terms of t if $\frac{ds}{dt} = 3t - \frac{8}{t^2}$, given that $s = 1\frac{1}{2}$ when $t = 1$.

17 a Find A in terms of x if $\frac{dA}{dx} = (2x + 1)(x^2 - 1)$, given that $A = 0$, when $x = 1$.

b Find the value of A when $x = -1$.

18 Find the general solution, and, for the conditions given, a particular solution of each of these differential equations.

a $\frac{dy}{dx} = 3x$, $y = 3$ when $x = 0$

b $\frac{dy}{dx} = \frac{4}{x^2} + 5$, $y = -10$ when $x = -4$

c $\frac{dv}{dt} = 6t + 3t^2$, $v = 12$ when $t = 2$

d $\frac{dy}{dx} = \left(1 + \frac{1}{x}\right)\left(1 - \frac{1}{x}\right)$, $y = 0$ when $x = -1$

19 a Find $\frac{d}{dx}\left(\int (x^2 + 5)\,dx\right)$.

b Find $\frac{d}{dx}\left(\int (ax^3 + bx^2 + cx + d)\,dx\right)$.

c Hence deduce $\frac{d}{dx}\left(\int f(x)\,dx\right)$.

Indefinite and definite integrals

The integrals in the previous section resulted in *functions* of the variable used.

$\int 2x\,dx = \underbrace{x^2 + c}_{\text{a function of } x}$

There was always a constant of integration which could or could not be found depending on information given.

Such integrals are called **indefinite integrals**.

There are situations where an integral has to be evaluated numerically.

Example 8 Given that the rate of change of displacement, s m, of a particle at time t s is given by

$$\frac{ds}{dt} = 3t^2 + 4t$$

find the total displacement from $t = 1$ to $t = 3$.

$$s = \int (3t^2 + 4t)\,dt$$

Integrate $\frac{ds}{dt}$ to find s in terms of t.

$$= t^3 + 2t^2 + c$$

When $t = 3$ $\quad s_3 = 3^3 + 2 \times 3^2 + c$

When $t = 1$ $\quad s_1 = 1^3 + 2 \times 1^2 + c$

Difference in displacement is the difference between s evaluated at $t = 3$ and at $t = 1$.

$$\therefore \quad s_3 - s_1 = 3^3 + 2 \times 3^2 + c - (1^3 + 2 \times 1^3 + c)$$

$$= 27 + 18 - 1 - 2$$

$$= 42$$

So displacement is 42 metres.

✓ ***Note*** The value of the integral was calculated at $t = 3$ and $t = 1$ and the difference found. The constant, c, cancelled out.

There is a special notation for evaluating an integral in this way.

Upper limit of integration

Square brackets

$$\int_1^3 (3t^2 + 4t)\,dt = \left[t^3 + 2t^2\right]_1^3$$

Lower limit of integration

Substitute 3 first and subtract value when 1 is substituted. *Note*: c does not appear.

$$= 3^3 + 2 \times 3^2 - (1^3 + 2 \times 1^2)$$

$$= 27 + 18 - 1 - 2$$

$$= 42$$

An integral evaluated in this way is called a **definite integral**. Such an integral is used when the *difference* in value between the integral at its lower and upper limits is required.

13.2 Area 'under' a curve, definite integrals

Consider a continuous curve $y = f(x)$. To find the area 'under' the curve (more precisely the area between the curve and the x-axis), bounded by the lines $x = a$ and $x = b$, several methods could be used.

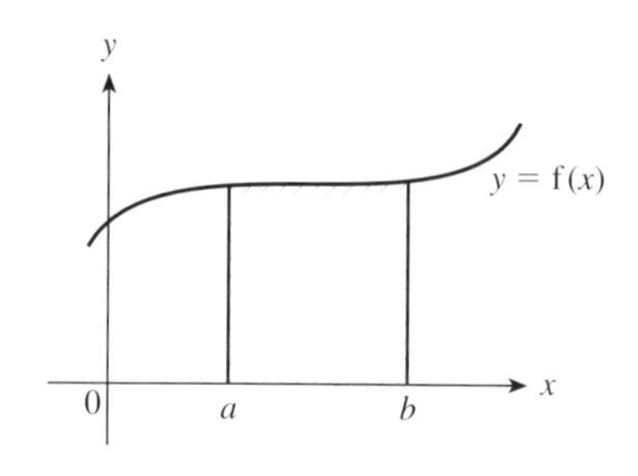

For a rough estimate, the graph could be plotted on graph paper and squares counted. Alternatively the area could be split into trapeziums or rectangles and their areas summed. (See Book 2.)

To find an area using integration

Let A be the area from the line $x = a$ up to PN where P is the point (x, y).

(Just as y depends on x, the area, A, also depends on x. The question is, how?)

Consider a point $Q(x + \delta x, y + \delta y)$ close to P, with ordinate QM.

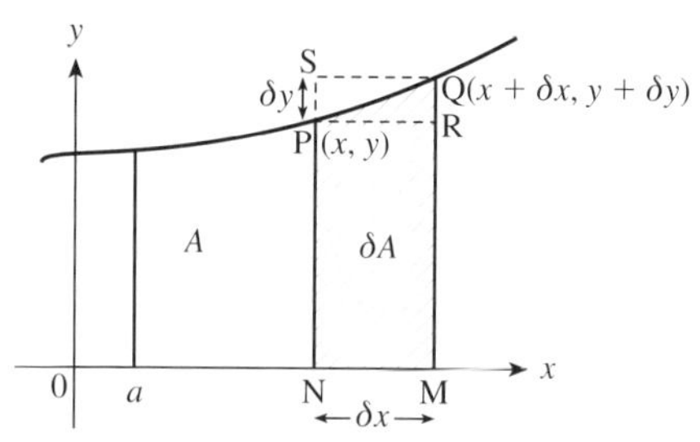

The shaded area will correspond to a small increase in area A. Let this increase be δA.

From the diagram,

Area NMRP $< \delta A <$ Area NMQS

$$y\delta x < \delta A < (y + \delta y)\,\delta x$$

Divide through by δx.

$$\therefore \quad y < \frac{\delta A}{\delta x} < y + \delta y$$

As $\delta x \to 0$, $\delta y \to 0$ and so $\frac{\delta A}{\delta x}$ lies between y and something which can be made as close to y as one wants.

$$\therefore \quad \lim_{\delta x \to 0} \frac{\delta A}{\delta x} = y$$

But $$\lim_{\delta x \to 0} \frac{\delta A}{\delta x} = \frac{dA}{dx}$$

$$\therefore \quad \frac{dA}{dx} = y$$

Integrating both sides with respect to x

$$A = \int y\,dx$$

So the area 'under' a curve can be found by integrating the equation of the curve.

The constant of integration can be ignored; it would depend on the value of x from which the area A is measured.

Since the required area from $x = a$ to $x = b$ is the *difference* between the areas up to $x = b$ and $x = a$ the definite integral is used.

$$A = \int_a^b y\,dx$$

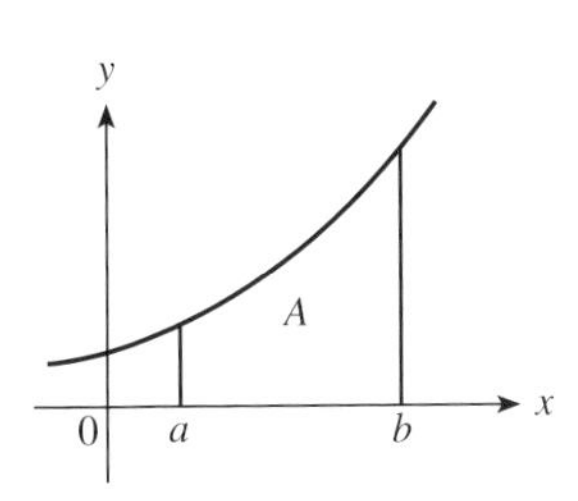

This result, namely that the area under a curve can be found by integration, is a version of the theorem called the ***Fundamental Theorem of Calculus.***

Example 9 Find the area bounded by $y = 3x^2$, $x = 2$, $x = 3$ and the x-axis.

$$A = \int_2^3 y\,dx$$

$$= \int_2^3 3x^2\,dx$$

$$= \left[x^3\right]_2^3$$

$$= 3^3 - 2^3$$

$$= 19$$

To show how c cancels out:
If A_x is the area from some arbitrary origin to x,

$$A_x = \int 3x^2\,dx = x^3 + c$$

$$A_3 = 3^3 + c$$

$$A_2 = 2^3 + c$$

$$\therefore\ A = A_3 - A_2 = 3^3 - 2^3 = 19$$

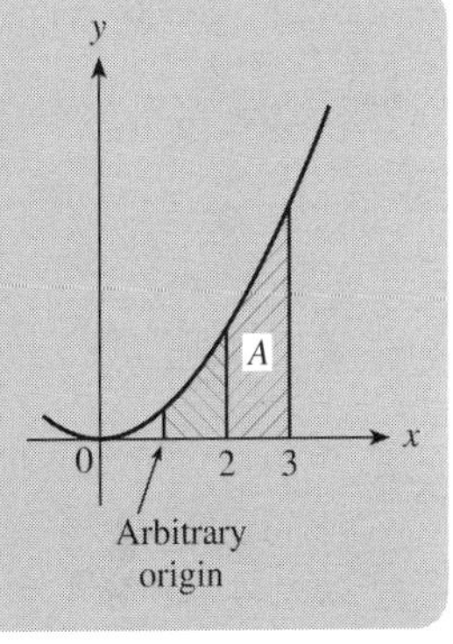

✓ ***Note*** In deriving $A = \int_a^b y\,dx$ the value of y was +ve.
If y is −ve, i.e. the area is below the x-axis, the integral A, will be −ve.
An area, however, is always +ve.

In the diagram, if $\int_a^b y\,dx = A$ then $A < 0$.
In this case, the area shaded $= |A|$.

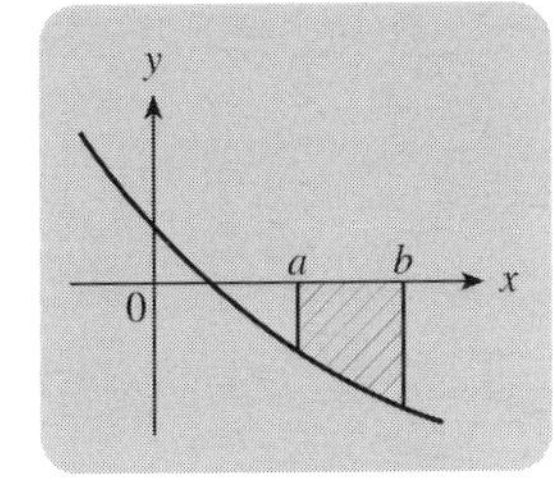

➤ Area between curve and x-axis

$$= \int_a^b y\,dx \begin{cases} \text{+ve for area above } x\text{-axis} \\ \text{−ve for area below } x\text{-axis} \end{cases}$$

Limits a and b are values of x.

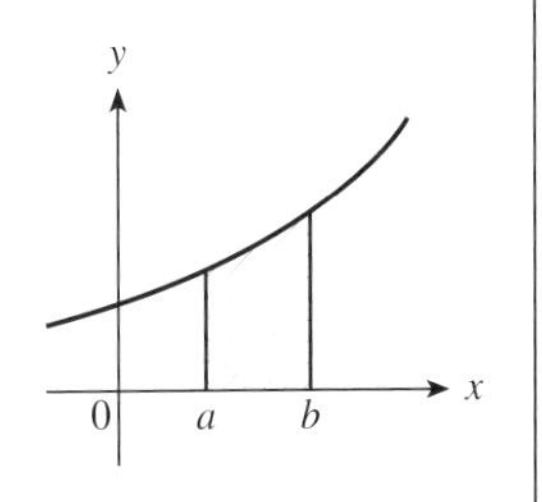

The area, A, between a curve and the y-axis from $y = c$ to $y = d$ is given by

$$A = \int_c^d x \, dy$$

The derivation is similar to that given on page 306.

➤ Area between curve and y-axis

$= \int_c^d x \, dy$ ↗ +ve for area to right of y-axis ↘ −ve for area to left of y-axis

Limits c and d are values of y.

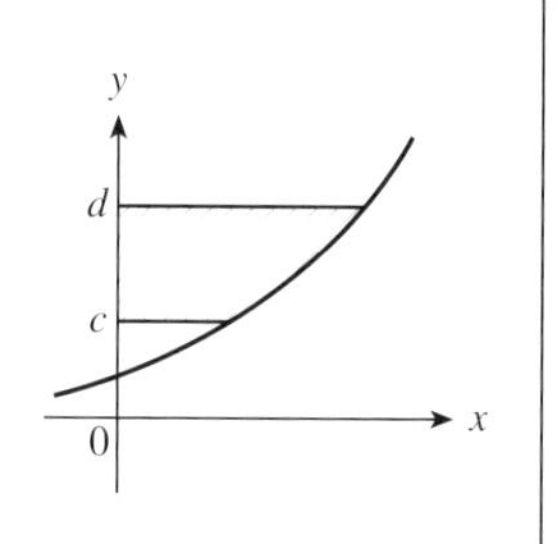

✓ ***Remember*** *Differentiating* gives the *gradient*. *Integrating* between limits gives the *area* under the curve between the limits.

Example 10

a Find $\int_0^3 (x^2 - 4x + 3) \, dx$.

b Find $\int_1^3 (x^2 - 4x + 3) \, dx$.

c Deduce the total shaded area.

d Find $\int_0^3 |x^2 - 4x + 3| \, dx$.

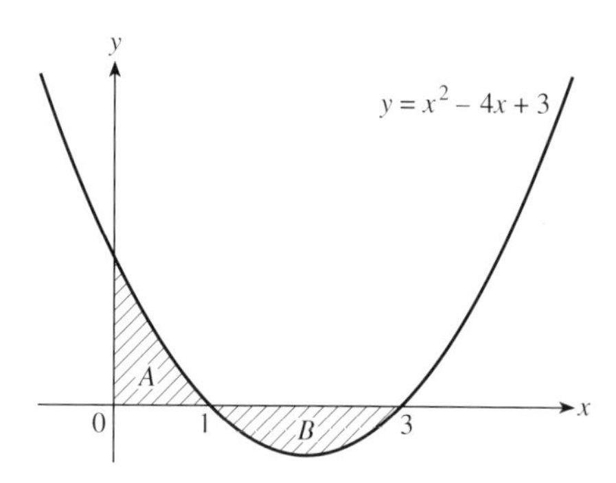

Solution

a $\int_0^3 (x^2 - 4x + 3) \, dx = \left[\frac{x^3}{3} - 2x^2 + 3x\right]_0^3$

$= \frac{3^3}{3} - 2 \times 3^2 + 3 \times 3 - 0$

$= 9 - 18 + 9$

$= 0$

Substitute $x = 3$ and $x = 0$. Substituting $x = 0$ gives zero.

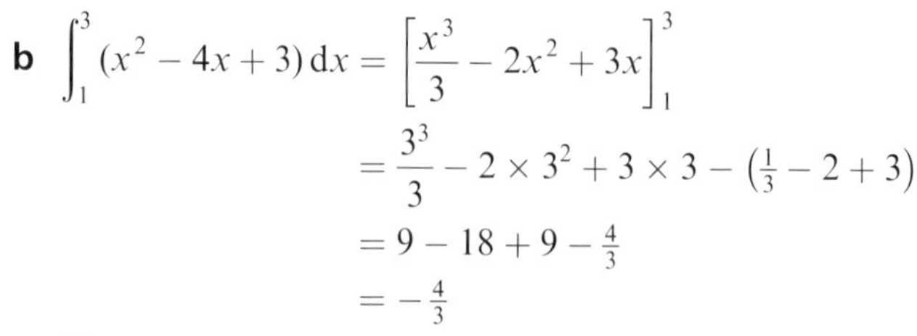

b $\int_1^3 (x^2 - 4x + 3) \, dx = \left[\frac{x^3}{3} - 2x^2 + 3x\right]_1^3$

$= \frac{3^3}{3} - 2 \times 3^2 + 3 \times 3 - \left(\frac{1}{3} - 2 + 3\right)$

$= 9 - 18 + 9 - \frac{4}{3}$

$= -\frac{4}{3}$

Substitute $x = 3$ and subtract value with $x = 1$.

The integral is −ve since the area is below the x-axis.

c From **a**

$\int_0^3 (x^2 - 4x + 3) \, dx = 0$

So Area A = Area B.

From **b** Area $B = \frac{4}{3}$

$\therefore$ Total shaded area $= \frac{4}{3} + \frac{4}{3} = \frac{8}{3}$

$\int_0^3 (x^2 - 4x + 3) \, dx = 0$ so the positive and negative integrals for A and B cancel each other out.

d $\displaystyle\int_0^3 |x^2 - 4x + 3|\,dx$

The integral equals the shaded area.

$$\therefore \quad \int_0^3 |x^2 - 4x + 3|\,dx = \tfrac{4}{3} + \tfrac{4}{3} = \tfrac{8}{3}$$

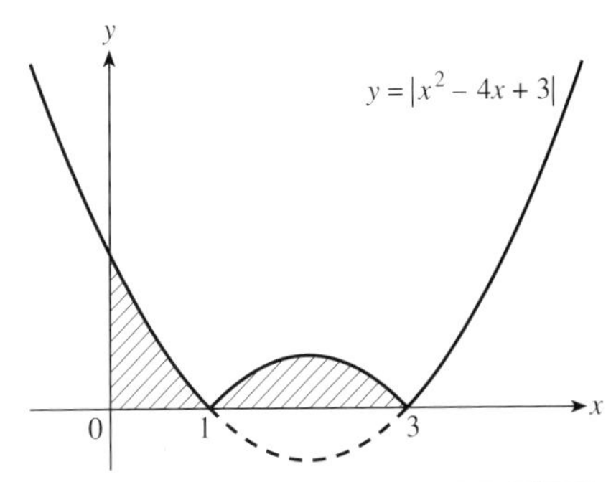

The integral is the area between the curve and the x-axis.

Even and odd functions

These results follow from the symmetry of the graphs.

- If $f(x)$ is an even function, then $\displaystyle\int_{-a}^{a} f(x)\,dx = 2\int_0^a f(x)\,dx$.

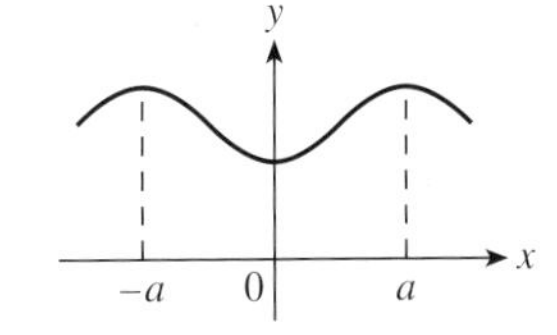

- If $f(x)$ is an odd function then $\displaystyle\int_{-a}^{a} f(x)\,dx = 0$.

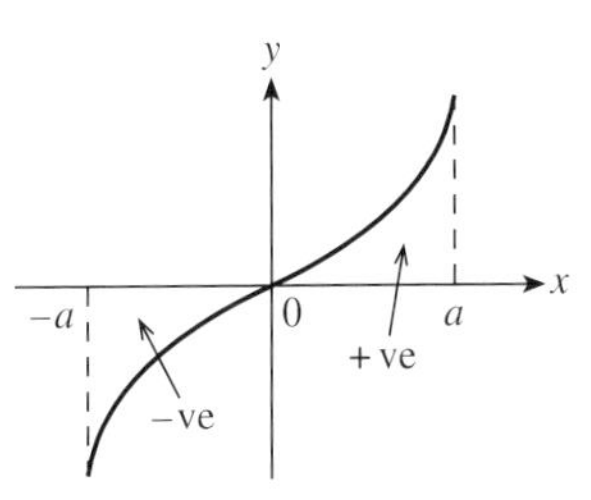

Example 11

a Find the area bounded by the curve $y = 2 - \sqrt{x}$, the y-axis and $y = -2$.

b Deduce the area A.

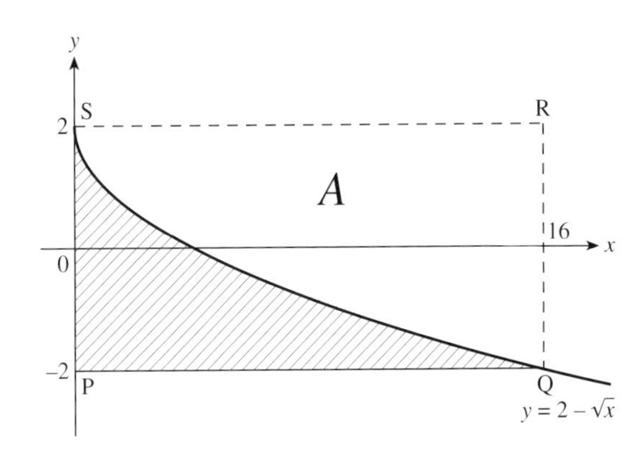

Solution

a Area required

$$= \int_{-2}^{2} x\,dy$$

Since integration is with respect to y the limits of integration refer to the y-axis.

$$= \int_{-2}^{2} (2 - y)^2\,dy$$

$y = 2 - \sqrt{x} \Rightarrow \sqrt{x} = 2 - y$ so $x = (2 - y)^2$

$$= \int_{-2}^{2} (4 - 4y + y^2)\,dy$$

$$= \left[4y - 2y^2 + \frac{y^3}{3}\right]_{-2}^{2}$$

$$= 4 \times 2 - 2 \times 2^2 + \frac{2^3}{3} - \left(4 \times (-2) - 2 \times (-2)^2 + \frac{(-2)^3}{3}\right)$$

$$= 16 + \tfrac{16}{3}$$

$$= 21\tfrac{1}{3}$$

Alternatively: notice odd/even functions

$$\int_{-2}^{2} -4y\,dy = 0$$

$$\int_{-2}^{2} (4 + y^2)\,dy = 2\int_{0}^{2} (4 + y^2)\,dy$$

$$= 2\left[4y + \frac{y^3}{3}\right]_0^2$$

$$= 2(8 + \tfrac{8}{3})$$

$$= 21\tfrac{1}{3}$$

b When $y = -2$ $\quad -2 = 2 - \sqrt{x}$

Substitute $y = -2$ in $y = 2 - \sqrt{x}$.

$\sqrt{x} = 4$

Square both sides to find x.

$\therefore \quad x = 16$

Area $A = 4 \times 16 - 21\tfrac{1}{3}$

$= 42\tfrac{2}{3}$

PS = 4. PQ = 16. Subtract area found in **a** from rectangle PQRS.

Example 12

At first sight, the integral in this example would seem to represent an infinitely extending area and, therefore, be infinite. However, the area tends to a finite limit. The situation is similar to an infinite series which tends to a finite limit.

Find $\displaystyle\int_2^{\infty} \frac{1}{x^2}\,dx$.

Find $\displaystyle\int_2^{k} \frac{1}{x^2}\,dx$ and work out the limit of the integral as $k \to \infty$.

$$\int_2^k \frac{1}{x^2}\,dx = \left[-\frac{1}{x}\right]_2^k$$

$$= -\frac{1}{k} + \frac{1}{2}$$

$$= \frac{1}{2} - \frac{1}{k}$$

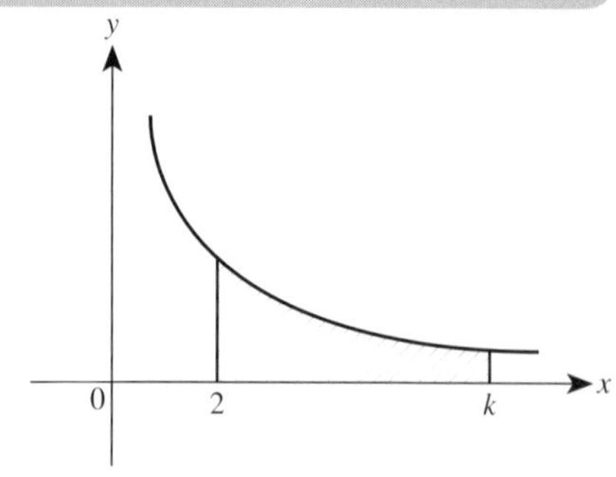

$$\int_2^{\infty} \frac{1}{x^2}\,dx = \lim_{k\to\infty} \int_2^k \frac{1}{x^2}\,dx$$

$$= \lim_{k\to\infty}\left(\frac{1}{2} - \frac{1}{k}\right)$$

$$= \frac{1}{2}$$

$\displaystyle\lim_{k\to\infty} \frac{1}{k} = 0$

Area between two curves

To find the area between the curves $y = \mathrm{f}(x)$ and $y = \mathrm{g}(x)$ bounded by $x = a$ and $x = b$ the method of subtraction is used.

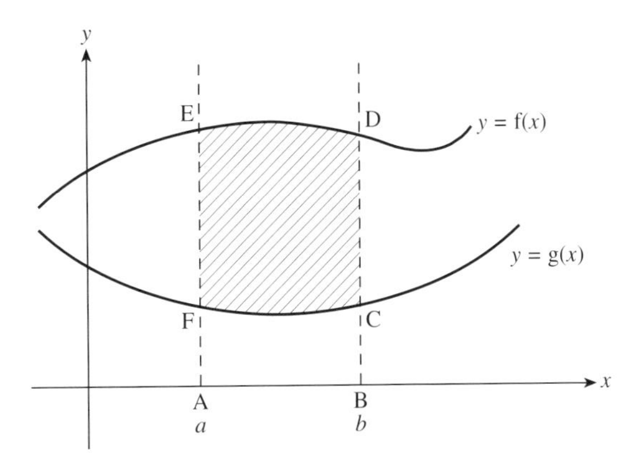

Area required = Area ABDE − Area ABCF

$$= \int_a^b \mathrm{f}(x)\,\mathrm{d}x - \int_a^b \mathrm{g}(x)\,\mathrm{d}x$$

$$= \int_a^b \left(\mathrm{f}(x) - \mathrm{g}(x)\right)\mathrm{d}x$$

✓ ***Note*** Even when one, or both, of the curves lies beneath the x-axis the same result, namely $\int(\mathrm{f}(x) - \mathrm{g}(x))\,\mathrm{d}x$, gives the area.

➤ Area between two curves $y = \mathrm{f}(x)$ and $y = \mathrm{g}(x)$

$$= \int_a^b \left(\mathrm{f}(x) - \mathrm{g}(x)\right)\mathrm{d}x$$

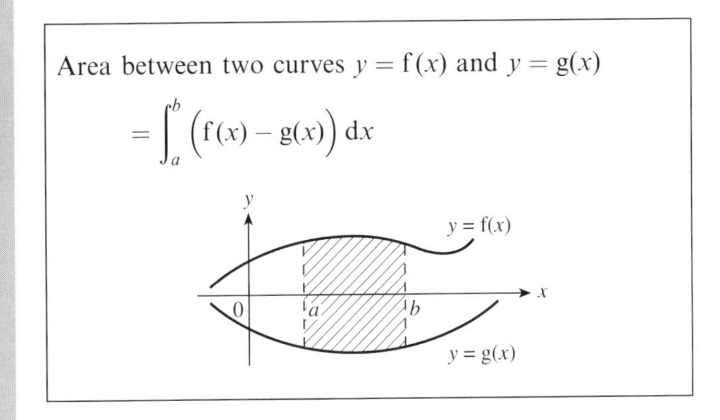

Example 13 Find the area enclosed between the curves $y = 16 - x^2$ and $y = x^2 - 4x$.

The curves intersect where

Draw a sketch.

$$16 - x^2 = x^2 - 4x$$
$$2x^2 - 4x - 16 = 0$$
$$x^2 - 2x - 8 = 0$$
$$(x - 4)(x + 2) = 0$$
$$\therefore \quad x = 4 \quad \text{or} \quad x = -2$$

So the limits of integration are -2 and 4.

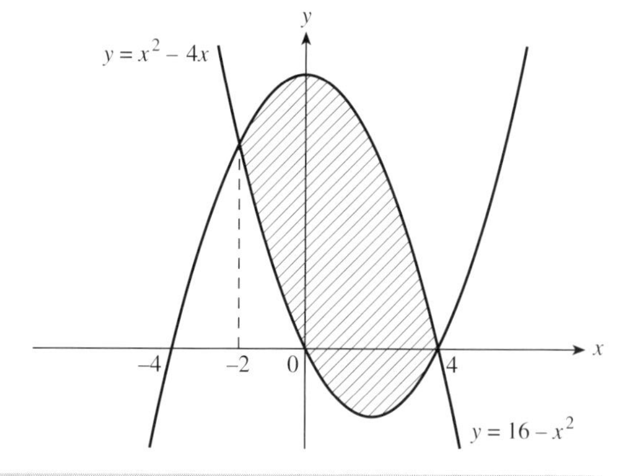

Area between curves $= \int_{-2}^{4} \big(f(x) - g(x)\big)\,dx$

The method deals correctly with the area below the x-axis.

$$\begin{aligned}\text{Area required} &= \int_{-2}^{4} \big(16 - x^2 - (x^2 - 4x)\big)\,dx \\ &= \int_{-2}^{4} (16 + 4x - 2x^2)\,dx \\ &= 2\int_{-2}^{4} (8 + 2x - x^2)\,dx \\ &= 2\left[8x + x^2 - \frac{x^3}{3}\right]_{-2}^{4} \\ &= 2\big(32 + 16 - \tfrac{64}{3} - (-16 + 4 + \tfrac{8}{3})\big) \\ &= 2\big(60 - \tfrac{72}{3}\big) \\ &= 72\end{aligned}$$

Take the common factor 2 outside the integral sign.

So area is 72 square units.

Interpretation of area 'under' a curve

Consider these two speed–time graphs:

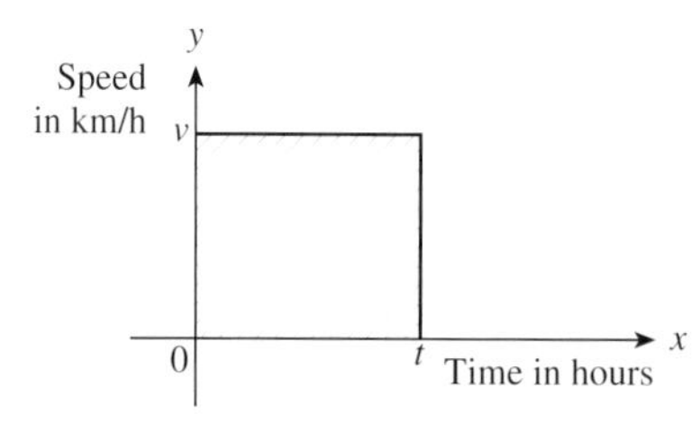

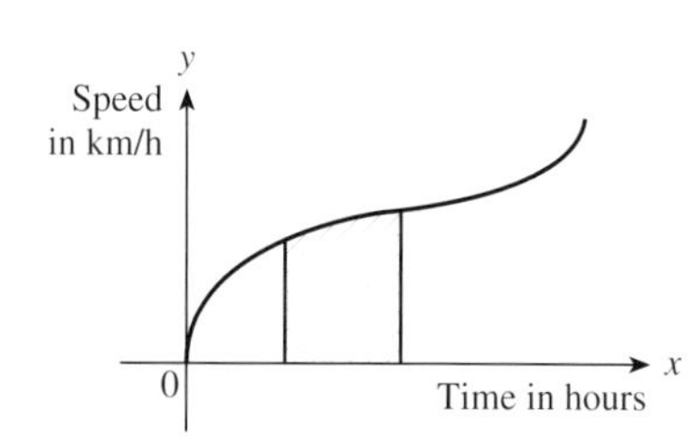

The area between the curve and the horizontal axis represents the distance travelled.

In the case of constant speed v, the distance travelled in time t is vt, which is the area shaded. The area is obtained by multiplying:

$$\frac{\text{km}}{\text{hour}} \times \text{hour} = \text{km}$$

Speed in kmh^{-1} (y-axis) | Time in h (x-axis) | Distance in km (area)

Similarly, for a graph of fuel consumption in litres per km plotted against distance travelled in km, the area under the curve represents litres used:

$$\frac{\text{litres}}{\text{km}} \times \text{km} = \text{litres}$$

Fuel consumption (y-axis) | Distance travelled (x-axis) | Fuel used (area)

This area represents the quantity obtained when the units on the axes are multiplied.

Example 14 The graph shows the area of the cross-section of a flask plotted against the height from the base at which the area is measured.

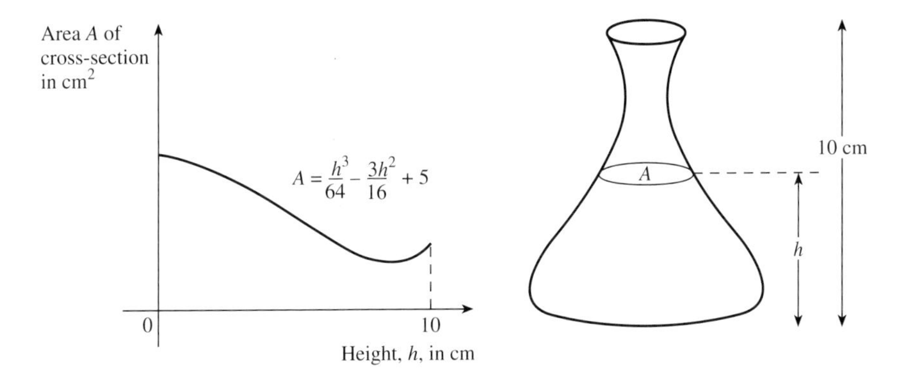

Find the area under the curve between $h = 0$ and $h = 10$ and interpret the answer.

Solution $A = \dfrac{h^3}{64} - \dfrac{3h^2}{16} + 5$

$$\text{Area under curve} = \int_0^{10} \left(\frac{h^3}{64} - \frac{3h^2}{16} + 5\right) \mathrm{d}h$$

$$= \left[\frac{h^4}{256} - \frac{h^3}{16} + 5h\right]_0^{10}$$

$$= \frac{10^4}{256} - \frac{10^3}{16} + 50$$

$$= 26.56$$

Area (cm^2) × Height (cm) = Volume (cm^3)

Interpret the result by multiplying the dimensions of the axes.

So the area under the curve represents the volume of the flask which is $26.6\,\text{cm}^3$.

EXERCISE 13b

1 Evaluate

a $\left[\dfrac{x^4}{4}\right]_1^2$ **b** $\left[x^3 - 3x\right]_{-2}^{0}$ **c** $\left[3x^3 - 4x\right]_{-1}^{1}$ **d** $\left[x^3 - \dfrac{1}{x^2}\right]_{-4}^{-3}$

2 Find the value of these definite integrals and draw sketches to show the area found.

a $\displaystyle\int_0^3 x^2\,dx$ **b** $\displaystyle\int_2^5 (2x^2 + 1)\,dx$ **c** $\displaystyle\int_{-2}^{2} x^3\,dx$ **d** $\displaystyle\int_1^2 \frac{1}{x^2}\,dx$

3 Evaluate

a $\displaystyle\int_{-1}^{3} (x + x^4)\,dx$ **b** $\displaystyle\int_8^{27} \frac{1}{2\sqrt[3]{x}}\,dx$ **c** $\displaystyle\int_1^4 \frac{3}{x^3}\,dx$ **d** $\displaystyle\int_1^8 \sqrt[3]{x}\,dx$

e $\displaystyle\int_4^9 \left(5 - \frac{2}{\sqrt{x}}\right) dx$ **f** $\displaystyle\int_{-3}^{-2} \frac{3x - 2}{x^3}\,dx$ **g** $\displaystyle\int_1^{\infty} \frac{1}{x^2}\,dx$ **h** $\displaystyle\int_2^{\infty} \frac{2}{x^3}\,dx$

4 Find the shaded areas.

a

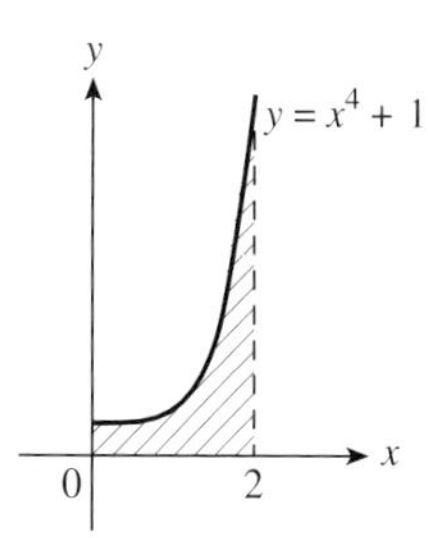

b

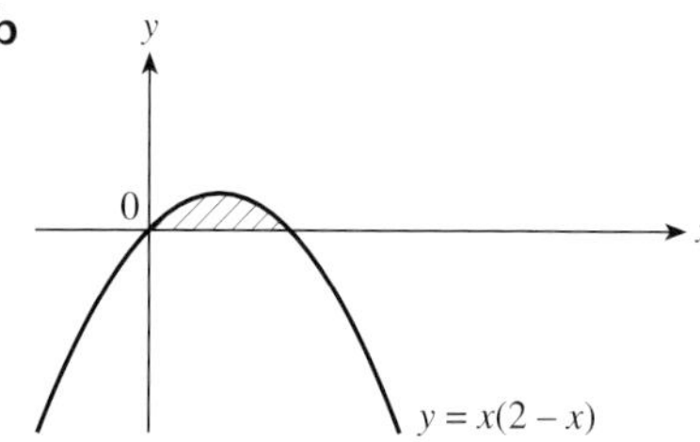

c

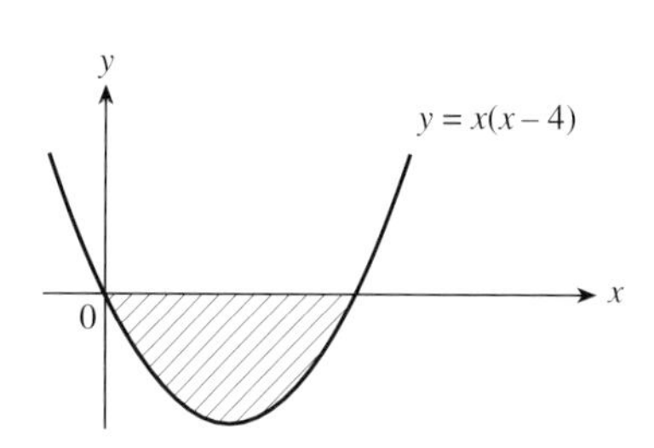

d

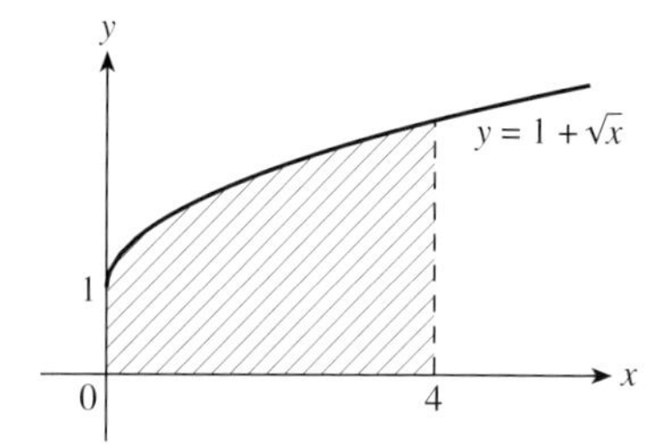

5 Find the areas enclosed by the x-axis and each of these curves and straight lines.

a $y = 3x^2$, $x = 1$, $x = 3$ **b** $y = x^2 + 2$, $x = -2$, $x = 5$

c $y = (x - 1)(x - 2)$, $x = -2$, $x = -1$ **d** $y = \dfrac{3}{x^2}$, $x = 1$, $x = 6$

6 Sketch the curve $y = x^2 - 5x + 6$ and find the area cut off below the x-axis.

7 Find, by integration, the area enclosed by $x + 4y - 20 = 0$ and the axes. Check by another method.

8 Sketch these curves and find the areas enclosed by them, and by the x-axis and the given straight lines.

a $y = x(4 - x)$, $x = 5$ **b** $y = -x^3$, $x = -2$

c $y = \dfrac{1}{x^2} - 1$, $x = 2$ **d** $y = (x - 2)^2$, $x = 1$

9 Find these shaded areas using $A = \int y\,dx$ and a method of subtraction.

a

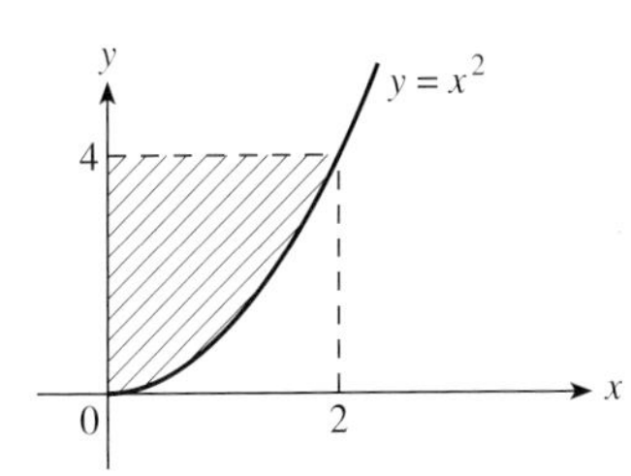

b

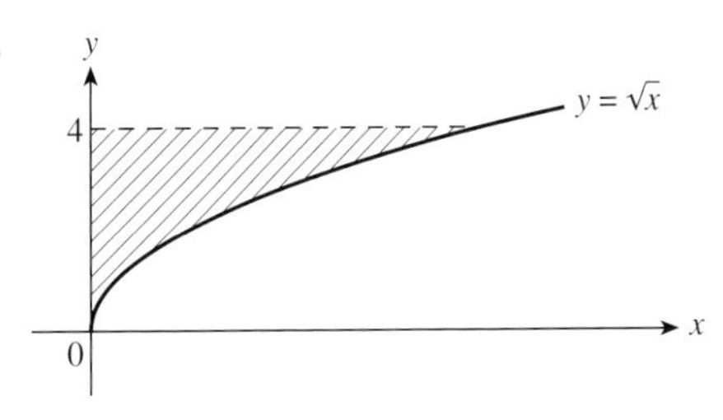

c

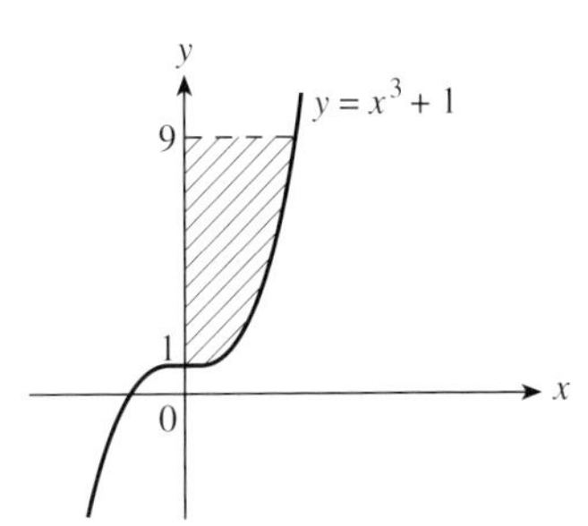

d

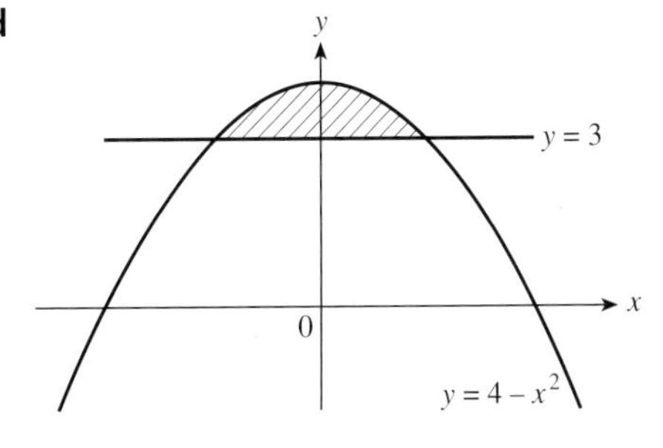

10 Find the shaded areas in parts **a** and **b** of Question 9 using $A = \int x\,dy$ i.e. by considering the area between the curve and the y-axis.

11 Find the area enclosed by the y-axis and these curves and straight lines.

a $x = y^2$, $y = 3$

b $y = x^3$, $y = 1$, $y = 8$

c $x - y^2 - 3 = 0$, $y = -1$, $y = 2$

d $x = \dfrac{1}{\sqrt{y}}$, $y = 2$, $y = 3$

12 Find these shaded areas.

a

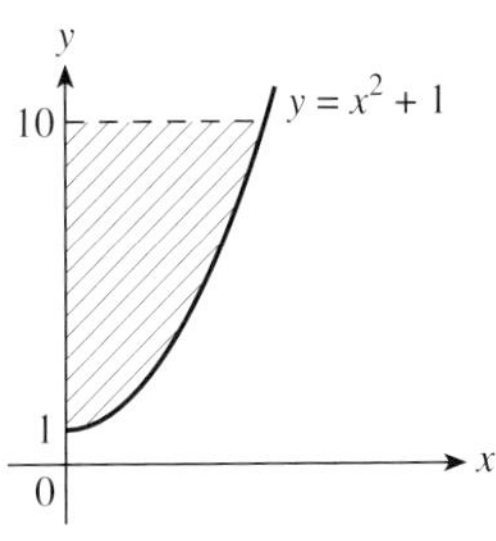

b

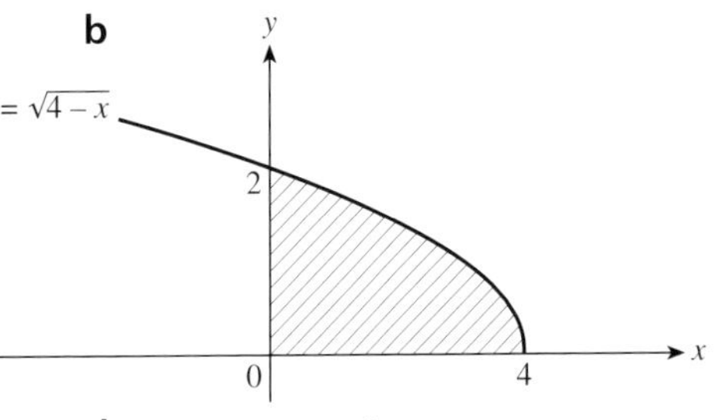

c

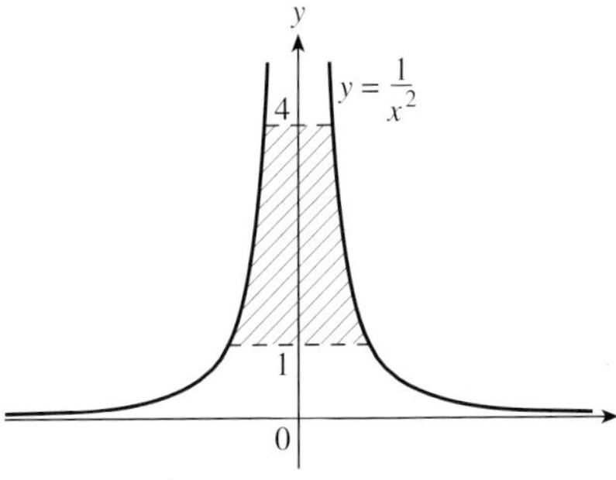

d

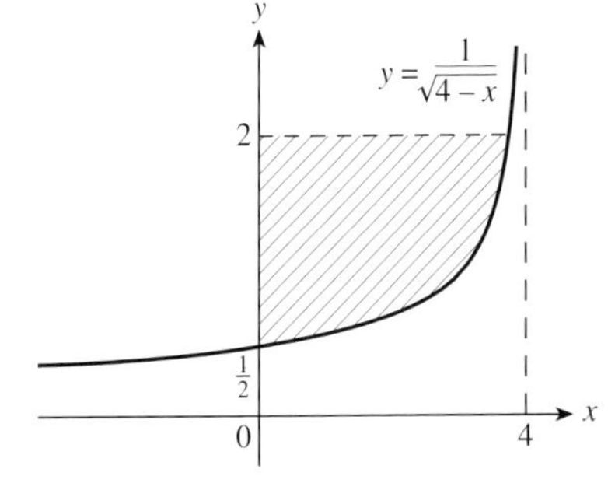

EXERCISE 13b *(continued)*

13 For these curves and straight lines find their points of intersection, draw a sketch on the same axes and find the area of the segment cut off from each curve by the corresponding straight line.

a $y = x^2 - 4x + 6$, $y = 3$ **b** $y = 7 - x - x^2$, $y = 5$

c $y = \frac{1}{2}x^2$, $y = 2x$ **d** $y = 3x^2$, $3x + y - 6 = 0$

e $y = (x + 1)(x - 2)$, $x - y + 1 = 0$ **f** $y = \sqrt{x} + 3$, $2y = x + 6$

14 The curves $y = x^2 + 2$ and $y = 4 - x^2$ meet at the points A and B.

a Find the coordinates of A and B and hence sketch the curves.

b Find the area enclosed by the two curves.

15 Find these shaded areas.

a

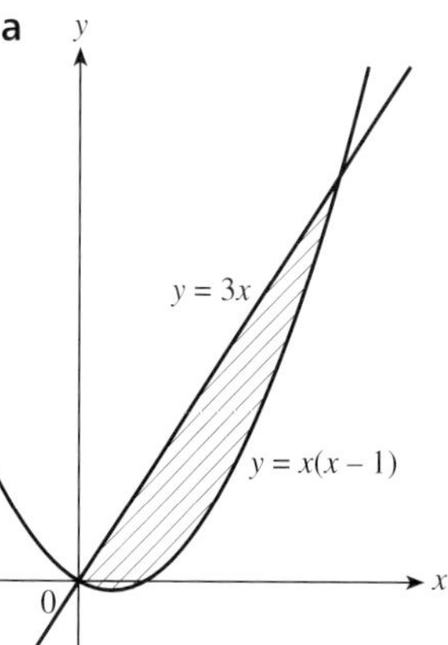

b

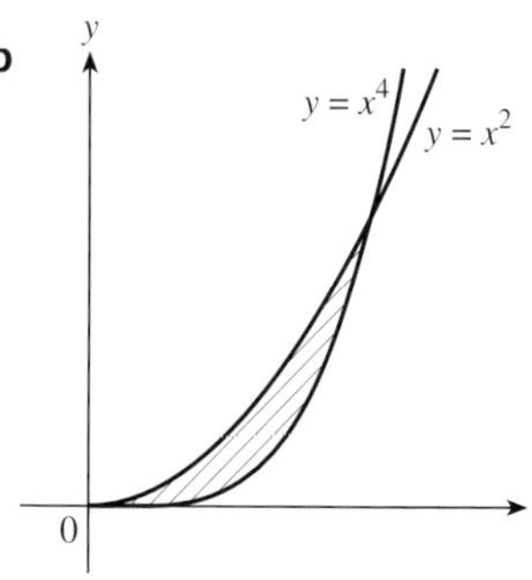

c

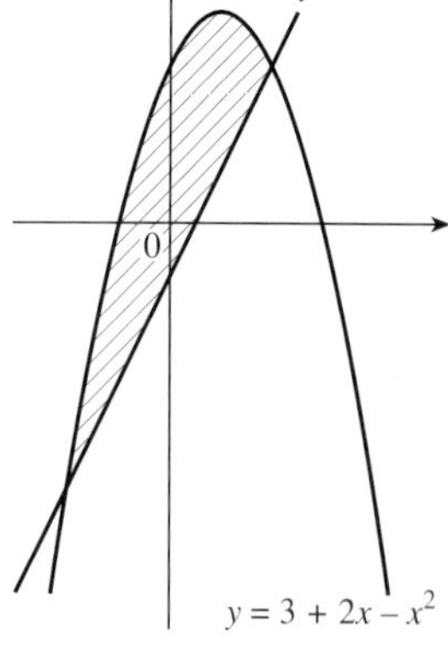

d

e

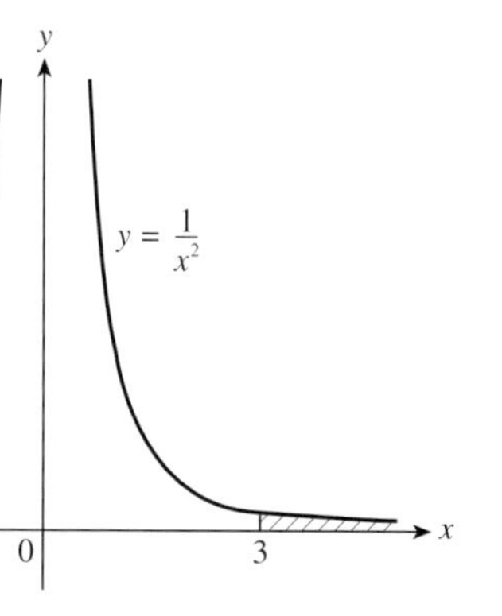

16 The diagram shows a sketch of $f(x) = x^2 - 3x + 2$.

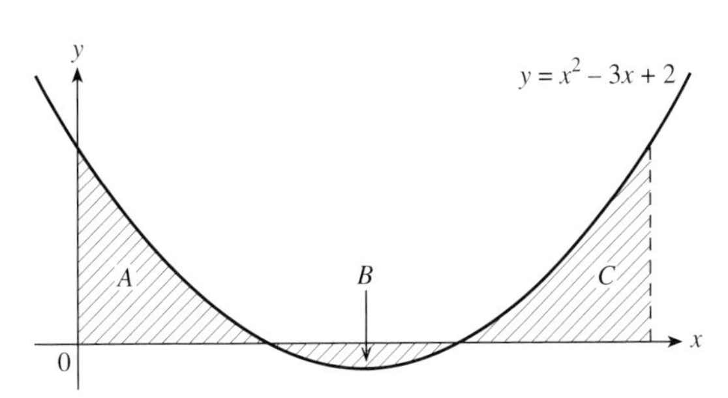

a Find $\int_0^3 f(x)\,dx$.

b Find the sum of the areas A, B and C.

c Explain the difference between the answers to parts **a** and **b**.

d Draw a sketch of $y = |f(x)|$.

e Find $\int_0^3 |f(x)|\,dx$.

17 A function $f(x)$ is defined as

$$f(x) = \begin{cases} 2x & 0 \leqslant x < 1 \\ x^2 - 2x + 3 & 1 \leqslant x < 2 \end{cases}$$

and $f(x)$ is a periodic function of period 2.

a Sketch $f(x)$ for $0 \leqslant x < 4$

b Find

i $\int_0^2 f(x)\,dx$ **ii** $\int_0^{10} f(x)\,dx$ **iii** $\int_0^{2n} f(x)\,dx,\ n \in \mathbb{Z}^+$

EXERCISE 13c (Extension)

1 **a** Draw diagrams to illustrate these results.

i If $f(x)$ is an odd function, then $\int_{-a}^{a} f(x)\,dx = 0$.

ii If $g(x)$ is an even function, then $\int_{-a}^{a} g(x)\,dx = 2\int_0^a g(x)\,dx$.

b Hence find

i $\int_{-1}^{1} (5x^4 + 3x^2 + 2)\,dx$

ii $\int_{-4}^{4} (3 + t + t^3)\,dt$

EXERCISE 13c
(continued)

2 Explain these results, using diagrams where helpful.

a $\int_a^c f(x)\,dx + \int_c^b f(x)\,dx = \int_a^b f(x)\,dx$

b $\int_a^b f(x)\,dx = -\int_b^a f(x)\,dx$

c $\int_a^b k\,dx = k(b-a)$ where k is constant

3 Using the symmetry of even and odd functions, and given $\int_0^1 x^2\,dx = \frac{1}{3}$, find

a $\int_{-1}^1 x^2\,dx$ **b** $\int_{-1}^1 x^3\,dx$ **c** $\int_{-1}^1 (x^3 + x^2)\,dx$

d $\int_{-1}^1 (x^5 + x^3 + 3)\,dx$ **e** $\int_{-1}^1 (x^3 + 4x^2 - 1)\,dx$ **f** $\int_0^1 6x^2\,dx$

g $\int_{-1}^1 (kx^2 + m)\,dx$ **h** $\int_{-1}^0 x^2\,dx$ **i** $\int_1^0 \frac{x^2}{2}\,dx$

j $\int_{-1}^1 (4 - x^2)\,dx$ **k** $\int_{-4}^4 (3x^5 + 2x)\,dx$

4 For the curve $y = 12x - x^3$, find the area bounded by the curve and the positive x-axis.

5 Find the equation of the curve which passes through the point $(-1, 0)$ and whose gradient at any point (x, y) is $3x^2 - 6x + 4$.
Find the area enclosed by the curve, the x-axis and the lines $x = 1$ and $x = 2$.

6 Find k if the areas A and B are equal.

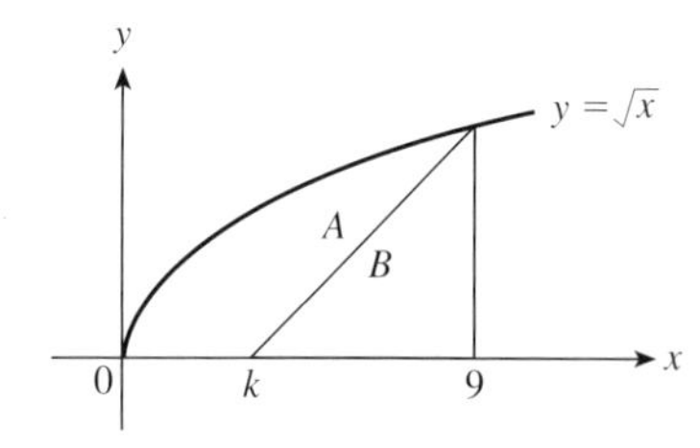

7 A child's kite, shown in the diagram, is symmetrical about the y-axis.
AB is two feet long.
Find the area of the kite in square feet.

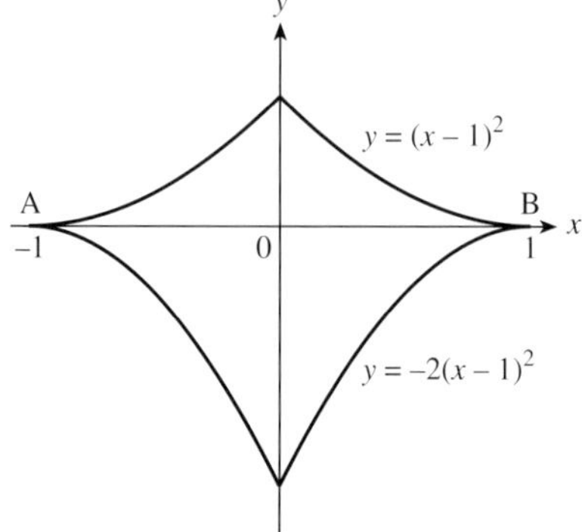

8 The parabola $y = 6x - x^2$ meets the x-axis at O and A. The tangents at O and A meet at T. Show that the curve divides the area of the triangle OAT into two parts in the ratio 2:1.

9 The curve $y = x(x - 1)^2$ touches the x-axis at the point A. B is the point (2, 2) on the curve and N is the foot of the perpendicular from B to the x-axis. Prove that the tangent at B divides the area between the arc AB, NB, and AN in the ratio 11:24.

10 Show that the curves $y = x^3$ and $y = 4 - 3x^2$ intersect at the point (1, 1) and touch at the point (−2, −8).
Find the area enclosed by the two curves.

11 **a** The diagram shows a set of seven parabolas, the kth parabola having equation $y = kx(1 - x)$.
Find the total area shaded.

b A similar set of $2n + 1$ parabolas is drawn, the kth parabola having equation $y = kx(1 - x)$ as in **a**. Alternate areas are shaded as in **a**. Find the total area shaded.

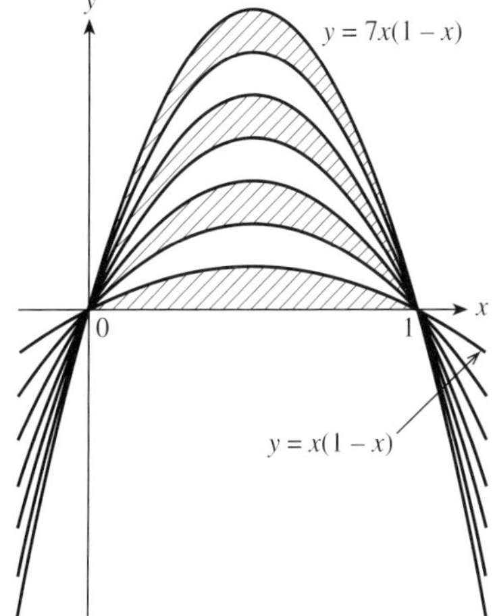

12 Find

a $\int_0^x (x^2 + 2x)\,dx$

b $\int_{-t}^{2t} (3x^2 + 2x)\,dx$

c $\int_{4-k}^{4+k} (x - 4)\,dx$

d $\int_1^{\infty} \frac{1}{\sqrt{x^3}}\,dx$

13 A small hole is made in a spherical gas-filled balloon of radius 6 m. At time t s after the hole is made, it is suspected that the gas is escaping at a rate of $2t\,\text{cm}^3\,\text{s}^{-1}$.

a Show that over half the gas will have escaped in 6 hours.

b Assuming a different model, namely that the gas escapes at $3t^2\,\text{cm}^3\,\text{s}^{-1}$, show that over half the gas will have escaped in 13 minutes.

EXERCISE 13d (Miscellaneous)

1 **a** Calculate $\int_{-1}^{1} x(x^2 - 1)\,dx$.

b Find the area bounded by the curve $y = x(x^2 - 1)$ and the x-axis
i between $x = -1$ and $x = 0$ **ii** between $x = 0$ and $x = 1$

2 Given that $\frac{dy}{dx} = x^2 + 2$ and that $y = 6$ when $x = 3$ find

a y in terms of x

b the value of y when $x = 1$

EXERCISE 13d *(continued)*

3 Find

a $\displaystyle\int \frac{x^3 + x}{\sqrt{x}}\,\mathrm{d}x$ **b** $\displaystyle\int_0^1 (2x+1)(3x+1)\,\mathrm{d}x$

c $\displaystyle\int_1^2 \frac{(x+1)^2}{x^4}\,\mathrm{d}x$ **d** $\displaystyle\int x^{2.5}\,\mathrm{d}x$

4 Given that $f'(x) = (3x+1)(x-2)$ and $f(-1) = \frac{1}{2}$, find $f(x)$.

5 The gradient of a curve is given by

$$\frac{\mathrm{d}y}{\mathrm{d}x} = ax + b$$

Given that the curve passes through (0, 0), (1, 2) and (−1, 4) find

a the values of a and b **b** the equation of the curve

6 The line $y = \frac{1}{2}x + 1$ meets the curve $y = \frac{1}{4}(7x - x^2)$ at the points A and B.

a Find the coordinates of A and B

b Find the length of AB

c Prove that the upper segment of the curve cut off by the line has area $1\frac{1}{8}$.

7 Find the ratio of area A to area B.

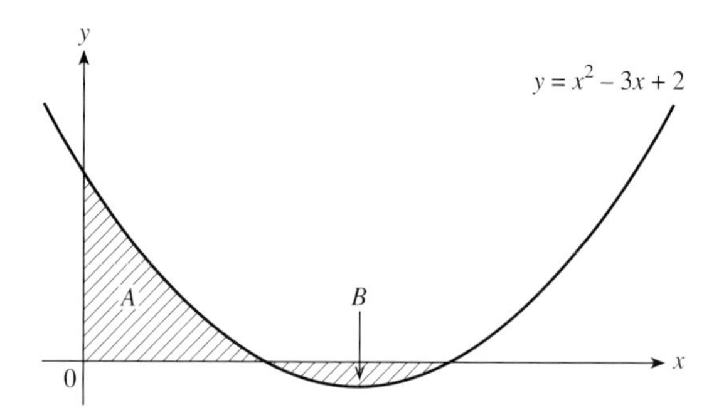

8 Find the area of the region lying between $y = 2x^2$ and $y = x^2$ from the origin up to the line $x = 4$.

9 Find these shaded areas.

a

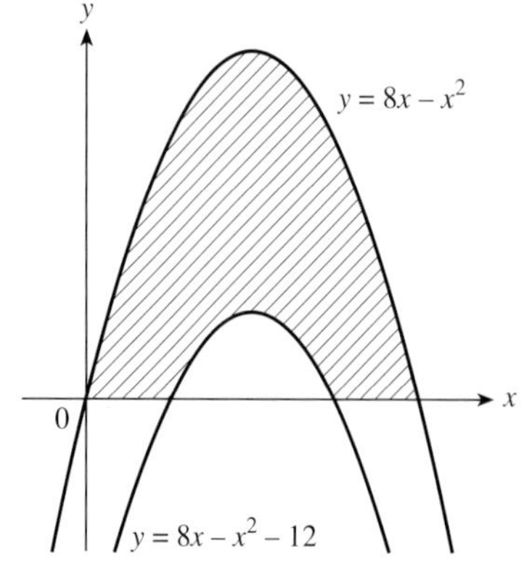

b

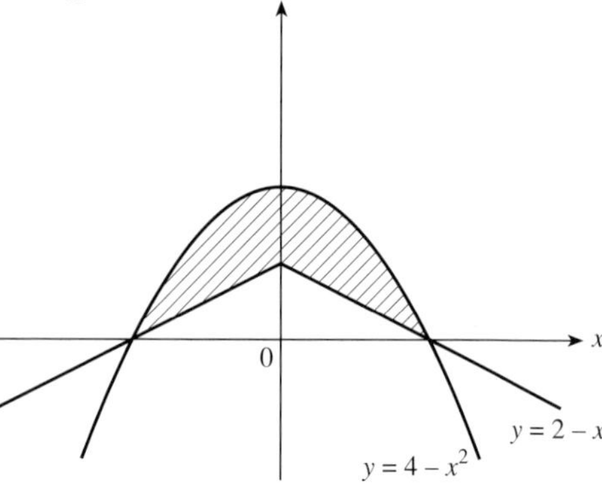

Test yourself

1 $\int (3x - 2)\,dx$ is equal to

A $3 + c$ **B** $3x^2 - 2x + c$ **C** $\frac{3x^2}{2} - 2c$ **D** $\frac{3x^2}{2} - 2x + c$ **E** $x^3 - x^2 + c$

2 A curve whose gradient is $-2x$ passes through (2, 0). Its equation is

A $y = 4 - x^2$ **B** $y = 8 - 2x^2$ **C** $y = x - 2$ **D** $y = (2 - x)^2$ **E** $y = 4 - 2x$

3 The area enclosed by the curve $y = 3x^2 - x$, the x-axis and the lines $x = 2$ and $x = 4$ is

A 50 **B** 34 **C** 12 **D** 156 **E** 46

4 If $\frac{dy}{dx} = 3\sqrt{x} + \frac{2}{x^3}$, then y is equal to

A $3\sqrt{x^3} - \frac{2}{x^2} + c$ **B** $\frac{3}{2\sqrt{x}} - \frac{6}{x^4} + c$ **C** $2\sqrt{x^3} - \frac{1}{x^2} + c$

D $2\sqrt{x^3} - \frac{1}{2x^4} + c$ **E** $2\sqrt{(x + c)^3} - \frac{1}{(x + k)^2}$

5 The rate of change of an object's mass at time t is $3t^2 - 4t - 2$.
Between $t = 1$ and $t = 2$, the object's mass

A increases by 1 **B** decreases by 1 **C** decreases by 7

D increases by 5 **E** remains constant

6 $f'(x) = 4x + 5$ and the curve $y = f(x)$ cuts the x-axis at $x = -3$.
Which of these points lies on $y = f(x)$?

A $(0, -1\frac{1}{4})$ **B** (1, 3) **C** (2, 18) **D** (−1, −6) **E** $(-\frac{1}{2}, 0)$

7 The area enclosed by the curve $y = (3 + x)(3 - x)$ and the x-axis is

A 0 **B** 54 **C** 18 **D** 36

E not able to be calculated from information given

8 What is the shaded area in this diagram?

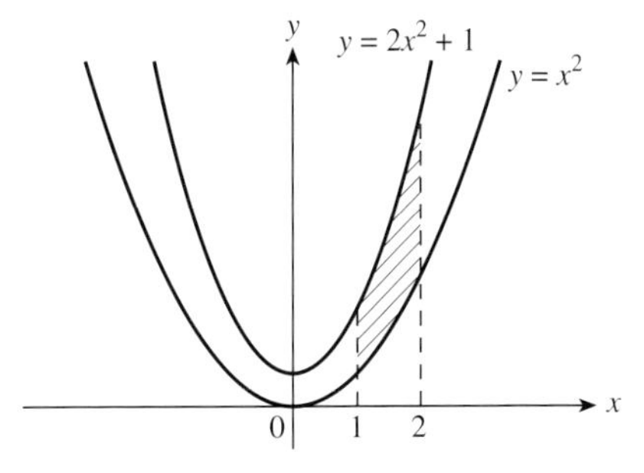

A 3 **B** $2\frac{1}{3}$ **C** $5\frac{2}{3}$ **D** 4 **E** $3\frac{1}{3}$

9 The area enclosed by the curve $y = 3\sqrt{x}$, the y-axis and the line $y = 6$ is

A 8 **B** 16 **C** $2\frac{10}{27}$ **D** $24 - 12\sqrt{6}$ **E** 24

Key points

Integration

$$\int x^n \, dx = \frac{x^{n+1}}{n+1} + c \quad n \neq -1$$

To integrate x^n add one to the power and divide by the new power.

If $\int f(x)\,dx = F(x)$ then $\int_a^b f(x)\,dx = F(b) - F(a)$

$$\int \{f(x) \pm g(x)\}\,dx = \int f(x)\,dx \pm \int g(x)\,dx$$

$$\int kf(x)\,dx = k\int f(x)\,dx$$

An **indefinite integral** results in a function being obtained.
Remember to add a constant.

A **definite integral** has limits, and results in a value being obtained.

Area

- Area between curve and x-axis

$= \int_a^b y\,dx$ → +ve for area above x-axis; −ve for area below x-axis

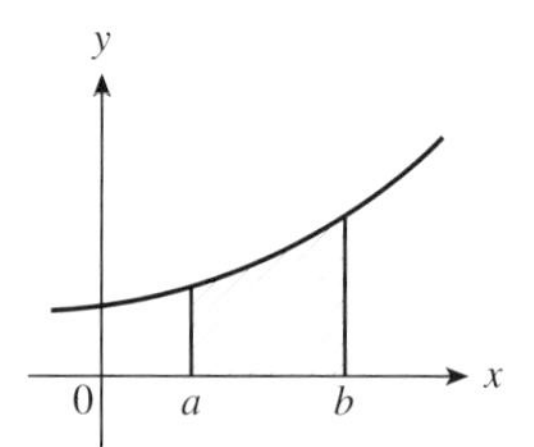

Limits a and b are values of x.

- Area between curve and y-axis

$= \int_c^d x\,dy$ → +ve for area above x-axis; −ve for area below x-axis

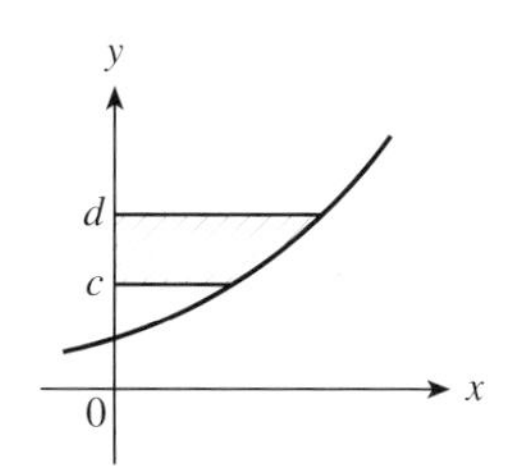

Limits c and d are values of y.

- Area between two curves $y = f(x)$ and $y = g(x)$.

$$= \int_a^b \left(f(x) - g(x)\right) dx$$

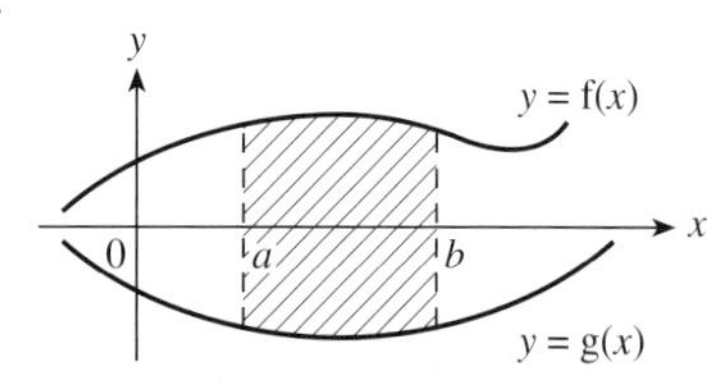

Even and odd functions

- If $f(x)$ is an even function then

$$\int_{-a}^{a} f(x)\,dx = 2\int_{0}^{a} f(x)\,dx$$

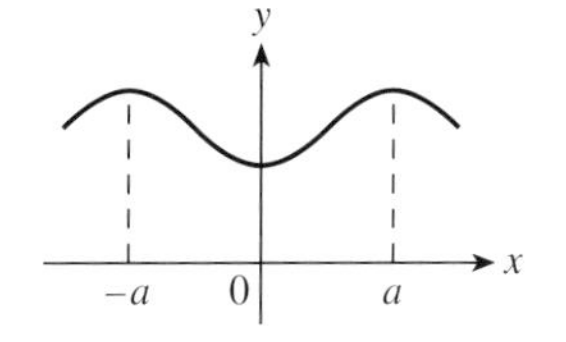

- If $f(x)$ is an odd function then

$$\int_{-a}^{a} f(x)\,dx = 0$$

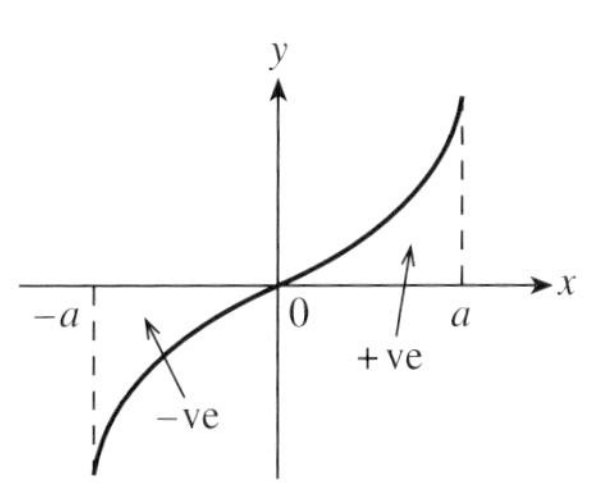

14 *Revision of Trigonometry, Geometry and Proportion*

This chapter covers problem solving using geometry, trigonometry and algebra. It is useful for revision or for those who did not follow the higher GCSE course.

14.1 Solution of right-angled triangles

Unknown sides and angles of right-angled triangles can be calculated using

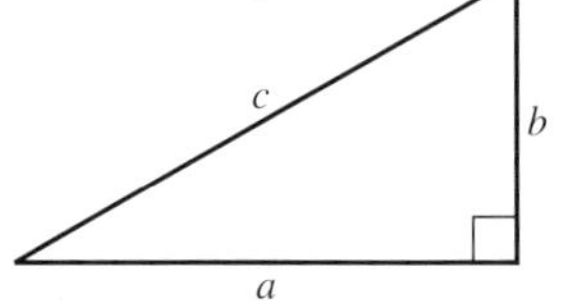

- **Pythagoras' Theorem**

  $c^2 = a^2 + b^2$

- The **trigonometrical ratios:** sine (sin), cosine (cos) and tangent (tan)

  In any right-angled triangle the side opposite the right angle is the **hypotenuse**. The other two sides are the **opposite** and **adjacent** depending on which of the two acute angles is being considered.

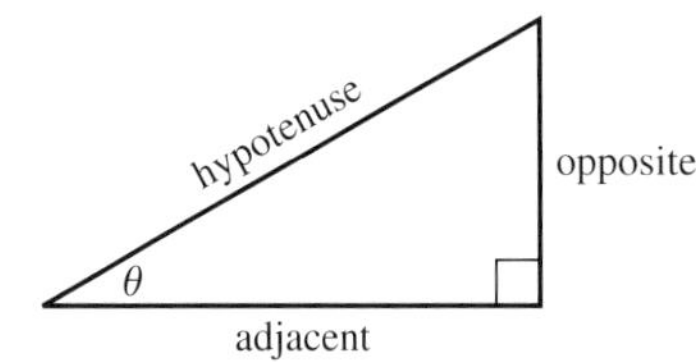

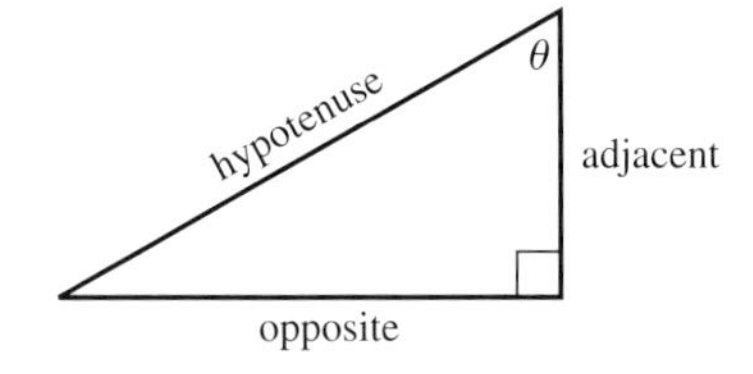

The adjacent side is adjacent (or next to) the angle being considered.
The opposite side is opposite the angle being considered.

$\sin\theta = \dfrac{\text{opposite}}{\text{hypotenuse}}$ $\quad\cos\theta = \dfrac{\text{adjacent}}{\text{hypotenuse}}$ $\quad\tan\theta = \dfrac{\text{opposite}}{\text{adjacent}}$

Use a mnemonic such as SOHCAHTOA, to remember these ratios.

14.2 Area of sector and length of arc (degrees)

Consider a circle, centre O, radius r and an arc, PQ, of the circle subtending an angle of θ (degrees) at the centre of the circle.

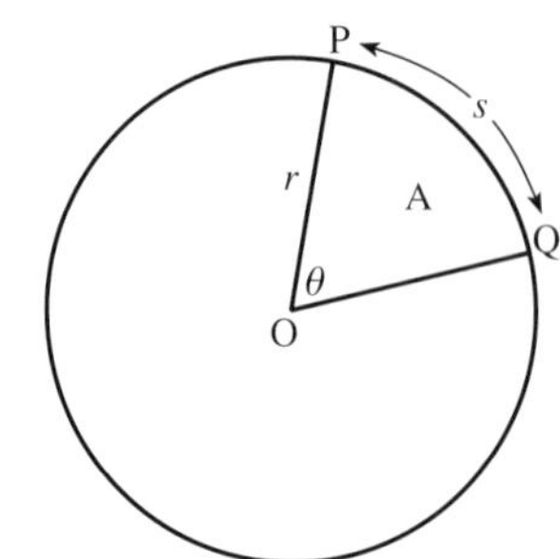

OPQ is a sector of the circle

Area of sector OPQ, $A = \dfrac{\theta}{360^\circ} \times \pi r^2$

Length of arc PQ, $s = \dfrac{\theta}{360^\circ} \times 2\pi r$

$\dfrac{\theta}{360^\circ}$ is the fraction of the circle required.

14.3 Similarity, ratio and proportion

Being **similar**, in mathematics, means having the same shape, although not usually the same size. If the shape and the size are the same, the figures (2D) or solids (3D) are said to be **congruent**.

Similar figures or solids have

- angles which are equal
- all corresponding lengths multiplied by scale factor k
- all corresponding areas multiplied by scale factor k^2
- all corresponding volumes multiplied by scale factor k^3.

Problems involving similar figures (2D)

Example 1

In this example, two methods are shown:
a *equivalent fractions, and* ***b*** *scale factor.*

a Find the length of EF.

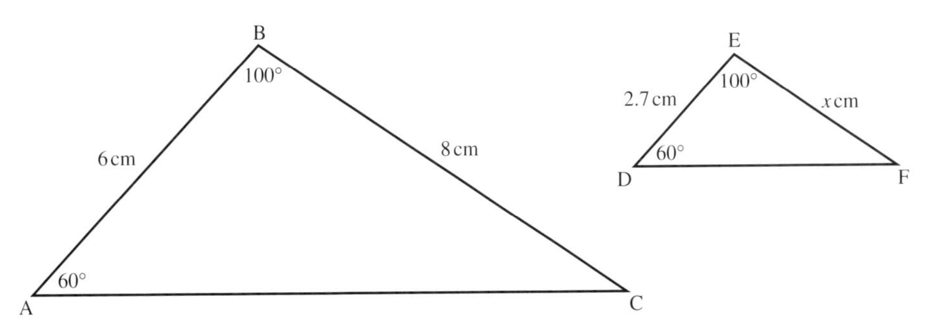

Triangles ABC and DEF are similar since their angles are equal.

AB corresponds to DE. BC corresponds to EF.

$$\therefore \quad \frac{AB}{DE} = \frac{BC}{EF}$$

Note: $\frac{AB}{BC} = \frac{DE}{EF}$ could also have been used.

$$\frac{6}{2.7} = \frac{8}{x}$$

Substitute the values. Omit all units, all lengths are in cm. Two equal fractions ∴ cross-multiply.

$$6x = 8 \times 2.7$$

$$x = \frac{\overset{4}{\cancel{8}} \times \overset{0.9}{\cancel{2.7}}}{\underset{1}{\cancel{6}}} = 3.6$$

So EF = 3.6 cm.

b These rectangles are similar. Find the value of y.

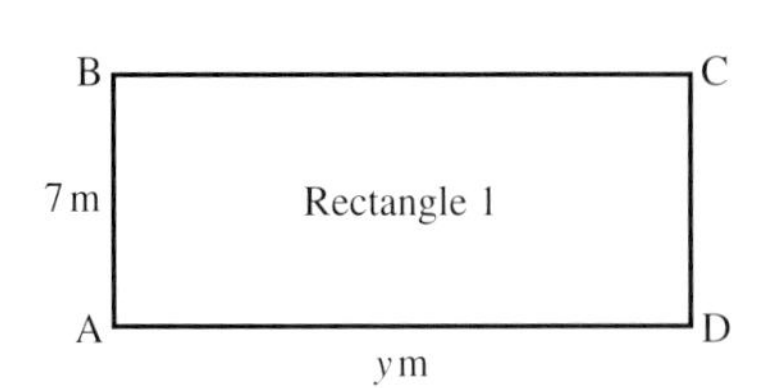

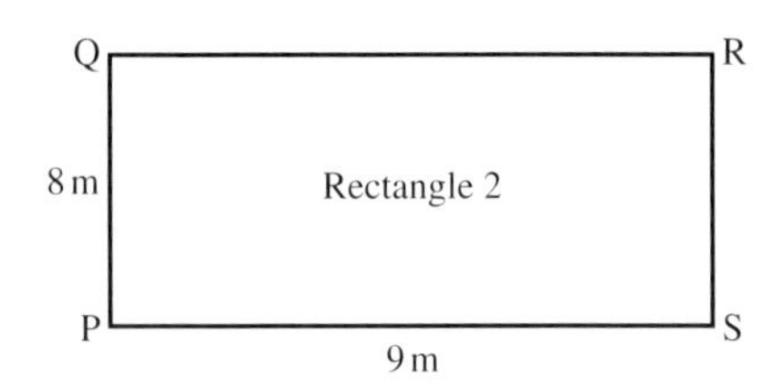

Let k be the scale factor for multiplying lengths of Rectangle 1 to obtain corresponding lengths of Rectangle 2.

Then $\quad 7k = 8$

Sides AB and PQ correspond, with scale factor k, so $AB \times k = PQ$.

$\therefore \quad k = \frac{8}{7}$

$\frac{8}{7}y = 9$

Sides AD and PS correspond, so $AD \times k = PS$.

$y = \frac{63}{8} = 7\frac{7}{8}$

Example 2 Find h in the diagram.

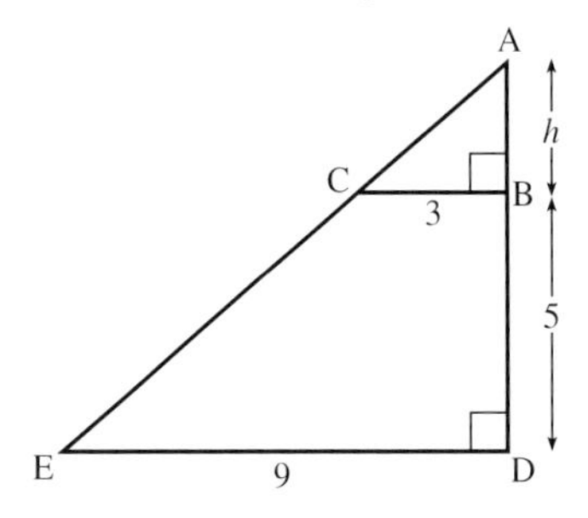

Sketch the triangles separately if there is any uncertainty which lengths correspond.

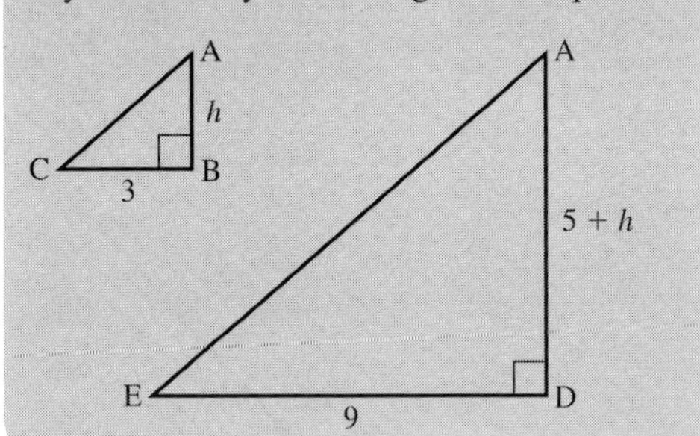

Triangles ABC and ADE are similar.

$$\frac{AB}{AD} = \frac{BC}{DE}$$

$$\frac{h}{5+h} = \frac{3}{9}$$

$$\frac{h}{5+h} = \frac{1}{3}$$

Two equal fractions $\therefore$ cross multiply.

$$3h = 5 + h$$

$$\therefore \quad h = 2\frac{1}{2}$$

Problems involving similar solids (3D)

Example 3 Two Russian dolls are similar. The diameters of their bases are 2 cm and 3 cm.

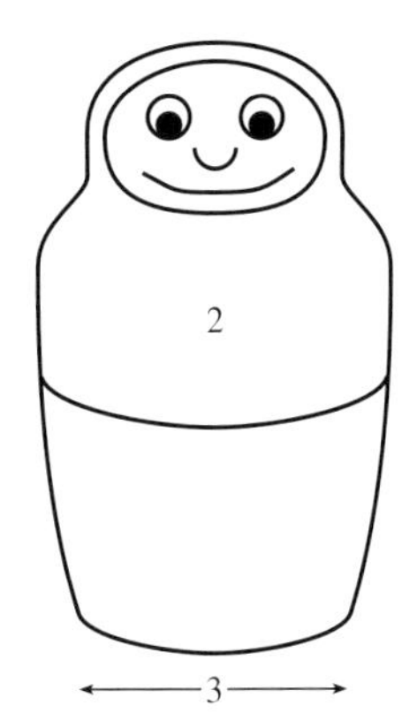

Part of each doll is painted red.

a If the height of doll 1 is 6 cm, find the height of doll 2.

b If the area painted red on doll 2 is 15 cm^2, find the area painted red on doll 1.

c If the volume of doll 1 is 16 cm^3, find the volume of doll 2.

Solution From the diameters of 2 cm and 3 cm the scale factor, k, can be found.

$$2k = 3$$
$$\therefore \quad k = \tfrac{3}{2}$$

So, length on doll 1 $\times \frac{3}{2}$ = corresponding length on doll 2.
Area on doll 1 $\times \left(\frac{3}{2}\right)^2$ = corresponding area on doll 2.
Volume on doll 1 $\times \left(\frac{3}{2}\right)^3$ = corresponding volume on doll 2.

a Height of doll 1 = 6 cm

so Height of doll 2 = $6 \times \frac{3}{2}$ cm = 9 cm

So the height of doll 2 is 9 cm.

Corresponding *lengths* are being compared $\therefore$ scale factor is k.

b Let red area of doll 1 = A cm^2.

Then red area of doll 2 = $A \times \left(\frac{3}{2}\right)^2$ cm^2

$$A\left(\tfrac{3}{2}\right)^2 = 15$$

$$\therefore \quad A = 15 \times \left(\tfrac{2}{3}\right)^2 = \tfrac{20}{3} = 6\tfrac{2}{3}$$

So area painted red on doll 1 is $6\frac{2}{3}$ cm^2.

Corresponding *areas* are being compared $\therefore$ scale factor is k^2.

c Volume of doll 1 = 16 cm^3

Volume of doll 2 = $16 \times \left(\frac{3}{2}\right)^3$ cm^3 = 54 cm^3

So the volume of doll 2 is 54 cm^3.

Corresponding *volumes* are being compared $\therefore$ scale factor is k^3.

✓ *Note* For problems involving surface areas, the scale factor for area (k^2) is needed.
For problems involving masses, the scale factor for volume (k^3) is needed.

Example 4 The area of a photograph is $16\,\text{cm}^2$. After enlargement the area is $100\,\text{cm}^2$.

Enlargement

Photograph

If the height of a tree in the photograph is 4 cm, what is its height in the enlargement?

Solution Let k be the scale factor for length.
Then k^2 is the scale factor for area.

$$k^2 = \frac{\text{Area of enlargement}}{\text{Area of photograph}} = \frac{100}{16}$$

Since two corresponding areas are given, the scale factor for area can be found.

$$\therefore \quad k = \sqrt{\frac{100}{16}} = \frac{10}{4} = \frac{5}{2}$$

Then, taking its square root, the scale factor for length can be obtained.

Now height of enlarged tree = k × height of original tree

so height of enlarged tree $= 4k$ cm

$= 4 \times \frac{5}{2}$ cm

$= 10$ cm

$$\frac{\text{Height of enlarged tree}}{\text{Height of original}} = k$$

So the height of the enlarged tree is 10 cm.

14.4 Geometry of a circle

Elementary properties of a circle

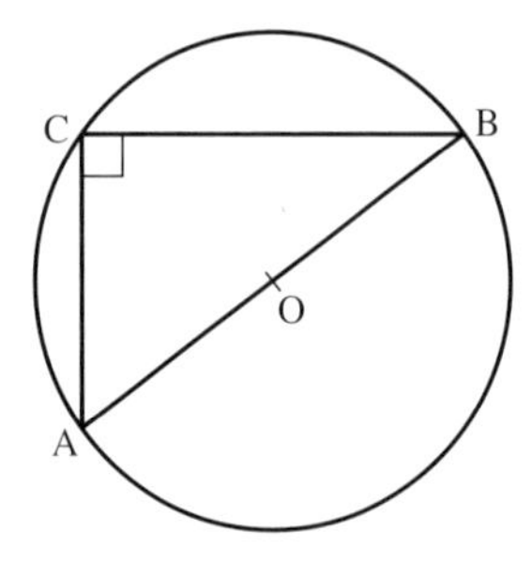

The angle in a semicircle is a right angle.

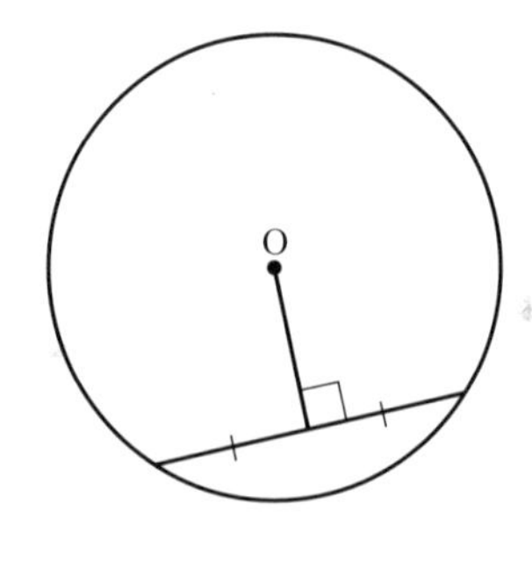

The perpendicular from the centre to a chord bisects the chord.

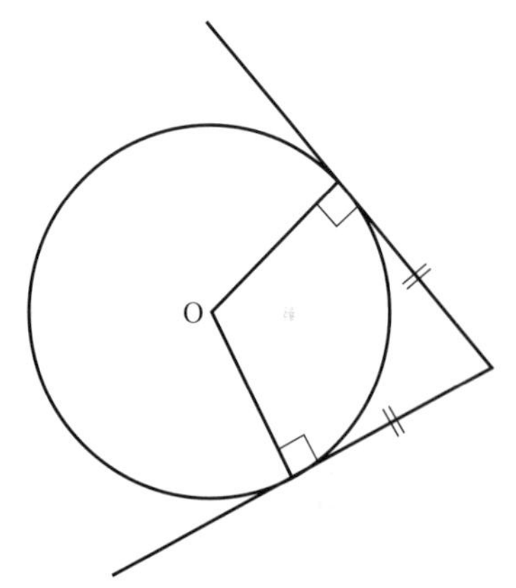

A tangent is perpendicular to the radius through the point of contact.

Tangents from an external point are of equal length.

14.5 Formulae for length, area and volume

Length *(1D)*	*Formula*	*Example*
Circumference of a circle	$C = 2\pi r$ $= \pi d$	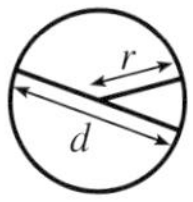

Area *(2D)*	*Formula*	*Example*
Triangle*	$A = \frac{1}{2}bh$	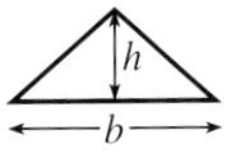 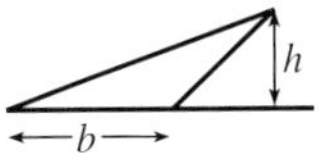
	$A = \frac{1}{2}ab \sin C$	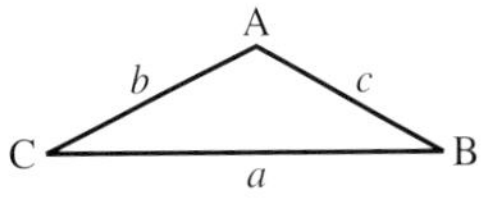
Parallelogram	$A = bh$	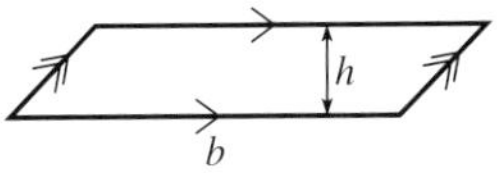
Trapezium	$A = \frac{h(a+b)}{2}$	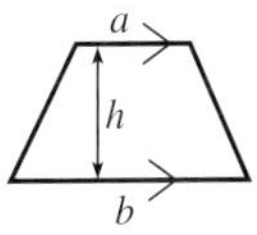
Quadrilateral with perpendicular diagonals, e.g. kite	$A = \frac{d_1 d_2}{2}$	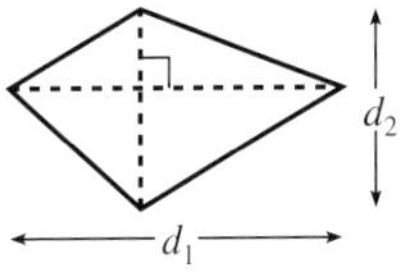
Circle	$A = \pi r^2$	
Surface of sphere	$A = 4\pi r^2$	

*See Chapter 16 for the derivation of the $A = \frac{1}{2}ab \sin C$ formula.

Volume *(3D)*	*Shape*	*Formula*	*Example*
Solid of uniform cross-section			
$V =$ Area of cross-section $\times$ length	Cuboid	$V = abc$	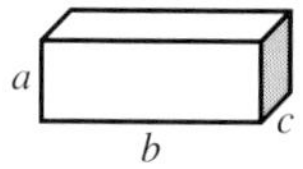
	Cylinder	$V = \pi r^2 h$	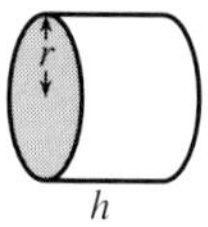
	Triangular prism	$V = \frac{1}{2}bhl$	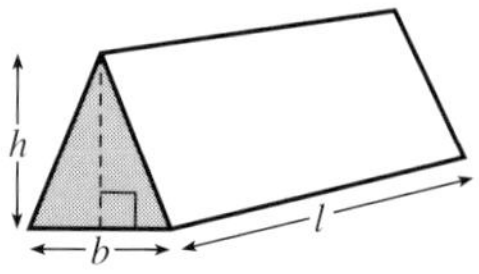
Solid which comes to a point			
$V = \frac{1}{3} \times$ base area $\times$ height	Cone	$V = \frac{1}{3}\pi r^2 h$	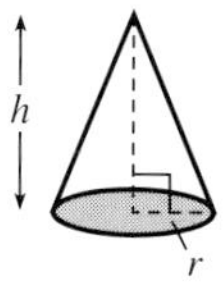
	Square-based pyramid	$V = \frac{1}{3}a^2 h$	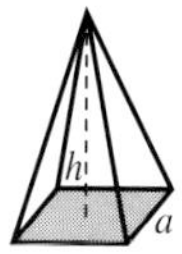
Sphere		$V = \frac{4}{3}\pi r^3$	

The dimension of a formula

Formulae contain letters for unknown lengths, for example, r, h and l and numbers, for example 2, π and $\sin C$.

- **Formulae for length**, such as $2\pi r$, contain a single letter (in this case r) for an unknown length.
- **Formulae for area**, such as $\frac{1}{2}ab\sin C$, contain a product of two letters (in this case a and b) for unknown lengths. ($\sin C$ is a ratio and has no dimension.)
- **Formulae for volume**, such as $\frac{1}{3}\pi r^2 h$, contain a product of three letters (in this case $r^2 h$) for unknown lengths.

Example 5

A solid cylinder, radius r cm, has volume 10 cm³. If S cm² is the total surface area of the cylinder, show that

$$S = 2\pi r^2 + \frac{20}{r}$$

Let h cm be the height of the cylinder.

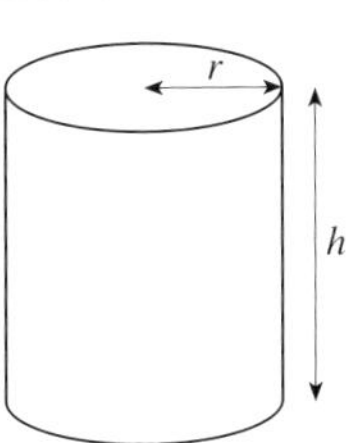

The surface area comprises two circles, (top and bottom, each of area πr^2) and the curved area, which, when opened out, would be a rectangle of area $2\pi r \times h$.

① contains r and h, whereas what is to be shown contains only r.

$$S = 2\pi r^2 + 2\pi rh \qquad ①$$

Now $\quad \pi r^2 h = 10$

Use the fact that the volume is 10cm³ to link r and h.

so $\quad h = \dfrac{10}{\pi r^2} \qquad ②$

To eliminate h, rearrange $\pi r^2 h = 10$ to give h in terms of r and substitute in ①.

Substituting ② into ① gives

$$S = 2\pi r^2 + 2\pi r \times \frac{10}{\pi r^2}$$
$$= 2\pi r^2 + \frac{20}{r}$$

EXERCISE 14a

Exercise 14a has numerical examples only. To avoid rounding errors, use full calculator values throughout.

1 Find these volumes.

a A cylinder of radius 4 cm and height 2.5 cm, correct to the nearest cm³

b A cone of base radius 12.1 cm and height 19 cm, correct to the nearest 10 cm³

c A sphere of radius 6370 km, in standard form correct to 3 significant figures

d A triangular prism of length 12 cm and cross-section an equilateral triangle of side 2 cm, giving the exact answer

e A cylinder of diameter 5 cm and height 8 cm, leaving π in the answer

The Earth is approximately a sphere of radius 6370 km.

2 A right cone has slant height 6.5 cm and perpendicular height 3.3 cm. Find

a the radius of the base

b the volume, correct to the nearest cm³.

EXERCISE 14a
(continued)

3 A sector of a circle of radius 10 cm has angle 130°. The sector is formed into a hollow cone with the arc AB forming the circumference of the base of the cone.

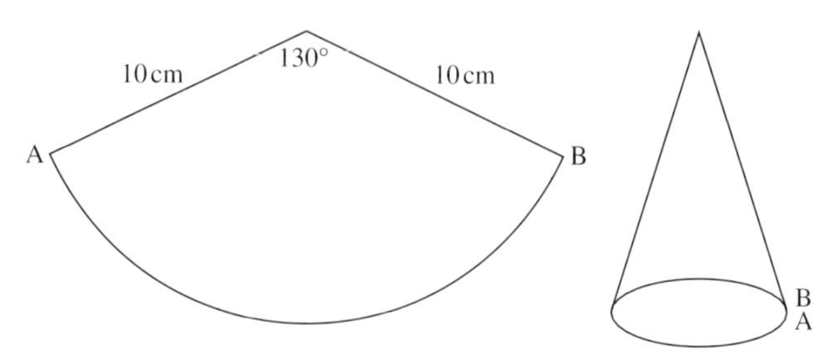

Find, correct to 3 significant figures

a the length of the arc AB

b the radius of the base of the cone

c the volume of the cone.

4 The cross-sectional area A of a pipe is the area between two concentric circles of radii R and r, $R > r$.

a Show that $A = \pi(R + r)(R - r)$.

b Find the volume of metal, in m^3, correct to 2 decimal places, in a pipe of length 25 m, where $R = 6.5$ cm and $r = 3.5$ cm.

5 All the triangles shown are similar either to triangle A or to triangle B.

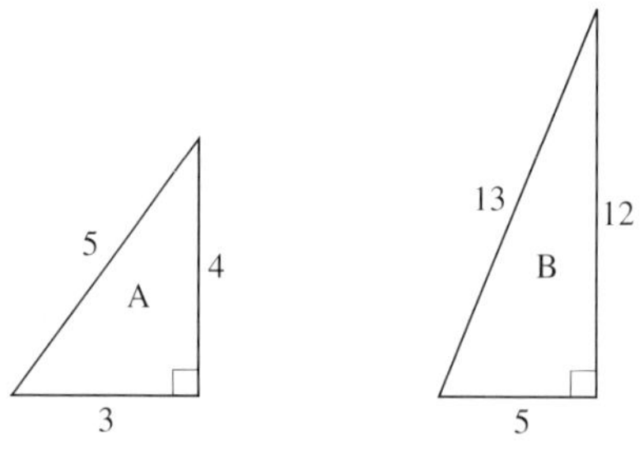

By considering HCFs, or otherwise, find, in each case, whether the triangles are similar to triangle A or to triangle B, and the value of x.

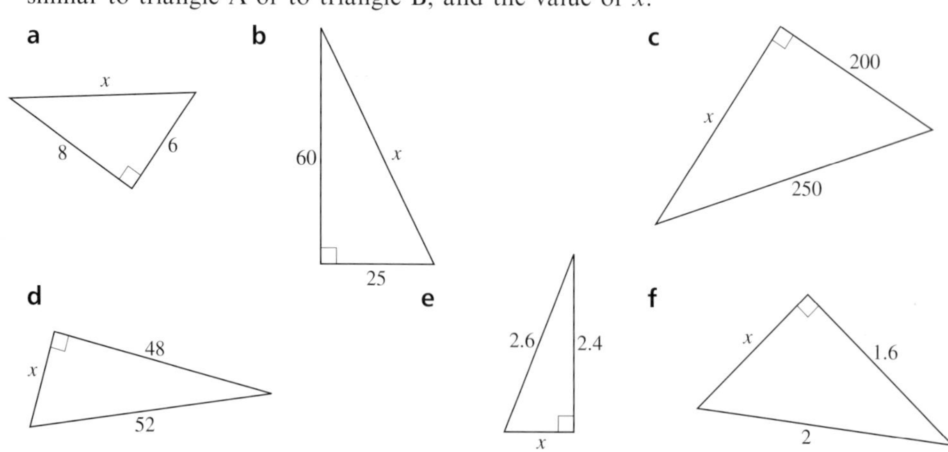

6 The model of a statue is $\frac{1}{12}$th full size.

a Suppose that the model and the statue are made from the same material and that the model has a mass of 1.5 kg. Find the mass of the statue.

b In fact, the statue is made of stone, 3.2 times as dense as the plaster of the model. Find the mass of the statue.

(Give answers in standard form.)

7 A plank AD is lying against a log of circular cross-section of radius 1 m as shown.

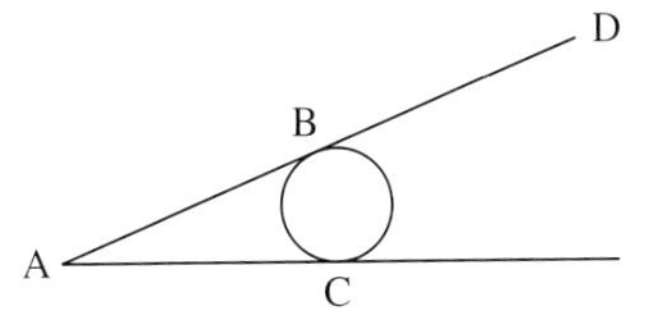

Given that AC = 5 m, find the height of B above the ground.

8 A bottle 14 inches high contains 4 pints of liquid when full.
A similar bottle, when full, contains half a pint.

a Calculate the height of the second bottle.

b Given that the surface area of the second bottle is 60 sq. in., calculate the surface area of the first bottle.

9 A sector of a circle of radius 1 m is to be folded to make a pointed witch's hat. Find the angle of the sector, correct to the nearest degree, given that the circumference of the hat is to be 50 cm.

10 Two designs, to be made of metal, are constructed entirely from semicircles. Find, for each design, in terms of π, the area and the perimeter.

a

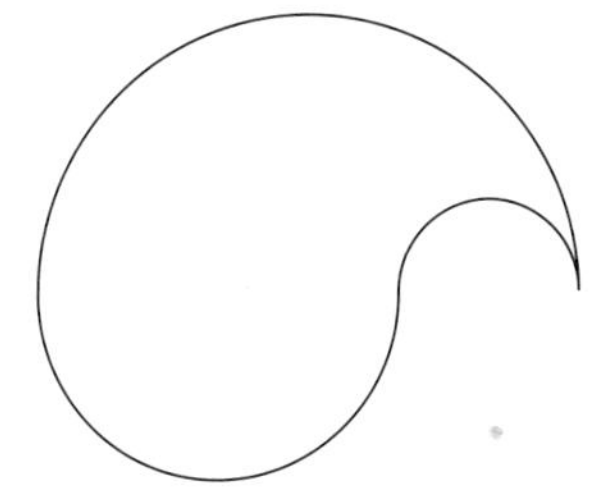

The two smaller circles have radii 7 cm and 14 cm.

b

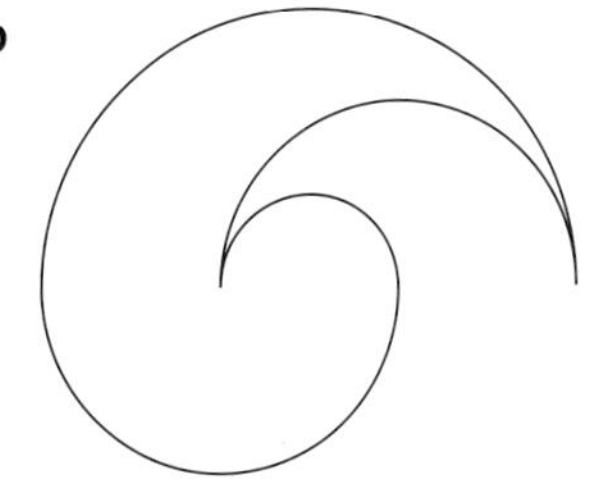

The circles have radii 2.1cm, 1.4 cm and 0.7 cm.

11 Television screens are rectangular with sides in the ratio 4:3 (standard) or 16:9 (wide screen).
The size of a television is defined by the length of the diagonal of the screen.
Find

a the dimensions of a 21-inch standard screen and of a 28-inch standard screen

b the dimensions of a 42-inch wide screen and of a 50-inch wide screen

c what fraction of the screen contains no picture when a wide screen film is shown on a standard screen

d what fraction of the screen contains no picture when a standard screen film is shown on a wide screen.

EXERCISE 14a *(continued)*

12 The points O, A, B and C have coordinates (0, 0), (0, 4), (14, 21) and (9, 0) respectively.
Show that the ratio of the area of triangle OAB to triangle OBC is 8:27.

13 The line $y = mx$ divides the triangle with vertices (0, 0), (12, 3) and (2, 7) into two equal areas. Find m.

14 **a** Find the number of sides of a regular polygon whose *exterior* angles are each 10°.

b Find the number of sides of a regular polygon whose *interior* angles are each 140°.

c By joining the vertices of a regular octagon to the centre of the octagon, or otherwise, find the area, correct to 3 significant figures, of a regular octagon with side 4 cm.

d Find the area, correct to 3 significant figures, of a regular octagon inscribed in a circle of radius 4 cm.

15 Triangle ABC is isosceles with AC = BC = 13 and AB = 10. M and N are the feet of the perpendiculars from A and B to BC and AC respectively.

a Find the area of triangle ABC.

b Explain why BC × AM = AC × BN.

c Find BN.

16 A chord of a circle AB of length 20 cm intersects a radius OC at D. OC and AB are perpendicular, CD = 2 cm and the circle has radius r cm.

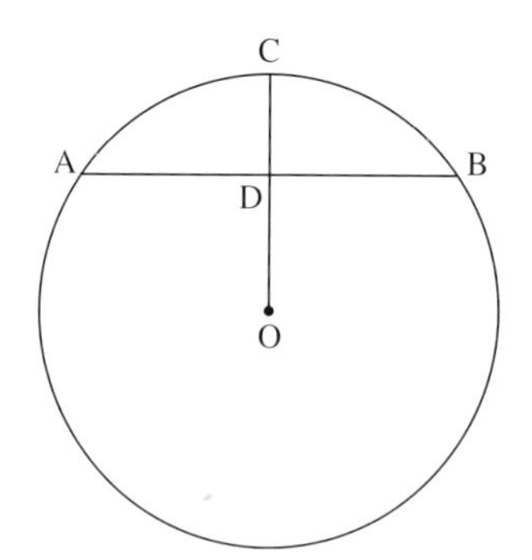

a Write down an expression for OD in terms of r.

b Form an equation in r and solve it to find the radius of the circle.

c Find angle DOB.

d Find the area of sector AOB.

e Find the area of segment ACB.

17 A cone of base radius 6 cm and height 12 cm is cut by a plane parallel to the base and 9 cm from the base.

a Explain why the cone cut off is similar to the original cone.

b Express the ratio of the volumes of the cone cut off to the original cone in the form $1:n$.

c Hence find the volume of the cone cut off and the volume of the frustum remaining. (Leave π in the answer.)

EXERCISE 14b

This exercise has examples using algebra.

1 Find an expression for these volumes.

a A cylinder of radius x and height $3x$

b A cone of base radius y and height $\frac{y}{2}$

c A cone of base radius r and slant height $\sqrt{3}r$

2 Find an expression for the total surface area of these.

a A solid cylinder of radius x and length y

b A cuboid of square cross-section and length l whose volume is V

3 A right cone has slant height l and vertical height h.

a Find an expression for its volume in terms of l and h.

b Given that $l = \sqrt{2}h$ and that the volume is 72π, find h.

4 An equilateral triangle has side $2x$. Find an expression for its area.

5 The length of the diagonal of a square is y. Find the length of a side.

6 A rectangle, x cm by y cm, has perimeter 60 cm and area $A\ \text{cm}^2$.

a Find an expression connecting x and y.

b Express A in terms of x.

7 A cuboid of volume $V\ \text{cm}^3$ has a square cross-section of side x cm.
The total length of all its edges is 90 cm. Express V in terms of x.

8 A cylinder, of radius r, is topped by a hemisphere. The total height is h.
Show that the volume V is given by

$$V = \frac{\pi r^2}{3}(3h - r)$$

9 In the diagram, AC is a diameter of a circle radius r and BD is perpendicular to AC.

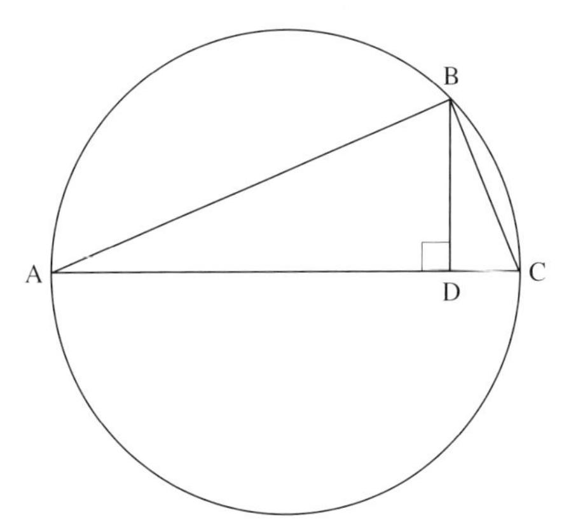

a Show that triangles ABC, ADB and BDC are similar

b Given that $\text{BC} = \frac{1}{2}r$, show that AD:DC = 15:1.

EXERCISE 14b
(continued)

10 A wine glass has the shape of a right circular cone. When full it holds x ml of wine and the depth is d cm. Find the depth of wine when the glass is only half full.

11 A cylinder with radius r cm and height h cm can hold 100π ml of liquid.

a Express r in terms of h.

b Express h in terms of r.

c Given that the cylinder is open and that its external surface area is $S\,\text{cm}^2$, show that

$$S = \frac{\pi}{r}(200 + r^3)$$

12 A piece of wire of length 48 cm is cut into two and formed into a square of side x cm and a rectangle x cm by y cm. Given that the total area of the two figures is $70\,\text{cm}^2$, find possible values for x and y.

13 Nine solid metal spheres of radius r and eighteen solid metal cones of base radius r and height $\frac{1}{3}r$ are melted down and the metal formed into solid cylinders of radius r and length $2r$.
Find the number of cylinders that can be formed.

14 An isosceles triangle has sides x cm, x cm and $2y$ cm, perimeter 32 cm and area $A\,\text{cm}^2$. Show that

a $x + y = 16$

b $A = y\sqrt{x^2 - y^2}$

c $A = 4(16 - x)\sqrt{2(x - 8)}$

15 The frames of a cube of side x cm and a cuboid x cm by x cm by y cm are made from a length of wire 96 cm long. The total volume of the cube and cuboid is $108\,\text{cm}^3$. Find x and y.

EXERCISE 14c
(Extension)

1 a A spotlight of radius 6 cm, 10 m above a stage, is emitting light as shown. The angle of the light to the vertical, as it emerges from the spotlight, is 1°. Calculate the radius of the circle of light on the stage.

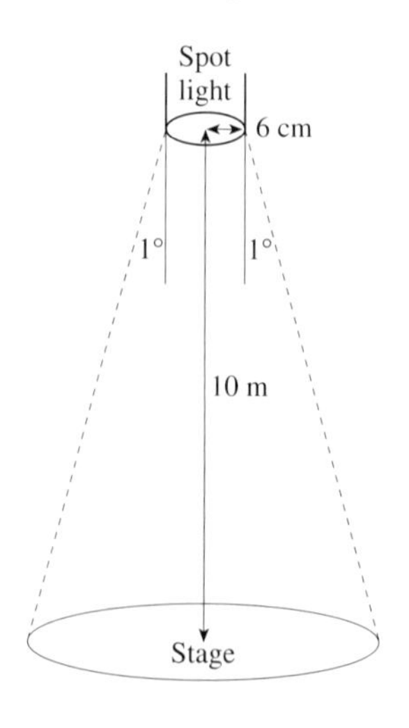

b A similar spotlight of radius r cm is h m above a stage. The angle of the light to the vertical is $x°$.

Find a formula for the radius R m of the circle of light on the stage.

Produce a spreadsheet for a lighting designer to give values of R for different values of r, x and h.

2 A graphics calculator has a screen of dimensions 6.2 cm by 3.8 cm.

a Find the ratio of the sides in the form $m{:}n$, where m and n are integers.

b A student wishes to draw a graph of a function with equal scales on each axis. He enters

X MIN −5

X MAX +5

Y MIN −4

What value should he enter for Y MAX so that the scales will be the same?

3 Two doorways of a cathedral are both 4.1m wide.

The first, ABCDE, has a semicircular arch with its centre at the mid-point of BD.

The second, JKLMN, has a Gothic arch consisting of circular arcs with their centres at K and M and radii 4.1m.

The verticals AB, DE, JK and MN are all the same height.

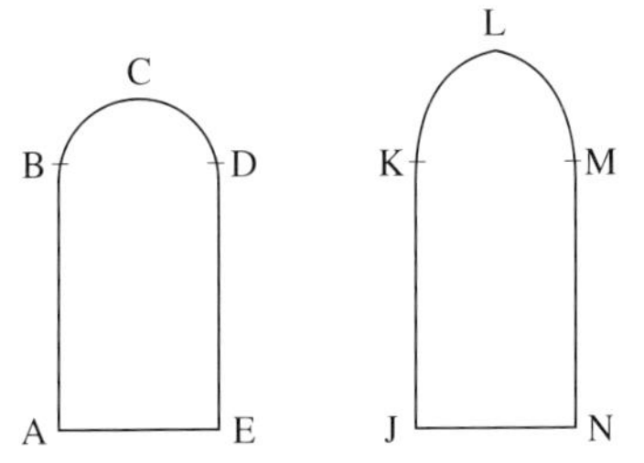

Show that, at their highest points, the Gothic arch is almost exactly 1.5 m higher than the semicircular arch.

4 The base of a tower is a regular heptagon with side 5 m.

Find its floor area, correct to the nearest square metre.

5 A circle is inscribed in a right-angled triangle.

Prove that the diameter is equal to the difference between the perimeter of the triangle and twice the hypotenuse.

EXERCISE 14c
(continued)

6 Triangle B_0AB_1 is right-angled at B_1, $AB_1 = 12$ and $B_0B_1 = 5$.

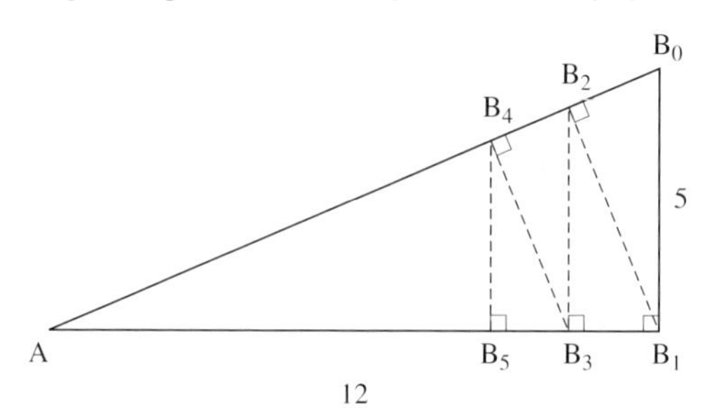

A sequence of right-angled triangles is formed:

$\Delta B_0B_1B_2$, $\Delta B_1B_2B_3$, $\Delta B_2B_3B_4$, $\Delta B_3B_4B_5$ and so on.

a Explain why all the triangles in the sequence are similar to each other and to ΔB_0AB_1.

b Find the lengths of B_1B_2, B_2B_3 and B_3B_4.

c Show that $B_0B_1 + B_1B_2 + B_2B_3 + B_3B_4 + \cdots$ is a geometric series.

d Find $\sum_{i=0}^{\infty} B_iB_{i+1}$.

7 An infinite spiral is formed as follows:
A square is divided in quarters and a quarter-circle drawn in one of the quarters.
The process is repeated, as shown in the diagram.

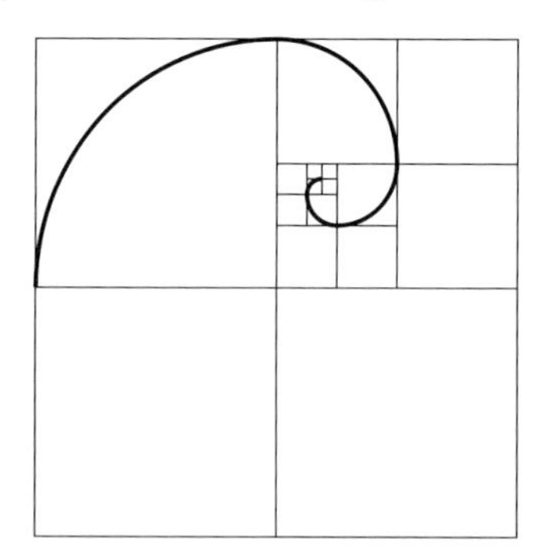

Show that, starting with a square of side 2, the length of the spiral will tend to π.

Test yourself

1 The ratio of the surface areas of two spheres is 1 : 4.

If the smaller has a radius of 2 cm, the volume of the larger is

A $\frac{2048}{3}\pi\,\text{cm}^3$ **B** $\frac{256}{3}\pi\,\text{cm}^3$ **C** $\frac{32}{3}\pi\,\text{cm}^3$ **D** $64\pi\,\text{cm}^3$ **E** $\frac{4}{3}\pi\,\text{cm}^3$

2 In triangles ABC, PQR angle A = angle P, angle B = angle Q, PQ = 6 cm, AB = 8 cm and BC = 7 cm.

QR =

A $9\frac{1}{3}$ cm **B** 5 cm **C** $6\frac{6}{7}$ cm **D** $5\frac{1}{4}$ cm

E not able to be found without more information

3 The tangents to a circle centre O, radius 5, from a point P meet the circle at A and B. PA = PB = 12.

The area of sector AOB is approximately

A 14.7 **B** 10.7 **C** 9.9 **D** 19.6 **E** 29.4

4 The points A, B and C lie on a circle, radius 7 cm. Triangle ABC is right-angled at A and angle B = 40°.

The length of AC is

A 7 cm **B** 14 cos 40° cm **C** 14 tan 40° cm **D** 14 cos 50° cm

E not able to be found without more information

5 A cone has volume $48\pi\,\text{cm}^3$.

If its base radius is 6 cm, its height is

A 4 cm **B** 24 cm **C** 8 cm **D** $2\sqrt{6}$ cm **E** $\frac{4}{3}$ cm

6 AB is a chord of length 12 cm of a circle centre O. Angle AOB = 80°.

The distance of O from AB is

A $\frac{6}{\tan 50^\circ}$ cm **B** 6 tan 40° cm **C** 6 sin 50° cm

D 6 tan 50° cm **E** 12 sin 50° cm

7 Two parallel chords, AB and CD, of a circle are 6 cm and 8 cm from the centre respectively.

The ratio AB : CD is

A 3:4 **B** 4:3 **C** 3:5 **D** 5:3

E not able to be found without more information

➤➤➤ Key points

Circles

Useful properties of a circle:

- The angle in a semicircle is a right angle.
- The perpendicular from the centre to a chord bisects the chord.
- A tangent is perpendicular to the radius through the point of contact.

Similarity, ratio and proportion

Being **similar**, in mathematics, means having the same shape, although not usually the same size.
If the shape and the size are the same, the figures (2D) or solids (3D) are said to be **congruent**.

Similar figures or solids have

- angles which are equal
- all corresponding lengths multiplied by scale factor k
- all corresponding areas multiplied by scale factor k^2
- all corresponding volumes multiplied by scale factor k^3.

Volume

Volume of a cone $= \frac{1}{3}\pi r^2 h$

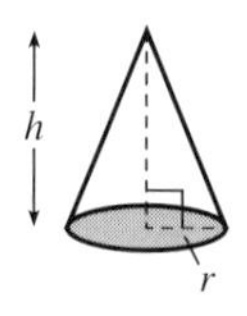

Volume of a sphere $= \frac{4}{3}\pi r^3$

15 Trigonometry

Before starting this chapter you will need to know

- about trigonometrical ratios ($\sin\theta$, $\cos\theta$ and $\tan\theta$) (Chapter 14)
- about transformations of graphs (Chapter 7).

A calculator or computer may be used for checking sketches and to become familiar with the power of the technology. It is important to understand the techniques of curve sketching with and without technological aids.

15.1 Radians

Angles can be measured in various units such as degrees, radians, right angles.

One complete turn $= 360^\circ =$ four right angles $= 2\pi$ radians

Radian measure is essential in higher level mathematics, particularly for calculus.

Definition of a radian

An arc of length r on a circle of radius r subtends an angle of 1 radian at the centre of the circle. So, if arc length, r, subtends 1 radian, the circumference, $2\pi r$, subtends 2π radians.

So $360^\circ = 2\pi$ rad

$$\pi \text{ rad} = 180^\circ$$

$$1 \text{ rad} = \frac{180^\circ}{\pi} \approx 57.3^\circ$$

$$1^\circ = \frac{\pi}{180} \text{ rad}$$

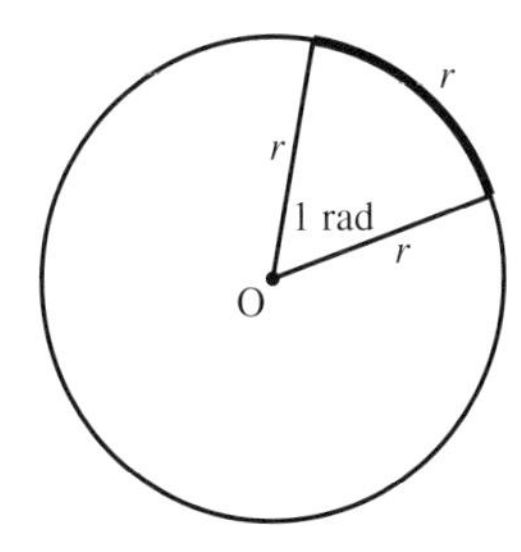

Converting radians to degrees

Using π rad $= 180^\circ$, simple fractions and multiples of π can easily be converted to degrees.

$\frac{\pi}{2}$ rad $= \frac{1}{2} \times 180^\circ = 90^\circ$

$\frac{\pi}{3}$ rad $= \frac{1}{3} \times 180^\circ = 60^\circ$

$\frac{\pi}{4}$ rad $= 45^\circ$

$\frac{\pi}{6}$ rad $= 30^\circ$

3π rad $= 540^\circ$

Example 1 Convert $\frac{7\pi}{15}$ rad to degrees.

$$1 \text{ rad} = \frac{180^\circ}{\pi}$$

$$\therefore \quad \frac{7\pi}{15} \text{ rad} = \frac{7\pi}{15} \times \frac{180^\circ}{\pi}$$

$$= 84^\circ$$

Converting degrees to radians

Some angles can easily be expressed as fractions or multiples of 180° ($= \pi$ rad).

$30^\circ = \frac{1}{6} \times 180^\circ = \frac{\pi}{6}$ rad $\qquad 150^\circ = \frac{5}{6} \times 180^\circ = \frac{5}{6}\pi$ rad $\qquad 720^\circ = 4\pi$ rad

Example 2 Convert 48° to radians.

$$1^\circ = \frac{\pi}{180} \text{ rad}$$

$$\therefore \quad 48^\circ = 48 \times \frac{\pi}{180} \text{ rad}$$

$$= \frac{4\pi}{15} \text{ rad}$$

15.2 Angles of any size

The x and y axes divide the plane into four quadrants.

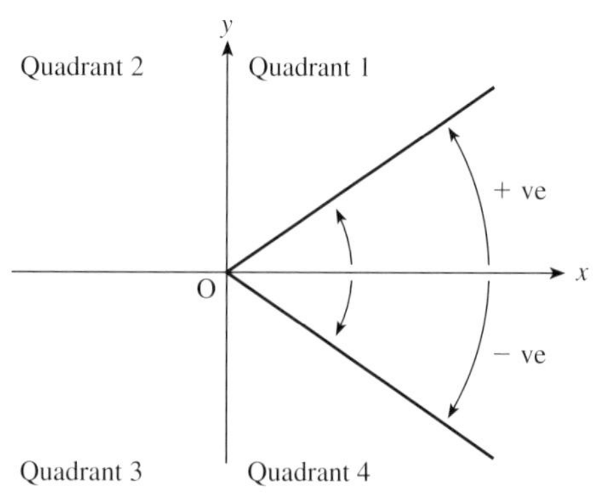

Angles are measured from Ox:

- Positive in an anticlockwise direction
- Negative in a clockwise direction

An angle can be of any size, positive or negative.
Elementary geometry and trigonometry deal with relatively small angles, usually less than 360°. There are many situations, however, which involve large angles. For example, think of the minute hand of a clock. In a year, it turns through 3153 600 degrees.

Example 3 In which quadrant would an angle of 560° terminate?

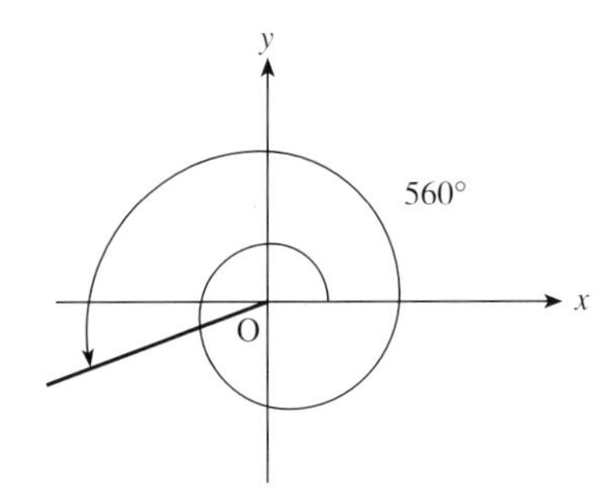

$560^\circ = 360^\circ + 200^\circ$

560° is one complete turn plus 200° anticlockwise.
This would terminate in quadrant 3.

EXERCISE 15a

In this exercise, remember that π radians $= 180^\circ$.

1 Copy and complete this table.

Degrees	30	45			120	**180**	360
Radians			$\frac{\pi}{3}$	$\frac{\pi}{2}$		$\boldsymbol{\pi}$	

2 Convert to degrees

a $\frac{\pi}{2}$ rad **b** $\frac{\pi}{4}$ rad **c** $\frac{\pi}{3}$ rad **d** $\frac{2\pi}{3}$ rad
e $\frac{\pi}{6}$ rad **f** $\frac{3\pi}{2}$ rad **g** $\frac{5\pi}{2}$ rad **h** 4π rad
i 5π rad **j** $\frac{4\pi}{3}$ rad **k** $\frac{7\pi}{2}$ rad **l** $\frac{3\pi}{4}$ rad

3 Convert to radians, leaving π in your answer

a 360° **b** 90° **c** 45° **d** 15°
e 60° **f** 120° **g** 300° **h** 270°
i 540° **j** 30° **k** 150° **l** 450°

4 In which quadrants do these angles terminate?

a 100° **b** $\frac{\pi}{3}$ **c** 70° **d** 190°
e $\frac{5\pi}{4}$ **f** $-\frac{5\pi}{6}$ **g** $-\frac{3\pi}{4}$ **h** $\frac{2\pi}{3}$
i 330° **j** -80° **k** 1000° **l** -140°

15.3 Trigonometrical ratios for any angle

Consider a line segment, OP′, of length r, lying along the positive direction of the x-axis.

Let OP′ rotate through θ to OP and let P have coordinates (x, y).

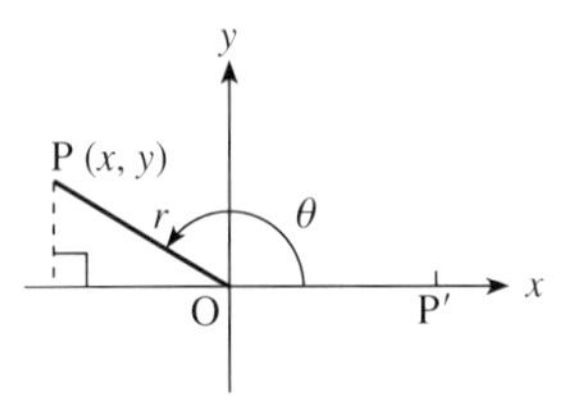

Three ratios are defined

$$\sin\theta = \frac{y}{r} \qquad \cos\theta = \frac{x}{r} \qquad \tan\theta = \frac{y}{x} \qquad x \neq 0$$

and their reciprocals

$$\operatorname{cosec}\theta = \frac{1}{\sin\theta} \qquad \sec\theta = \frac{1}{\cos\theta} \qquad \cot\theta = \frac{1}{\tan\theta} = \frac{\cos\theta}{\sin\theta}$$

The full names for these reciprocals are cosecant, secant and cotangent.

✓ ***Note*** $\tan\theta = \dfrac{\sin\theta}{\cos\theta}$ and $\cot\theta = \dfrac{\cos\theta}{\sin\theta}$

Since the coordinates, x and y, will sometimes be positive, sometimes negative, the signs of the ratios will also vary. The length, r, is always positive.

To find the trigonometrical ratio for any angle it is necessary to find its sign, and its magnitude.

To determine the sign of any trigonometrical ratio

By considering the signs of the x and y coordinates in each quadrant, and remembering that the length, r, is always positive, the signs of $\sin\theta$, $\cos\theta$ and $\tan\theta$ can be found.

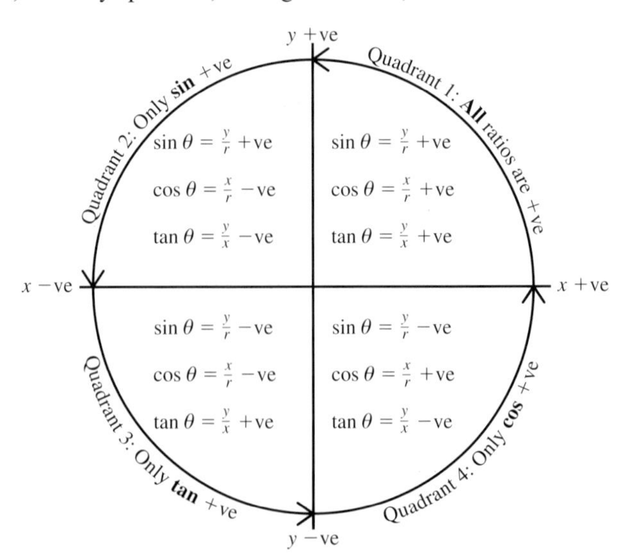

✓ ***Note*** To remember in which quadrants ratios are positive, one mnemonic is

All **S**illy **T**om **C**ats

S	A
T	C

The signs of cosec θ, sec θ and cot θ are the same as the signs of their reciprocals.

To determine the magnitude of any trigonometrical ratio

The magnitude for a ratio of an angle of any size can always be linked to the ratio of an *acute* angle: the acute equivalent angle.

Example 4 Express given ratios, in terms of trigonometrical ratios of an acute angle.

a $\cos 122° = \frac{x}{r}$

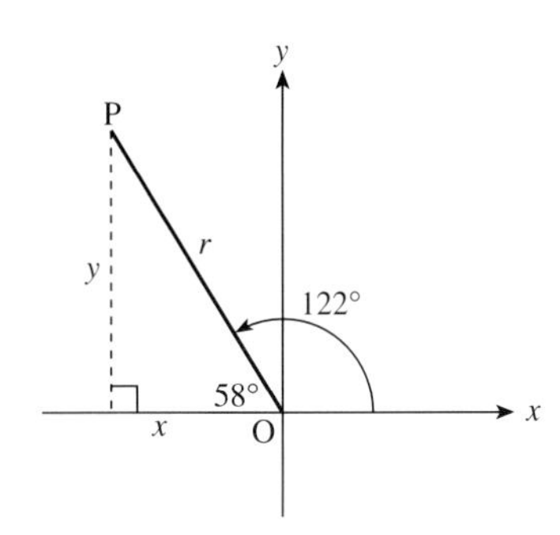

The numerical value of $\frac{x}{r}$ (ignoring the sign) will be the same as for $180° - 122° = 58°$.

122° is in quadrant 2 $\therefore$ cos 122° is −ve.

So, $\cos 122° = -\cos 58°$.

b $\tan 560° = \frac{y}{x}$

560° is one complete turn (360°) plus 200°. 560° − 360° = 200°.

The numerical value of $\frac{y}{x}$ (ignoring the sign) will be the same as for $200° - 180° = 20°$.

The angle is in quadrant 3 $\therefore$ tan 560° is +ve.

So, $\tan 560° = \tan 20°$.

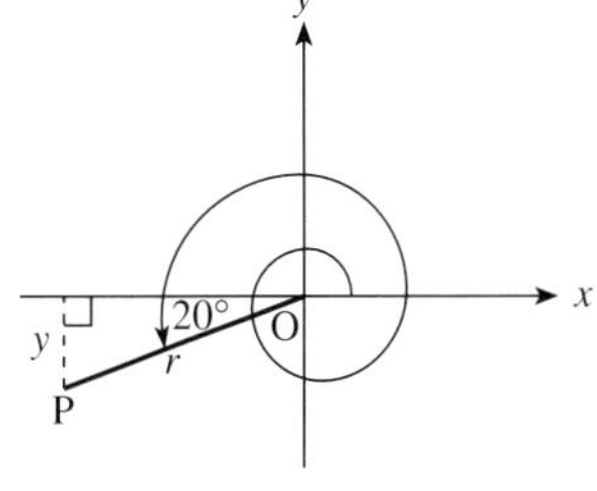

c $\sin(-70°) = \frac{y}{r}$

The numerical value of $\frac{y}{r}$ (ignoring the sign) will be the same as for 70°.

The angle is in quadrant 4 $\therefore$ sin(−70°) is −ve.

So, $\sin(-70°) = -\sin 70°$.

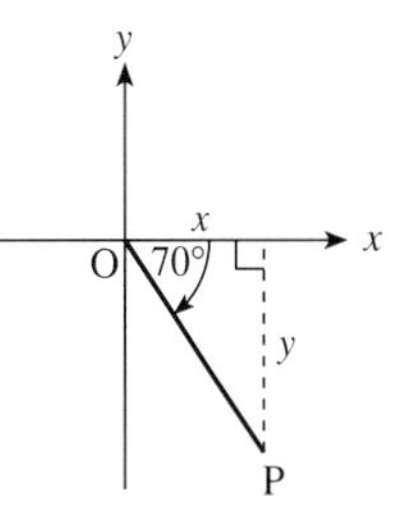

✓ ***Note*** In each of the above examples, a line is drawn from P perpendicular to the x-axis.

➤ To link the ratio for any angle with its acute equivalent angle:

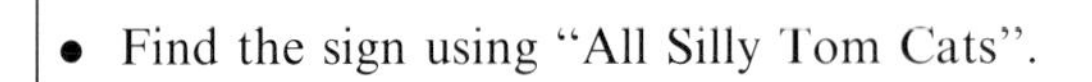

- Find the sign using "All Silly Tom Cats".

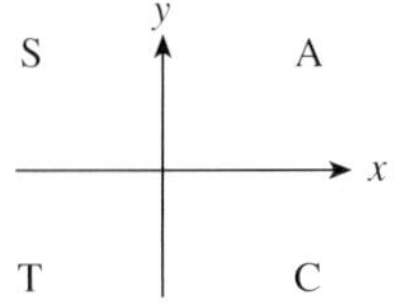

- Find the acute equivalent angle by rotating through the given angle to OP, drawing the perpendicular from P to the x-axis.

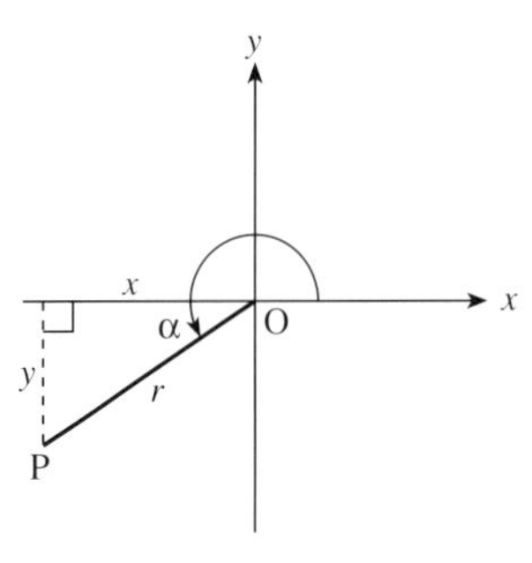

The acute equivalent angle, α, is the angle between OP and the x-axis.

A quick method for tackling examples is to think 'Which quadrant?' and 'How far from the x-axis?'

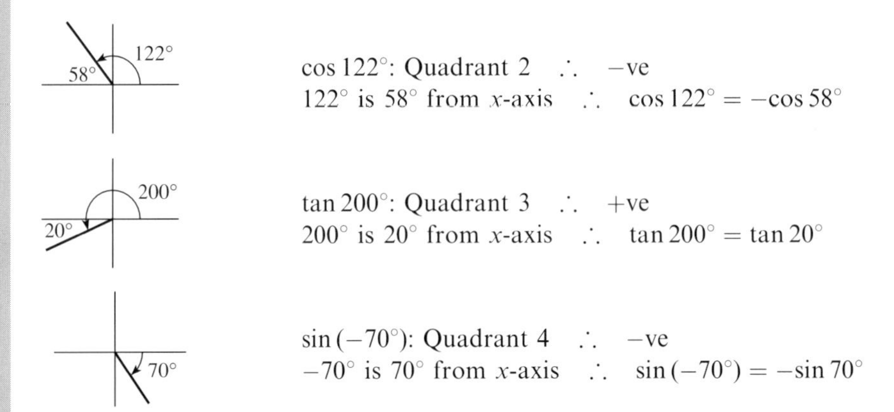

$\cos 122°$: Quadrant 2 $\therefore$ $-$ve
$122°$ is $58°$ from x-axis $\therefore$ $\cos 122° = -\cos 58°$

$\tan 200°$: Quadrant 3 $\therefore$ $+$ve
$200°$ is $20°$ from x-axis $\therefore$ $\tan 200° = \tan 20°$

$\sin(-70°)$: Quadrant 4 $\therefore$ $-$ve
$-70°$ is $70°$ from x-axis $\therefore$ $\sin(-70°) = -\sin 70°$

For every acute angle there are four angles between 0° and 360° with the same numerical ratio.

Two will be positive, two negative. For example,

$$\sin 37° = \sin(180° - 37°) = \sin 143°$$
$$= -\sin(180° + 37°) = -\sin 217°$$
$$= -\sin(360° - 37°) = -\sin 323°$$

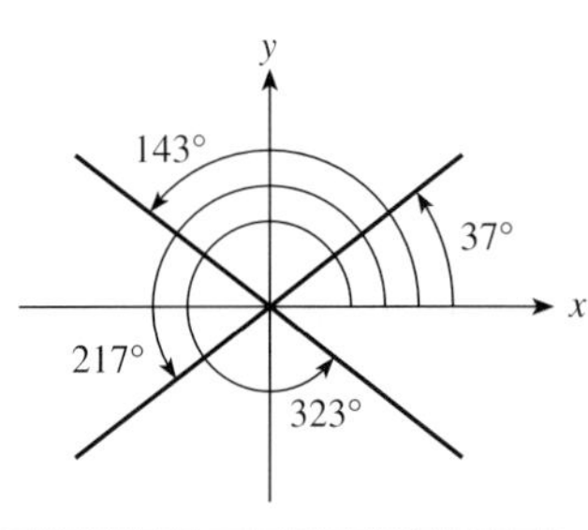

Each angle is 37° from the x-axis.

Special cases

For $\theta = 0°$, P has coordinates $(r, 0)$. So

$$\sin\theta = \frac{0}{r} = 0 \qquad \cos\theta = \frac{r}{r} = 1 \qquad \tan\theta = \frac{0}{r} = 0$$

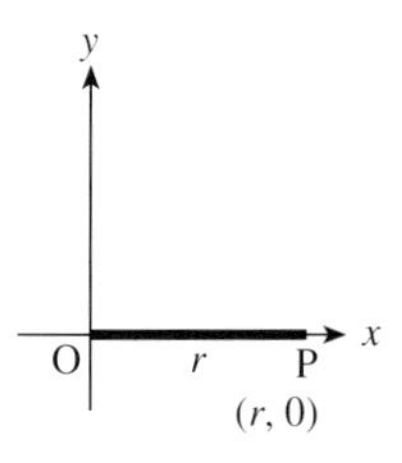

For $\theta = 90°$, P has coordinates $(0, r)$. So

$$\sin\theta = \frac{r}{r} = 1 \qquad \cos\theta = \frac{0}{r} = 0$$

$\tan 90°$ is not defined because division by zero is not defined.

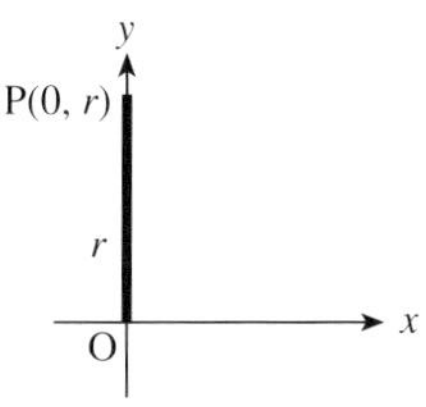

15.4 Graphs of trigonometrical functions

Plotting graphs of $\sin\theta$, $\cos\theta$ and $\tan\theta$ shows clearly how the functions vary.

Using the definition

$$\sin\theta = \frac{y}{r} \quad \text{and} \quad \cos\theta = \frac{x}{r}$$

and taking a circle of unit radius so that $r = 1$ gives $\sin\theta = y$ and $\cos\theta = x$. Then rotating OP through θ and plotting the y coordinate of P for each value of θ gives the sine curve.

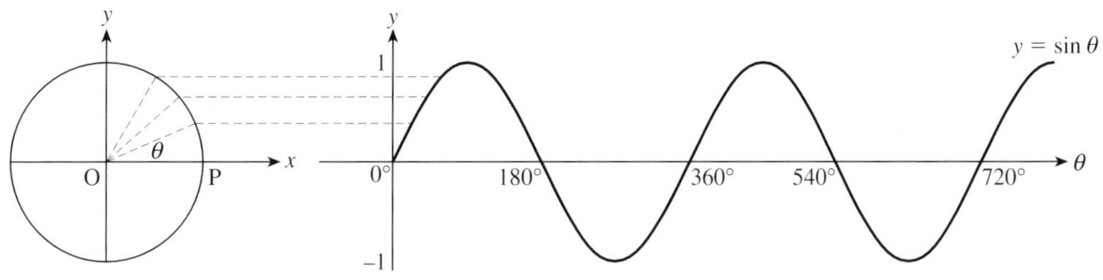

The graph repeats itself after 360°. The function $\sin\theta$ is periodic of period 360°.

The graph of $\cos\theta$ may be drawn in a similar way. It also has period 360°.

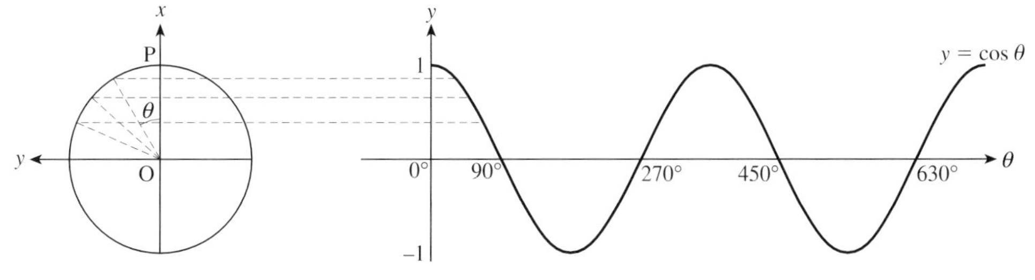

Since $\cos\theta = x$ the axes should be rotated through 90°. Rotating OP through θ and plotting the x coordinate for each value of θ gives the cosine curve.

✓ ***Note*** The sine and cosine curves are translations of each other.

For the graph of $\tan\theta$ the tangent at (1, 0) is drawn to the unit circle and OP is extended to meet the tangent at Q.
The y coordinate at Q is equal to $\tan\theta$.

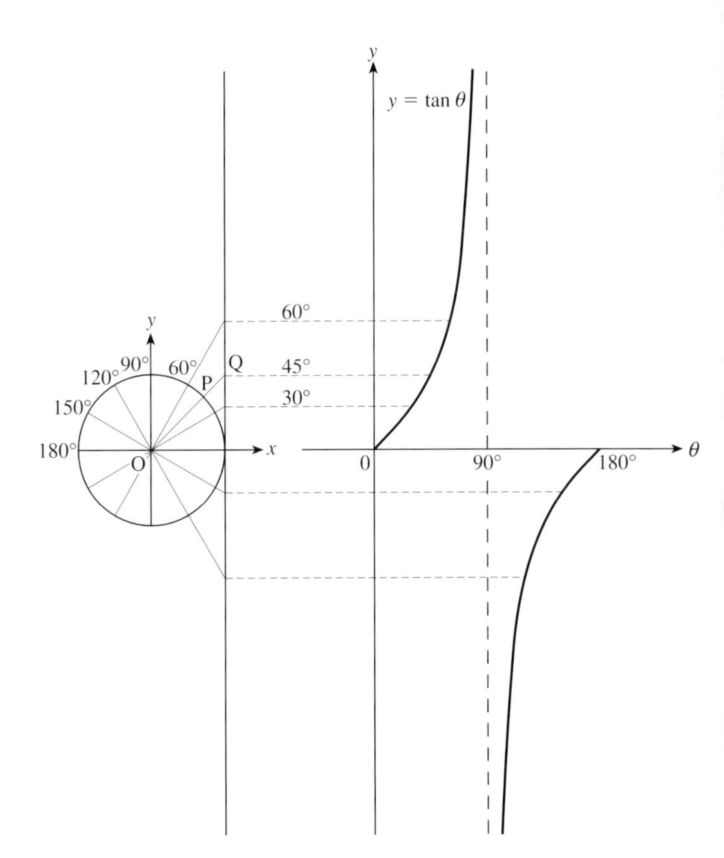

For $\tan\theta$, the period is 180°.

It is important to be familiar with the graphs of $y = \sin\theta$, $y = \cos\theta$ and $y = \tan\theta$.

$y = \sin\theta$

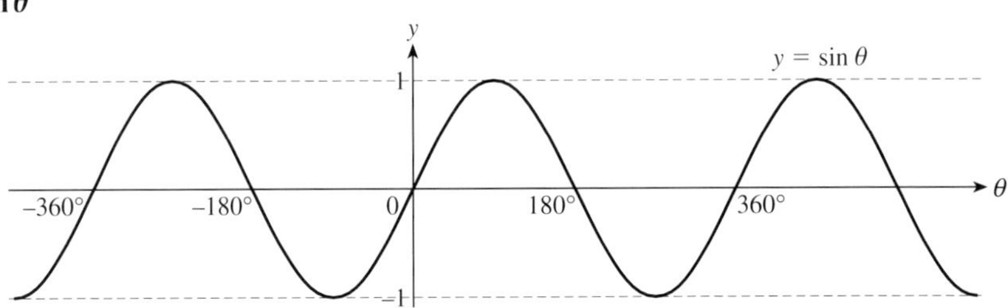

- $\sin 0° = 0$ so the curve passes through the origin.
- Maximum value of $\sin\theta$ is 1.
- Minimum value of $\sin\theta$ is -1.
- Graph repeats every 360° (2π radians) i.e. $\sin\theta$ is periodic of period 360° (2π radians):

  $\sin\theta = \sin(\theta + 360°) = \sin(\theta + 2 \times 360°) = \cdots = \sin(\theta + 360n°)$

  In radians: $\sin\theta = \sin(\theta + 2\pi) = \sin(\theta + 4\pi) = \cdots = \sin(\theta + 2n\pi)$

  $n \in \mathbb{Z}$, i.e. n is an integer.
- $\sin\theta = -\sin(-\theta)$
  $\therefore$ $\sin\theta$ is an odd function. The graph has 180° rotational symmetry about the origin.
- Domain is $\theta \in \mathbb{R}$. Range is $-1 \leqslant y \leqslant 1$.
- $f(\theta) = \sin\theta$ is a many-to-one function.

$y = \cos\theta$

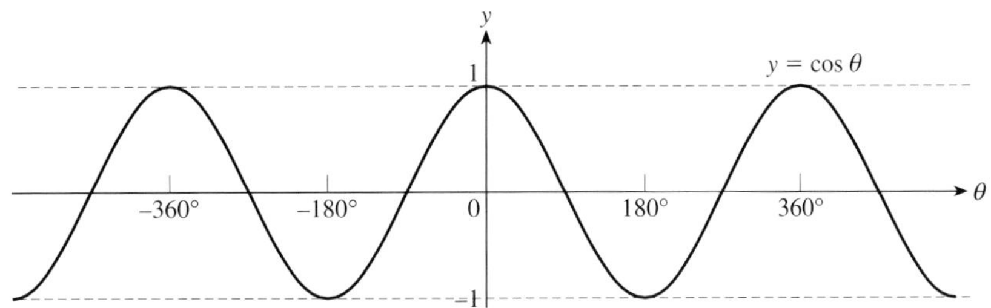

- $\cos 0° = 1$ so the curve cuts the y-axis at (0, 1).
- Maximum value of $\cos\theta$ is 1.
- Minimum value of $\cos\theta$ is -1.
- Graph repeats every 360° (2π radians) i.e. $\cos\theta$ is periodic of period 360° (2π radians):

  $\cos\theta = \cos(\theta + 360°) = \cos(\theta + 2 \times 360°) = \cdots = \cos(\theta + 360n°)$ $\quad n \in \mathbb{Z}$.

  In radians: $\cos\theta = \cos(\theta + 2\pi) = \cos(\theta + 4\pi) = \cdots = \cos(\theta + 2n\pi)$
- $\cos\theta = \cos(-\theta)$
  $\therefore$ $\cos\theta$ is an even function. The graph has the y-axis as an axis of symmetry.
- Domain is $\theta \in \mathbb{R}$. Range is $-1 \leqslant y \leqslant 1$.
- $f(\theta) = \cos\theta$ is a many-to-one function.

$y = \tan\theta$

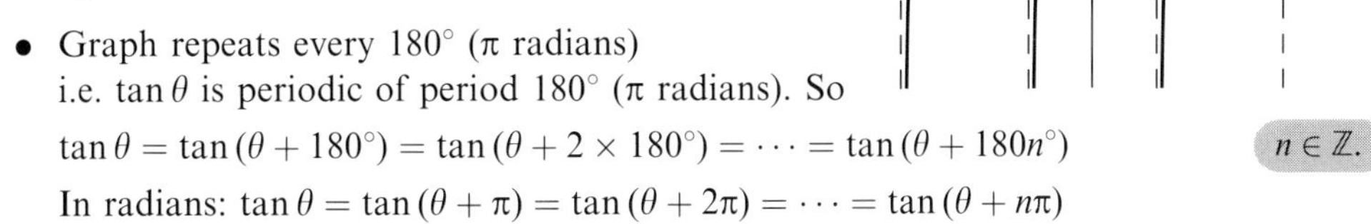

- $\tan 0° = 0$ so curve passes through the origin (0, 0).
- No maximum or minimum values.
- Asymptotes at $\theta = \pm 90°, \pm 270°, \pm 450°, \ldots$
  In radians: $\theta = \pm \frac{1}{2}\pi, \pm \frac{3}{2}\pi, \ldots$
  That is, at all odd multiples of $90°(\frac{1}{2}\pi$ radians).
  This can be summed up by saying:
  asymptotes occur at
  $\theta = (2n + 1)90°$ or $\theta = (2n + 1)\frac{\pi}{2}$.

✓ ***Remember*** $(2n + 1)$, where n is an integer, will give an odd number.

- Graph repeats every 180° (π radians)
  i.e. $\tan\theta$ is periodic of period 180° (π radians). So

  $\tan\theta = \tan(\theta + 180°) = \tan(\theta + 2 \times 180°) = \cdots = \tan(\theta + 180n°)$ $\quad n \in \mathbb{Z}$.

  In radians: $\tan\theta = \tan(\theta + \pi) = \tan(\theta + 2\pi) = \cdots = \tan(\theta + n\pi)$
- $\tan\theta = -\tan(-\theta)$
  $\therefore$ $\tan\theta$ is an odd function.
  The graph has 180° rotational symmetry about the origin.
- Domain is $\theta \in \mathbb{R}$, $\theta \neq (2n + 1)90°$; in radians $\theta \neq (2n + 1)\frac{\pi}{2}$. Range is $y \in \mathbb{R}$.
- $f(\theta) = \tan\theta$ is a many-to-one function.

Example 5

This example illustrates how the graphs can be used to find any number of angles with a particular ratio.

Find three angles with the same trigonometrical ratio as

a $\sin 135°$ **b** $\cos 118°$ **c** $\tan(-37°)$

Solution

a $135°$ is $45°$ from $180°$. Locate 135° on a sketch of the sine graph.

So, by symmetry, $\sin 45°$ has the same value as $\sin 135°$.

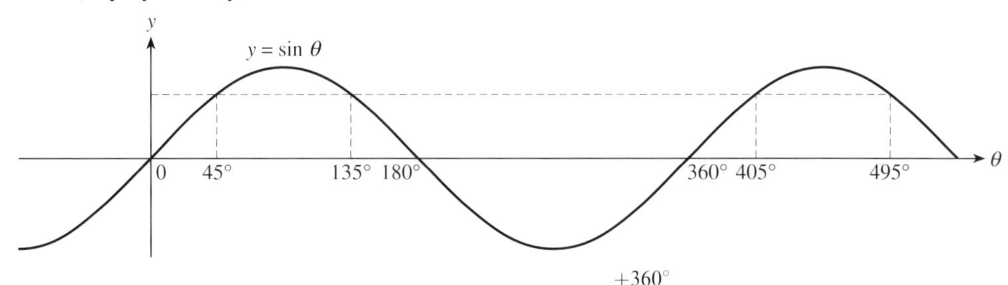

The graph then repeats every $360°$:

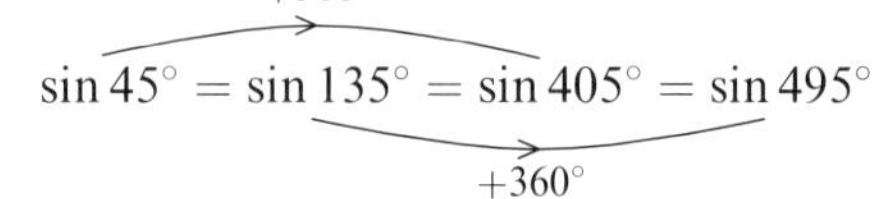

So the sines of $45°$, $135°$, $405°$ and $495°$ all have the same value.

b $118°$ is $28°$ from $90°$. Locate 118° on a sketch of the cosine graph.

By symmetry $\cos(270° - 28°) = \cos 242°$ has the same value as $\cos 118°$.

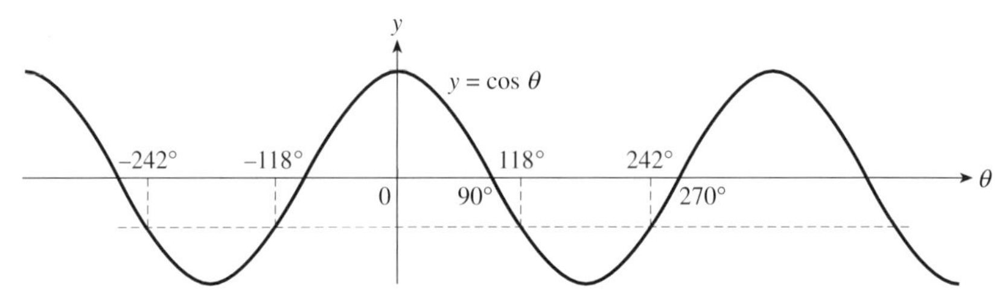

The graph is symmetrical about the y-axis so $\cos(-118°)$ and $\cos(-242°)$ have the same value as $\cos 118°$.

Alternatively, since the graph repeats every $360°$, $360°$ could be subtracted from, or added to, the two values already found.

$\cos(118° - 360°) = \cos(-242°)$ $\qquad$ $\cos(242° - 360°) = \cos(-118°)$

So the cosines of $-242°$, $-118°$, $118°$ and $242°$ all have the same value.

c The tan graph repeats every $180°$. So given one angle, others can be found by adding or subtracting multiples of $180°$. So

$-180°$ $\qquad$ $+180°$ $\qquad$ $+180°$

$\tan(-217°) = \tan(-37°) = \tan 143° = \tan 323°$

So the tangents of $-37°$, $143°$, $-217°$ and $323°$ all have the same value.

✓ ***Note*** By adding or subtracting multiples of the period, an infinite number of possible solutions can be found to questions like those in Example 5.

Transformations of trigonometrical graphs

The graphs of $\sin\theta$, $\cos\theta$ and $\tan\theta$ can be transformed using the methods of Chapter 7.

A graphical calculator or computer package is a great help for studying these transformations and for checking sketches. Try to resist the temptation to use the calculator before attempting a sketch.

Example 6 For given functions, sketch the graphs, state the range, and state the period.

a $y = 4\cos 3x \quad 0° \leqslant x \leqslant 360°$

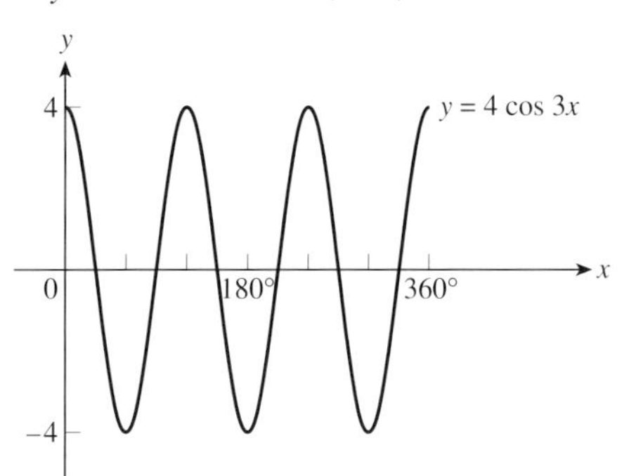

The curve $y = \cos x$ undergoes two stretches with one parallel to each of the axes. (The stretches can be done in either order.)

Stretching $y = \cos x$ parallel to the y-axis, scale factor 4, gives $y = 4\cos x$. Hence the range will be $-4 \leqslant y \leqslant 4$.

Range: $-4 \leqslant y \leqslant 4$

Period: $120°$

Stretching $y = 4\cos x$ parallel to the x-axis, scale factor $\frac{1}{3}$, gives $y = 4\cos 3x$.
The graph is compressed towards the y-axis. Three periods of $y = 4\cos 3x$ fit into one of $y = 4\cos x$. The period of $y = \cos x$ is $360°$, so the period of $y = 4\cos 3x$ is $\frac{360°}{3} = 120°$.

b $y = 1 - \tan\frac{x}{3} \quad -3\pi \leqslant x \leqslant 3\pi \quad x \neq \pm\frac{3\pi}{2}$

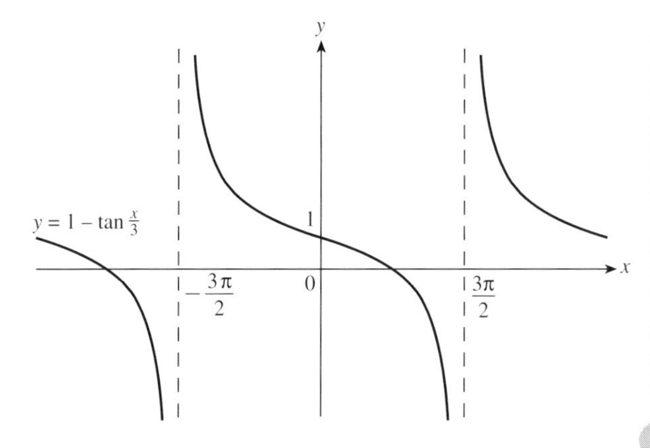

The curve $y = \tan x$ undergoes three transformations (the order is important).

- Stretch parallel to x-axis scale factor 3 gives $y = \tan\frac{x}{3}$.
- Reflection in x-axis gives $y = -\tan\frac{x}{3}$.
- Move 1 unit up, i.e. translation $\binom{0}{1}$ gives $y = 1 - \tan\frac{x}{3}$.

The range is any real value of y.

Range: $y \in \mathbb{R}$

Period: 3π

The graph is stretched away from the y-axis.
One period of $y = \tan x$ fits into a third of the period of $y = \tan\frac{x}{3}$.
Since the period of $y = \tan x$ is π, the period of $y = 1 - \tan\frac{x}{3}$ is 3π.

c $y = \frac{1}{2}\sin(x + 30^\circ) \quad -180^\circ \leqslant x \leqslant 180^\circ$

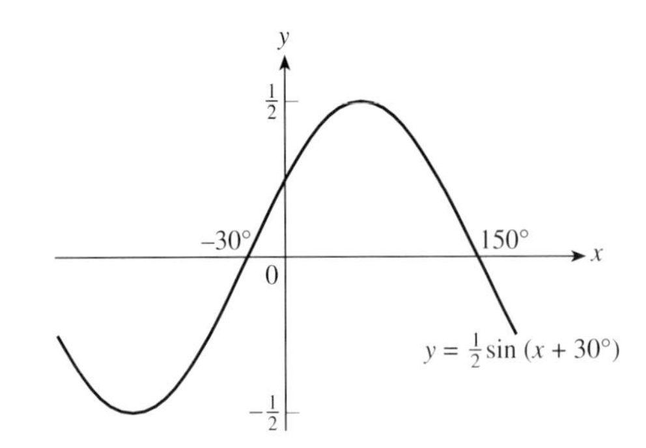

The curve $y = \sin x$ undergoes two transformations (in either order).

- Move 30° to the left, i.e. translation $\binom{-30^\circ}{0}$, gives $y = \sin(x + 30^\circ)$.
- 'Stretch' (compress) parallel to y-axis scale factor $\frac{1}{2}$, gives $y = \frac{1}{2}\sin(x + 30^\circ)$.

Range: $-\frac{1}{2} \leqslant y \leqslant \frac{1}{2}$

Period: 360°

The period is the same as for $y = \sin x$, i.e. 360°.

✓ ***Note*** $\sin kx$ and $\cos kx$ have period $\dfrac{360^\circ}{k}$ $\left(\dfrac{2\pi}{k} \text{ radians}\right)$.

$\tan kx$ has period $\dfrac{180^\circ}{k}$ $\left(\dfrac{\pi}{k} \text{ radians}\right)$.

15.5 Special triangles: Trigonometrical ratios of 30°, 45° and 60°

For 30° and 60° draw an **equilateral triangle** with sides of 2 units. Split it in half. Work out the height using Pythagoras' theorem. From this half equilateral triangle the sin, cos and tan of 30° and 60° can then be written down.

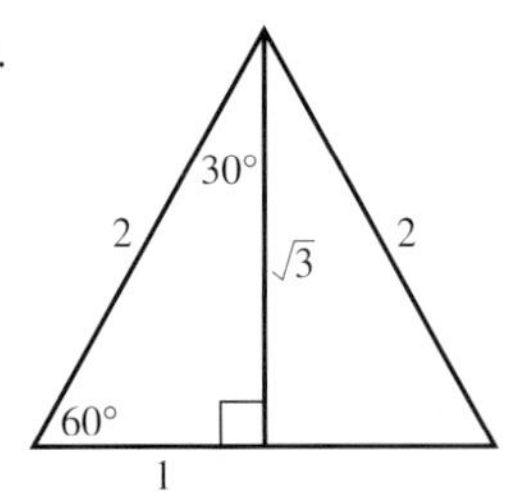

For 45° draw an **isosceles right-angled triangle** with equal sides of 1 unit. Work out the length of the hypotenuse by Pythagoras' theorem. From this triangle the sin, cos and tan of 45° can then be written down.

θ in degrees	$\sin\theta$	$\cos\theta$	$\tan\theta$	θ in radians
0°	0	1	0	0
30°	$\frac{1}{2}$	$\frac{\sqrt{3}}{2}$	$\frac{1}{\sqrt{3}}$	$\frac{\pi}{6}$
45°	$\frac{1}{\sqrt{2}}$	$\frac{1}{\sqrt{2}}$	1	$\frac{\pi}{4}$
60°	$\frac{\sqrt{3}}{2}$	$\frac{1}{2}$	$\sqrt{3}$	$\frac{\pi}{3}$
90°	1	0	Undefined	$\frac{\pi}{2}$

The values in the table should be at your fingertips. It is not necessary to learn them although, with use, many will become familiar. Learn ways of working them out.

Example 7

For this example, the answers are to be given in surds. So, a calculator, unless it is a very sophisticated one, is not helpful.

Write down, leaving surds in the answer

a $\sin 300^\circ$ **b** $\tan(-45^\circ)$ **c** $\cos 330^\circ$

Solution

a 300° is in quadrant 4.

$\therefore \quad \sin 300^\circ$ is $-$ve.

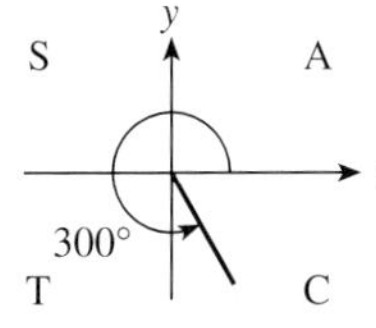

Alternatively, $\sin 300^\circ$ is $-$ve and has the same numerical value as $\sin 60^\circ$.

300° is 60° from the x-axis so

$\sin 300^\circ = -\sin 60^\circ$

$\sin 60^\circ = \dfrac{\sqrt{3}}{2}$

So $\sin 300^\circ = -\dfrac{\sqrt{3}}{2}$.

From the special triangle, $\sin 60^\circ = \dfrac{\sqrt{3}}{2}$.

b -45° is in quadrant 4.

$\therefore \quad \tan(-45^\circ)$ is $-$ve.

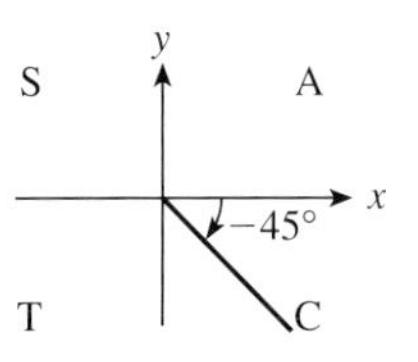

Alternatively, $\tan(-45^\circ)$ is $-$ve and has the same numerical value as $\tan 45^\circ$.

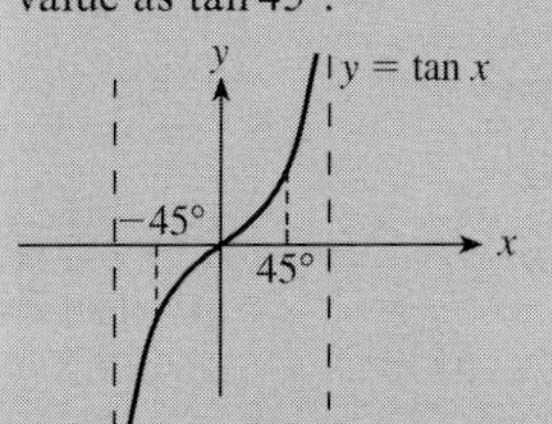

-45° is 45° from the x-axis so

$\tan(-45^\circ) = -\tan 45^\circ$

$\tan 45^\circ = 1$

So $\tan(-45^\circ) = -1$.

From the special triangle, $\tan 45^\circ = 1$.

c 330° is in quadrant 4.

$\therefore \quad \cos 330^\circ$ is $+$ve.

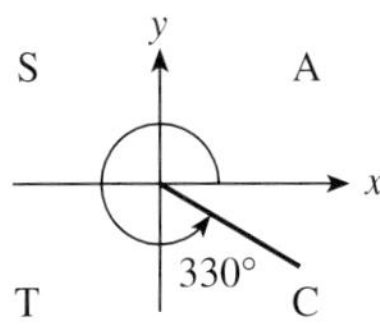

Alternatively, $\cos 330^\circ$ is $+$ve and has the same numerical value as $\cos 30^\circ$.

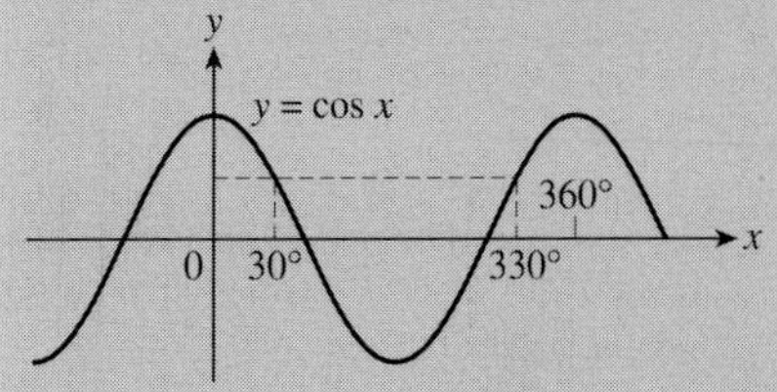

330° is 30° from the x-axis so

$\cos 330^\circ = \cos 30^\circ$

$\cos 30^\circ = \dfrac{\sqrt{3}}{2}$

So $\cos 330^\circ = \dfrac{\sqrt{3}}{2}$.

From the special triangle, $\cos 30^\circ = \dfrac{\sqrt{3}}{2}$.

EXERCISE 15b

1 Express in terms of the trigonometrical ratios of acute angles

a $\sin 170^\circ$ **b** $\tan 300^\circ$ **c** $\cos 200^\circ$ **d** $\sin(-50^\circ)$

e $\cos(-20^\circ)$ **f** $\sin 325^\circ$ **g** $\tan(-140^\circ)$ **h** $\cos 164^\circ$

i $\tan 143^\circ$ **j** $\cos(-130^\circ)$ **k** $\sin 250^\circ$ **l** $\tan(-50^\circ)$

m $\cos 293^\circ$ **n** $\sin(-230^\circ)$ **o** $\sin 1000^\circ$ **p** $\tan 904^\circ$

2 Express in terms of the trigonometrical ratios of acute angles

a $\operatorname{cosec} 230^\circ$ **b** $\cot 200^\circ$ **c** $\sec 142^\circ$ **d** $\cot 156^\circ$

e $\operatorname{cosec}(-53^\circ)$ **f** $\sec(-172^\circ)$ **g** $\operatorname{cosec} 111^\circ$ **h** $\sec 721^\circ$

3 Using the special triangles, write down the values of

a $\sin 30^\circ$ **b** $\cos 30^\circ$ **c** $\cos 45^\circ$ **d** $\tan 30^\circ$

e $\tan 45^\circ$ **f** $\cos 135^\circ$ **g** $\sin 330^\circ$ **h** $\tan 300^\circ$

i $\sin 225^\circ$ **j** $\cos(-60^\circ)$ **k** $\tan(-150^\circ)$ **l** $\sin(-300^\circ)$

m $\sin 405^\circ$ **n** $\cos(-135^\circ)$ **o** $\tan 210^\circ$ **p** $\sin 660^\circ$

4 Using the special triangles, write down the values of

a $\sec 30^\circ$ **b** $\operatorname{cosec} 120^\circ$ **c** $\cot(-30^\circ)$ **d** $\operatorname{cosec} 135^\circ$

e $\sec(-120^\circ)$ **f** $\operatorname{cosec} 225^\circ$ **g** $\cot 330^\circ$ **h** $\sec 150^\circ$

5 Write down the values of

a $\sin 270^\circ$ **b** $\cos 0^\circ$ **c** $\tan 180^\circ$ **d** $\sin 0^\circ$

e $\tan 2\pi$ **f** $\cos \frac{\pi}{2}$ **g** $\sin \pi$ **h** $\cos \pi$

6 Write down the values of these, leaving surds in the answers where appropriate.

a $\cos \frac{\pi}{4}$ **b** $\sin \frac{\pi}{6}$ **c** $\sin \frac{2\pi}{3}$ **d** $\tan \pi$

e $\sin \frac{3\pi}{4}$ **f** $\tan \frac{\pi}{3}$ **g** $\sin\left(-\frac{\pi}{3}\right)$ **h** $\cos \frac{\pi}{3}$

i $\tan \frac{\pi}{4}$ **j** $\cos \frac{11\pi}{6}$ **k** $\tan \frac{5\pi}{6}$ **l** $\sin \frac{4\pi}{3}$

7 Using a sketch of the graph of the trigonometrical function, or otherwise, find all values of θ, where

a $\sin\theta = \sin 30^\circ \quad 0^\circ \leqslant \theta \leqslant 720^\circ$ **b** $\cos\theta = \cos 140^\circ \quad 0^\circ \leqslant \theta \leqslant 720^\circ$

c $\tan\theta = \tan(-20^\circ) \quad -360^\circ \leqslant \theta \leqslant 360^\circ$ **d** $\sin\theta = \sin\left(-\frac{\pi}{4}\right) \quad 0 \leqslant \theta \leqslant 4\pi$

e $\cos\theta = \cos\pi \quad -2\pi \leqslant \theta \leqslant 2\pi$ **f** $\tan\theta = \tan\frac{\pi}{3} \quad 0 \leqslant \theta \leqslant 4\pi$

8 Draw sketches of $\sin\theta$, $\cos\theta$ and $\tan\theta$, on separate axes, for $0^\circ \leqslant \theta \leqslant 360^\circ$.

9 These graphs can be sketched by transformations of the graph of $\sin\theta$.
Draw a sketch of each graph for $0° \leqslant \theta \leqslant 360°$, state the transformation of $\sin\theta$ required, and state the period of the graph.

a $1 + \sin\theta$ **b** $\sin(\theta + 60°)$ **c** $\sin 2\theta$
d $\sin\frac{1}{2}\theta$ **e** $-\sin\theta$ **f** $\sin(-\theta)$

10 **a** Describe the transformations of the graph of $\cos\theta$ which would give $3\cos(\theta - 30°) - 1$.

b The graph of $y = \tan\theta$ undergoes these transformations. State the equation of the resulting graph.
i Stretch parallel to x-axis, scale factor 3, followed by a translation $\binom{10°}{-2}$
ii A translation $\binom{60°}{4}$, followed by a stretch parallel to the y-axis, scale factor 2

11 These functions have domain $\theta \in \mathbb{R}$.
For each function, find the range and the period in radians.

a $\sin\theta$ **b** $\cos 2\theta$ **c** $\tan\theta$ **d** $\tan 3\theta$
e $4\cos\theta$ **f** $\sin\frac{\theta}{2}$ **g** $\sin k\theta$ **h** $\tan k\theta$

12 For each of these functions, state the range, state whether the function is even, odd or neither, and sketch the graph of $y = f(x)$.

a $f(x) = 1 + \sin x$ **b** $f(x) = 2 + 3\cos x$ **c** $f(x) = 5\sin x + 10$
d $f(x) = 1 - \cos x$ **e** $f(x) = -\sin 3x$ **f** $f(x) = 2\cos 2x$

15.6 Trigonometrical identities

Two important identities will be proved.

$$\frac{\sin\theta}{\cos\theta} = \tan\theta \qquad \text{and} \qquad \sin^2\theta + \cos^2\theta = 1$$

Remember: An identity is true for all values of the variable. The sign $\equiv$ may be used in place of $=$.

✓ ***Note*** $(\sin\theta)^2$ is written as $\sin^2\theta$ and pronounced 'sine squared theta'.
To work out, for example, $\sin^2 42°$ on a calculator, evaluate $\sin 42°$ and square it.

Proof

To prove: $\dfrac{\sin\theta}{\cos\theta} = \tan\theta$

State result to be proved, and start with known information.

By definition: $\sin\theta = \dfrac{y}{r}$ $\quad\cos\theta = \dfrac{x}{r}$

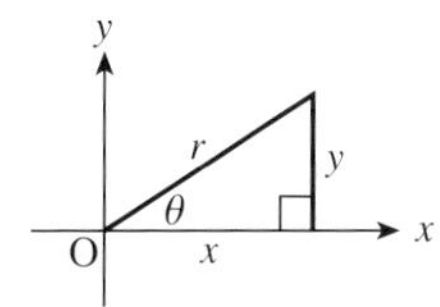

$$\therefore \quad \frac{\sin\theta}{\cos\theta} = \frac{y}{r} \div \frac{x}{r} = \frac{y}{r} \times \frac{r}{x} = \frac{y}{x}$$

$$= \tan\theta$$

Start with one side (in this case LHS). Use known facts to show LHS = RHS.

So $\dfrac{\sin\theta}{\cos\theta} = \tan\theta.$

State conclusion.

Proof

To prove: $\sin^2\theta + \cos^2\theta = 1$

State result to be proved.

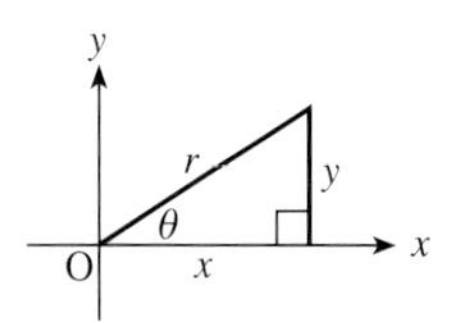

Draw diagram if required.

Start with one side (in this case LHS). Use known facts and theorems to show LHS = RHS.

$$\sin^2\theta + \cos^2\theta = \left(\frac{y}{r}\right)^2 + \left(\frac{x}{r}\right)^2$$

$$= \frac{y^2 + x^2}{r^2}$$

By Pythagoras' theorem $\quad y^2 + x^2 = r^2$

$\therefore \quad \sin^2\theta + \cos^2\theta = \frac{r^2}{r^2} = 1$

So $\sin^2\theta + \cos^2\theta = 1$.

State conclusion.

➤ For all values of θ:

$$\frac{\sin\theta}{\cos\theta} = \tan\theta \qquad \sin^2\theta + \cos^2\theta = 1$$

The identity $\sin^2\theta + \cos^2\theta = 1$ can be rearranged to give

$$\sin^2\theta = 1 - \cos^2\theta \quad \text{or} \quad \cos^2\theta = 1 - \sin^2\theta$$

Dividing the identity $\sin^2\theta + \cos^2\theta = 1$ by $\cos^2\theta$ gives

$$\tan^2\theta + 1 = \sec^2\theta$$

Dividing the identity $\sin^2\theta + \cos^2\theta = 1$ by $\sin^2\theta$ gives

$$1 + \cot^2\theta = \text{cosec}^2\theta$$

➤ $\tan^2\theta + 1 = \sec^2\theta \qquad 1 + \cot^2\theta = \text{cosec}^2\theta$

$\cot\theta = \frac{\cos\theta}{\sin\theta}$

From the diagram $\quad \sin\theta = \frac{b}{c} = \cos(90^\circ - \theta)$

$$\cos\theta = \frac{a}{c} = \sin(90^\circ - \theta)$$

$$\tan\theta = \frac{b}{a} = \cot(90^\circ - \theta)$$

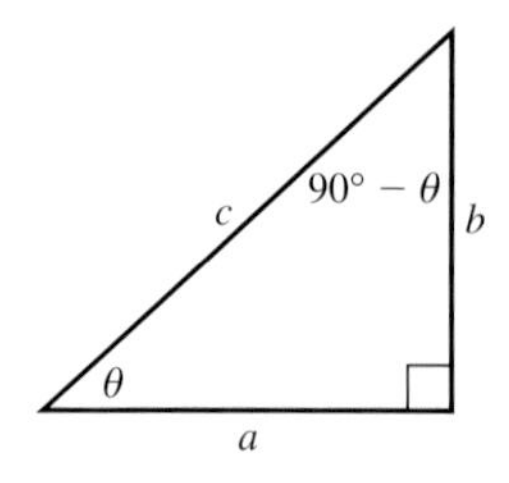

➤ $\sin\theta = \cos(90^\circ - \theta) \qquad \cos\theta = \sin(90^\circ - \theta) \qquad \tan\theta = \cot(90^\circ - \theta)$

✓ ***Note*** Although the diagram only illustrates the results for $0^\circ < \theta < 90^\circ$, they are true for all values of θ.

Example 8

This example, and the ones that follow, use the identity as a known result.

Prove the identity: $\cos^4\theta - \sin^4\theta = \cos^2\theta - \sin^2\theta$

Proof

To prove: $\cos^4\theta - \sin^4\theta = \cos^2\theta - \sin^2\theta$ — State result to be proved.

$\cos^4\theta - \sin^4\theta$ — Start with one side (in this case LHS).

$= (\cos^2\theta - \sin^2\theta)(\cos^2\theta + \sin^2\theta)$ — Factorise using difference of squares.

But $\cos^2\theta + \sin^2\theta = 1$

$\therefore \quad \cos^4\theta - \sin^4\theta = \cos^2\theta - \sin^2\theta$ — State conclusion.

Example 9

In this example, the identity is used in the form $1 - \sin^2\theta = \cos^2\theta$.

If $x = a\sin\theta$, simplify $\dfrac{x}{\sqrt{a^2 - x^2}}$. — Substitute for x.

$\dfrac{x}{\sqrt{a^2 - x^2}} = \dfrac{a\sin\theta}{\sqrt{a^2 - a^2\sin^2\theta}}$ — Factorise the expression under the root sign.

1 $\quad = \dfrac{a\sin\theta}{\sqrt{a^2(1 - \sin^2\theta)}}$ — Use $1 - \sin^2\theta = \cos^2\theta$.

1 $\quad = \dfrac{a\sin\theta}{\sqrt{a^2\cos^2\theta}}$

1 $\quad = \dfrac{a\sin\theta}{a\cos\theta}$ — Cancel a, use $\dfrac{\sin\theta}{\cos\theta} = \tan\theta$

$= \tan\theta$

Example 10

In this example, the identity $\sin^2\theta + \cos^2\theta = 1$ will enable θ to be eliminated.

Eliminate θ from $x = a\sin\theta$, $y = b\cos\theta$.

$x = a\sin\theta \Rightarrow \sin\theta = \dfrac{x}{a}$ — Rearrange to give $\sin\theta$ and $\cos\theta$ in terms of x, y, a and b.

$x = b\cos\theta \Rightarrow \cos\theta = \dfrac{y}{b}$

But $\quad \sin^2\theta + \cos^2\theta = 1$ — Substitute into the identity.

$\therefore \quad \left(\dfrac{x}{a}\right)^2 + \left(\dfrac{y}{b}\right)^2 = 1$

or $\quad \dfrac{x^2}{a^2} + \dfrac{y^2}{b^2} = 1$ — θ is eliminated.

Example 11

This example uses the identity and then offers an alternative solution, using Pythagoras' theorem.

If $\sin\theta = \frac{15}{17}$ and θ is obtuse, find $\cos\theta$.

To find $\cos\theta$, both the sign and the magnitude are needed.

θ is obtuse $\therefore$ $\cos\theta$ is $-$ve

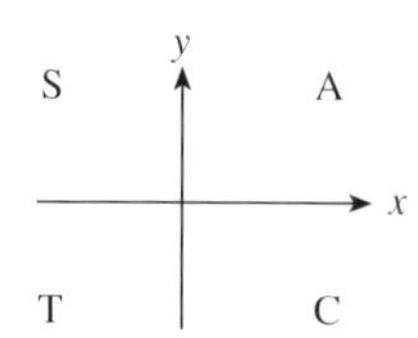

To find the magnitude, two methods are possible.

Using the identity $\sin^2\theta + \cos^2\theta = 1$

Substitute for $\sin\theta$.

$$\sin^2\theta + \cos^2\theta = 1$$

$$\left(\tfrac{15}{17}\right)^2 + \cos^2\theta = 1$$

$$\cos^2\theta = 1 - \tfrac{225}{289} = \tfrac{64}{289}$$

$$\therefore \quad \cos\theta = \pm\sqrt{\tfrac{64}{289}} = \pm\tfrac{8}{17}$$

Note: It is not necessary to find θ.

But since $\cos\theta$ is $-$ve, $\cos\theta = -\frac{8}{17}$.

Using Pythagoras' theorem

Draw a right-angled triangle with $\sin\alpha = \frac{15}{17}$. α is the acute equivalent angle.

$$x^2 = 17^2 - 15^2$$
$$= (17-15)(17+15)$$
$$= 2 \times 32$$
$$= 64$$
$$\therefore \quad x = 8$$

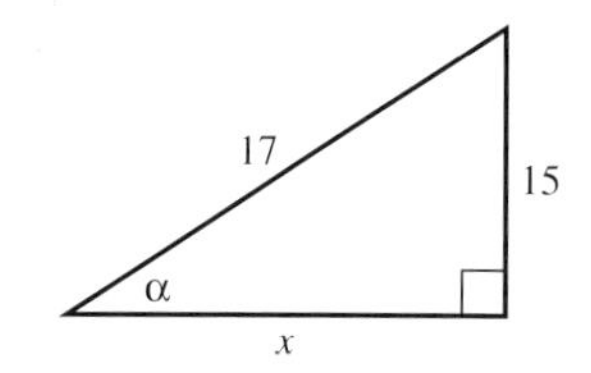

But $\cos\theta$ is $-$ve, and $\cos\alpha = \frac{8}{17}$ so $\cos\theta = -\frac{8}{17}$.

15.7 Solution of trigonometrical equations

There are many instances when a solution of an equation, such as $\sin\theta = \frac{1}{4}$, is needed.

One solution can be found by using either the calculator or the special triangles. From this one solution other solutions can be found either by the symmetry of the graph, or by considering the quadrants.

On calculators, the inverse sine function is marked arcsin or $\sin^{-1}$. So, one solution of $\sin\theta = \frac{1}{4}$ is $\theta = \arcsin\frac{1}{4}$ from the calculator. In this book, arcsin, arccos and arctan are used in preference to $\sin^{-1}$, $\cos^{-1}$, $\tan^{-1}$. The inverse trigonometrical functions are covered in Book 2.

✓ ***Note*** Answers to trigonometrical equations (and to other equations) can be checked on a calculator.

Answers to Examples 12–19 are given as exact answers, or correct to 1 decimal place if the answer is not exact.

Example 12 Solve this equation: $\cos\theta = -\frac{1}{4}$ for $0° < \theta < 360$

$\cos\theta = -\frac{1}{4}$ — Find one solution on the calculator using $\arccos(-\frac{1}{4})$.

$\arccos(-\frac{1}{4}) = 104.5°$

So one solution is $\theta = 104.5°$.

$180° - 104.5° = 75.5°$

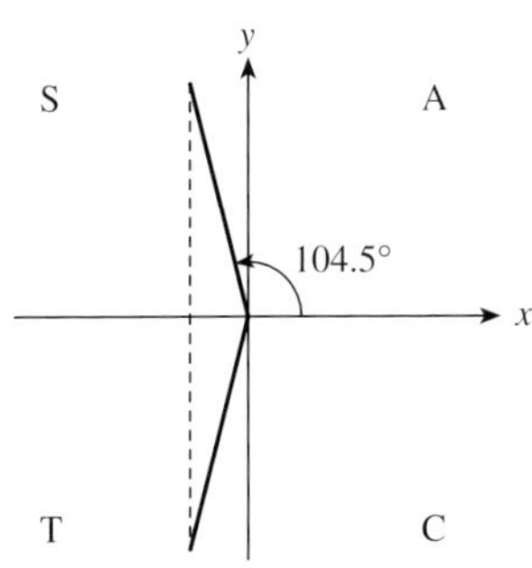

cos is −ve
∴ solutions are in quadrants 2 and 3, 75.5° from the x-axis.

So the second solution is $\theta = 180° + 75.5° = 255.5°$

So $\theta = 104.5°$ or $\theta = 255.5°$.

Example 13 Solve $\sin\left(\theta - \frac{\pi}{4}\right) = \frac{\sqrt{3}}{2}$ for $0 < \theta < 2\pi$.

Find solutions for $\theta - \frac{\pi}{4}$.

$$\sin\left(\theta - \frac{\pi}{4}\right) = \frac{\sqrt{3}}{2}$$

$\arcsin\frac{\sqrt{3}}{2} = \frac{\pi}{3}$ from special triangles.

so $\quad \theta - \frac{\pi}{4} = \frac{\pi}{3} \quad$ or $\quad \theta - \frac{\pi}{4} = \pi - \frac{\pi}{3}$

Find other angles which, when $\frac{\pi}{4}$ is added, will still be in range.

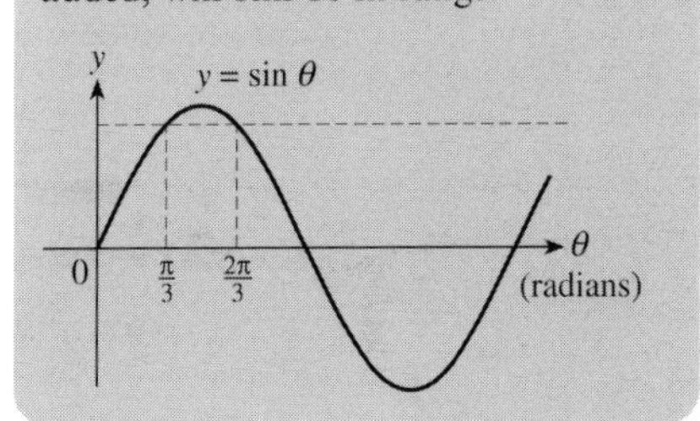

so $\quad \theta = \frac{\pi}{3} + \frac{\pi}{4} \quad$ or $\quad \theta = \frac{2\pi}{3} + \frac{\pi}{4}$

$\quad = \frac{7\pi}{12} \quad\quad = \frac{11\pi}{12}$

$\therefore\ \theta = \frac{7\pi}{12}$ or $\frac{11\pi}{12}$.

Example 14 Solve $\tan 3\theta = 1$ for $0° \leqslant \theta \leqslant 360°$.

Since $0° \leqslant \theta \leqslant 360°$, it follows that $0° \leqslant 3\theta \leqslant 3 \times 360°$. So all solutions for 3θ up to $3 \times 360° = 1080°$ must be listed.

From the special triangles, $\tan 45° = 1$. So $3\theta = 45°$ is one solution. More values of 3θ can be obtained by adding (or subtracting) multiples of 180°.

$$3\theta = 45°,\ 45° + 180°,\ 45° + 360°,\ 45° + 540°,\ 45° + 720°,\ 45° + 900°$$
$$= 45°,\ 225°,\ 405°,\ 585°,\ 765°,\ 945°$$
$$\therefore\ \theta = 15°,\ 75°,\ 135°,\ 195°,\ 255°,\ 315°.$$

Note All values in the range must be listed for 3θ. *Then* divide the values for 3θ by 3. Do *not* divide by 3 at an earlier stage.

Use of a general solution is more efficient. Put $n = 0, 1, 2, 3, 4, 5$ to find the solutions.

$3\theta = 45° + 180n°$ where n is an integer

$\theta = 15° + 60n°$

Example 15 Find one point of intersection of $y = \sqrt{3}\sin x$ and $y = \cos x$, where x is in radians.

The curves intersect where

$$\sqrt{3}\sin x = \cos x$$

$$\sqrt{3}\tan x = 1$$

Dividing both sides by $\cos x$ is permitted because $\cos x = 0$ does not lead to a solution.

$$\therefore \quad \tan x = \frac{1}{\sqrt{3}}$$

Use $\frac{\sin x}{\cos x} = \tan x$.

$$\text{so} \quad x = \arctan\frac{1}{\sqrt{3}}$$

One value of x is $x = \frac{\pi}{6}$.

When $x = \frac{\pi}{6}$, $y = \cos\frac{\pi}{6} = \frac{\sqrt{3}}{2}$

So coordinates of one point of intersection are $\left(\frac{\pi}{6}, \frac{\sqrt{3}}{2}\right)$.

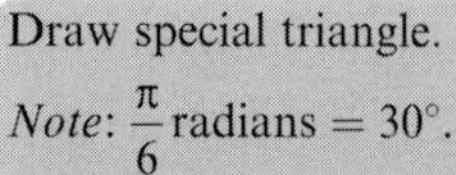

Draw special triangle.

Note: $\frac{\pi}{6}$ radians $= 30°$.

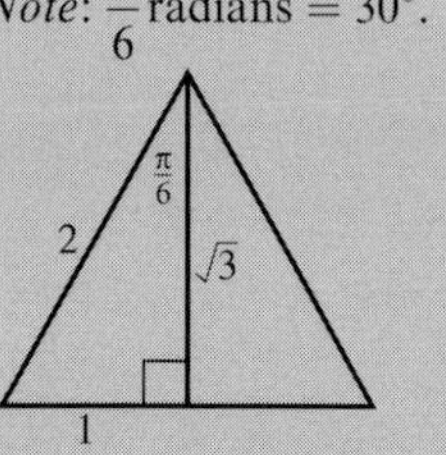

Try illustrating this on a graphics calculator. The point of intersection can be found only approximately.

Solving trigonometrical equations which are quadratic

These are some examples of quadratic equations involving trigonometrical functions:

$$2\sin^2\theta - \sin\theta = 0$$

$$\cos^2\theta - 4\cos\theta - 5 = 0$$

$$2\sin x\cos x - 4\cos x + \sin x - 2 = 0$$

$$6\cos^2\theta + 5\sin\theta - 7 = 0$$

Example 16 Solve $2\sin^2\theta - \sin\theta = 0$ for $-180° \leqslant \theta \leqslant 180°$.

This is a quadratic equation in $\sin\theta$.

$$2\sin^2\theta - \sin\theta = 0$$

$$\sin\theta(2\sin\theta - 1) = 0$$

$\sin\theta$ could be zero so do not divide through by $\sin\theta$. Put $\sin\theta$, the common factor, outside the bracket.

$$\therefore \quad \sin\theta = 0 \text{ or } \sin\theta = \tfrac{1}{2}$$

Use a sketch and the special triangles to find the solution in the given range.

When $\sin\theta = 0 \quad \theta = -180°, 0°, 180°$

When $\sin\theta = \frac{1}{2} \quad \theta = 30°, 150°$

So $\theta = -180°, 0°, 30°, 150°, 180°$.

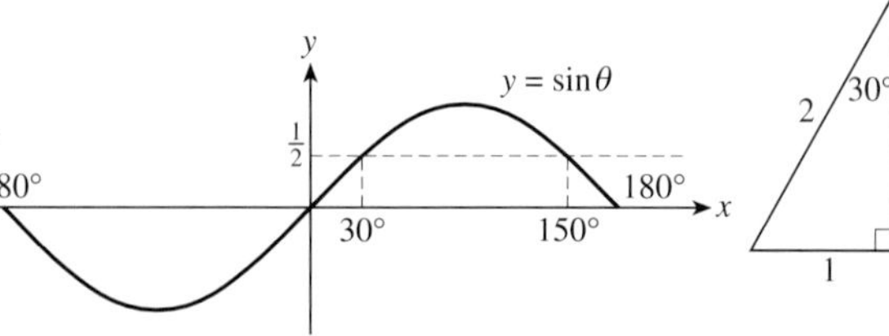

If preferred, Example 16 can be solved by substituting y for $\sin\theta$ to give $2y^2 - y = 0$, and solving for y.

Example 17

Solve $3\sin\theta + \tan\theta = 0$ for $0 \leqslant \theta \leqslant 2\pi$.

$$3\sin\theta + \tan\theta = 0$$

Sometimes, it can be helpful to express trigonometrical equations in terms of $\sin\theta$ and $\cos\theta$ only.

$$3\sin\theta + \frac{\sin\theta}{\cos\theta} = 0$$

Use $\frac{\sin\theta}{\cos\theta} = \tan\theta$ and multiply both sides by $\cos\theta$.

$$3\sin\theta\cos\theta + \sin\theta = 0$$

$$\sin\theta(3\cos\theta + 1) = 0$$

$\sin\theta$ is a common factor.

$\therefore \quad \sin\theta = 0 \quad \text{or} \quad \cos\theta = -\frac{1}{3}$

If $\sin\theta = 0 \quad \theta = 0, \pi, 2\pi$

If $\cos\theta = -\frac{1}{3} \quad \theta = 1.9, 2\pi - 1.9$

$= 1.9, 4.4$

So $\quad \theta = 0, 1.9, \pi, 4.4, 2\pi$.

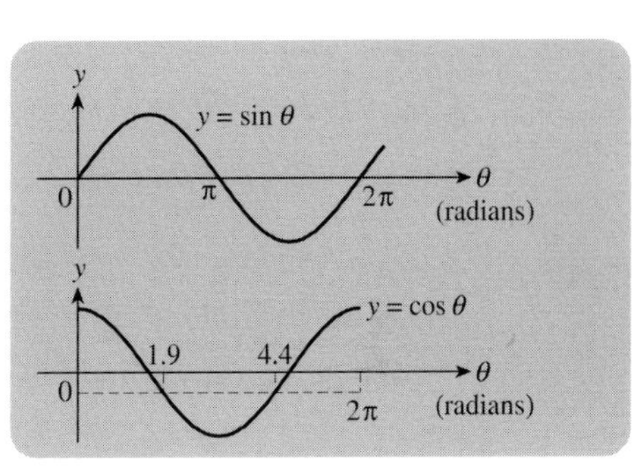

✓ ***Note*** Since the range given for solutions is in radians the answers should be given in radians.

Example 18

Solve $2\sin x\cos x - 4\cos x - \sin x + 2 = 0$ for $-\pi < x < \pi$.

$$2\sin x\cos x - 4\cos x - \sin x + 2 = 0$$

Try factorising by grouping.

$$2\cos x(\sin x - 2) - (\sin x - 2) = 0$$

$$(\sin x - 2)(2\cos x - 1) = 0$$

$(\sin x - 2)$ is a common factor.

so $\quad \sin x - 2 = 0 \quad \text{or} \quad \cos x = \frac{1}{2}$

When $\sin x - 2 = 0 \quad \sin x = 2$

$|\sin x| \leqslant 1$ so there is no solution to $\sin x = 2$.

When $\cos x = \frac{1}{2} \quad x = \pm\frac{\pi}{3}$

So solution is $x = \pm\frac{\pi}{3}$.

cos +ve $\therefore$ quadrants 1 and 4.

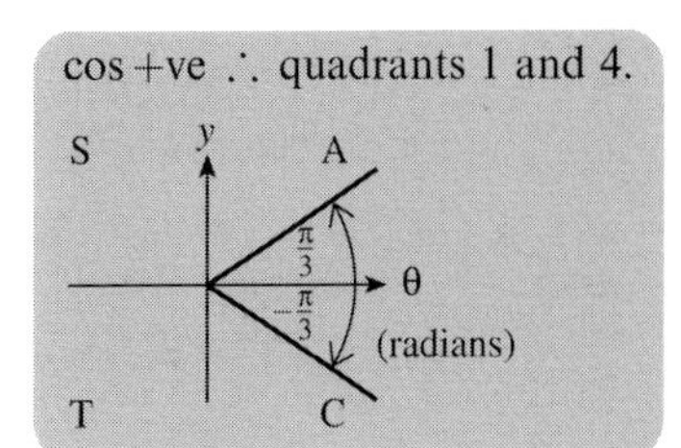

Example 19 Solve $7 - 6\cos^2\theta = 5\sin\theta, \quad 0^\circ \leqslant \theta \leqslant 360^\circ$.

$$7 - 6\cos^2\theta = 5\sin\theta$$

By substituting $\cos^2\theta = 1 - \sin^2\theta$ the equation will be a quadratic in $\sin\theta$.

$$7 - 6(1 - \sin^2\theta) = 5\sin\theta$$

$$7 - 6 + 6\sin^2\theta - 5\sin\theta = 0$$

$$6\sin^2\theta - 5\sin\theta + 1 = 0$$

Put $y = \sin\theta$ if preferred:
$6y^2 - 5y + 1 = 0$
$(3y - 1)(2y - 1) = 0$

$$(3\sin\theta - 1)(2\sin\theta - 1) = 0$$

$\therefore \qquad \sin\theta = \frac{1}{3} \quad \text{or} \quad \sin\theta = \frac{1}{2}$

When $\sin\theta = \frac{1}{3}$

Find one value on the calculator: $\theta = \arcsin\frac{1}{3} = 19.5^\circ$. Find other solutions by symmetry of the graph.

$\theta = 19.5^\circ$

or $\theta = 180^\circ - 19.5^\circ = 160.5^\circ$

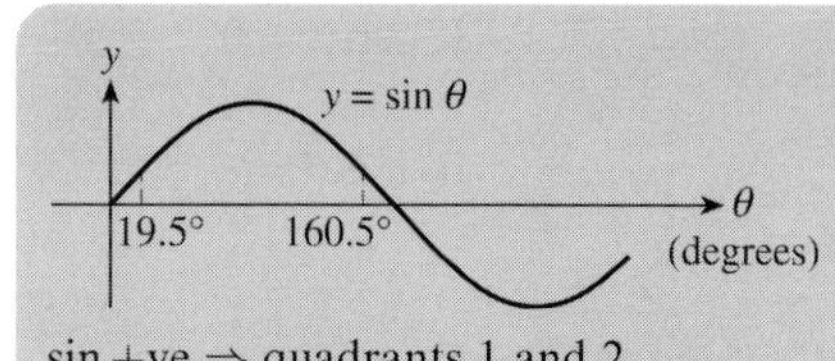

sin +ve ⇒ quadrants 1 and 2.
Solutions are 19.5° from the x-axis.

When $\sin\theta = \frac{1}{2}$

$\theta = 30^\circ$

or $\theta = 180^\circ - 30^\circ = 150^\circ$

So $\theta = 19.5^\circ, 30^\circ, 150^\circ, 160.5^\circ$.

Remember: From special triangles, $\sin 30^\circ = \frac{1}{2}$.

15.8 Small angle approximations

When x is small and measured in radians then

$$\sin x \approx x \qquad \cos x \approx 1 - \frac{x^2}{2} \qquad \tan x \approx x$$

These results are proved in Book 2.

Example 20 Find the approximate value of $\dfrac{\cos 2\theta - 1}{\theta\tan\theta}$ when θ is small.

When θ is small $\quad \cos 2\theta \approx 1 - \dfrac{(2\theta)^2}{2}$

$\qquad = 1 - 2\theta^2$

Replace x by 2θ in the approximation for $\cos x$ and then simplify.

When θ is small $\quad \tan\theta \approx \theta$

So $\quad \dfrac{\cos 2\theta - 1}{\theta\tan\theta} \approx \dfrac{1 - 2\theta^2 - 1}{\theta^2}$

$\qquad = \dfrac{-2\theta^2}{\theta^2}$

$\qquad = -2$

Substitute the approximate values for $\cos 2\theta$ and $\tan\theta$, and then simplify.

Check, with the calculator in radian mode, and $\theta = 0.001$, for example.

So the approximate value of $\dfrac{\cos 2\theta - 1}{\theta\tan\theta}$ when θ is small is -2.

EXERCISE 15c

In this exercise, answers should be left in terms of π where appropriate.

1 If $s = \sin\theta$ and $c = \cos\theta$ simplify

a $\sqrt{1-s^2}$ **b** $\sqrt{1-c^2}$ **c** $\dfrac{s}{\sqrt{1-s^2}}$ **d** $\dfrac{sc}{\sqrt{1-s^2}}$

e $\dfrac{\sqrt{1-c^2}}{c}$ **f** $\dfrac{c^4-s^4}{c^2-s^2}$ **g** $\dfrac{s\sqrt{1-s^2}}{c\sqrt{1-c^2}}$

2 Find a solution, where $0 \leqslant x \leqslant \frac{\pi}{2}$, to these equations.
Do *not* use a calculator if the answer can be found from the special triangles.

a $\sin x = \frac{1}{2}$ **b** $\tan x = \sqrt{3}$ **c** $\tan x = 1$ **d** $\tan x = \frac{1}{2}$

e $\sin x = \dfrac{1}{\sqrt{3}}$ **f** $\cos x = \dfrac{1}{\sqrt{3}}$ **g** $\cos x = \dfrac{\sqrt{3}}{2}$ **h** $\tan x = \dfrac{1}{\sqrt{2}}$

3 Find, without using a calculator, the values of

a $\sin\theta$, $\tan\theta$ if $\cos\theta = \frac{4}{5}$ and θ is acute

b $\cos\theta$, $\tan\theta$ if $\sin\theta = \frac{5}{13}$ and θ is obtuse

c $\sin\theta$, $\cos\theta$ if $\tan\theta = -\frac{7}{24}$ and θ is reflex

4 Find the values of θ, from 0° to 360° inclusive which satisfy

a $\cos\theta = \frac{1}{2}$ **b** $\tan\theta = 1$ **c** $\sin\theta = 1$ **d** $\cos\theta = -\dfrac{\sqrt{3}}{2}$

e $\tan\theta = -\sqrt{3}$ **f** $\sin\theta = 0.6$ **g** $\cos(\theta + 60°) = 0.5$ **h** $\tan(\theta - 10°) = -0.1$

5 For $0 \leqslant x \leqslant 2\pi$, solve

a $\tan\theta = \dfrac{1}{\sqrt{3}}$ **b** $\sin\theta = 0.7$ **c** $\cos\left(\theta + \dfrac{\pi}{3}\right) = \dfrac{1}{2}$

d $\sin\left(\theta - \dfrac{\pi}{6}\right) = 1$ **e** $\sqrt{3}\cos\theta = -1$ **f** $\tan\theta = 0.2$

6 For $0 \leqslant x \leqslant 2\pi$, solve

a $\sin^2 x = \dfrac{1}{4}$ **b** $\tan^2 x = \dfrac{1}{3}$ **c** $\sin 2x = \dfrac{1}{2}$

d $\tan 2x = -1$ **e** $\cos 3x = \dfrac{\sqrt{3}}{2}$ **f** $\sin 3x = -1$

7 For $-180° \leqslant \theta \leqslant 180°$, solve

a $\sin^2 2\theta = 1$ **b** $\tan\theta = 3$ **c** $\tan^2 3\theta = 1$

d $4\cos 2\theta = 1$ **e** $\sin(2\theta + 30°) = 0.8$ **f** $\tan(3\theta - 45°) = \frac{1}{2}$

8 For $0° \leqslant \theta \leqslant 360°$, solve

a $\sin\theta(2\sin\theta - 1) = 0$ **b** $(2\cos\theta - 1)(\cos\theta + 1) = 0$

c $\sin\theta = \cos\theta$ **d** $\tan^2\theta + \tan\theta = 0$

e $2\cos^2\theta = \cos\theta$ **f** $3\sin^2\theta + \sin\theta = 0$

g $2\sin^2\theta - \sin\theta - 1 = 0$ **h** $2\cos^2\theta + 3\cos\theta + 1 = 0$

i $4\cos^3\theta = \cos\theta$ **j** $\tan\theta = \sin\theta$

k $4\sin^2\theta = 3\cos^2\theta$ **l** $\sin^2\theta = 4\cos^2\theta$

EXERCISE 15c
(continued)

9 For $-\pi \leqslant x \leqslant \pi$, solve

a $3 - 3\cos\theta = 2\sin^2\theta$

b $\cos^2\theta + \sin\theta + 1 = 0$

c $3\sin^2\theta - \sin\theta\cos\theta - 4\cos^2\theta = 0$

d $(3\sin\theta - 2)(\tan\theta - 1) = 0$

e $6\sin\theta\cos\theta - 3\cos\theta + 2\sin\theta - 1 = 0$

f $\sin 2\theta = \cos 2\theta$

10 Eliminate θ from these equations.

a $x = a\cos\theta,\ y = b\sin\theta$

b $x = 1 - \sin\theta,\ y = 1 + \cos\theta$

c $x = 4 - \cos\theta,\ y = 2 + \sin\theta$

11 Prove these identities.

a $\tan\theta + \dfrac{1}{\tan\theta} = \dfrac{1}{\sin\theta\cos\theta}$

b $\dfrac{1}{\sin\theta} + \dfrac{\tan\theta}{\cos\theta} = \dfrac{1}{\sin\theta\cos^2\theta}$

c $\dfrac{1 - \cos\theta}{\sin\theta} = \dfrac{\sin\theta}{1 + \cos\theta}$

d $\left(\dfrac{1}{\cos\theta} + \tan\theta\right)\left(\dfrac{1}{\cos\theta} - \tan\theta\right) = 1$

12 Find approximations for these functions when θ is small. (θ in radians.)

a $\dfrac{\sin 3\theta}{2\theta}$

b $\dfrac{\sin 4\theta}{\sin 2\theta}$

c $\dfrac{1 - \cos\theta}{\theta^2}$

d $\dfrac{\theta\sin\theta}{1 - \cos 2\theta}$

e $\dfrac{\sin\theta\tan\theta}{1 - \cos 3\theta}$

f $\sin\theta\operatorname{cosec}\frac{1}{2}\theta$

g $\tan^2\dfrac{\theta}{2} + 2\cos\dfrac{\theta}{2}$

h $\dfrac{1 - \cos 2\theta}{\theta\sin 3\theta}$

13 Given that $f(x) = 2 - x\cos x$, x in radians, show that $f(x) = 0$ has a root between 7 and 8.

14 Show that $\theta - \sin\theta = \frac{\pi}{3}$ has a root between 1 and 2.

15 Plot on graph paper, or draw on a graphics calculator, the graphs of $y = 1 - \sin\frac{x}{3}$ and $y = x$ for $0 \leqslant x \leqslant \pi$.
Hence find a solution to $1 - \sin\frac{x}{3} = x$ correct to 1 decimal place.

16 Plot on graph paper, or draw on a graphics calculator, the graphs of $y = \sin(x + 30^\circ)$ and $y = 2 + \tan x$ for $0^\circ \leqslant x \leqslant 180^\circ$. Hence find a solution to $\sin(x + 30^\circ) = 2 + \tan x$, correct to the nearest degree.

17 For these equations sketch the graphs for $0 \leqslant x \leqslant 2\pi$, state the range, describe the required transformation of $y = \tan x$ or $y = \cos x$, and state the period.

a $y = \dfrac{1}{2}\cos\left(x - \dfrac{\pi}{4}\right) - 2$

b $y = 1 - \tan\dfrac{x}{2}$

c $y = \cos\left(\dfrac{\pi}{3} - 2x\right)$

d $y = \tan(-3x)$

18 Write down the maximum and minimum values of these expressions, giving the smallest positive or zero value of θ, in degrees, for which they occur.

a $\sin\theta$

b $3\cos\theta$

c $2\cos\frac{1}{2}\theta$

d $-\frac{1}{2}\sin 2\theta$

e $1 - 2\sin\theta$

f $3 + 2\cos 3\theta$

g $\dfrac{1}{2 + \sin\theta}$

h $\dfrac{1}{4 - 3\cos\theta}$

19 State, with reasons, which of these equations have no real roots.

a $2\sin\theta = 3$ **b** $\sin\theta + \cos\theta = 0$ **c** $\sin\theta + \cos\theta = 2$ **d** $\tan\theta = 2$

The rest of the questions in this exercise use $\sec\theta$, $\operatorname{cosec}\theta$ *and* $\cot\theta$.

20 If $s = \sin\theta$, $c = \cos\theta$ and $t = \tan\theta$, simplify

a $\dfrac{1-s^2}{s}$ **b** $\dfrac{c}{1-c^2}$ **c** $\sqrt{1+t^2}$ **d** $\dfrac{1-s^2}{1-c^2}$

e $c(1+t^2)$ **f** $\dfrac{s}{c^2-1}$ **g** $\dfrac{t}{\sqrt{1+t^2}}$ **h** $\dfrac{c}{s}+\dfrac{s}{c}$

21 If $x = a\operatorname{cosec}\theta$, $y = b\cot\theta$ and $z = c\sec\theta$ simplify

a $\sqrt{x^2-a^2}$ **b** b^2+y^2 **c** $y\sqrt{b^2+y^2}$ **d** z^2-c^2

e $\dfrac{1}{\sqrt{z^2-c^2}}$ **f** $\dfrac{x}{x^2-a^2}$ **g** $\dfrac{y}{b^2+y^2}$ **h** $\dfrac{\sqrt{z^2-c^2}}{z}$

22 If $\cos\theta = -\frac{8}{17}$ and θ is obtuse, find the values of

a $\cot\theta$ **b** $\operatorname{cosec}\theta$

23 If $\tan\theta = \frac{7}{24}$ and θ is reflex, find the values of

a $\operatorname{cosec}\theta$ **b** $\sec\theta$

24 Eliminate θ from these equations.

a $x = a\cot\theta,\quad y = b\operatorname{cosec}\theta$ **b** $x = a\sec\theta,\quad y = b\tan\theta$

c $x = a\tan\theta,\quad y = b\cos\theta$ **d** $x = a\cot\theta,\quad y = b\sin\theta$

25 For $-180° \leqslant \theta \leqslant 180°$, solve

a $\operatorname{cosec}\theta = 2$ **b** $\sec 2\theta = 3$ **c** $3\cos\theta + 2\sec\theta + 7 = 0$

d $\cot\theta = 5\cos\theta$ **e** $3\cos\theta = 2\cot\theta$ **f** $\tan\theta = 4\cot\theta + 3$

26 Prove these identities.

a $\sec^2\theta - \operatorname{cosec}^2\theta = \tan^2\theta - \cot^2\theta$ **b** $\sec\theta + \tan\theta = \dfrac{1}{\sec\theta - \tan\theta}$

c $\sec\theta + \operatorname{cosec}\theta\cot\theta = \sec\theta\operatorname{cosec}^2\theta$ **d** $\sin^2\theta(1+\sec^2\theta) = \sec^2\theta - \cos^2\theta$

EXERCISE 15d (Miscellaneous)

1 Sketch $y = 2\cos 3x$ for $0° \leqslant x \leqslant 180°$, state the range of y and hence the number of solutions in the range $0° \leqslant x \leqslant 180°$ for

a $\cos 3x = \frac{1}{2}$ **b** $\cos 3x = 1$ **c** $\cos 3x = 2$

2 For these functions sketch the graphs for $0° \leqslant x \leqslant 360°$, state the range, describe the required transformation of $y = \sin x$, and state the period.

a $y = -\sin x$ **b** $y = \sin 2x$ **c** $y = 3\sin x$ **d** $y = \sin(x + 40°)$

e $y = 2 + \sin x$ **f** $y = \sin(20° - x)$ **g** $y = 1 + \sin\dfrac{x}{2}$

EXERCISE 15d
(continued)

3 $f(x) = 2\sin x$, $x \in \mathbb{R}$ and $g(x) = x + \frac{\pi}{4}$, $x \in \mathbb{R}$.

a Find $f(\frac{\pi}{6})$ and $g(\frac{\pi}{5})$.

b Write down the range of f, and the range of g.

c Calculate $fg(x)$ and $gf(x)$.

d Solve $fg(x) = -1$ for $0 \leqslant x \leqslant 2\pi$.

4 Solve $(1 + \cos x)^2 = \frac{1}{4}$ for $-180° \leqslant x \leqslant 180°$.

5 Find one point of intersection of the curve $y = \tan(x + \frac{\pi}{5})$ and the line $y = \sqrt{3}$.

6 $f(x) = 2x^3 - 7x^2 + 7x - 2$.

a Show that $f(1) = 0$ and hence factorise $f(x)$.

b Solve $f(x) = 0$.

c Hence, or otherwise, solve for $0 \leqslant x \leqslant 2\pi$

i $2\tan^3 x - 7\tan^2 x + 7\tan x - 2 = 0$
ii $2\sin^3 x - 7\sin^2 x + 7\sin x - 2 = 0$
iii $2\cos^3 x - 7\cos^2 x + 7\cos x - 2 = 0$

7 Simplify, giving exact answers as a single fraction with rational denominator

a $\sin^2 \frac{\pi}{4} + \tan \frac{\pi}{6}$ **b** $\tan \frac{\pi}{6} + \tan \frac{\pi}{3}$ **c** $\sin 45° + \cos 60°$

d $\dfrac{\sin 120° + \tan 120°}{\sin 150° + \tan 150°}$ **e** $\tan 30° + \dfrac{1}{\cos 30°}$ **f** $2\tan \frac{11\pi}{6} + \dfrac{1}{\cos \frac{11\pi}{6}}$

8 a Given that $f(x) = 2\sin(x - \frac{\pi}{4})$ for the domain $-\frac{\pi}{2} \leqslant x \leqslant \frac{\pi}{2}$, find the range of $f(x)$ and sketch $y = f(x)$. Solve $f(x) = -\sqrt{3}$ for $-\frac{\pi}{2} \leqslant x \leqslant \frac{\pi}{2}$.

b Given also that $g(x) = \sin x$, find functions $h_1(x)$ and $h_2(x)$ such that $h_2 g h_1(x) = f(x)$.

9 The approximate depth of water, d m, in a harbour at time t hours after midnight is modelled by the equation $d = d_0 + 6\sin ct$, where $c > 0$ and c is measured in radians per hour.

a Given that the greatest depth of water is 25 m, find d_0 and the least depth of water.

b Given that $c = 0.5$, find the length of time between successive low tides, to the nearest five minutes.

c What is the depth of water in the harbour at 8 a.m., correct to the nearest metre?

10 Sketch, on the same axes, the graphs of $y = |2\sin x|$, $y = x$ and $y = \frac{x}{4}$ for $0 \leqslant x \leqslant 2\pi$. Hence state the number of solutions, for $0 \leqslant x \leqslant 2\pi$, of

a $|2\sin x| = x$ **b** $|8\sin x| = x$

11 A pendulum is swinging through an angle of 80°. The angle, θ (degrees), between the pendulum and the vertical, at time t seconds, is given by $\theta = a\cos(60t°)$. Find the value of a and the period of the pendulum (i.e. the time taken to swing through $2 \times 80° = 160°$).

12 Given that $\sin x = k$, where x is acute, find, in terms of k

a $\cos x$ **b** $\cos(90° - x)$ **c** $\sin(-x)$ **d** $\sin(180° - x)$ **e** $\sin(x - 90°)$

13 Find, for these functions, the range and, if the functions are periodic, the period in radians.

a $\cos|x|$ **b** $|\cos x|$ **c** $\sin|2x|$ **d** $|\tan x|$

14 Find x and y, given that $0 < x < \frac{\pi}{2}$ and $0 < y < \frac{\pi}{2}$ and that

$$\sin x + \cos y = \frac{\sqrt{6}+2}{2\sqrt{2}} \quad \text{and} \quad 3\sin x - \cos y = \frac{3\sqrt{6}-2}{2\sqrt{2}}$$

15 The graph of $y = a + b\cos 2x$, where x is in radians, passes through the point $\left(\frac{\pi}{2}, c\right)$ and cuts the x- and y-axes at $\frac{\pi}{6}$ and -1 respectively. Find a, b and c and state the sequence of transformations of $y = \cos x$ which would result in the graph of $y = a + b\cos 2x$.

16 The triangles below are similar to these two special triangles. In each case, state to which special triangle they are similar, the scale factor to obtain the given triangle from the special triangle and the value of x and, where relevant, y.

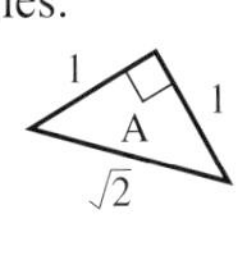

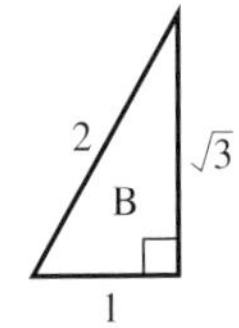

a

b

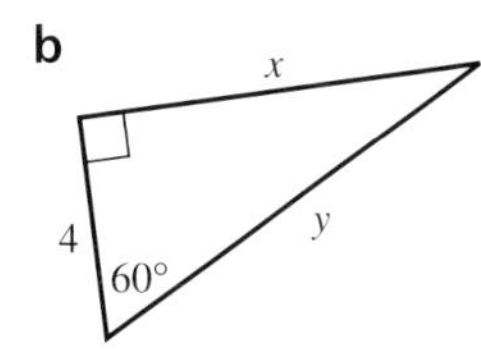

c

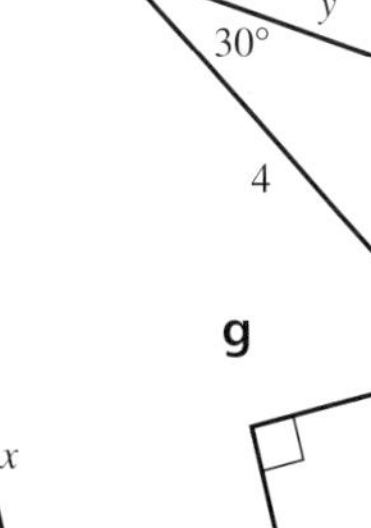

d

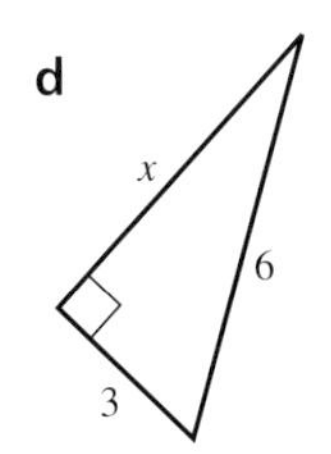

e

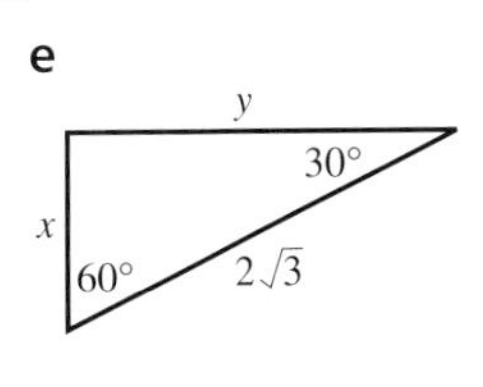

f

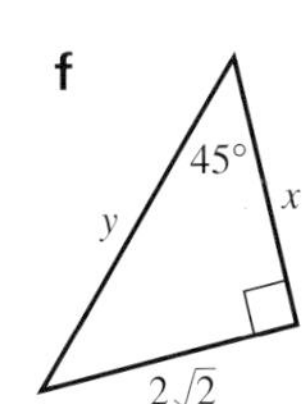

g

17 $\cos\frac{2\pi}{5} = \frac{\sqrt{5}-1}{4}$.

a Find $\sec\frac{2\pi}{5}$ in the form $A + B\sqrt{5}$, where A and B are constants.

b Show that

$$\sin\frac{2\pi}{5} = \frac{\sqrt{10+2\sqrt{5}}}{4}$$

18 Prove the identity: $(\sin\theta + \cos\theta)(1 - \sin\theta\cos\theta) = \sin^3\theta + \cos^3\theta$.

19 The curves $y = 2\sin^2 x$ and $y = 3\sin x - 1$ in the domain $0 \leqslant x \leqslant \frac{\pi}{2}$ intersect at A and B. Show that $AB = \frac{1}{6}\sqrt{4\pi^2 + 81}$.

20 Given that $f(x) = \cos x$, x in radians, find ff(1) and fff(1). Using a calculator show that the sequence defined by $u_n = f^n(1)$, where f^n indicates that the function is applied n times, converges to a limit. Find this limit correct to 6 decimal places.

Test yourself

1 $\frac{7\pi}{15}$ radians is equivalent to

A 1.46° **B** $\left(\frac{7}{2700}\right)^\circ$ **C** 168° **D** 12° **E** 84°

2 $\cos 30^\circ$ is equal to

A $\frac{1}{2}$ **B** $\frac{2}{\sqrt{3}}$ **C** $\frac{1}{\sqrt{2}}$ **D** $\frac{\sqrt{3}}{2}$ **E** 2

3 $\tan 290^\circ$ is equal to

A $\tan 70^\circ$ **B** $-\tan 290^\circ$ **C** $\tan 360^\circ - \tan 290^\circ$

D $-\tan 70^\circ$ **E** $\tan(-290^\circ)$

4 The solutions of $\cos^2\theta = \frac{1}{2}\cos\theta$ in the range $0 \leqslant \theta \leqslant 2\pi$ are

A $\frac{\pi}{3}$ and $\frac{5\pi}{3}$ **B** $\frac{\pi}{6}$ and $\frac{5\pi}{6}$ **C** 0, π and 2π

D $\frac{\pi}{3}, \frac{\pi}{2}, \frac{3\pi}{2}$ and $\frac{5\pi}{3}$ **E** $0, \frac{\pi}{6}, \pi$ and $\frac{5\pi}{6}$

5 330° is equivalent to

A $\frac{\pi}{6}$ radians **B** $-\frac{\pi}{3}$ radians **C** $\frac{11\pi}{6}$ radians **D** $\frac{\pi}{3}$ radians **E** $\frac{7\pi}{6}$ radians

6 If $\cos\theta = -\frac{7}{25}$ and $\frac{\pi}{2} \leqslant \theta \leqslant \pi$, then $\sin\theta$ is equal to

A $\frac{18}{25}$ **B** $\frac{24}{25}$ **C** $-\frac{48}{625}$ **D** $\pm\frac{24}{25}$ **E** $\pm\frac{576}{625}$

7 The number of solutions of the equation $\sin 4\theta = \frac{1}{\sqrt{2}}$, where $0 \leqslant \theta \leqslant 360^\circ$, is

A 2 **B** 4 **C** 6 **D** 8 **E** 10

8 $\dfrac{1+\cos\frac{5\pi}{4}}{1-\sin\frac{5\pi}{4}}$ is equal to

A $1-2\sqrt{2}$ **B** $3-2\sqrt{2}$ **C** 1 **D** $\frac{1}{\sqrt{2}+1}$ **E** $2+2\sqrt{3}$

9 The solutions to $\cos^2 x = \frac{1}{2}(1+\cos x)$ in the range $-180^\circ < x \leqslant 180^\circ$ are

A -120°, 0° and 120° **B** -60°, 60° and 180° **C** -60°, 0° and 120°

D -120° and 60° **E** 0°, $\pm 60^\circ$ and 180°

10 If $p = \frac{\cos\theta}{2}$ and $q = \sin^3\theta$ then

A $8p^3 + q = 1$ **B** $(2p + \sqrt[3]{q})^2 = 1$ **C** $4p^2 = 1 - q^{\frac{2}{3}}$ **D** $2\cos^{-1} p = \sin^{-1}(\sqrt[3]{q})$

E no simple relationship connects p with q

Key points

Trigonometrical ratios

π radians $= 180°$

$\sin\theta = \frac{y}{r}$ $\cos\theta = \frac{x}{r}$ $\tan\theta = \frac{y}{x}$ $x \neq 0$

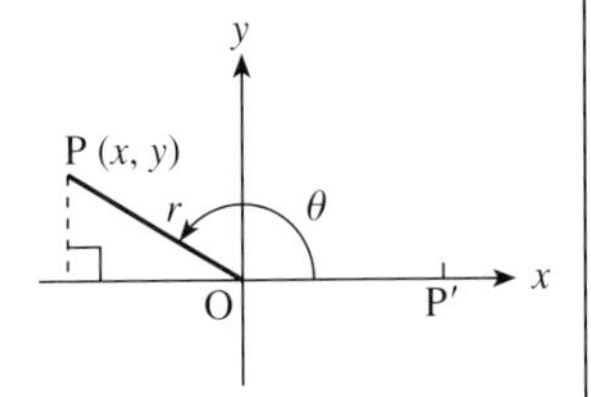

To find the trigonometrical ratios of any angle use either the symmetry of the graph or find

- the **sign** from 'All Silly Tom Cats''
- and the **magnitude** by finding the acute equivalent angles.

S A T C (quadrant diagram with x and y axes)

Use the special triangles for ratios of 45°, 30°, 60°.

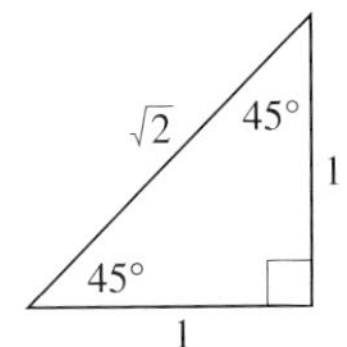

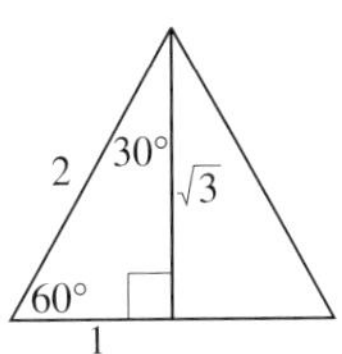

Identities

For all values of θ:

$\frac{\sin\theta}{\cos\theta} = \tan\theta$ $\frac{\cos\theta}{\sin\theta} = \cot\theta$

$\sin^2\theta + \cos^2\theta = 1$ $\tan^2\theta + 1 = \sec^2\theta$ $1 + \cot^2\theta = \operatorname{cosec}^2\theta$

$\sin\theta = \cos(90° - \theta)$ $\cos\theta = \sin(90° - \theta)$ $\tan\theta = \cot(90° - \theta)$

Solving trigonometrical equations

- Use identities.
- Recognise quadratic equations.
- $a\sin x = b\cos x \Rightarrow \tan x = \frac{b}{a}$.
- Find one solution with a calculator or using the special triangle and think 'what else?'
- Give answer in degrees if degrees are specified in the question; otherwise use radians.
- Remember that a calculator will *check* all solutions even though it will not find them.
- For equations such as $\cos 3x = 0.2$ or $\sin(x + 40°) = 0.5$, list solutions for $3x$ or $x + 40°$ before dividing by 3 or subtracting 40°.

Graphs

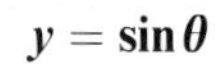

$y = \sin\theta$

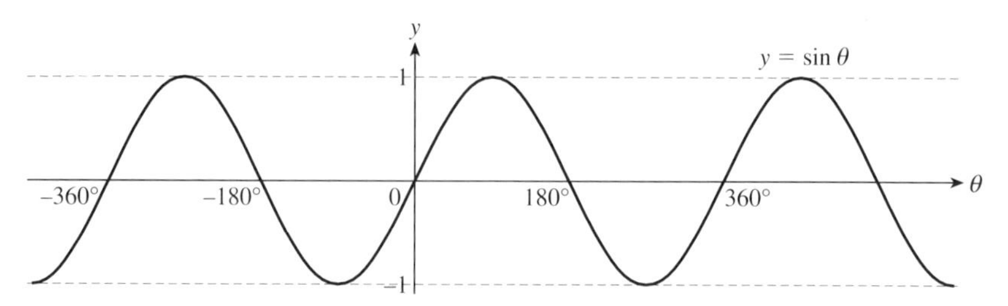

$y = \cos\theta$

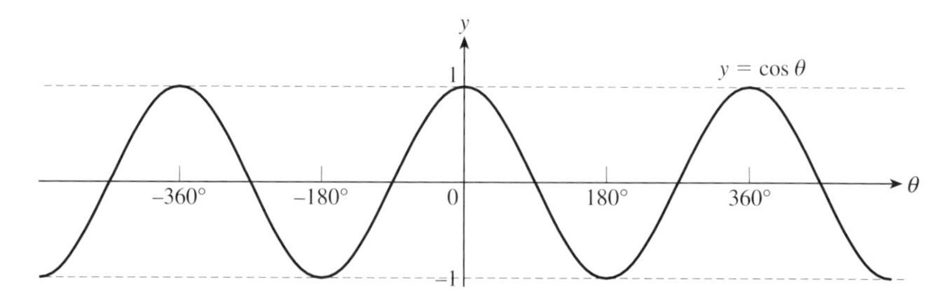

$y = \tan\theta$

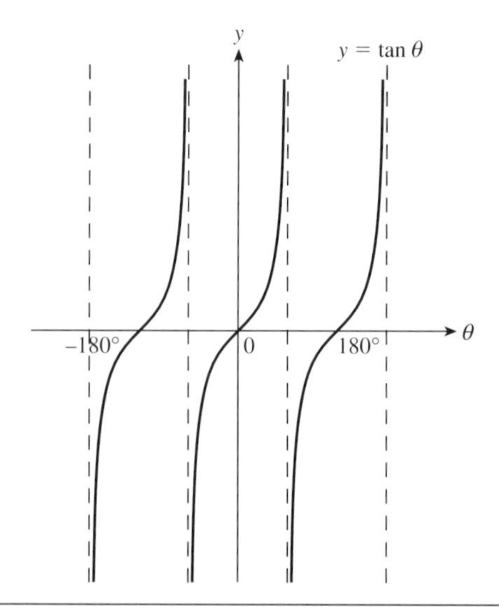

Proving identities

Use the trigonometrical identities on page 369.

For equations or identities it is often helpful, as a first step, to put all the trigonometric functions in terms of sines and/or cosines.

16 Further Applications of Trigonometry

Before starting this chapter you will need to know

- about elementary trigonometry, geometry and proportion (Chapter 14)
- about trigonometrical ratios of acute and obtuse angles (Chapter 15).

16.1 Area of sector and length of arc (radians)

Consider a circle, centre O, radius r and an arc, PQ, of the circle subtending an angle of θ radians at the centre of the circle. OPQ is a sector of the circle.

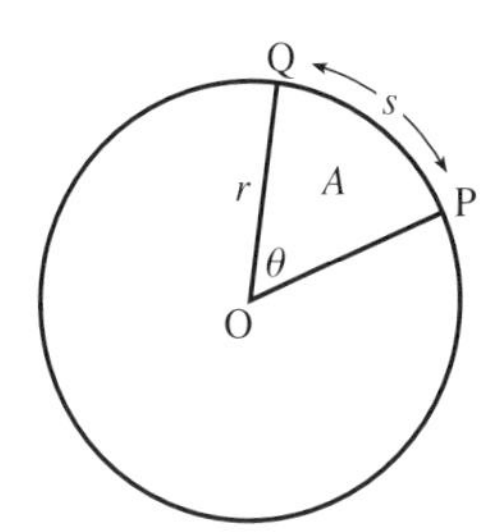

Area of sector OPQ, $A = \dfrac{\theta}{2\pi} \times \pi r^2 = \dfrac{1}{2}r^2\theta$

Length of arc PQ, $s = \dfrac{\theta}{2\pi} \times 2\pi r = r\theta$

$\dfrac{\theta}{2\pi}$ is the fraction of the circle required.

➤

Area of sector, $A = \frac{1}{2}r^2$
Length of arc, $s = r\theta$ (θ in radians)

Remember π radians $= 180°$

Example 1

The arc, AB, subtends an angle of $\frac{\pi}{3}$ at the centre, O, of a circle radius 6 cm. Find the length of arc AB and the area of sector OAB.

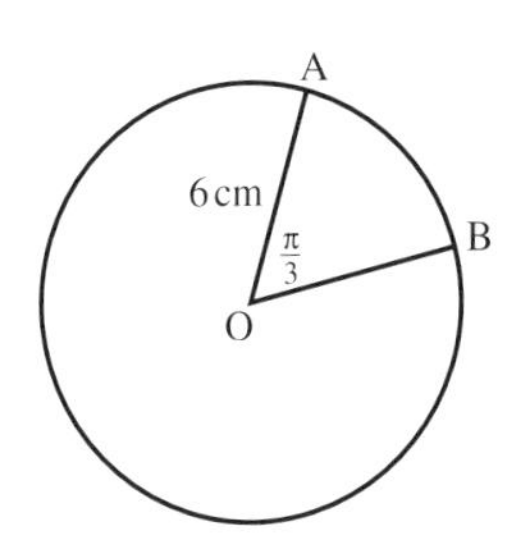

$s = r\theta$

Here, $r = 6$ and $\theta = \dfrac{\pi}{3}$.

So, arc AB $= 6 \times \dfrac{\pi}{3}$ cm $= 2\pi$ cm

$A = \frac{1}{2}r^2\theta$

$\therefore$ area sector OAB $= \dfrac{1}{2} \times 6^2 \times \dfrac{\pi}{3}$ cm^2

$= 6\pi$ cm^2

Note θ must be in radians to use these formulae.

Example 2 The perimeter of the sector of a circle, radius 3 cm is 8 cm. Find the area of the sector.

Perimeter $= (3 + 3 + s)$ cm

But perimeter $= 8$ cm

So arc AB is 2 cm.

The perimeter of OAB includes the radii. $r = 3$ cm.

$$s = r\theta$$

$$2 = 3\theta$$

$$\therefore \quad \theta = \tfrac{2}{3}$$

θ in radians.

Then $\quad A = \frac{1}{2}r^2\theta = \frac{1}{2} \times 3 \times 3 \times \frac{2}{3} = 3$

$\therefore$ area of sector AOB is 3 cm^2.

Example 3 OAB is a sector of a circle centre O. OC = OD = a. Angle COD = 2θ. Show that the shaded area is given by $a^2 \cos\theta(\sin\theta - \theta\cos\theta)$

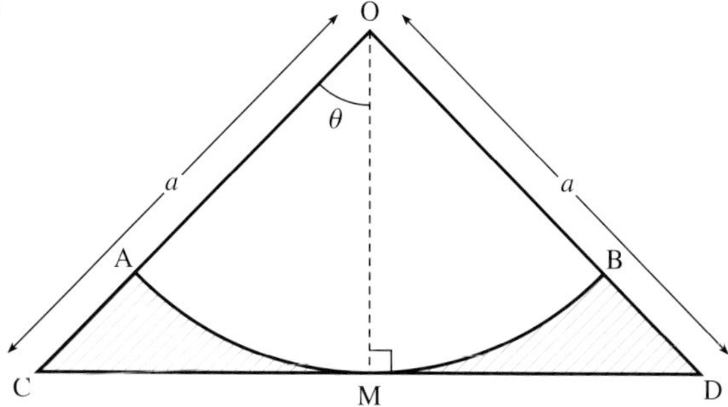

Let the area of the $\triangle$COD be A_t and the area of the sector OAB be A_s.

Join O to mid-point M of CD.

Shaded area, $A = A_t - A_s$

Angle OMD = 90° because tangent is perpendicular to radius.

$A_t = \frac{1}{2}bh \quad \sin\theta = \dfrac{\text{CM}}{a} \quad \cos\theta = \dfrac{\text{OM}}{a}$

$$A_t = \text{CM} \times \text{OM}$$

$$= a\sin\theta \times a\cos\theta$$

$$= a^2 \sin\theta\cos\theta$$

$$A_s = \tfrac{1}{2}\text{OM}^2 \times 2\theta$$

Area of the sector $= \frac{1}{2}r^2\theta$. Here the angle of the sector is 2θ.

$$= a^2\theta\cos^2\theta$$

$$A = A_t - A_s$$

$$= a^2\sin\theta\cos\theta - a^2\theta\cos^2\theta$$

$a^2\cos\theta$ is a common factor.

$$= a^2\cos\theta(\sin\theta - \theta\cos\theta)$$

EXERCISE 16a

All angles in this exercise (apart from Question 13) are measured in radians. Exact answers should be given where appropriate.

1 A disc makes 100 revolutions in three minutes.
Find the angle through which it turns every second, in radians and in degrees.

2 Find the length of the arcs and the areas of the sectors.

a

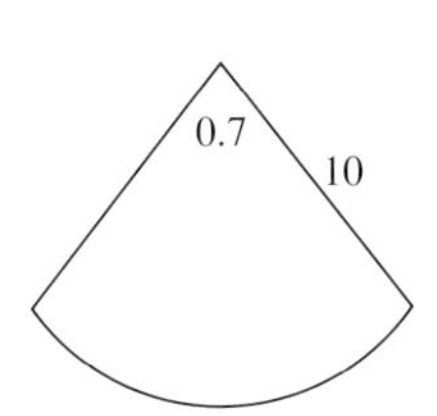

b

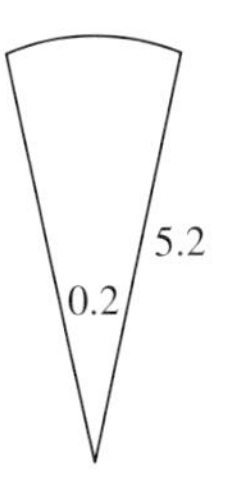

c

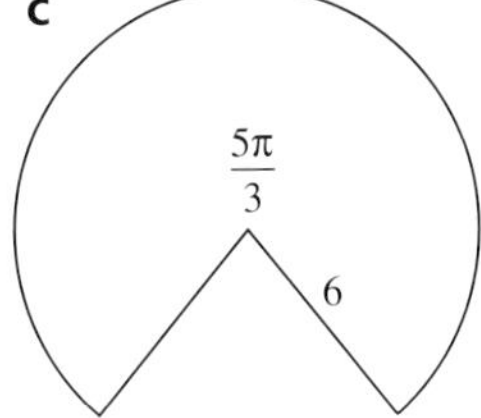

3 Find the length of an arc which subtends an angle of 0.8 radians at the centre of a circle of radius 10 cm.

4 An arc of a circle subtends an angle of 0.5 radians at the centre.
Given that the length of the arc is 3 cm, find the radius of the circle.

5 Find the angle subtended at the centre of a circle of radius 2.5 cm by an arc 2 cm long.

6 Find the area of a sector containing an angle of 1.5 radians in a circle of radius 2 cm.

7 The radius of a circle is 3 cm. Find the angle contained by a sector of area 18 cm^2.

8 A round cake with diameter 20 cm is shared equally between six people.
Find the perimeter and the area of the top of each piece.
(Leave π in your answers.)

9 A 1.5 m long pendulum travels from one extreme of its swing to the other extreme in half a second. In this time, the bob at the bottom of the pendulum travels $\frac{\pi}{10}$ m.
Find how long it takes the pendulum to sweep out the equivalent of a complete circle.

10 A coin rolls on its edge along a slope. The coin travels 40 cm and makes n complete revolutions. Show that the face of the coin has an area of

$$\frac{400}{\pi n^2} \text{ cm}^2$$

11 The face of a town hall clock carries a design of concentric circles.
The inner circle has radius 0.5 m and the outer circle has radius 1 m, which is also the length of the minute hand. The region between the circles is shaded.

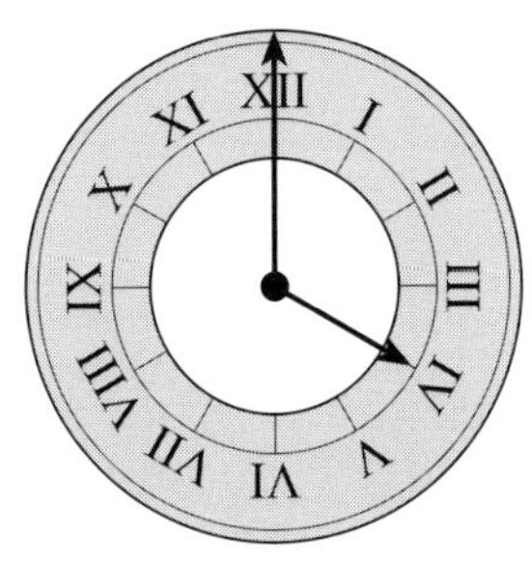

Find the area of the shaded region swept out by the minute hand in ten minutes.
(Leave π in the answer.)

EXERCISE 16a
(continued)

12 An arc subtends an angle of 1 radian at the centre of a circle, and a sector of area $72\,\text{cm}^2$ is bounded by this arc and the two radii.
Find the radius of the circle.

13 The chord AB of a circle subtends an angle of 60° at the centre.
Find the ratio of the lengths of chord AB to arc AB.

14 A segment is cut off a circle of radius 5 cm by a chord AB, of length 6 cm.
Find the length of the minor arc AB.

15 A circular dartboard is divided into 20 equal sectors one of which is shown in the diagram.

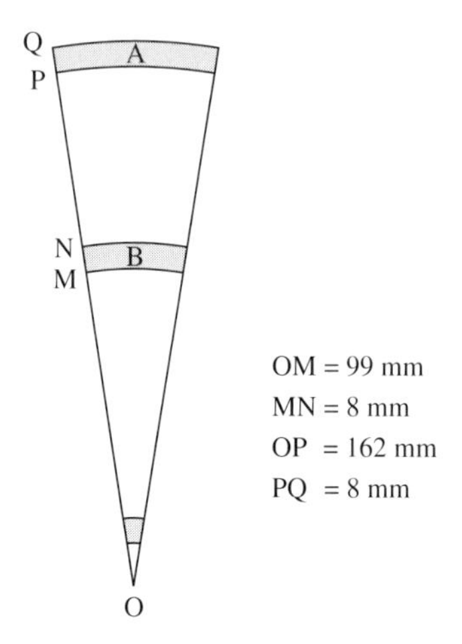

O is the centre of the circle. The areas for scoring double and treble 20 are marked A and B respectively.
Find the ratio area A:area B in the form n:1, giving n correct to 1 d.p.

16 An oar of length l has the tips of its handle and its blade at A and B respectively. It is pivoted at P, a quarter of the way from A to B.

During a stroke, A travels along an arc of length $\dfrac{l}{3}$.

a Find the area of the sector swept out by PB during a stroke.

The oar is moved so that P is now three-tenths of the way from A to B, and the angle turned by the oar in a stroke is not changed.

b Find the length of the arc along which B travels during a stroke.

16.2 Area of a triangle

The usual **notation for labelling triangles** is to use capital letters for vertices, the same capitals to represent the size of the angles at the vertices and the corresponding lower case letters to represent the length of sides opposite the vertices. So, for example, the angle at B will be of size B and the side opposite B will be of length b.

This elegantly simple idea was first used by Euler and was one of his many contributions to mathematics.

To prove Area of triangle $= \frac{1}{2}ab\sin C$

This proof is for an acute-angled triangle, but the formula holds for any triangle.

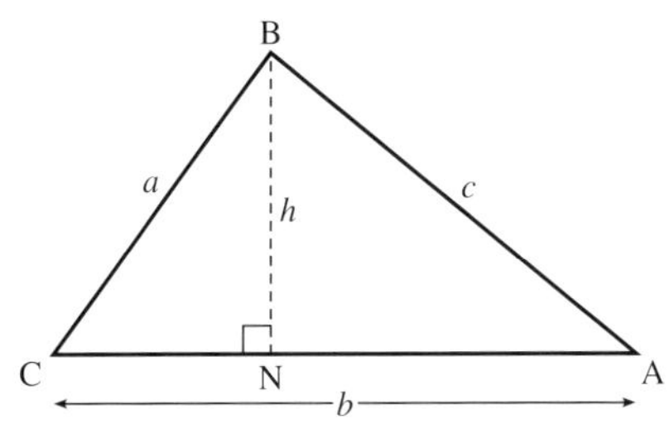

Area of $\triangle$ABC $= \frac{1}{2}bh$

Using area $= \frac{1}{2} \times$ base $\times$ height.

In $\triangle$CBN, $h = a\sin C$

$\sin C = \frac{h}{a}$

$\therefore$ Area of $\triangle$ABC $= \frac{1}{2} \times b \times a\sin C$

$= \frac{1}{2}ab\sin C$

➤ **Area of a triangle $= \frac{1}{2}ab\sin C$**

Similarly: Area $= \frac{1}{2}bc\sin A$
Area $= \frac{1}{2}ac\sin B$

✓ ***Note*** Two sides and the included angle are needed.

Example 4 Find the area of this triangle.

Two sides and the included angle are given.

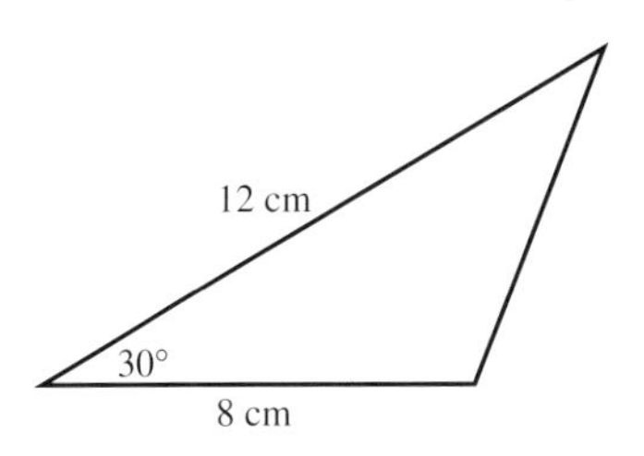

$A = \frac{1}{2}ab\sin C$

$a = 8, b = 12, C = 30°$

$= \frac{1}{2} \times 8 \times 12 \times \sin 30°$

$= 4 \times 12 \times \frac{1}{2} = 24$

So the area of the triangle is $24\,\text{cm}^2$.

Example 5 Given that chord $AB = 2\sqrt{3}$, show that the area of the minor (shaded) segment ACB of the circle, centre O, radius 2, is $\frac{1}{3}(4\pi - 3\sqrt{3})$.

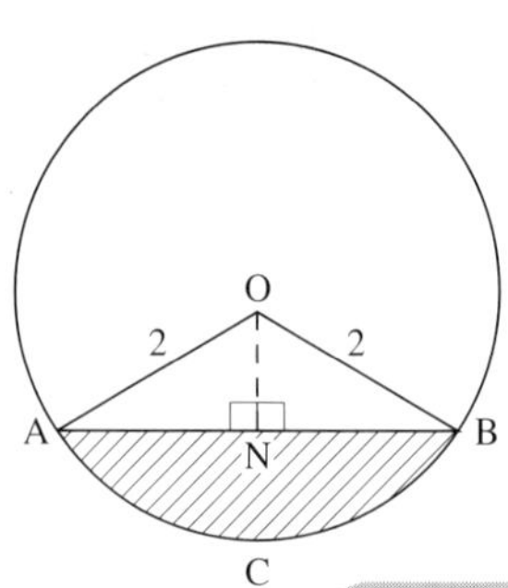

$OA = OB$ (radii) $\therefore$ $\triangle AOB$ is isosceles.

$AB = 2\sqrt{3}$ so $AN = \sqrt{3}$

ON, the perpendicular from the centre to the chord, bisects AB.

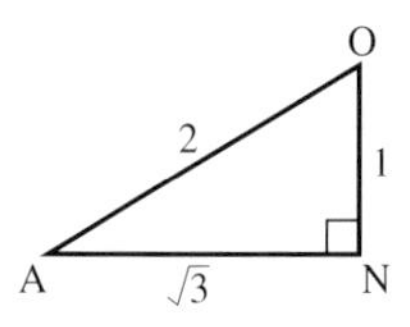

$\sin A\hat{O}N = \dfrac{\sqrt{3}}{2}$, so from the special triangles $A\hat{O}N = \dfrac{\pi}{3}$ and $ON = 1$.

ON can also be calculated using Pythagoras' theorem.

$ON = \frac{1}{2}OA$ and $\triangle AON$ is half an equilateral triangle of side 2.

So $A\hat{O}N = \dfrac{\pi}{3}$.

$\therefore \quad A\hat{O}B = \dfrac{2\pi}{3}$

Area of segment ACB = Area of sector OAB – Area of $\triangle AOB$

$$\begin{aligned}\text{Area of sector OAB} &= \frac{1}{2}r^2\theta \\ &= \frac{1}{2} \times 2^2 \times \frac{2\pi}{3} \\ &= \frac{4\pi}{3}\end{aligned}$$

$\theta = \dfrac{2\pi}{3}$.

Remember: The angle must be in radians when using this formula.

$$\begin{aligned}\text{Area of } \triangle OAB &= \frac{1}{2}ab\sin C \\ &= \frac{1}{2} \times OA \times OB \sin A\hat{O}B \\ &= \frac{1}{2} \times 2^2 \sin\frac{2\pi}{3} \\ &= \frac{2\sqrt{3}}{2} \\ &= \sqrt{3}\end{aligned}$$

$$\begin{aligned}\text{Area of segment ACB} &= \frac{4\pi}{3} - \sqrt{3} \\ &= \frac{1}{3}(4\pi - 3\sqrt{3})\end{aligned}$$

➤ Area of segment, S = Area of sector – Area of triangle

$$= \tfrac{1}{2}r^2(\theta - \sin\theta)$$

(θ in radians)

Example 6

Three identical cylinders of radius 3 cm are placed in contact with each other with their axes parallel and a band is placed round the cylinders.

This diagram shows a cross-section.

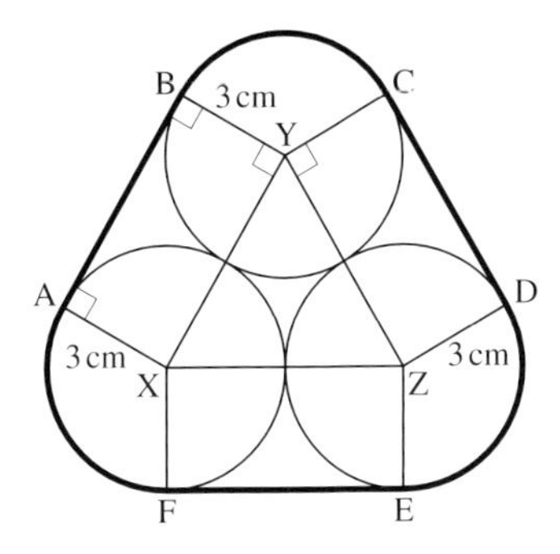

The band is made up of 3 straight parts and 3 arcs.

Calculate the length of the band.

Solution

The part of the band AB is a straight line which is a tangent to the circles centres X and Y at A and B respectively.

$Y\hat{B}A = X\hat{A}B = 90^\circ$

$AX = BY = 3\,\text{cm}$

Radius ⊥ tangent.

Therefore ABYX is a rectangle and XY = AB.

By symmetry, XY = YZ = ZX.

Therefore △XYZ is equilateral.

Also by symmetry, CD = EF = AB.

$XY = 2 \times 3\,\text{cm} = 6\,\text{cm}$

XY is twice the radius of the cylinder.

So AB = CD = EF = 6 cm.

The part of the band BC is the arc of a circle subtending $B\hat{Y}C$ at the centre Y.

$$B\hat{Y}C = 360^\circ - B\hat{Y}X - C\hat{Y}Z - X\hat{Y}Z$$
$$= 360^\circ - 2 \times 90^\circ - 60^\circ = 120^\circ$$

$B\hat{Y}X = C\hat{Y}Z = 90^\circ$ (angles of a rectangle).
$X\hat{Y}Z = 60^\circ$ (△XYZ is equilateral).

So the three arcs BC, DE and FA will together form a circle of radius 3.

$$\text{Therefore length of band} = 3AB + BC + DE + FA$$
$$= (3 \times 6 + 6\pi)\,\text{cm}$$
$$= (18 + 6\pi)\,\text{cm}$$

EXERCISE 16b

Exact answers should be given where appropriate. Otherwise correct to 3 significant figures.

1 Find the area of these triangles.

a

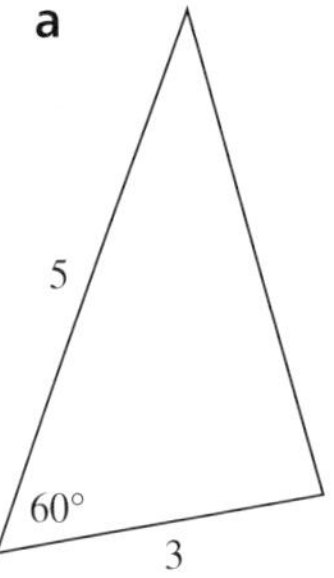

b

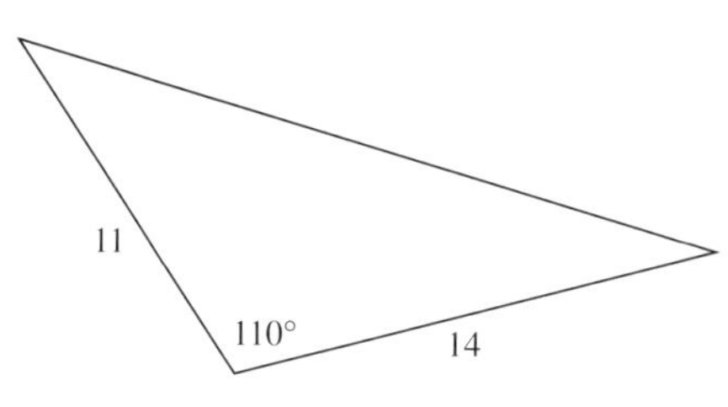

c

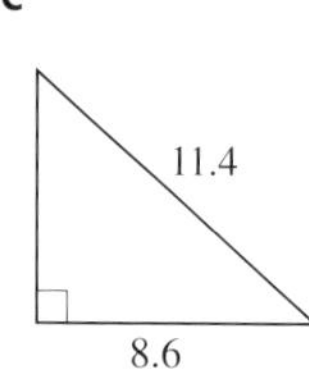

d

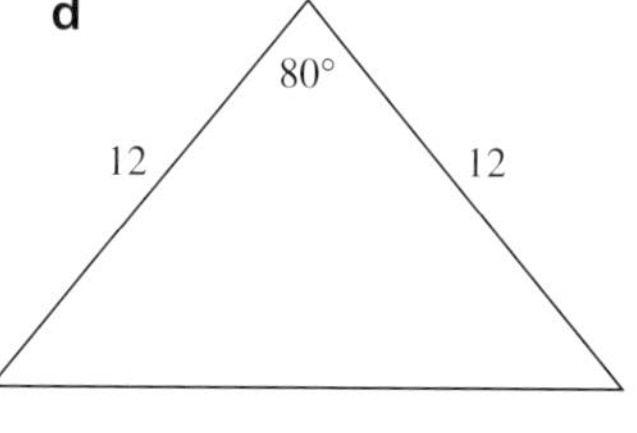

e

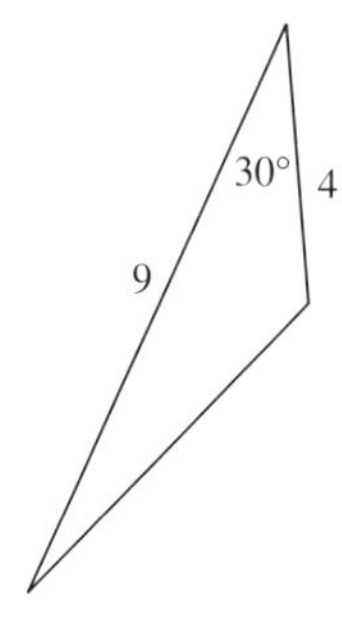

2 Find the area of the triangle ABC in which

a $A = 90°$ $B = 27°$ $a = 15$ **b** $C = 90°$ $A = 42°$ $a = 10$

c $a = b = 12$ $c = 4$ **d** $a = b = 12$ $A = 80°$

3 The arc, AB, of a sector of a circle, centre O, radius 2 cm, is 4 cm long. Find

a the area of the sector AOB

b the area of triangle AOB

c the area of the minor segment cut off by the line AB.

4 In each diagram, find the area of sector AOB, and the area of triangle AOB, and hence deduce the area of segment ABC.

a

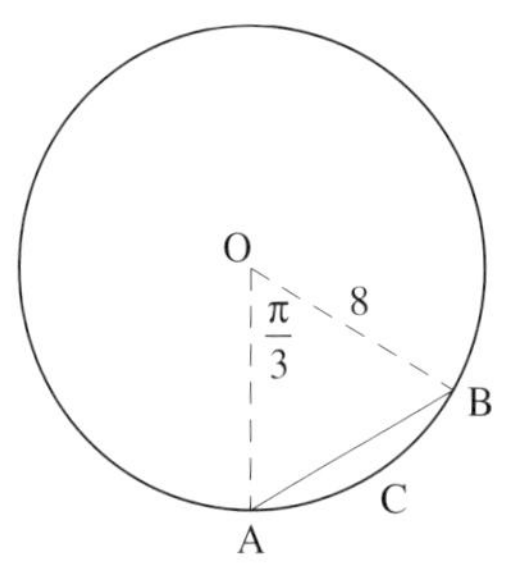

b

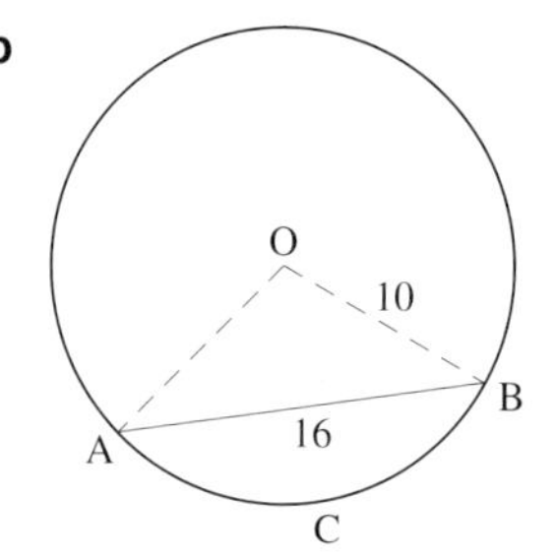

5 A chord AB subtends an angle of $\frac{2\pi}{3}$ at O, the centre of a circle with radius 12 cm. Find the area of

a sector AOB **b** triangle AOB **c** the major segment cut off by AB.

6 A chord PQ of a circle with radius r, subtends an angle θ at the centre.

a Show that the area of the minor segment cut off by PQ is $\frac{1}{2}r^2(\theta - \sin\theta)$.

b Write down the area of the major segment cut off by PQ in terms of r and θ.

c Hence show that if the ratio of the areas of the segments is 1:3 then

$2\theta - 2\sin\theta = \pi$

7 The diagram shows the cross-section of a ball, radius r, floating in water. The surface of the water touches the ball at A and B. AB subtends an angle of $\dfrac{2\pi}{3}$ at the centre of the ball.

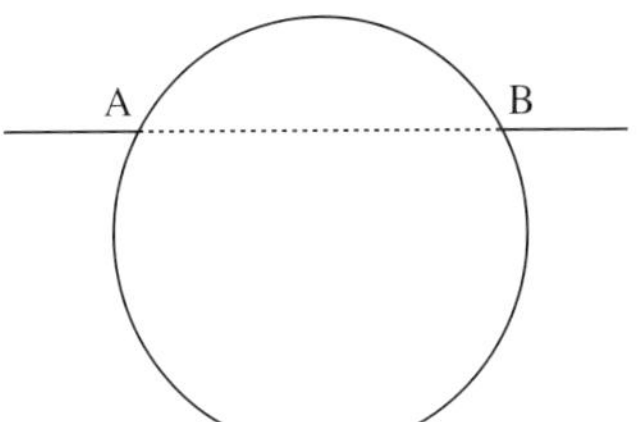

a Find the length of AB in terms of r.

b Hence find, in terms of r, the circumference of the circle where the ball crosses the surface of the water.

8 Two circles with equal radii r are drawn. Their centres, O and P, are a distance r apart so that the centre of each circle lies on the circumference of the other. The circles intersect at A and B.

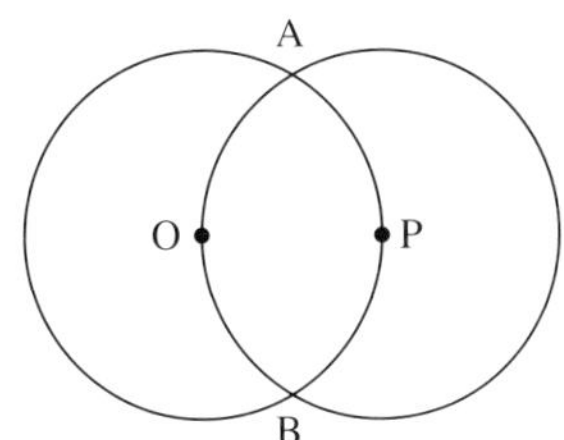

a Show that angle AOP $= \dfrac{\pi}{3}$ and find angle AOB.

b Hence find the area of the sector PAOB of the circle centre P.

c Show that the length of AB is $\sqrt{3}r$ and that the area of overlap of the circles is

$2r^2\left(\dfrac{\pi}{3} - \dfrac{\sqrt{3}}{4}\right)$

9 Three circular beer mats of radius 5 cm are placed on a table so that each touches the other two.
Find the area of the space between the mats.

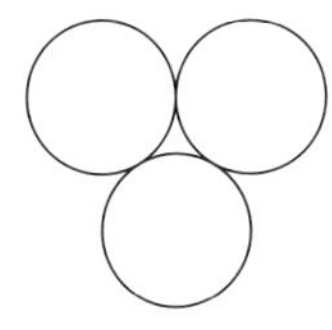

10 The diagram shows a circle, radius r, inscribed and circumscribed by regular hexagons.

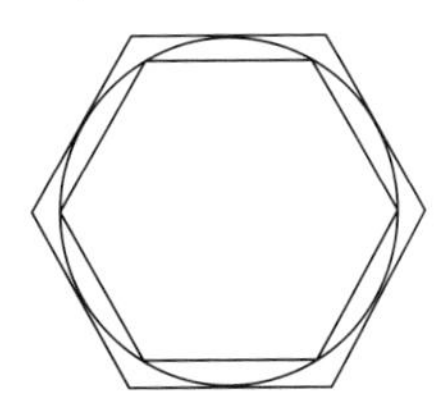

a Find exact expressions for the perimeters of both hexagons in terms of r.

b Hence show that π must lie between 3 and $2\sqrt{3}$.

16.3 Solution of triangles

Solution of triangles or solving triangles means finding sides and/or angles given certain data. Right-angled triangles were solved in Chapter 14. The sine and cosine rules enable non-right-angled triangles to be solved. It is interesting, before introducing the rules, to discover exactly what is required to specify a triangle.

Given data for drawing a triangle, there are cases where

- no triangle is possible
- just one triangle is possible
- more than one triangle is possible.

EXERCISE 16c

For this exercise, it may be helpful to try to construct the triangles with ruler and compasses or, at least, to plan such a construction.

1 Consider these sets of data and decide into which category they fall: no triangle ABC possible, just one triangle ABC possible, or more than one triangle ABC possible.

a $A = 60^\circ$ $B = 100^\circ$ $c = 10\text{ cm}$ **b** $A = 60^\circ$ $B = 100^\circ$ $C = 10^\circ$

2 Repeat Question 1 for these sets of data.

a $a = 8\text{ cm}$ $A = 60^\circ$ $b = 9\text{ cm}$ **b** $a = 10\text{ cm}$ $A = 60^\circ$ $b = 9\text{ cm}$

c $a = 8\text{ cm}$ $b = 7\text{ cm}$ $c = 6\text{ cm}$ **d** $a = 8\text{ cm}$ $A = 75^\circ$ $b = 9\text{ cm}$

e $a = 8\text{ cm}$ $C = 126^\circ$ $b = 9\text{ cm}$ **f** $a = 8\text{ cm}$ $b = 9\text{ cm}$ $c = 1\text{ cm}$

g $a = 10\text{ cm}$ $b = 4\text{ cm}$ $c = 5\text{ cm}$ **h** $A = 25^\circ$ $B = 100^\circ$

i $a = 10\text{ cm}$ $c = 5\text{ cm}$ $C = 30^\circ$ **j** $a = 10\text{ cm}$ $c = 8\text{ cm}$ $A = 90^\circ$

Triangle facts

Some useful facts about triangles should be noted from Exercise 16c.

- The largest angle of a triangle is opposite the longest side and the smallest angle opposite the shortest side.
- There can only be one obtuse angle in a triangle.
  If there is one, it will be opposite the longest side.
- The sum of the lengths of any two sides of a triangle must exceed the length of the third side.
- There are some sets of data which will result in identical triangles being drawn. All such triangles will be **congruent**. For example,

  SSS: (given 3 sides): Exercise 16c Question 2c
  SAS: (given 2 sides and the included angle): Exercise 16c Question 2e
  AAS: (given 2 angles, so the third is known, and one side): Exercise 16c Question 1a
  RHS: (given a right angle, the hypotenuse and one side): Exercise 16c Question 2j

- When three angles are given all the triangles will be **similar**: Exercise 16c, Question 2h.
- When two sides and an angle (not the included angle) are given there may be 0, 1 or 2 possible triangles. (See Exercise 16c Questions 2a, 2b, 2d, 2i.)

16.4 The sine and cosine rules

The sine and cosine rules provide a method of solving triangles.

- To use the sine rule, an angle and the corresponding side, plus one more side or angle are needed.
- To use the cosine rule, either two sides and the included angle or three sides are needed.

The **sine rule**: For any triangle,

$$\frac{a}{\sin A} = \frac{b}{\sin B} = \frac{c}{\sin C} \quad \text{or alternatively} \quad \frac{\sin A}{a} = \frac{\sin B}{b} = \frac{\sin C}{c}$$

Proof

To prove the sine rule: $\dfrac{a}{\sin A} = \dfrac{b}{\sin B} = \dfrac{c}{\sin C}$

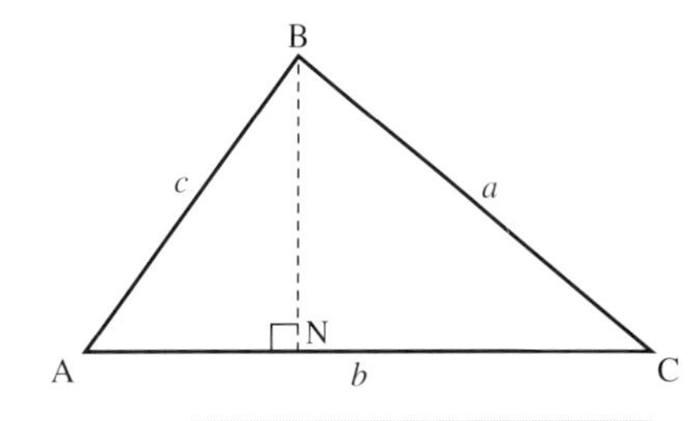

For an acute-angled triangle
BN is perpendicular to AC.

In $\triangle$ABN $\quad BN = c \sin A$

In $\triangle$CBN $\quad BN = a \sin C$

So $\quad a \sin C = c \sin A$

$\therefore \quad \dfrac{a}{\sin A} = \dfrac{c}{\sin C}$

$\sin A = \dfrac{BN}{c} \qquad \sin C = \dfrac{BN}{a}$

Similarly $\quad \dfrac{a}{\sin A} = \dfrac{b}{\sin B}$

The perpendicular from C to AB would give this result.

$\therefore \quad \dfrac{a}{\sin A} = \dfrac{b}{\sin B} = \dfrac{c}{\sin C}$

For an obtuse-angled triangle
BN is perpendicular to AC produced.

AC produced means AC is extended.

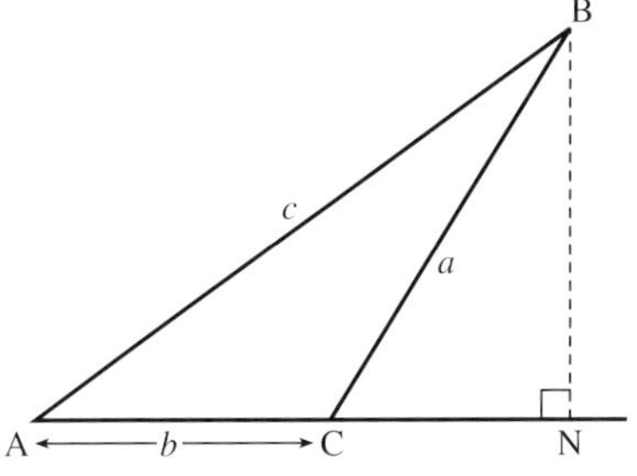
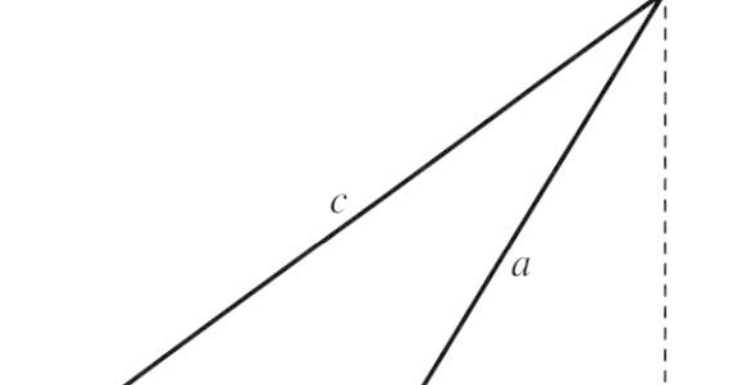

$\sin A = \dfrac{BN}{c}$

$\sin(180° - C) = \sin C$

In $\triangle$ABN $\quad BN = c \sin A$

In $\triangle$CBN $\quad BN = a \sin(180° - C) = a \sin C$

So $\quad a \sin C = c \sin A$

$\therefore \quad \dfrac{a}{\sin A} = \dfrac{c}{\sin C}$

Similarly $\quad \dfrac{c}{\sin C} = \dfrac{b}{\sin B}$

The perpendicular from A to BC produced would give this result.

$\therefore \quad \dfrac{a}{\sin A} = \dfrac{b}{\sin B} = \dfrac{c}{\sin C}$

➤ The **cosine rule**: For any triangle,

$a^2 = b^2 + c^2 - 2bc\cos A$

Proof

To prove the cosine rule: $a^2 = b^2 + c^2 - 2bc\cos A$

For an acute-angled triangle
Draw CN perpendicular to BA.

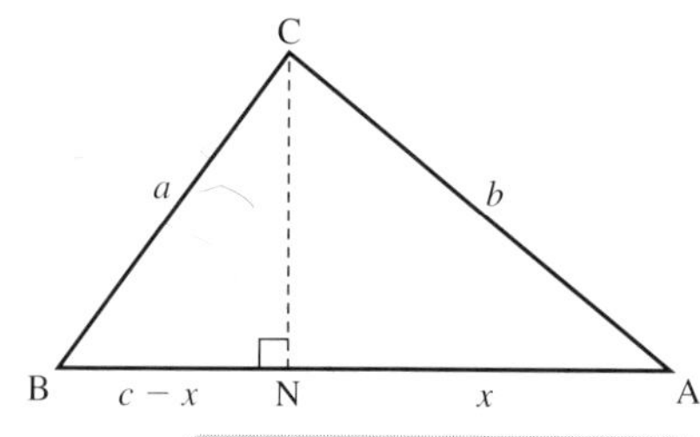

Let AN = x, then BN $= c - x$

In △BCN $\quad \text{CN}^2 = a^2 - (c - x)^2$

$= a^2 - c^2 + 2cx - x^2$

In △ACN $\quad \text{CN}^2 = b^2 - x^2$

Using Pythagoras' theorem

So $\quad a^2 - c^2 + 2cx - x^2 = b^2 - x^2$

$\therefore \quad a^2 = b^2 + c^2 - 2cx$

But, in △ACN $\quad x = b\cos A$

$\cos A = \dfrac{x}{b}$

so $\quad a^2 = b^2 + c^2 - 2bc\cos A$

Similarly $\quad b^2 = a^2 + c^2 - 2ac\cos B$

Putting BN = x gives this result.

and $\quad c^2 = a^2 + b^2 - 2ab\cos C$

The perpendicular from B to AC gives this result.

For an obtuse-angled triangle
Draw BN perpendicular to CA produced.

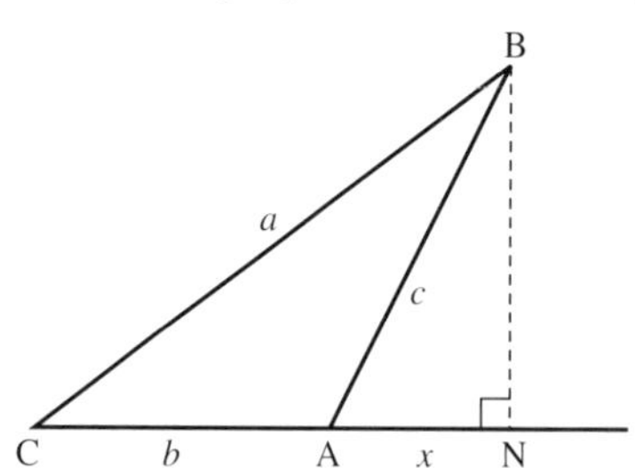

In △BCN $\quad \text{BN}^2 = a^2 - (b + x)^2$

$= a^2 - b^2 - 2bx - x^2$

In △BAN $\quad \text{BN}^2 = c^2 - x^2$

So $\quad a^2 - b^2 - 2bx - x^2 = c^2 - x^2$

$\therefore \quad a^2 = b^2 + c^2 + 2bx$

But, in △ABN $\quad x = c\cos(180° - A)$

$\cos(180° - A) = \dfrac{x}{c}$

$= -c\cos A$

$\cos(180° - A) = -\cos A$

so $\quad a^2 = b^2 + c^2 - 2bc\cos A$

Similarly $\quad b^2 = a^2 + c^2 - 2ac\cos B$

and $\quad c^2 = a^2 + b^2 - 2ab\cos C$

➤ Rearranging the cosine rule gives $\cos A = \dfrac{b^2 + c^2 - a^2}{2bc}$

Given three sides of a triangle, the rearrangement can be used to find the angles.

✓ ***Note*** For right-angled triangles, the sine rule gives

$$\frac{a}{\sin 90^\circ} = \frac{b}{\sin B}$$

But $\sin 90^\circ = 1$, so $\sin B = \dfrac{b}{a}$.

For right-angled triangles, the cosine rule gives

$$a^2 = b^2 + c^2 - 2bc\cos 90^\circ$$

But $\cos 90^\circ = 0$, so $a^2 = b^2 + c^2$, which is Pythagoras' theorem.

In Examples 7–13, all answers are given exactly or correct to 1 decimal place for lengths and for angles.

Example 7 Given $a = 8$ cm, $C = 126^\circ$ and $b = 9$ cm, find AB and angle B.

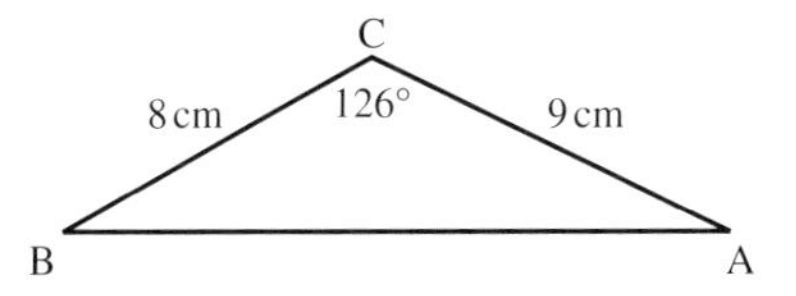

See Exercise 16c, Question 2e.

Two sides and the included angle are given: the cosine rule can be used.

Using the cosine rule

$$c^2 = a^2 + b^2 - 2ab\cos C$$

$$= 8^2 + 9^2 - 2 \times 8 \times 9\cos 126^\circ$$

$\therefore \quad c = 15.2$

So AB = 15.2 cm.

Work out c^2 on the calculator and take the square root. State AB correct to 3 s.f. Keep accurate value of c in memory on calculator for use in the sine rule.

Using the sine rule

$$\frac{\sin B}{b} = \frac{\sin C}{c}$$

$$\frac{\sin B}{9} = \frac{\sin 126^\circ}{c}$$

$$\sin B = \frac{9\sin 126^\circ}{c}$$

$\therefore \quad B = 28.7^\circ$

$B = \arcsin\left(\dfrac{9\sin 126^\circ}{c}\right)$

Since C is obtuse, B must be acute.

Example 8 Given $a = 8\,\text{cm}$, $b = 7\,\text{cm}$ and $c = 6\,\text{cm}$, find all angles of the triangle.

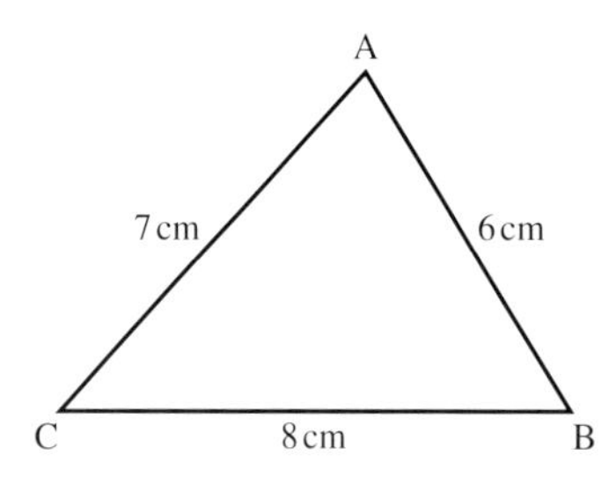

See Exercise 16c, Question 2c.

Given 3 sides, the cosine rule can be used.

$a = 8$, $b = 7$, $c = 6$

The cosine rule gives

No angle is given so the sine rule cannot be used first. Instead, use the cosine rule to find one angle.

$$\begin{aligned}\cos A &= \frac{b^2 + c^2 - a^2}{2bc} \\ &= \frac{7^2 + 6^2 - 8^2}{2 \times 7 \times 6} \\ &= \frac{49 + 36 - 64}{2 \times 7 \times 6} \\ &= \frac{21}{2 \times 7 \times 6} \\ &= \tfrac{1}{4}\end{aligned}$$

cos A could be evaluated on the calculator. The method shown can lead to more elegant solutions.

$$\therefore \quad A = \arccos \tfrac{1}{4} = 75.5^\circ$$

Using the sine rule

$$\frac{\sin A}{a} = \frac{\sin B}{b}$$

$$\frac{\sin A}{8} = \frac{\sin B}{7}$$

$$\text{so} \quad \sin B = \frac{7 \sin A}{8} = \frac{7 \times \sqrt{15}}{8 \times 4}$$

For sin A either use the calculator or, since $\cos A = \frac{1}{4}$, draw a triangle with $\cos A = \frac{1}{4}$ and use Pythagoras' theorem to find the third side.

$\sin A = \dfrac{\sqrt{15}}{4}$

$$\begin{aligned}\therefore \quad B &= \arcsin \frac{7\sqrt{15}}{32} \\ &= 57.9^\circ\end{aligned}$$

Accurate values of A and B should be kept on the calculator and used to calculate C.

$$\begin{aligned}C &= 180^\circ - A - B \\ &= 180^\circ - 75.5^\circ - 57.9^\circ \\ &= 46.6^\circ\end{aligned}$$

Example 9

Given $A = 60°$, $B = 100°$ and $c = 10\,\text{cm}$, find AC.

See Exercise 16c, Question 1a.

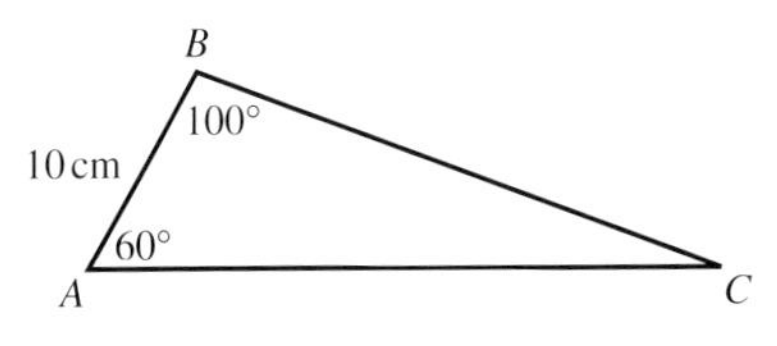

$C = 180° - 100° - 60° = 20°$

Given two angles, the third can be calculated.

Using the sine rule $\dfrac{c}{\sin C} = \dfrac{b}{\sin B}$

Substitute $c = 10$, and $C = 20°$.

$$\frac{10}{\sin 20°} = \frac{b}{\sin 100°}$$

Multiply both sides by sin 100°

$$b = \frac{10 \sin 100°}{\sin 20°}$$

$$= 28.8$$

So $AC = 28.8\,\text{cm}$.

Example 10

In this example, given two sides and an angle (not the included angle), more than one triangle may satisfy the data. This is called the 'ambiguous case'.

Given $a = 8\,\text{cm}$, $A = 60°$ and $b = 9\,\text{cm}$, find the possible values of B and C and sketch the triangles.

See Exercise 16c, Question 2a.

Using the sine rule

$$\frac{\sin A}{a} = \frac{\sin B}{b}$$

$$\frac{\sin 60°}{8} = \frac{\sin B}{9}$$

$$\sin B = \frac{9 \sin 60°}{8}$$

$$B = \arcsin\left(\frac{9 \sin 60°}{8}\right)$$

$$\therefore \quad B = 77.0° \text{ or } B = 180° - 77.0° = 103.0°$$

There are two possible positions for B (marked B_1 and B_2) and $\therefore$ 2 possible values for angle B.

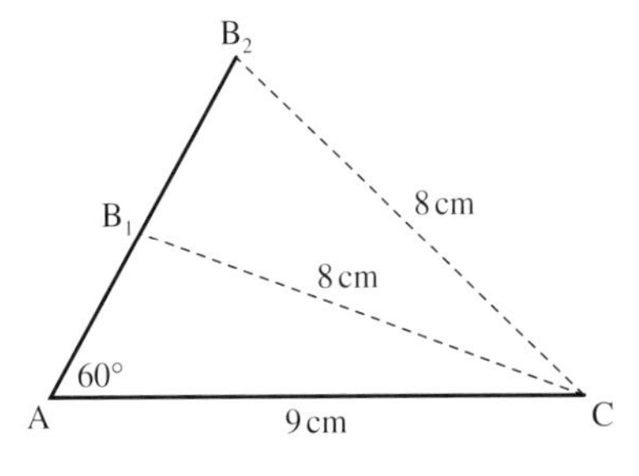

When $B = 77.0°$ $C = 180° - 60° - 77.0° = 43.0°$

When $B = 103.0°$ $C = 180° - 60° - 103.0° = 17.0°$

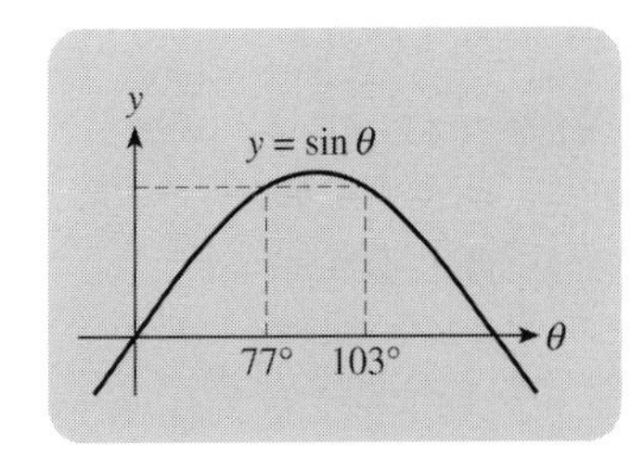

There are two possible triangles.

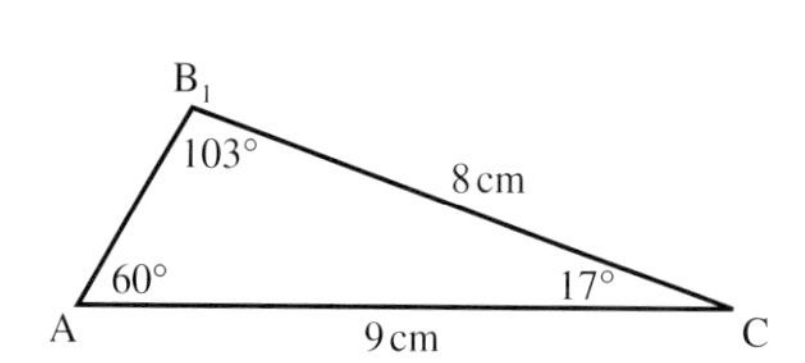

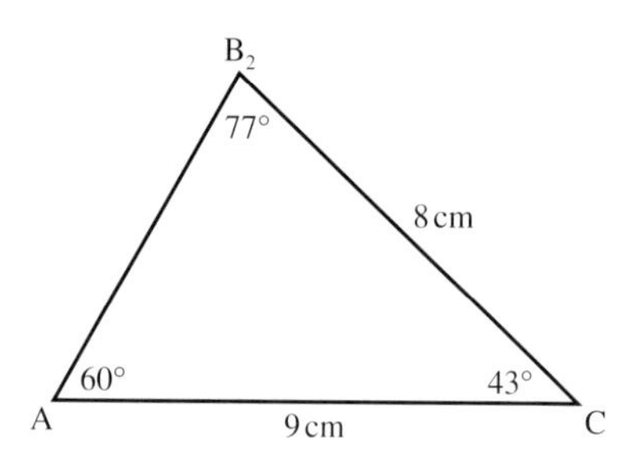

Example 11

How many triangles can be drawn with $a = 10\,\text{cm}$, $A = 60^\circ$ and $b = 9\,\text{cm}$?

For each possible triangle find angle B.

See Exercise 16c, Question 2b.

By the sine rule: $\dfrac{\sin B}{b} = \dfrac{\sin A}{a}$

$b = 9,\ a = 10.$

$$\frac{\sin B}{9} = \frac{\sin 60^\circ}{10}$$

$$\sin B = \frac{9 \sin 60^\circ}{10}$$

$$B = \arcsin\left(\frac{9 \sin 60^\circ}{10}\right)$$

$\therefore$ $B = 51.2^\circ$

or $B = 180^\circ - 51.2^\circ = 128.8^\circ$

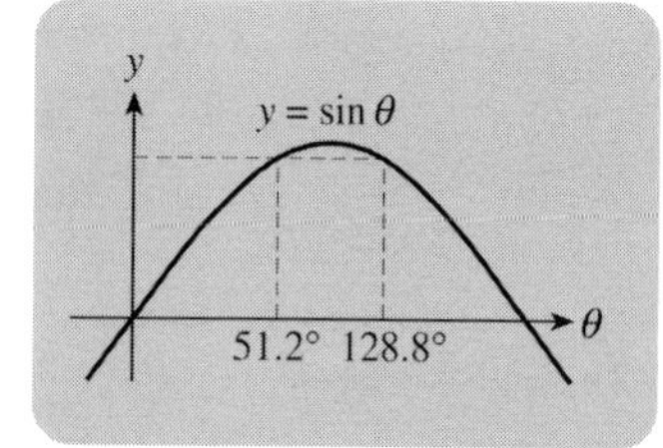

Angle B cannot be 128.8°, because angle $A = 60^\circ$ and the sum of the angles of a triangle is 180°.

So only one triangle can be drawn, with angle $B = 51.2^\circ$

y

$y = \sin\theta$

51.2° 128.8° θ

Example 12

In the triangle shown, find Q.

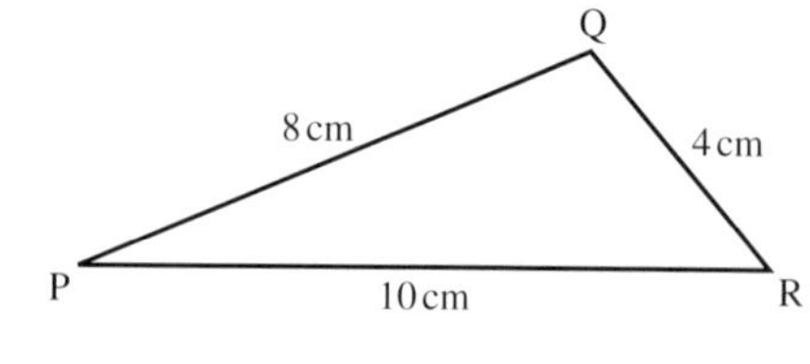

By the cosine rule

$p = 4,\ q = 10,\ r = 8.$

$$q^2 = p^2 + r^2 - 2pr\cos Q$$

$$\cos Q = \frac{p^2 + r^2 - q^2}{2pr}$$

so $$\cos Q = \frac{4^2 + 8^2 - 10^2}{2 \times 4 \times 8}$$

cos Q could be evaluated here on a calculator.

$$= \frac{16 + 64 - 100}{2 \times 4 \times 8}$$

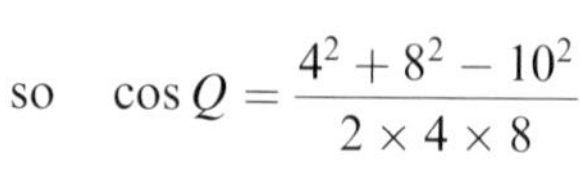

$$= \frac{-\cancel{20}^{5}}{2 \times \cancel{4} \times 8}$$

$$= -\frac{5}{16}$$

$Q = \arccos\left(-\frac{5}{16}\right)$

$\cos Q$ is $-$ve $\therefore$ angle Q is obtuse, so $Q = 108.2^\circ$.

Example 13 In triangle LMN, with LN = 6 cm, MN = 5 cm and $N = 40°$, find angles L and M.

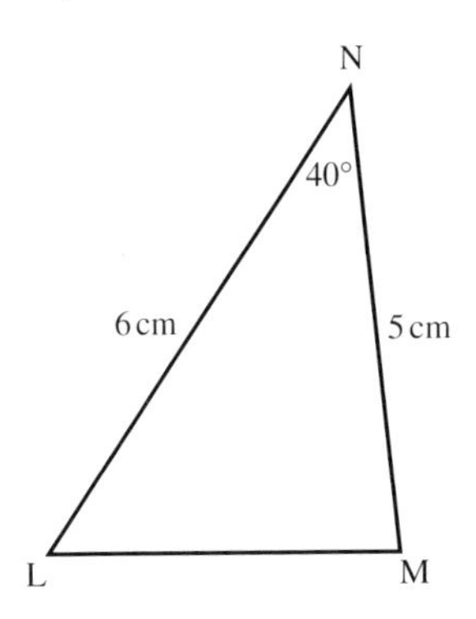

Using the cosine rule

$$LM^2 = 5^2 + 6^2 - 2 \times 5 \times 6 \cos 40°$$
$$= 25 + 36 - 60 \cos 40°$$
$$= 61 - 60 \cos 40°$$

The sine rule cannot be used as there is no side and its corresponding angle. The cosine rule can be used to find LM.

$$\therefore \quad LM = \sqrt{61 - 60 \cos 40°} = 3.877\ldots$$

Store LM in memory for future use.

✓ ***Note*** To find angles L and M, the sine rule can be used. However, when the sine rule is used to find an angle two possibilities are obtained, one acute and one obtuse. The obtuse angle may not be a possible solution.

Angle M (opposite the longest side) could be obtuse.

Angle L (not opposite the longest side) must be acute, so angle L should be calculated first.

Using the sine rule: $$\frac{\sin L}{5} = \frac{\sin 40°}{LM}$$

Recall LM from calculator memory or use original expression for LM.

$$\sin L = \frac{5 \sin 40°}{LM}$$

$$\therefore \quad L = 56.0°$$

L must be acute because it is not opposite the longest side.

Now, $$N = 40°$$

$$\therefore \quad M = 180° - 40° - 56.0° = 84.0°$$

So angles L and M are 56.0° and 84.0° respectively.

EXERCISE 16d

This exercise gives practice in solving triangles.
Give answers correct to 3 significant figures unless stated otherwise.

1 Use the sine rule to find the values of the unknown sides and angles.
In any ambiguous case, give both solutions.

a

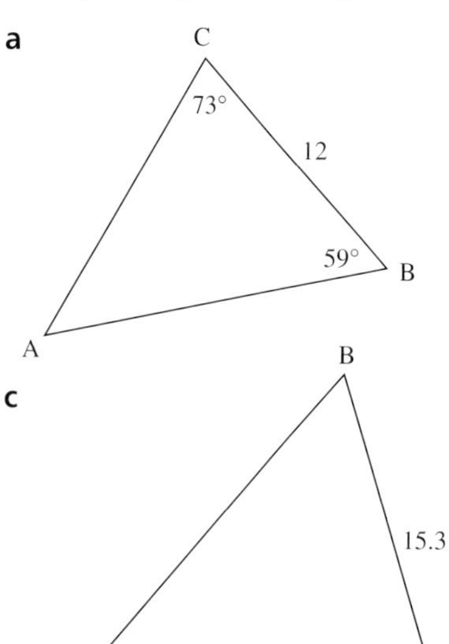

b

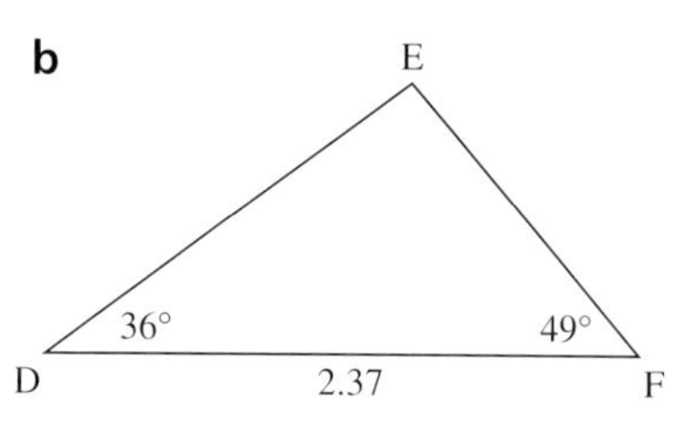

c

d

e

f

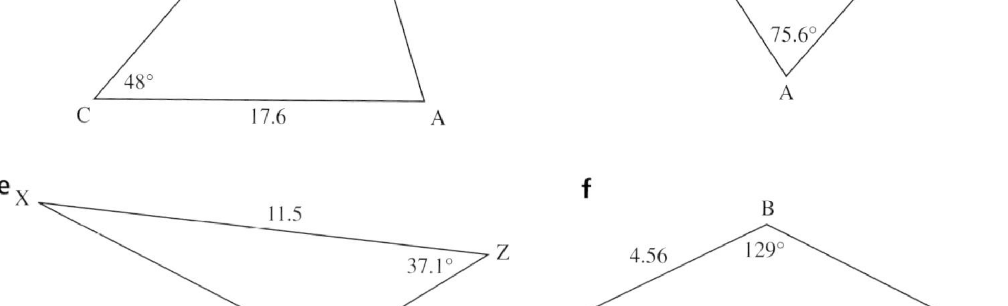

2 Use the cosine rule to find the values of the unknown sides and angles.

a **b** **c** **d** **e**

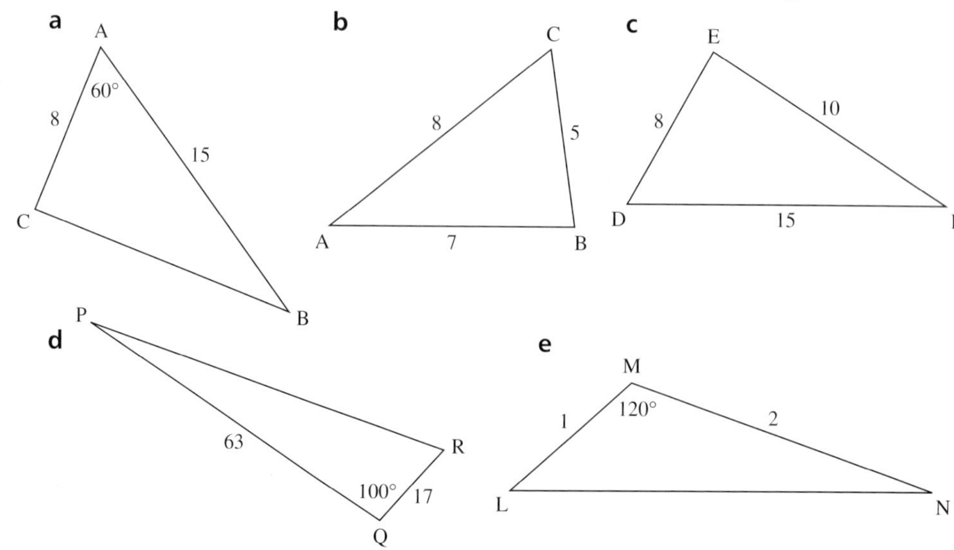

3 Find all missing sides and angles in these triangles.

a $A = 73.2^\circ$ $B = 61.7^\circ$ $c = 171$ **b** $a = 10$ $b = 12$ $c = 9$

c $a = 136$ $B = 102^\circ$ $C = 43^\circ$ **d** $a = 31$ $b = 42$ $C = 104^\circ$

e $A = 28^\circ$ $a = 8.5$ $b = 14.8$ **f** $a = 22$ $b = 62$ $c = 48$

4 Find the values of the unknowns in these triangles, without using a calculator. Give exact answers.

a

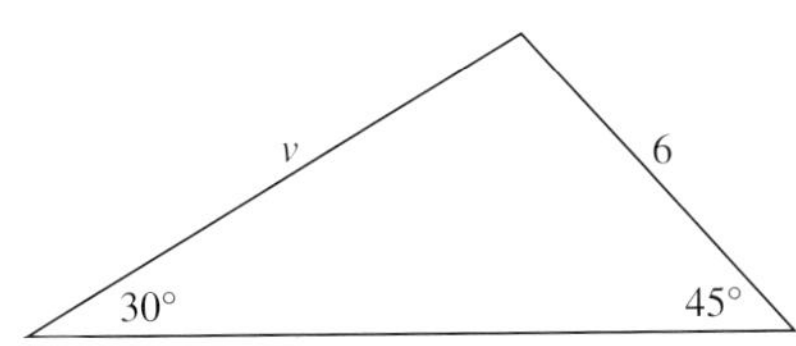

b

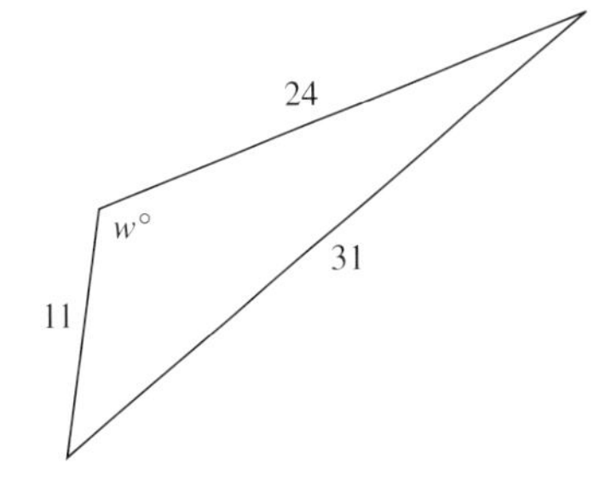

c

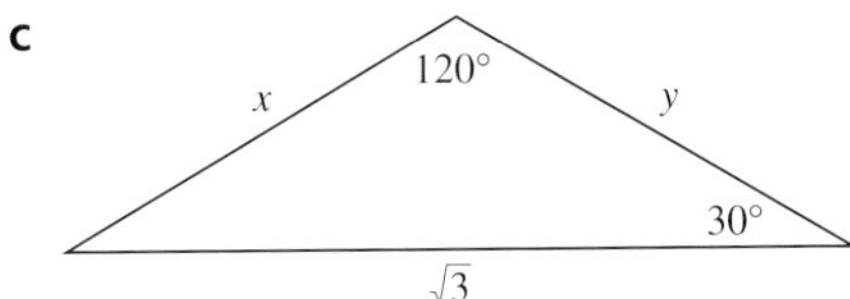

d

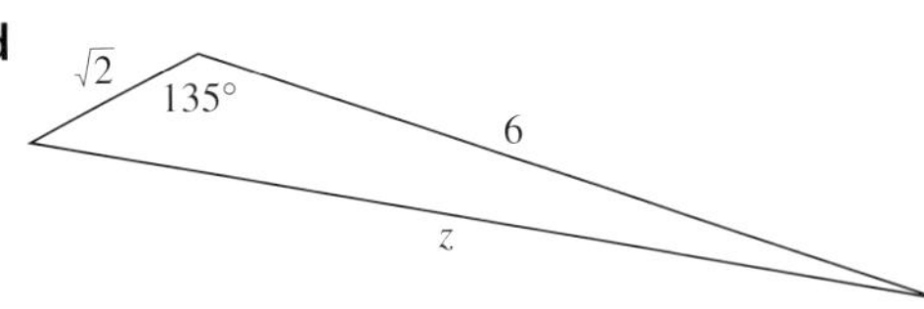

5 Two points A and B on a straight coastline are 1km apart, B being due east of A. If a ship is observed on bearings 167° and 205° from A and B respectively, what is its distance from the coastline?

6 A boat is sailing directly towards a cliff.
The angle of elevation of a point on the top of the cliff and straight ahead of the boat increases from 10° to 15° as the ship sails a distance of 50 m.
Find the height of the cliff.

7 A triangle has sides 10 cm, 11 cm and 15 cm.
By how much does its largest angle differ from a right angle?

8 A ship rounds a headland by sailing first 4 nautical miles on a course of 069° then 5 nautical miles on a course of 295°.
Calculate the distance and bearing of its new position from its original position.

9 A motorist travelling along a straight level road in the direction 053° observes a pylon on a bearing of 037°. 800 m further along the road the bearing of the pylon is 296°. Calculate the distance of the pylon from the road.

10 Two light ropes hang 1.5 m apart from the ceiling of a gym. One is 4 m long and just reaches the ground. The other is 3.8 m long. The ends of the ropes are pulled together so that, with the ropes taut, their free ends touch at P. Find

a the angle between the free ends of the ropes at P

b the height of P above the ground.

EXERCISE 16d
(continued)

Questions 11–14 are of types that could have been set in the context of astronomy, stage (and other) design, surveying, sailing, engineering etc. A strength of mathematics is that the same problem-solving techniques can apply in so many fields.

11 Two points, A and B, are marked, on level ground, 30 m apart and in line with a tower. The angles of elevation from A and B are 29° and 37° respectively. Find the height of the tower to the nearest metre.

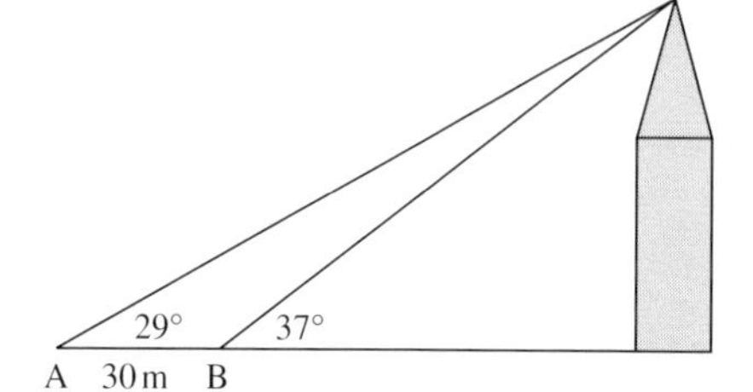

12 From the top of a building the angles of depression of the top and bottom of a tower 100 m tall are 41° and 52°. Assuming that the tower and the building are on level ground, find the height of the building, correct to the nearest metre.

13 From a point A, 25 m due south of a tree, the angle of elevation of the top of the tree is 27°. From a point B the bearing of the tree is 204° and the angle of elevation of its top is 18°. The points A, B and the foot of the tree are on level ground. Find, correct to the nearest 0.1 m

a the height of the tree

b the distance from B to the foot of the tree

c the distance AB.

14 From a point A the bearing of the base of a tower 60 m high is 053° and the angle of elevation of the top of the tower is 16°. From a point B the bearing is 300° and the angle of elevation is 20°. Find the distance AB.

EXERCISE 16e
(Extension)

1 Two concentric circles are drawn. The larger one has a radius a times that of the smaller one. A pair of radii are drawn with an angle θ between them, dividing each circle into two arcs.
Show that if the major arc of the smaller circle has the same length as the minor arc of the larger circle, then

$$\theta = \frac{2\pi}{a+1}$$

2 The base of a traffic cone is made from a square piece of plastic, side $2a$ and centre C, by cutting off the corners with circular arcs, centre C. The radius of the arcs is chosen so that the curved sides of the base subtend an angle of $\frac{\pi}{6}$ at C, while the straight sides subtend an angle of $\frac{\pi}{3}$. Finally, a circular hole, centre C and radius b, is removed.

Find an expression for the area of the base.

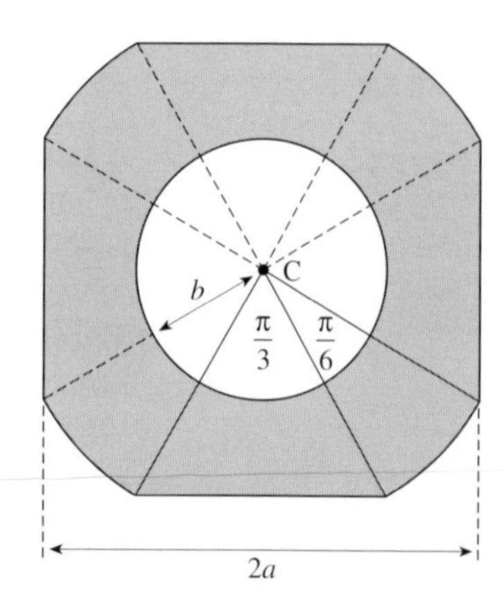

3 A hexagonal nut 2 mm thick has its centre at C. The distance from C to the mid-point of a side of the nut is 4 mm. The hole in the centre of the nut has radius 2 mm. The thread in the central hole may be ignored.

a Find the volume of metal in the nut.

The nut is to be treated with a protective coating.

b Show that the surface area of the nut is $96\sqrt{3}\,\text{mm}^2$.

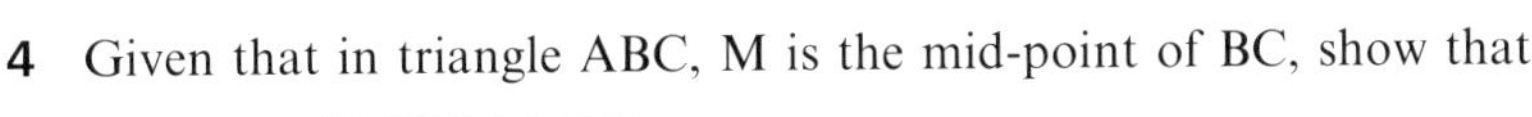

4 Given that in triangle ABC, M is the mid-point of BC, show that

$\text{AM} = \frac{1}{2}\sqrt{2(c^2 + b^2) - a^2}$

5 Show that the area A of any quadrilateral whose diagonals intersect at an angle θ is given by

$A = \frac{1}{2}d_1 d_2 \sin\theta$

where d_1, d_2 are the lengths of the diagonals.

6 The first diagram shows two concentric circles with radii 1 and 2 units.

a Is it possible to find a value of θ such that

Area of region A = Area of region B?

If so, find the appropriate value of θ.

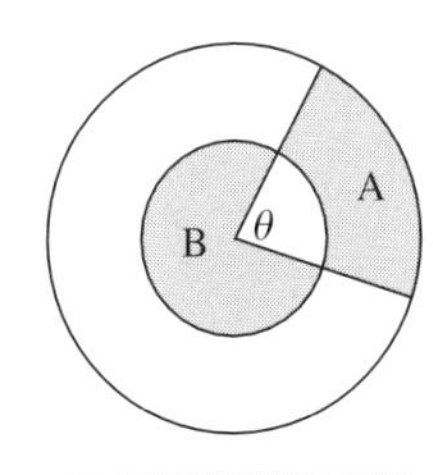

b Is it possible to find a value of θ such that

Perimeter of region A = Perimeter of region B?

If so, find the appropriate value of θ.

Work in radians.

The second diagram shows three concentric circles with radius 1, 2 and 3 units.

c Repeat parts **a** and **b**.

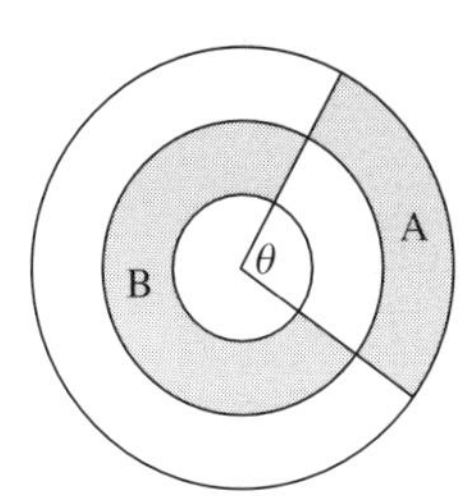

Notice that in the third diagram the regions are between the circles of radii 4 and 3 and those of radii 3 and 2. The circle radius 1 is not used at all.

d Repeat parts **a** and **b** for four concentric circles.

e Predict, from the results so far, the result for 5, 6 and n concentric circles.

f Given that the largest circle has radius $n + 1$ units, find an expression for θ in terms of n.

g Find the limiting value of θ as the number of circles increases.

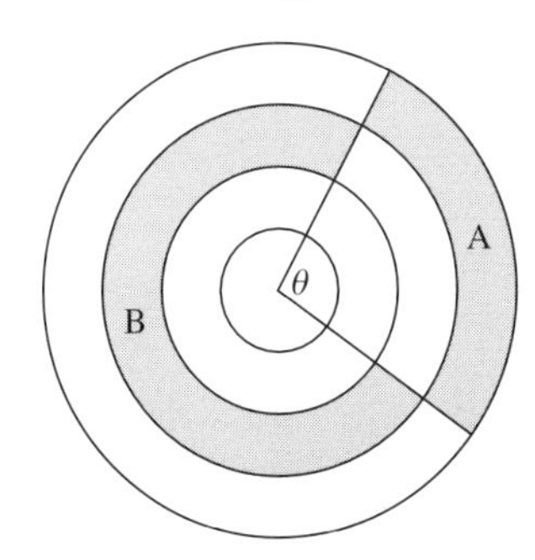

EXERCISE 16e
(continued)

7 Work in radians, giving all the answers as exact expressions. All the discs in this question have radius 1 and are placed flat on a table.

a Three discs are placed so that their centres form an equilateral triangle of side 2. Find the area between the discs.

b Four discs are placed so that their centres form a square of side 2. Find the area between the discs.

c Five discs are placed so that their centres form a regular pentagon of side 2, as shown.

i Find the size of each interior angle of a regular pentagon.

ii Given that O is the centre of the regular pentagon, find the area of triangle AOB.

iii Find the area between the discs.

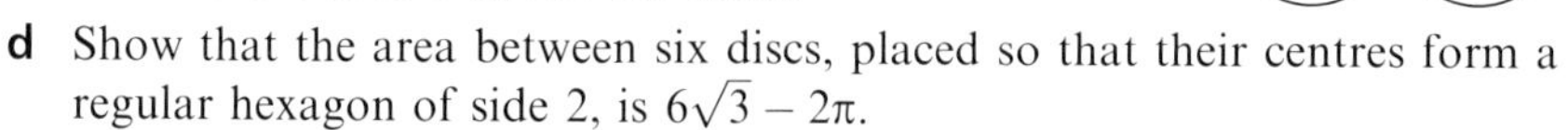

d Show that the area between six discs, placed so that their centres form a regular hexagon of side 2, is $6\sqrt{3} - 2\pi$.

e Show that the area, A_n, between n discs, placed so that their centres form a regular polygon of side 2, is given by

$$A_n = n\cot\frac{\pi}{n} + \frac{\pi}{2}(2 - n)$$

8 Work in radians, giving all the answers as exact expressions. All the discs in this question have radius 1 and are placed flat on a table. The perimeter, in each case, is defined as the length of a taut string passing round the outside of the discs.

a Three discs are placed so that the lines joining their centres form an equilateral triangle. (See Example 6 on page 377.) Find the perimeter.

b Four discs are placed so that the lines joining their centres form a square. Find the perimeter.

c n discs are placed so that the lines joining their centres form a regular polygon. Find the perimeter when **i** $n = 5$, **ii** $n = 6$.

d Show that the perimeter, P_n, for n discs, is given by $P_n = 2(n + \pi)$.

9 Show that, with the usual notation, given angle A and sides a and c, there will be

a only one possible triangle if $\frac{a}{c} > 1$

b two possible triangles if $\sin A < \frac{a}{c} < 1$

c no possible triangle if $\frac{a}{c} < \sin A$.

10 Draw a triangle ABC and its circumcircle (i.e. the circle through the vertices A, B and C) marking the centre, O. Show that $\angle BOC = 2A$, where $\angle BAC = A$. By considering the isosceles triangle OBC, show that, where R is the radius of the circumcircle

$$\frac{a}{\sin A} = 2R$$

Similarly, it can be shown that $\frac{b}{\sin B}$ *and* $\frac{c}{\sin C}$ *equal 2R. This gives a more general form of the sine rule (see page 381):* $\frac{a}{\sin A} = \frac{b}{\sin B} = \frac{c}{\sin C} = 2R$

11 The area $\triangle$ of a triangle can be calculated from the formula, known as Heron's formula

$$\triangle = \sqrt{s(s-a)(s-b)(s-c)}$$

where $s = \frac{1}{2}(a+b+c)$. Prove the formula by eliminating A from the formulae $a^2 = b^2 + c^2 - 2bc\cos A$ and $\triangle = \frac{1}{2}bc\sin A$.

12 The sides of a triangle are three terms of a geometric sequence with common ratio r.

a Show that $\dfrac{\sqrt{5}-1}{2} < r < \dfrac{\sqrt{5}+1}{2}$.

b Show further that if $\sqrt{\dfrac{\sqrt{5}-1}{2}} < r < \sqrt{\dfrac{\sqrt{5}+1}{2}}$ the triangle is acute angled.

EXERCISE 16f (Miscellaneous)

1 Find any missing angles, missing sides and the area of these triangles.

a **b** 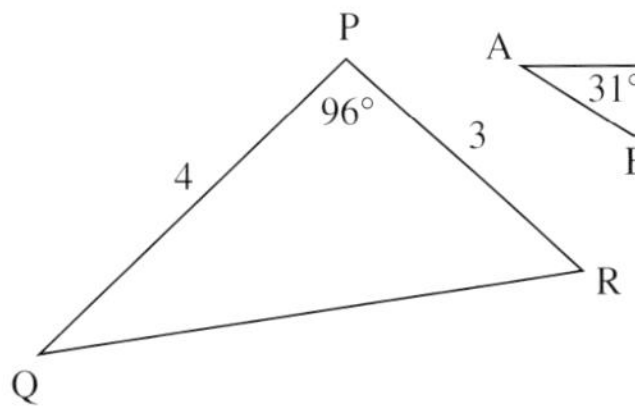 **c**

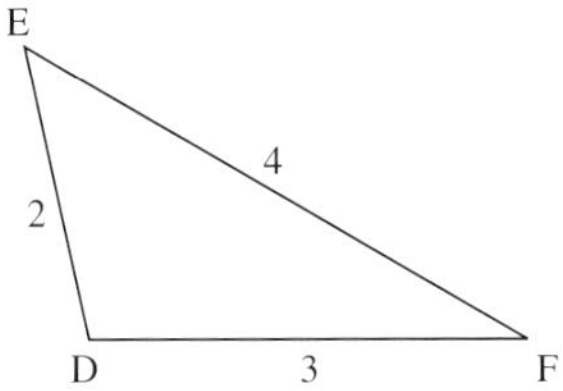

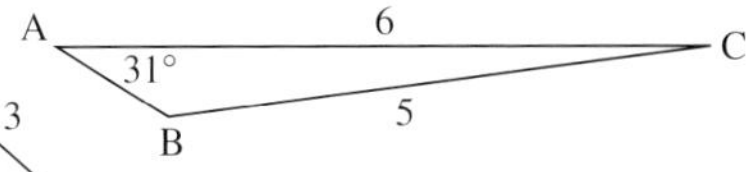

E D F 2 4 3

P Q R 96° 4 3

A B C 31° 6 5

2 Find the area of these triangles, without using a calculator.

a **b**

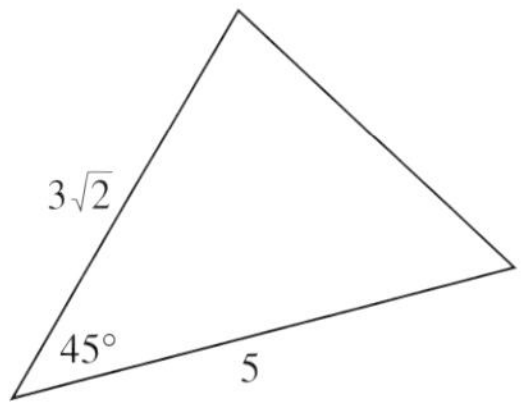

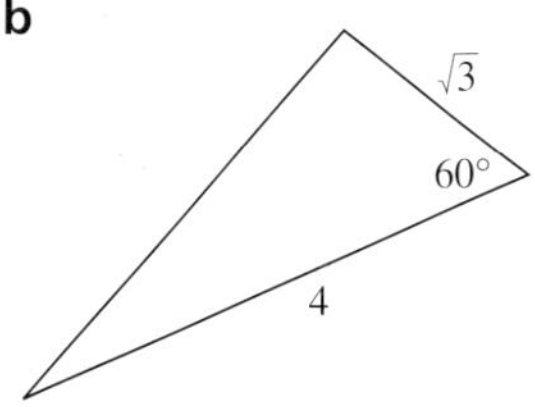

$3\sqrt{2}$ 45° 5

$\sqrt{3}$ 60° 4

3 A circular coin is held stationary on a flat horizontal surface while an identical coin rolls around its perimeter, without slipping.
Find through how many radians the second coin turns.

4 The lengths of the sides of a triangle are 10, x and $x-2$.
The side of length $x-2$ is opposite an angle of 60°. Find x.

5 In triangle XYZ, $x = 29$, $y = 21$ and $z = 20$. Find

a the area of the triangle

b the length of the perpendicular from X to YZ.

6 The area of a sector of a circle, diameter 7 cm, is 18.375 cm^2.
Find, without using a calculator, the length of the arc of the sector.

EXERCISE 16f
(continued)

7 A flower bed is designed as follows: Triangle DEF is an equilateral triangle of side 8 m. Arcs EF, FD and DE have radii 8 m and centres D, E and F respectively.

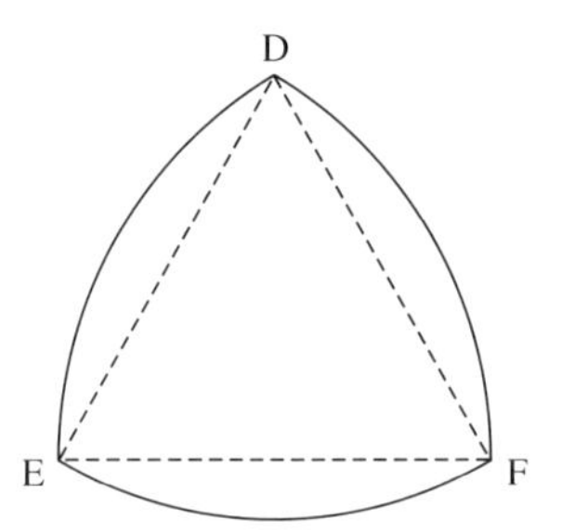

Find the area of the flower bed correct to the nearest 0.1m^2.

8 O is the centre of a circle radius r. AB and CD subtend angles $\frac{3\pi}{4}$ and $\frac{\pi}{4}$ at O.

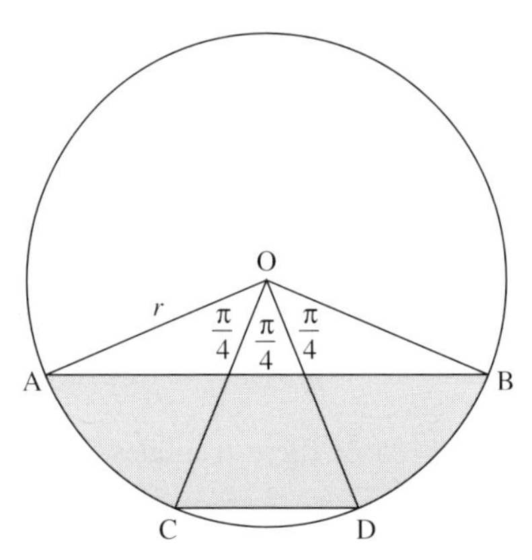

Show that the area shaded is equal to $\frac{1}{4}$ of the area of the circle.

9 Using the usual notation, state what can be deduced about a triangle with the property:

a $a^2 > b^2 + c^2$ **b** $a^2 = b^2 + c^2$ **c** $a^2 < b^2 + c^2$

d $a^2 = b^2 + c^2 - bc$ **e** $a^2 = b^2 + c^2 + bc$

10 In any triangle, show that $a = b\cos C + c\cos B$.

11 The sides of a triangle are in the ratio 2:3:4. Show that the cosine of the largest angle is $-\frac{1}{4}$.

12 Find the area of

a the largest square **b** the largest circle **c** the largest triangle

d the largest inverted semicircle

which can be inscribed in a semicircle of radius r.

13 Given a right-angle triangle, one could construct, on each side, shapes such as **i** semicircles or **ii** equilateral triangles or **iii** regular hexagons.

a Using Pythagoras' theorem, or otherwise, show that in each of cases **i–iii** above, the area of the shape on the hypotenuse is equal to the sum of the areas of the shapes on the other two sides.

b State a general rule.

Test yourself

1 In triangle ABC, AB = 12, BC = 5 and angle $C = 80°$.

Angle A is equal to

A 33.3° **B** 24.2° **C** 24.6° **D** 65.4° **E** 22.6°

2 A sector of angle 3 radians and radius 4 has an area of

A $\frac{12}{\pi}$ **B** $\frac{16\pi}{3}$ **C** 48 **D** 24 **E** $\frac{2\pi}{15}$

3 In triangle ABC, $a = 15$, $c = 8$ and angle $B = 2$ radians.

Side b is equal to

A 11.1 **B** 49.1 **C** 13.8 **D** 19.7 **E** 30.0

4 A circle of radius 5 is cut by a chord of length 8.

The minor segment has area approximately equal to

A 23.2 **B** 12 **C** 11.6 **D** 11.2 **E** 5.6

5 A triangle has sides 10, 20 and 25.

Correct to 3 significant figures, the largest angle is

A 108° **B** 129° **C** 71.8° **D** 88.6° **E** 144°

6 In triangle ABC, $A = 25°$, $a = 27$ and $b = 57$.

Correct to 1 decimal place, angle B may be equal to

A 11.5° **B** 38.2° **C** 63.0° **D** 116.8° **E** 88.2°

7 Triangle PQR has PQ = 2, PR = $\sqrt{8}$ and angle $P = 135°$.

The area of triangle PQR is

A $\sqrt{20}$ **B** 4 **C** 2 **D** $6\sqrt{2}$ **E** $2 - \frac{1}{\sqrt{2}}$

8 $\cos\theta = \frac{\sqrt{3}}{2}$. A sector of radius $\frac{12}{\pi}$ and angle θ has arc length

A $\frac{12}{\pi}$ **B** 2 or 22 **C** 10 or 14 **D** $\frac{5\pi}{6}$ **E** 2π or 10π

9 A triangle ABC, whose area is $3\,\text{cm}^2$, has sides AB = 4 cm and BC = $\sqrt{3}$ cm.
Angle ABC =

A 90° **B** 60° **C** 120° **D** 30° **E** 60° or 120°

10 In triangle PQR, PQ = $a + 1$, PR = $2a + 1$, QR = $4a - 1$ and angle P = 120°.

$a =$

A $\frac{1}{9}$ **B** $\frac{11}{13}$ **C** 3 **D** 2 **E** $2\frac{1}{2}$

Key points

Applications of Trigonometry

When θ is measured in radians

- area of sector $= \frac{1}{2}r^2\theta$
- length of arc $= r\theta$

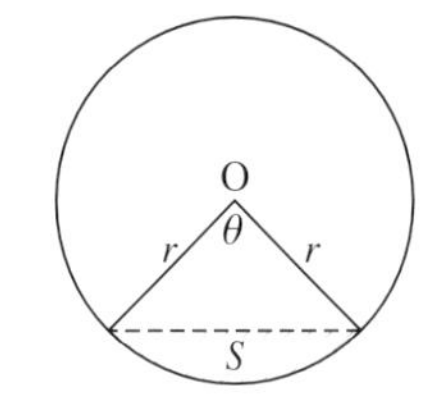

Area of triangle $= \frac{1}{2}ab\sin C$

Area of segment $S =$ Area of sector $-$ Area of triangle

$$= \frac{1}{2}r^2(\theta - \sin\theta)$$

Sine rule

$$\frac{a}{\sin A} = \frac{b}{\sin B} = \frac{c}{\sin C}$$

or alternatively

$$\frac{\sin A}{a} = \frac{\sin B}{b} = \frac{\sin C}{c}$$

(Remember the ambiguous case: if $\sin A = k < 1$, there may be two possible values for A.)

Cosine rule

$$a^2 = b^2 + c^2 - 2bc\cos A$$

or alternatively

$$\cos A = \frac{b^2 + c^2 - a^2}{2bc}$$

In multistage problems, avoid rounding errors by using full calculator values throughout.

Revision Exercise 3

1 An arithmetic progression has a first term 1 and a common difference of $\frac{1}{2}$.

a Find the least value of n such that the nth term exceeds 17.5.

b Solve the inequality $S_n \geqslant \frac{209}{2}$ where S_n denotes the sum of the first n terms.

2 Obtain an expression for $\sum_{r=1}^{n} \left(\frac{1}{2} - 2^r + 2r\right)$ in terms of n.

3 A sequence is defined by $10x$, $9x + y$, $8x + 2y$, $\cdots$, $10y$

a Show that the sequence is an arithmetic progression. State the common difference.

b Find the sum of the sequence in terms of x and y.

c Find the values of x and y given that the second term of the sequence is 29 and the sum of the sequence is 275.

4 A geometric progression has the first term 6 and common ratio $\frac{5}{6}$.

a Find the least value of n for which the nth term is less than $\frac{1}{10}$.

b Find the least value of n for which the sum of the first n terms exceeds 35.

5 The sum of the first n terms of a geometric progression is $\dfrac{4(1-(-0.5)^n)}{1.5}$.

a State the first term and the common ratio.

b The sum to infinity of a geometric series is $\dfrac{p}{1-q^2}$.

State the first term and the common ratio.

6 **a** Show that $\log m + \log(m^2) + \log(m^3) + \cdots$ is an arithmetic series.

b Evaluate $\sum_{i=1}^{100} \log_{10}(3^i)$ correct to 1 decimal place.

7 The nth term of a series is given by $u_n = \sum_{r=1}^{n-1} u_r$, $n > 1$, $u_1 = 1$.

a Find a simpler expression for u_n.

b Find the sum of the first n terms of the series, i.e. $u_1 + u_2 + u_3 + \cdots + u_n$.

8 **a** Find the sum of all the integers up to 120.

b Find the sum of all the integers up to 120 which are not multiples of 6.

c Find the sum of all the integers up to 120 which are not multiples of 2 or 3.

9 A pagoda is a tall oriental building. One particular pagoda is constructed from twelve storeys. The heights of the storeys are in arithmetic progression. The total height of the pagoda is known to be 34.8 metres. The top storey is 1.8 metres high. Find the height of the first and second storeys.

10 The functions f and g are defined for all real values by $f(x) = 2x - 3$ and $g(x) = (x+1)^2$.
The functions p and q are the composite functions fg and gf respectively.
Find $\int p(x)\,dx$ and $\int q(x)\,dx$.

11 The functions f and g are defined for positive values of x by

$f(x) = 2x^2 + 6x + 4 \quad g(x) = x^2 + 2x$

a Simplify $\dfrac{f(x)}{g(x)}$.

b Find $\displaystyle\int \frac{f(x)}{x^2 g(x)}\,dx$.

12 **a** Sketch the curve $y = -x^2 + 6x - 5$. Show clearly the maximum point and all points where the curve crosses the axes.

b Find the area of the finite region bounded by the curve and the x-axis.

c Find the coordinates of the points where the line $y = 3$ cuts the curve.

d Find the area of the finite region bounded by the curve and the line $y = 3$.

13 **a** Find the values of x for which the straight line $y = 2x + 6$ meets the curve $y = 9x - x^3$.

b Sketch on one diagram the graphs of $y = 2x + 6$ and $y = 9x - x^3$. Show clearly all the points found in part **a** and also all intercepts.

c Find the area of the finite region which lies entirely in the first quadrant and which is bounded by the straight line $y = 2x + 6$ and the curve $y = 9x - x^3$

14 Sketch these graphs on separate diagrams for $0° \leqslant x \leqslant 720°$.

a $y = \sin x$ **b** $y = \sin 2x$ **c** $y = \sin\left(\frac{x}{2}\right)$ **d** $y = 2\sin x$

15 Sketch these graphs on separate diagrams for $0 \leqslant x \leqslant 2\pi$.

a $y = 2\cos x - 1$ **b** $y = 2(\cos 2x + 1)$ **c** $y = \frac{1}{2}\cos\left(x + \frac{\pi}{2}\right)$

16 State how many solutions each of these equations has for $-\pi \leqslant x \leqslant \pi$. Do not solve the equations.

a $\sin x = 1$ **b** $2\sin x = 1$ **c** $2\sin 2x = 1$ **d** $2\sin\left(\frac{x}{2}\right) = 1$

17 Find the exact solutions of the equation $2\cos^2 x = 3(1 + \sin x)$, for $0 \leqslant x \leqslant 2\pi$.

18 Solve each of these equations correct to 1 decimal place.

a $\tan x = \frac{1}{3}$ $\quad -90° \leqslant x \leqslant 90°$ **b** $\tan 2x = \frac{1}{3}$ $\quad -90° \leqslant x \leqslant 90°$

c $\sin x = -\frac{1}{3}$ $\quad -180° \leqslant x \leqslant 180°$ **d** $\sin(x - 30°) = -\frac{1}{3}$ $\quad -180° \leqslant x \leqslant 180°$

e $\cos x = \frac{1}{3}$ $\quad 0° \leqslant x \leqslant 360°$ **f** $\cos(2x + 10°) = \frac{1}{3}$ $\quad 0° \leqslant x \leqslant 360°$

19 $f(x) = x^2$, $g(x) = \sin x$ and $h(x) = x - \frac{\pi}{2}$.
For $-\pi \leqslant x \leqslant \pi$, find all the solutions of these equations .

a $fg(x) = \frac{1}{4}$ **b** $fgh(x) = \frac{3}{4}$

20 Some of these are equations and some are identities.
Prove the identities, and solve the equations for $0 \leqslant x \leqslant 2\pi$.

a $\frac{\sin x}{\cos x} + \frac{\cos x}{\sin x} = \frac{1}{\sin x \cos x}$ **b** $(1 - \sin x)^2 = 1 - \sin^2 x$

c $(\sin x + \cos x)^2 = \sin^2 x + \cos^2 x$ **d** $\frac{\cos x}{1 + \sin x} + \frac{1 + \sin x}{\cos x} = \frac{2}{\cos x}$

e $\frac{\cos^2 x}{\cos x - \sin x} + \frac{\sin^2 x}{\sin x - \cos x} = \sin x + \cos x$

21 Eliminate θ from this pair of equations.

$2y - 1 = 3\cos\theta$

$x + 4 = \frac{1}{2}\sin\theta$

22 $f(x) = 3\sin x - 2\cos x$ and $g(x) = 2\sin x + \cos x$.
Find the exact solutions to the equation $3f(x) = g(x)$ for $0 \leqslant x \leqslant 2\pi$.

23 Prove these identities.

a $(\sin A + \cos A)^2 + (\sin A - \cos A)^2 = 2$

b $\cos^2 A - \sin^2 A = 2\cos^2 A - 1$

c $\dfrac{1 - \tan^2 A}{1 + \tan^2 A} = 2\cos^2 A - 1$

d $(\cos^2 A - 2)^2 - 4\sin^2 A = \cos^4 A$

24 An arc of length 2 cm subtends an angle θ at the centre of a circle of radius r cm. The corresponding sector of the circle has area $5\,\text{cm}^2$.

a Find the values of r and θ

b Find the perimeter of the sector.

25 Two circles each of radius r, with centres at A and D, intersect at B and C. Angle BAC is θ radians.

a Find the area of the triangle ABC.

b Find the area of the sector ABC.

c Show that the overlap of the two circles has area $r^2(\theta - \sin\theta)$.

A solar eclipse can be modelled by two overlapping circles, each of radius r.

d When the distance between the centres of the circles is $\frac{3}{2}r$, show that $\cos\frac{\theta}{2} = \frac{3}{4}$. Hence show that the area of the overlap is approximately 14% of the total area of one of the circles.

e Find the corresponding percentage when the distance between the centres is r.

f Find the corresponding percentage when the distance between the centres is $\frac{r}{2}$.

Examination Questions 3

Sequences and series

1 The 12th term of an arithmetic progression is 17 and the sum of the first 12 terms is 105. Find the first term. *UCLES*

2 The sum of the second and third terms of a geometric series is equal to six times the first term. Find the possible values of the common ratio. *WJEC*

3 An arithmetic series has first term 7 and common difference 4. The sum of the first n terms if 3567. Find the value of n. *WJEC*

4 The ninth term of an arithmetic series is 17 and the sum of the first five terms is 10. Determine the first term and the common difference of the series. *AEB*

5 The second term of a geometric series is 80 and the fifth term of the series is 5.12.

a Find the common ratio and the first term of the series.

b Find the sum to infinity of the series, giving your answer as an exact fraction.

c Find the difference between the sum to infinity of the series and the sum of the first 14 terms of the series, giving your answer in the form $a \times 10^n$, where $1 \leqslant a < 10$ and n is an integer. *EDEXCEL*

6 In an arithmetic progression, the ninth term is 7, and the twenty-ninth term is equal to twice the fifth term.

a Determine the first term and the common difference of the progression.

b Calculate the sum of the first 200 terms of the progression. *AEB*

7 **a** Find the sum of the integers which are divisible by 3 and lie between 1 and 400.

b Hence, or otherwise, find the sum of the integers, from 1 to 400 inclusive, which are *not* divisible by 3. *LONDON*

8 A small company producing children's toys plans an increase in output. The number of toys produced is to be increased by 8 each week until the weekly number produced reaches 1000. In week 1, the number to be produced is 280; in week 2, the number is 288; etc. Show that the weekly number produced will be 1000 in week 91.

From week 91 onwards, the number produced each week is to remain at 1000. Find the total number of toys to be produced over the first 104 weeks of the plan. *UCLES*

9 The sequence $u_1, u_2, u_3, \ldots$ is defined by $u_1 = 0, \quad u_{n+1} = (1 + u_n)^2$.
Find the value of u_5.
Describe the behaviour of the sequence as n becomes large. *UCLES*

10 Evaluate $\sum_{r=1}^{40} (5r + 7)$. *UCLES*

11 **a** Find

i the sum of all the integers from 1 to 300 inclusive

ii the sum of all the integers from 1 to 300 which are *not* multiples of 10.

b For a certain value of x, the first three terms of a geometric progression are $x + 20$, $x - 4$ and $x - 20$ respectively. Calculate this value of x and hence find

i the common ratio **ii** the sum to infinity. *UCLES*

12 The nth term of a sequence is u_n, where $u_n = 95\left(\frac{4}{5}\right)^n$, $n = 1, 2, 3, \ldots$

a Find the values of u_1 and u_2.

Giving your answers to 3 significant figures, calculate

b the value of u_{21}

c $\sum_{n=1}^{15} u_n$.

d Find the sum to infinity of the series whose first term is u_1 and whose nth term is u_n. *LONDON*

13 The fourth term of an arithmetic series is 20 and the ninth term is 40. Find

a the common difference,

b the first term,

c the sum of the first twenty terms. *WJEC*

14 The nth term of a sequence is defined by $t_n = \frac{1}{2}n(n+1)$ for all positive integers n.

a Find the value of $t_1 + t_2$ and of $t_2 + t_3$.

b By simplifying an expression for $t_n + t_{n+1}$, show that the sum of any two consecutive terms is a perfect square. *UCLES*

Integration

1 **a** Evaluate $\int_0^4 x(4-x)\,dx$.

b The diagram shows the curve $y = x(4-x)$, together with a straight line. This line cuts the curve at the origin O and at the point P with x-coordinate k, where $0 < k < 4$.

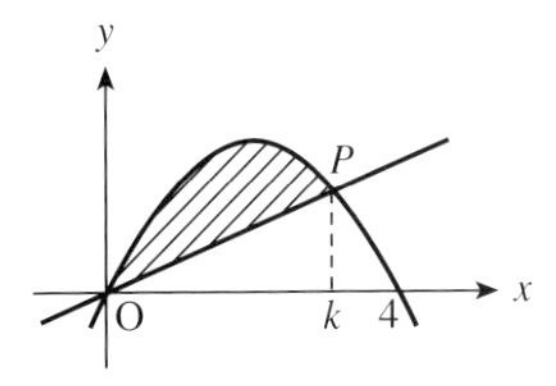

i Show that the area of the shaded region, bounded by the line and the curve, is $\frac{1}{6}k^3$.

ii Find, correct to 3 decimal places, the value of k for which the area of the shaded region is half of the total area under the curve between $x = 0$ and $x = 4$. *OCR*

2 **a** Differentiate $\left(x + \frac{1}{x}\right)^2$ with respect to x.

b Find the equation of the curve which passes through the point (1, −1) and for which $\frac{dy}{dx} = x^2(2x + 1)$. *UCLES*

3 The diagram shows a sketch of part of the curve with equation $y = f(x)$ where $f(x) = -x^3 + 27x - 34$.

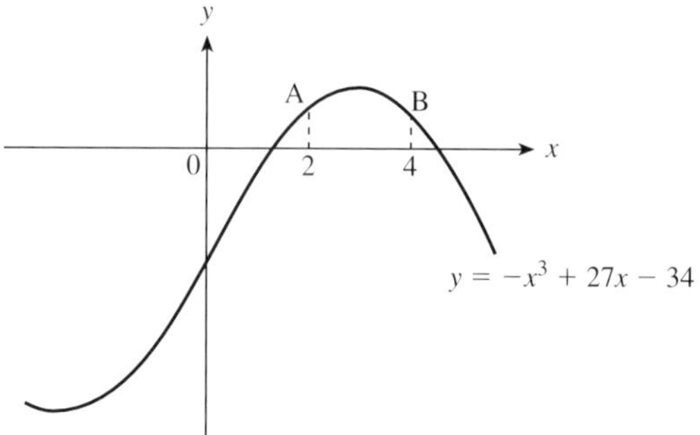

a Find $\int f(x)\,dx$.

The lines $x = 2$ and $x = 4$ meet the curve at points A and B as shown.

b Find the area of the finite region bounded by the curve and the lines $x = 2$, $x = 4$ and $y = 0$.

c Find the area of the finite region bounded by the curve and the straight line AB. *LONDON*

4 The diagram shows the curve $y = 3x - x^2$. The curve meets the x-axis at the origin O and at the point A. The tangent to the curve at the point B(2, 2) intersects the x-axis at C.

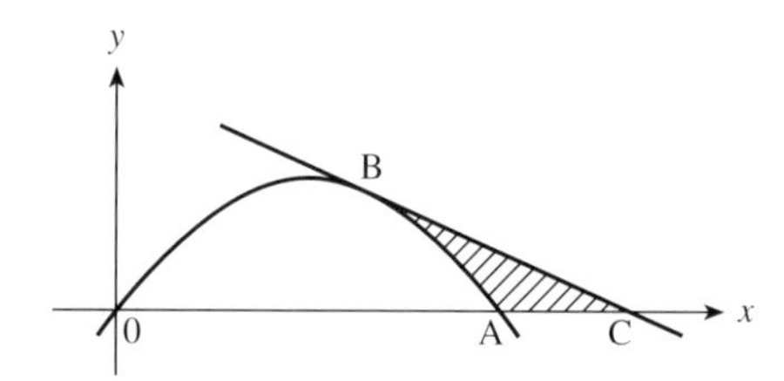

a Find the equation of the tangent to the curve at B.

b Find the shaded area. *WJEC*

5 $y = 3x^{\frac{1}{2}} - 4x^{-\frac{1}{2}}$, $x > 0$.

a Find $\frac{dy}{dx}$.

b Find $\int y\,dx$.

c Hence show that

$$\int_1^3 y\,dx = A + B\sqrt{3}$$

where A and B are integers to be found. *LONDON*

6 The diagram shows a sketch of the curve with equation $y = 16 - 4x^2$.

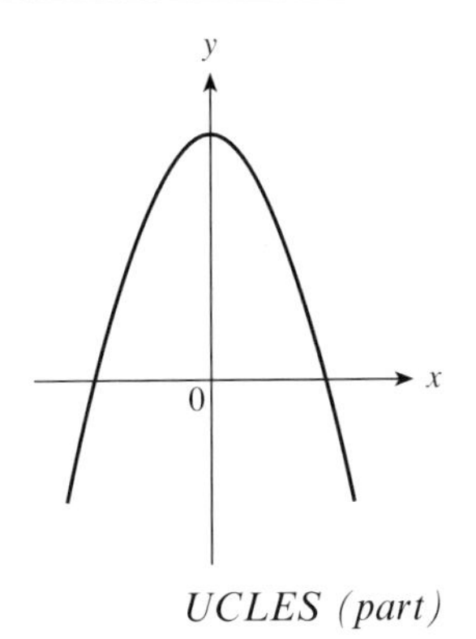

a Find an equation of the tangent to this curve at the point where $x = k$.

Obtain the value of k for which this tangent is parallel to the line $y = 2x + 5$.

UCLES (part)

7 The diagram shows a sketch of the graph of $y = x^2$ and the normal to the curve at the point A(1, 1).

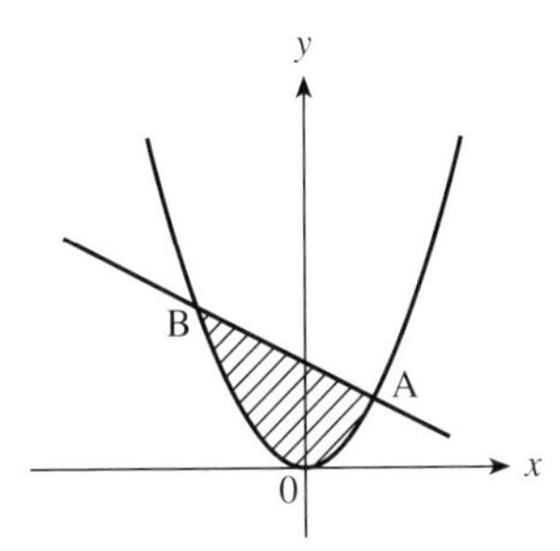

a Use differentiation to find the equation of the normal at A. Verify that the point B where the normal cuts the curve again has coordinates $\left(-\frac{3}{2}, \frac{9}{4}\right)$.

b The region which is bounded by the curve and the normal is shaded in the diagram. Calculate its area, giving your answer as an exact fraction. *UCLES*

8 The line $y = 3x - 2$ intersects the curve $y = x^2$ at points A and B, where the x-coordinate of A is less than the x-coordinate of B.

a Find the coordinates of A and B.

b Show that the equation of the tangent to the curve at A is $y = 2x - 1$.

c The tangent to the curve at A intersects the line $x = 2$ at C(2, 3). Sketch the graphs of $y = x^2$ and $y = 2x - 1$ on the same diagram showing the points A, B and C.

d Shade the region R enclosed by the arc AB, the line AC and the line BC.

e Find the area of the region R. *WJEC*

9 The curve C has equation $y = x^3 - 3x^2$.

a Find the coordinates of the stationary points of C and determine their nature.

b Sketch the curve C.

c Find the area of the region bounded by the curve C and the x-axis. *WJEC*

10 The equation of a curve is $y = x + \dfrac{4}{x^2}$.

Find

a the coordinates of the turning point of the curve

b the equation of the tangent to the curve at the point (1, 5)

c the area enclosed by the curve, the x-axis and the lines $x = 1$ and $x = 3$. *UCLES*

Trigonometry

1 Show that the equation

$15\cos^2\theta = 13 + \sin\theta$

may be written as a quadratic equation in $\sin\theta$.

Hence solve the equation, giving all values of θ such that $0^\circ \leqslant \theta \leqslant 360^\circ$. *OCR*

2 Sketch the graph of $y = \cos x^\circ$, for values of x from 0 to 360.

Sketch, on the same diagram, the graph of $y = \cos(x - 60)^\circ$.

Use your diagram to solve the equation

$\cos x^\circ = \cos(x - 60)^\circ$

for values of x between 0 and 360. Indicate clearly on your diagram how the solutions relate to the graphs.

State how many values of x satisfying the equation

$\cos(10x)^\circ = \cos(10x - 60)^\circ$

lie between 0 and 360. (You should explain your reasoning briefly, but no further detailed working or sketching is necessary.) *OCR*

3 Find, in degrees, the values of θ in the interval $0 \leqslant \theta \leqslant 360^\circ$ for which

$4\sin^2\theta - 2\sin\theta = 4\cos^2\theta - 1.$

State which of your answers are exact and which are given to a degree of accuracy of your choice, which you should give. *EDEXCEL*

4 Find in degrees to 1 decimal place, the values of x which lie in the interval $-180^\circ \leqslant x \leqslant 180^\circ$ and satisfy the equation $\sin 2x = -0.57$. *LONDON*

5 The figure shows the triangle OCD with $OC = OD = 17$ cm and $CD = 30$ cm. The mid-point of CD is M. With centre M, a semicircular arc A_1 is drawn on CD as diameter. With centre O and radius 17 cm, a circular arc A_2 is drawn from C to D. The shaded region R is bounded by the arcs A_1 and A_2.

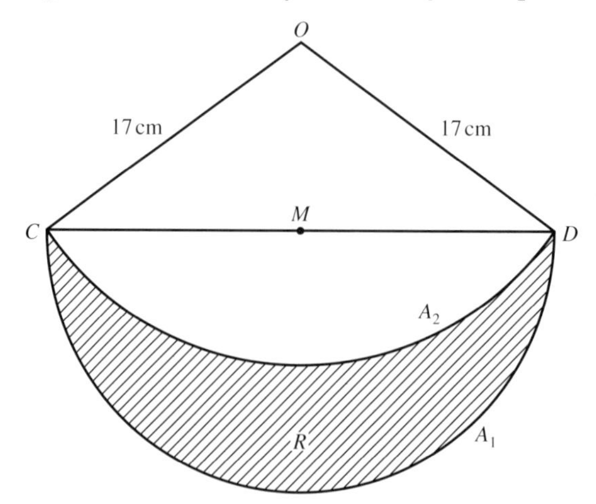

Calculate, giving answers to 2 decimal places,

a the area of the triangle OCD,

b the angle COD in radians,

c the area of the shaded region R. *LONDON*

6 The figure shows a minor sector OMN of a circle centre O and radius r cm. The perimeter of the sector is 100 cm and the area of the sector is A cm^2.

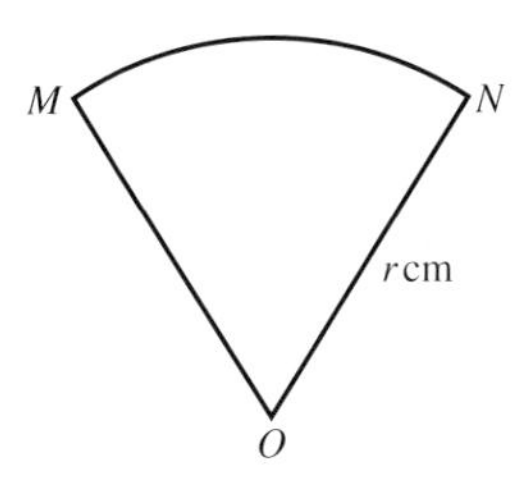

a Show that $A = 50r - r^2$.

Given that r varies, find

b the value of r for which A is a maximum and show that A is a maximum,

c the value of $\angle MON$ for this maximum area,

d the maximum area of the sector OMN. *LONDON*

7 There is a straight path of length 70 m from the point A to the point B. The points are joined also by a railway track in the form of an arc of the circle whose centre is C and whose radius is 44 m, as shown in the figure.

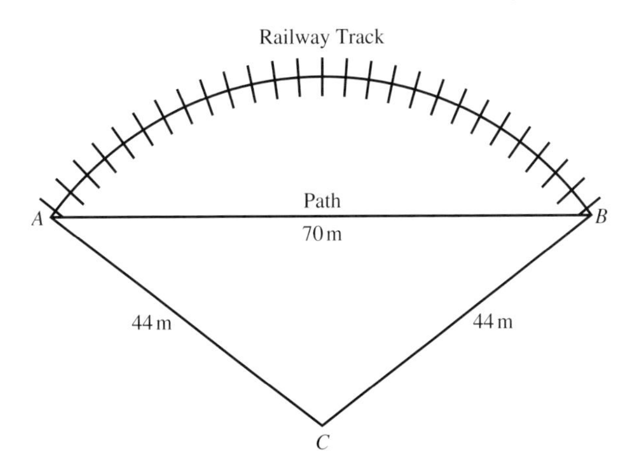

a Show that the size, to 2 decimal places, of $\angle ACB$ is 1.84 radians.

Calculate

b the length of the railway track,

c the shortest distance from C to the path,

d the area of the region bounded by the railway track and the path. *LONDON*

8 **a** Find the coordinates of the point where the graph of $y = 2\sin\left(2x + \frac{5}{6}\pi\right)$ crosses the y-axis.

b Find the values of x, where $0 \leqslant x \leqslant 2\pi$, for which $y = \sqrt{2}$. *LONDON*

9 **a** Given that $\tan 75^\circ = 2 + \sqrt{3}$, find in the form $m + n\sqrt{3}$, where m and n are integers, the values of **i** $\tan 15^\circ$, and **ii** $\tan 105^\circ$.

b Find, in radians to two decimal places, the values of x in the interval $0 \leqslant x \leqslant 2\pi$, for which $3\sin^2 x + \sin x - 2 = 0$. *LONDON*

10 Find all values of θ in the range 0° to 360° satisfying $6\cos^2\theta + \sin\theta - 4 = 0$. *WJEC*

11 Given that x is an obtuse angle and y is a reflex angle, solve the simultaneous equations

$$18\sin x - 12\cos y = 13$$
$$4\sin x + 3\cos y = 1$$

WJEC

12 The diagram, which is not drawn to scale, shows a chord AB of a circle, centre C. The area of the shaded region is $77\,\text{cm}^2$ and $A\hat{C}B = 80°$.

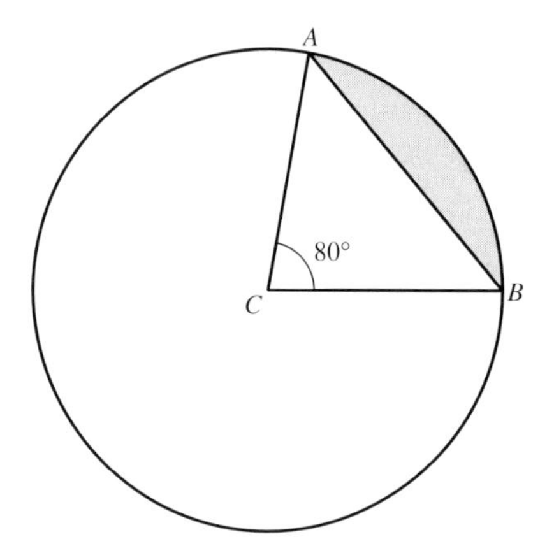

Find the radius of the circle.

WJEC

13 The triangle ABC has $AB = 5\,\text{cm}$, $BC = 3\,\text{cm}$, $CA = 7\,\text{cm}$.

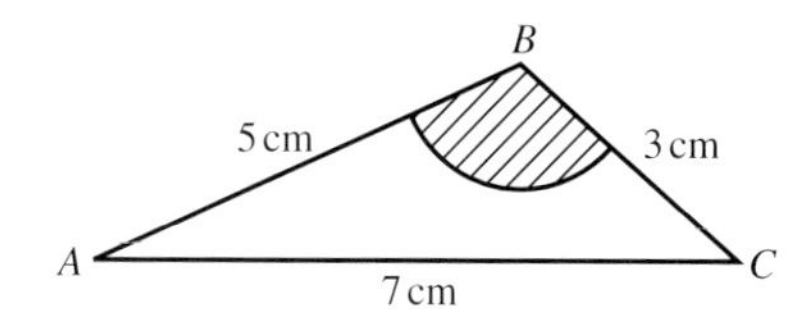

a Use the cosine rule to find the size of angle ABC, giving your answer in radians in terms of π.

b The circular sector centre B and radius r cm is removed from the triangle. The area of the sector, shaded in the diagram, is equal to one tenth of the area of the original triangle. Calculate the value of r, giving your answer to three significant figures.

AEB

14 Find all solutions in the interval $0° < \theta < 180°$ of the equation

$2\sin(3\theta - 48°) - 1 = 0$.

AEB

15 **a** Given that

$$\frac{\sin\theta - \cos\theta}{\sin\theta + \cos\theta} = \frac{6\sin\theta}{\cos\theta}$$

find the exact values of $\tan\theta$. Hence find θ, for $0° \leqslant \theta \leqslant 360°$.

b Show that the equation

$$\frac{\sin\theta - \cos\theta}{\sin\theta + \cos\theta} = \frac{\sin\theta}{\cos\theta}$$

has no solutions for θ.

UCLES

16 The diagram shows a triangle ABC in which angle $C = 30°$, $BC = x$ cm and $AC = (x + 2)$ cm.

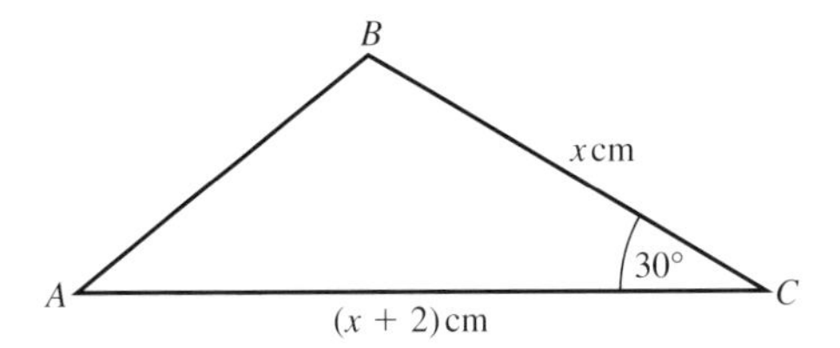

Given that the area of triangle ABC is $12\,\text{cm}^2$, calculate the value of x. *UCLES*

17 Prove the identity

$$\frac{1 + \sin x}{\cos x} + \frac{\cos x}{1 + \sin x} \equiv 2 \sec x.$$ *UCLES*

18 Triangle ABC is such that $AB = 5$ cm, $BC = 7$ cm and $CA = 8$ cm. The point R is the foot of the perpendicular from A to BC. With centre A and radius AR, a circular arc is drawn, from a point P on AB to a point Q on AC, touching the line BC at R (see diagram)

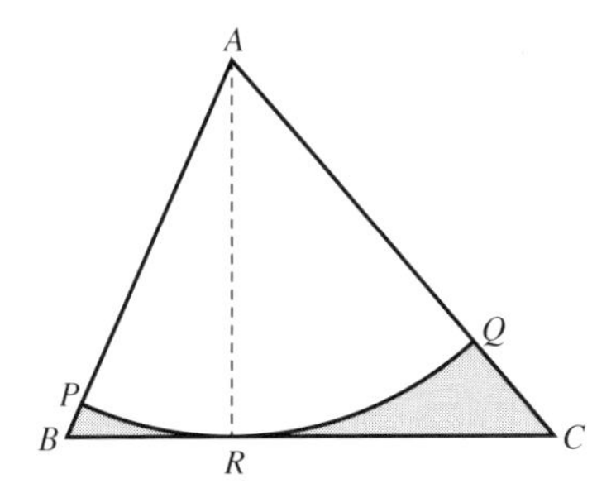

a Show that angle $BAC = \frac{1}{3}\pi$ radians, and that $\sin B = \frac{4}{7}\sqrt{3}$.

b Show that the area of the shaded region, which lies inside triangle ABC but outside sector APQ, is

$$\left(10\sqrt{3} - \frac{200}{49}\pi\right)\text{cm}^2$$ *UCLES*

19 A circle has centre O and radius r. The chord AB is such that angle $AOB = \theta$ radians and the minor segment cut off by the chord is shaded in the diagram.

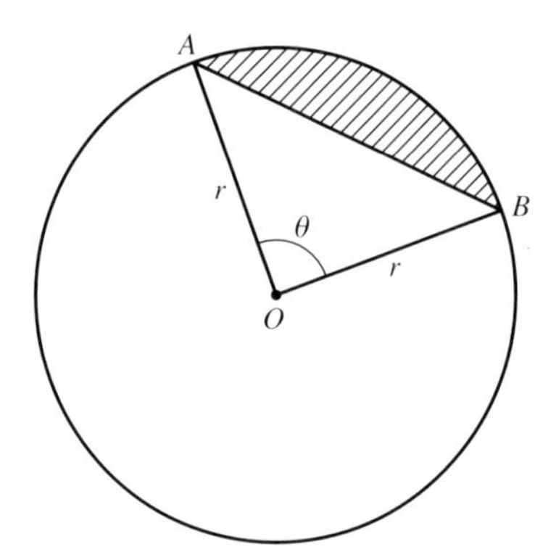

a Determine an expression for the area of the shaded region, in terms of r and θ.

b Given that the shaded region has area equal to one quarter of the area of the circle, show that θ satisfies the equation

$$\theta = \sin\theta + \frac{\pi}{2}.$$

Show that this equation has a root between 2.3 and 2.4. *AEB*

20 A circle with centre O and radius 1.25 cm has a chord AB such that $A\hat{O}B = 2\theta$ radians, where $\theta < \frac{\pi}{2}$.

The length of the minor arc AB exceeds the length of the chord AB by 0.75 cm.

a Show that $\theta - \sin\theta - 0.3 = 0$.

b Show that the value of θ lies between 1.2 and 1.3. *WJEC (part)*

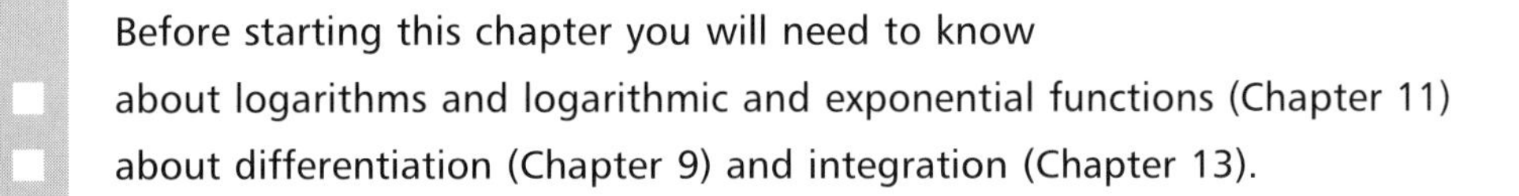

17 The functions e^x and ln x

Before starting this chapter you will need to know

- about logarithms and logarithmic and exponential functions (Chapter 11)
- about differentiation (Chapter 9) and integration (Chapter 13).

17.1 The function e^x and its inverse, ln x

In Chapter 11 exponential functions, for example 2^x, 3^{2x^2}, $10^{\cos x}$, where the variable is in the index (or exponent), and their inverses, log functions, were introduced.

✓ ***Remember*** $f(x) = 2^x \Leftrightarrow f^{-1}(x) = \log_2 x$

A particularly important exponential function, $f(x) = e^x$, is called *the* exponential function. The function e^x can be defined in many ways. One way is by an infinite series which can be shown to be convergent.

$$e^x = 1 + \frac{x}{1!} + \frac{x^2}{2!} + \frac{x^3}{3!} + \cdots$$

$n! = n(n-1)(n-2)\cdots \times 2 \times 1$

so $\quad e^1 = e = 1 + \dfrac{1}{1!} + \dfrac{1}{2!} + \dfrac{1}{3!} + \cdots = 2.718\,28\ldots$

➤ $$\boxed{f(x) = e^x \Leftrightarrow f^{-1}(x) = \ln x}$$

Remember: $\ln x$ means $\log_e x$.

Alternative approaches to defining e are given in Book 2.

The two numbers, e and π, (particularly e) are fundamental in describing many natural phenomena in physics, biology, chemistry, statistics and economics.

Space scientists ask the question, if intelligent life exists in our universe, how could it be recognised? Space explorers include, in any exploring craft, the numbers e and π, expressed in binary form. These numbers are so fundamental that all intelligent species would eventually discover (or invent) them.

Differentiation and integration of e^x

By definition

$$e^x = 1 + \frac{x}{1!} + \frac{x^2}{2!} + \frac{x^3}{3!} + \cdots$$

Assuming that an infinite series can be differentiated term by term

$$\begin{aligned}\frac{d}{dx}(e^x) &= \frac{1}{1!} + \frac{2x}{2!} + \frac{3x^2}{3!} + \frac{4x^3}{4!} + \cdots \\ &= 1 + \frac{x}{1!} + \frac{x^2}{2!} + \frac{x^3}{3!} + \cdots \\ &= e^x\end{aligned}$$

So e^x remains unchanged when differentiated. That is, the gradient of the curve $y = e^x$ is equal to its ordinate (y value) at each point.

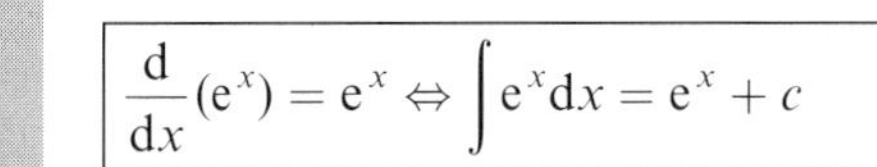

$$\frac{d}{dx}(e^x) = e^x \Leftrightarrow \int e^x dx = e^x + c$$

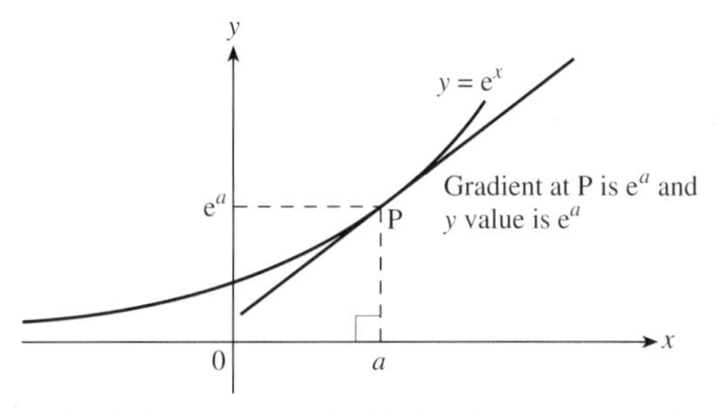

Similarly $\frac{d}{dy}(e^y) = e^y$

(Differentiation of e^x from first principles is covered in Book 2.)

Note $f(x) = ke^x \Rightarrow f'(x) = ke^x$

$f(x) = ke^x$ is the only elementary function which remains unchanged when differentiated.

One reason the exponential function is of such importance mathematically is that it leads to the solution of differential equations of the form $\frac{dy}{dx} = ky$.

These, and similar, equations arise when growth and decay, for example in science or economics, are described mathematically.

A useful result that is needed for differentiating $\ln x$ is $\quad \frac{dy}{dx} = \frac{1}{\frac{dx}{dy}}$

If δx and δy are increments in x and y respectively $\quad \frac{\delta y}{\delta x} = \frac{1}{\frac{\delta x}{\delta y}}$

As $\delta x \to 0$, $\delta y \to 0$, $\frac{\delta y}{\delta x} \to \frac{dy}{dx}$ and $\frac{\delta x}{\delta y} \to \frac{dx}{dy}$ $\quad \therefore \quad \frac{dy}{dx} = \frac{1}{\frac{dx}{dy}}$

Differentiation of $\ln x$

If $y = \ln x$, $e^y = x$. (Expressing $y = \ln x$ in index form.)

Differentiating with respect to y,

$$e^y = \frac{dx}{dy}$$

But $\quad \frac{dx}{dy} = \frac{1}{\frac{dy}{dx}}$

$\therefore \quad \frac{dy}{dx} = \frac{1}{e^y} = \frac{1}{x}$

So $\quad \frac{d}{dx}(\ln x) = \frac{1}{x}$

$$\frac{d}{dx}(\ln x) = \frac{1}{x} \Leftrightarrow \int \frac{1}{x}\, dx = \ln x + c$$

So $\frac{1}{x}$, i.e. x^{-1}, the only power of x which could not be integrated in Chapter 13, can now be integrated by using the function, $\ln x$.

Limits of the definite integral $\int_a^b \frac{1}{x}\,dx$

If a and b are both positive

$$\int_a^b \frac{1}{x}\,dx = \Big[\ln x\Big]_a^b = \ln b - \ln a = \ln\frac{b}{a}$$

Since a and b are positive, $\ln a$ and $\ln b$ can be evaluated.

If a and b are both negative, a problem arises since $\ln x$ is not defined for $x < 0$.

✓ ***Remember*** The domain of $\ln x$ is $x \in \mathbb{R}$, $x > 0$.

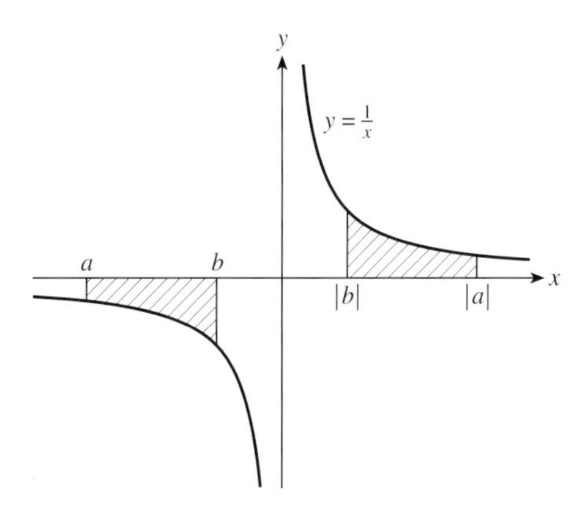

By the symmetry of the graph, it can be seen that, for a and b negative,

$$\int_a^b \frac{1}{x}\,dx = \Big[\ln|x|\Big]_a^b = \ln|b| - \ln|a| = \ln\frac{b}{a}$$

Note: $\ln|b| < \ln|a|$. The integral is $-$ve because the area is below the x-axis.

If a and b have different signs the integral

$$\int_a^b \frac{1}{x}\,dx$$

cannot be evaluated because $\frac{1}{x}$ is not defined for $x = 0$.

➤ The definite integral

$$\int_a^b \frac{1}{x}\,dx$$

can be evaluated if *both* limits have the same sign, i.e. the discontinuity ($x = 0$) does not lie between a and b. Then

$$\int_a^b \frac{1}{x}\,dx = \Big[\ln|x|\Big]_a^b$$

Example 1 Find $\int_2^3 \frac{1}{x}\,dx$ and $\int_{-2}^{-1} \frac{1}{x}\,dx$

and explain why $\int_{-1}^{2} \frac{1}{x}\,dx$

cannot be evaluated.

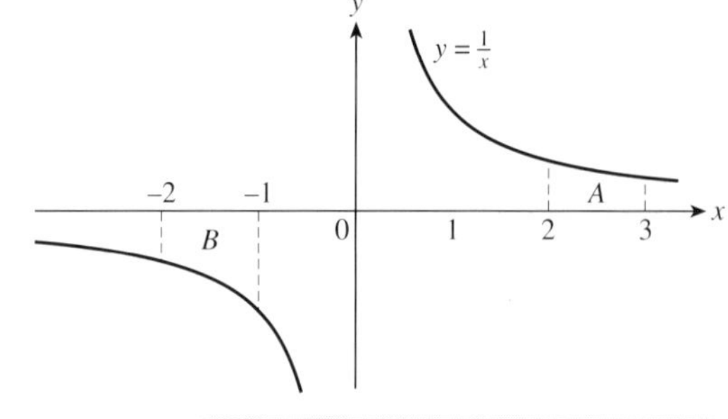

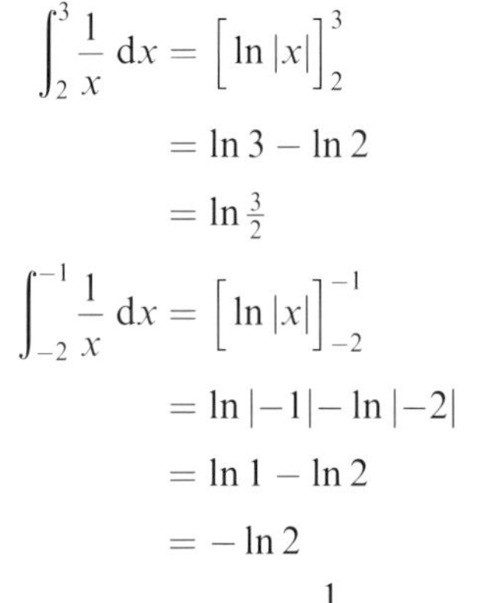

$$\int_2^3 \frac{1}{x}\,dx = \Big[\ln|x|\Big]_2^3$$

$$= \ln 3 - \ln 2$$

$$= \ln \tfrac{3}{2}$$

This integral represents area A. The limits of integration are both +ve.

$\log a - \log b = \log \frac{a}{b}$

$$\int_{-2}^{-1} \frac{1}{x}\,dx = \Big[\ln|x|\Big]_{-2}^{-1}$$

$$= \ln|-1| - \ln|-2|$$

$$= \ln 1 - \ln 2$$

$$= -\ln 2$$

This integral represents area B. The limits of integration are both −ve.

Remember: $\ln 1 = 0$

Integral is −ve because the area is below x-axis.

The graph of $y = \dfrac{1}{x}$ is undefined at $x = 0$.

So the area between $x = -1$ and $x = 2$ is not defined. Therefore

$$\int_{-1}^{2} \frac{1}{x}\,dx$$

cannot be evaluated.

Limits of integration have different signs, so the integral cannot be evaluated.

Graphs of e^x and $\ln x$

As x increases, the graph of e^x eventually becomes steeper than any polynomial graph. Conversely, the graph of $\ln x$, the reflection of e^x in the line $y = x$, tends very slowly to infinity, more slowly than any polynomial graph.

For e^x the domain is $x \in \mathbb{R}$ and the range is $y \in \mathbb{R}$, $y > 0$.

For the inverse function, $\ln x$, the domain is $x \in \mathbb{R}$, $x > 0$ and the range is $y \in \mathbb{R}$.

Note that the graphs of e^x and $\ln x$ are reflections of each other in $y = x$.

The x-axis is an asymptote to $y = e^x$.
The y-axis is an asymptote to $y = \ln x$.

The graphs of e^x and $\ln x$ can be transformed using the methods of Chapter 7.

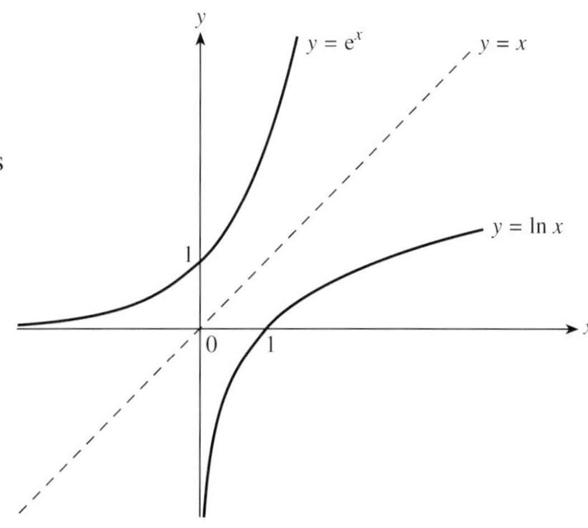

Example 2 Sketch $y = f(x)$ where $f(x) = 1 - e^x$. State the domain and range of the function and any asymptotes of the curve.

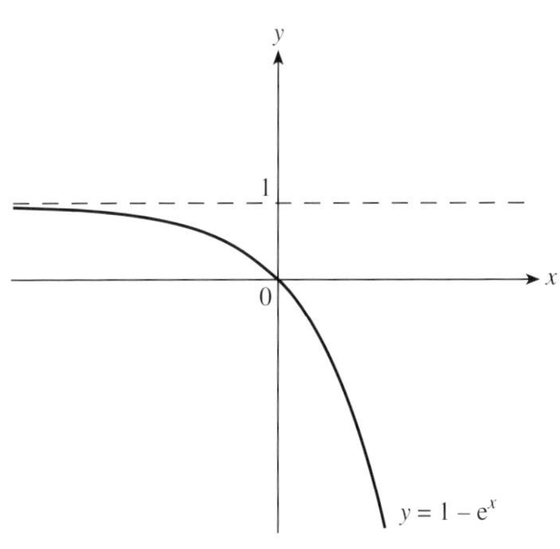

$y = -e^x$ is a reflection of $y = e^x$ in the x-axis. $y = 1 - e^x$ is a translation of $\begin{pmatrix} 0 \\ 1 \end{pmatrix}$ of $y = -e^x$.

(1 is added to the function.)

The x-axis is an asymptote to $y = e^x$ and $y = -e^x$ so $y = 1$ will be an asymptote to the translated curve.

Domain: $x \in \mathbb{R}$. Range: $y \in \mathbb{R}$, $y < 1$. Asymptote: $y = 1$.

Example 3 Find the area enclosed by the curve $y = e^x$, the y-axis and the tangent to $y = e^x$ at (1, e).

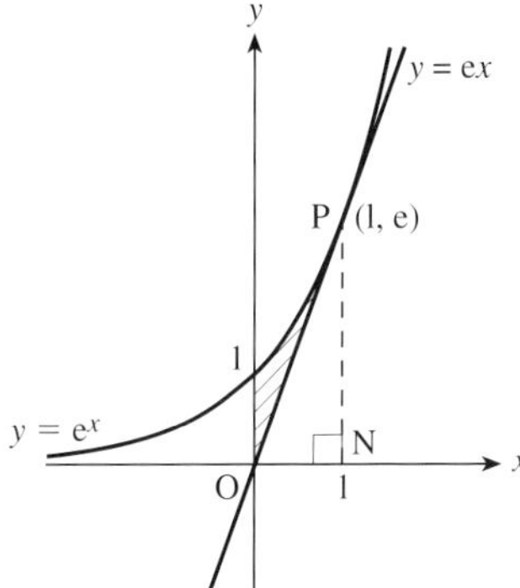

$$y = e^x$$

$$\Rightarrow \quad \frac{dy}{dx} = e^x$$

At (1, e) $\quad \frac{dy}{dx} = e$

$\therefore$ tangent has gradient e and passes through (1, e).

$\therefore$ equation of tangent is $y - e = e(x - 1)$

Using $y - y_1 = m(x - x_1)$

i.e. the equation of the tangent is $y = ex$. So the tangent passes through O.

$$\begin{aligned}\text{Area required} &= \int_0^1 e^x \, dx - \text{area } \triangle \text{ OPN} \\ &= \left[e^x\right]_0^1 - \frac{e \times 1}{2} \\ &= e^1 - e^0 - \frac{e}{2} \\ &= \frac{e}{2} - 1\end{aligned}$$

PN = e, ON = 1.

Remember: $e^0 = 1$

EXERCISE 17a

1 Find, correct to 3 significant figures

a e^3 **b** $\ln 4$ **c** $e^{-2.7}$ **d** $\ln \frac{1}{4}$

2 Find $\frac{dy}{dx}$ when

a $y = 2e^x$ **b** $y = \ln x$ **c** $y = 3x^2 - 5e^x$

d $y = x^{\frac{1}{2}} + 2\ln x$ **e** $y = e^x - \ln x$ **f** $y = \frac{4}{x}$

3 Evaluate, giving an exact answer

a $\left[e^x\right]_{-1}^{1}$ **b** $\left[\ln|x|\right]_{2}^{6}$ **c** $\left[3e^x + x\right]_{0}^{4}$

d $\left[\ln|x|\right]_{-3}^{-1}$ **e** $\left[e^x + \ln|x|\right]_{2}^{3}$ **f** $\left[2e^{-x} - 3\ln|x|\right]_{1}^{5}$

4 Simplify

a $e^{\ln 4}$ **b** $e^{\ln x}$ **c** $\ln e^3$ **d** $e^{\ln(2x+1)}$

e $\ln(e^{3-x})$ **f** $\ln e^x$ **g** $e^{2\ln 2}$ **h** $e^{-3\ln 4}$

5 Sketch these functions, stating the range.

a $f(x) = 1 + e^x \quad x \in \mathbb{R}$ **b** $f(x) = 2 + \ln x \quad x \in \mathbb{R}, x > 0$

c $f(x) = e^{x-1} \quad x \in \mathbb{R}$ **d** $f(x) = \ln(4 + x) \quad x \in \mathbb{R}, x > -4$

6 Find, at the point where $x = 1$, **i** the y-coordinate and **ii** the gradient of

a $y = e^x$ **b** $y = \ln x$

c $y = e^x + 4$ **d** $y = \ln x + 4$

e $y = e^x + \ln x + x^2$ **f** $y = e^x - 6\sqrt{x}$

Explain, with the help of sketches, why the gradients are the same for **a** and **c**, and why the gradients are the same for **b** and **d**.

7 Evaluate

a $2\int_0^6 e^x \, dx$ **b** $\int_{2.5}^{7.5} \frac{1}{x} \, dx$ **c** $\int_1^e \frac{1}{x} \, dx$

8 Find the coordinates of the points on these curves where the gradient is $\frac{1}{2}$ and where the gradient is 2.

a $y = e^x$ **b** $y = \ln x$

9 Find the area enclosed by the curve $y = e^x$, the axes and $x = 3$.

10 Find the area enclosed by the curve $y = \frac{1}{x}$, the x-axis, $x = 2$ and $x = 4$.

11 Find the area enclosed by the curve $y = e^x - x$, the x-axis, $x = -1$ and $x = 1$.

12 Find the area enclosed by the curve $y = \frac{1}{x}$, the x-axis, $x = -6$ and $x = -1$.

13 **a** Show that the curve $y = \frac{1}{x} + 4x^2$ has a minimum point and find its coordinates.

b Find the area enclosed by the curve, the x-axis, $x = \frac{1}{2}$ and $x = 2$.

14 **a** Find the coordinates of the points on the curve $y = \ln x + x^2$ where the gradient is 3.

b Find the equation of the tangent at each point.

15 **a** Show that the curve $y = e^x - x$ has a minimum point at (0, 1).

b Sketch $y = e^x - x$.

16 **a** Show that the curve $y = \ln x - x$ has a maximum point at (1, −1).

b Sketch $y = \ln x - x$.

17 **a** Find the equation of the tangent to the curve $y = \ln x$ at $x = \frac{1}{2}$.

b The tangent meets the x and y axes at A and B respectively. Find the coordinates of A and B.

c Hence show that the area of triangle OAB is $\frac{1}{4}(1 + \ln 2)^2$.

18 **a** Find the points of intersection of the curve $y = \frac{2}{x}$ and the line $y = 3 - x$.

b Find the area enclosed by the line and the curve.

19 Find the area in the first quadrant enclosed by the curve $y = \frac{4}{x} - x$, the line $y = x$ and the x-axis.

20 **a** Find the equation of the tangent to the curve $y = e^x + \frac{1}{x}$ at the point where $x = 1$.

b Show that, correct to 3 significant figures, the area enclosed by the curve, the tangent and $x = 2$ is 0.786.

21 **a** Find the equation of the normal to the curve $y = e^x$ at the point (1, e).

b Find the point of intersection of the normal with the x-axis.

c Find the area enclosed by the curve, the normal and both axes.

17.2 Differentiation and integration of e^{kx}

The **chain rule** is an important method of differentiation. It is used here to differentiate e^{kx} and is discussed more fully in Book 2.

The chain rule states that if $y = f(t)$ and $t = g(x)$ then

$$\frac{dy}{dx} = \frac{dy}{dt} \times \frac{dt}{dx}$$

Proof

Suppose y is a function of t, and t itself a function of x. If δy, δt and δx are corresponding small increments in the variables y, t and x then

$$\frac{\delta y}{\delta x} = \frac{\delta y}{\delta t} \times \frac{\delta t}{\delta x} \qquad ①$$

When δy, δt and δx tend to zero $\frac{\delta y}{\delta x} \to \frac{dy}{dx}$, $\frac{\delta y}{\delta t} \to \frac{dy}{dt}$ and $\frac{\delta t}{\delta x} \to \frac{dt}{dx}$

So equation ① becomes

$$\frac{dy}{dx} = \frac{dy}{dt} \times \frac{dt}{dx}$$

➤ The chain rule: $\frac{dy}{dx} = \frac{dy}{dt} \times \frac{dt}{dx}$

The chain rule will now be used to differentiate e^{kx}.

Let $y = e^{kx}$ and $t = kx$, then $y = e^t$.

y is expressed as a function of t and t as a function of x.

$y = e^t \qquad t = kx$

Both functions can be differentiated.

$\frac{dy}{dt} = e^t \qquad \frac{dt}{dx} = k$

Differentiate y with respect to t and t with respect to x.

By the chain rule,

$$\frac{dy}{dx} = \frac{dy}{dt} \times \frac{dt}{dx}$$
$$= e^t \times k$$
$$= ke^{kx}$$

Substitute for t.

➤ $\frac{d}{dx}(e^{kx}) = ke^{kx} \Leftrightarrow \int e^{kx}\,dx = \frac{1}{k}e^{kx} + c$

Example 4

Find $\frac{dy}{dx}$, given y.

a $y = e^{6x} + e^{-\frac{x}{3}}$

Apply $\frac{d}{dx}(e^{kx}) = ke^{kx}$ with $k = 6$ and $k = -\frac{1}{3}$.

$$\frac{dy}{dx} = 6e^{6x} - \tfrac{1}{3}e^{-\frac{x}{3}}$$

b $y = \ln(5x^4)$

Rewrite using log rules.

$= \ln 5 + 4\ln x$

Note: ln 5 is a constant, $\therefore \frac{d}{dx}(\ln 5) = 0$.

$$\frac{dy}{dx} = \frac{4}{x}$$

Example 5 Find $\int_{\ln 2}^{\ln 4} e^{-x}\,dx$.

$$\int_{\ln 2}^{\ln 4} e^{-x}\,dx = \left[-e^{-x}\right]_{\ln 2}^{\ln 4}$$

Apply $\int e^{kx}\,dx = \frac{1}{k}e^{kx}$ with $k = -1$.

$$= -e^{-\ln 4} - (-e^{-\ln 2})$$

$-\ln a = \ln (a)^{-1} = \ln\left(\frac{1}{a}\right)$

$$= -e^{\ln(\frac{1}{4})} + e^{\ln(\frac{1}{2})}$$

$e^{\ln a} = a$

$$= -\tfrac{1}{4} + \tfrac{1}{2}$$

$$= \tfrac{1}{4}$$

EXERCISE 17b

1 Differentiate

a e^x b e^{4x} c e^{-x} d e^{-2x} e $-3e^{-5x}$ f $e^{3x/2}$

2 Integrate

a e^x b $8e^{4x}$ c $-e^{-x}$ d $\frac{1}{3}e^{-4x}$ e $5e^{-5x}$ f $-3e^{3x/2}$

3 Differentiate

a $\ln x$ b $\ln 6x$ c $\ln x^3$ d $\ln 3x^2$ e $-7\ln x$ f $2\ln\frac{x}{4}$

4 Integrate

a $\frac{1}{x}$ b $\frac{4}{x}$ c $\frac{1}{2x}$ d $\frac{1}{3x}$ e $-\frac{2}{3x}$ f $-\frac{5}{x}$

5 Find the area bounded by $y = e^{3x} - \frac{1}{x}$, the x-axis, $x = \frac{1}{2}$ and $x = 1$.

6 Find the area enclosed by the curve $y = e^{-2x}$, the axes and $x = 2$.

7 a Find the coordinates of any points where $y = e^{-x} - 1$ cuts the axes.
b Find the area bounded by the curve $y = e^{-x} - 1$, the x-axis and $x = 4$.

8 Show that the curve $y = e^{3x} - 2x$ has a minimum point at $\left(\frac{1}{3}\ln\frac{2}{3}, \frac{2}{3}\left(1 - \ln\frac{2}{3}\right)\right)$

9 a Find the gradient of $y = 2\ln x - x^2$ at the point where $x = 2$.
b Find the coordinates of the turning point on $y = 2\ln x - x^2$.

10 Given that $y = e^{2x} + e^{-x}$, find
a the intercept of the curve on the y-axis
b any stationary points of the curve and determine their nature
c the area bounded by the curve, the axes and $x = 1$.

EXERCISE 17c (Extension)

1 Using a spreadsheet, or otherwise, find an approximate value of e by evaluating the first twelve terms of the series

$$e = 1 + \frac{1}{1!} + \frac{1}{2!} + \frac{1}{3!} + \cdots$$

2 A generous banker offers a rate of interest of 100% per annum. An investor deposits £1 for a year, so, at the end of the year the investment is worth £2.
The banker now decides to calculate the interest twice yearly, i.e. 6 every months, so that the investment of £1 will be worth, at the end of the year, $£\left(1 + \frac{1}{2}\right)^2$.

a Work out the value, at the end of the year, of £1 invested, when the interest is calculated regularly 2, 3, 4, 5 and 6 times a year. Show that when the interest is paid at n regular intervals throughout the year, the total sum at the end of the year will be

$$£\left(1 + \frac{1}{n}\right)^n$$

b Investigate the value of $\left(1 + \frac{1}{n}\right)^n$ as $n \to \infty$.

3 Investigate the value of this continued fraction.

$$2 + \cfrac{1}{1 + \cfrac{1}{2 + \cfrac{2}{3 + \cfrac{3}{4 + \cfrac{4}{5 + 5 \cdots}}}}}$$

4 a Using a spreadsheet or otherwise, find the gradient of $y = 2^x$ at the point (0, 1). Use the method given on pages 177–8.

b Repeat **a** for $y = 3^x$.

c By trying different values of a in $y = a^x$, find the value of a for which the gradient of $y = a^x$ is 1 at (0, 1).

5 Maximizing a product

a Find positive integers whose sum is 30 and whose product is as large as possible, using
i 2 **ii** 3 **iii** 4 such integers

b If *any* positive number is allowed, find the maximum product using
i 4 **ii** 5 **iii** 6 **iv** 7 **v** 10 **vi** 15 numbers

c Find the maximum product possible if any numbers to any power are allowed.

EXERCISE 17d (Miscellaneous)

1 a Show that the equation of the tangent $y = e^{-3x}$ at the point (0, 1), is $y = 1 - 3x$.

b Find the area bounded by $y = e^{-3x}$, the axes and $x = -1$.

2 The function f is defined by $f(x) = ke^x$, $x \in \mathbb{R}$ and k is a positive constant.

a State the range of f.

b Find $f\left(\ln \frac{1}{k}\right)$.

c Find $f^{-1}(x)$ and state its domain.

d Sketch on the same axes $y = f(x)$ and $y = f^{-1}(x)$.

e Given that the graphs of $y = f(x)$ and $y = f^{-1}(x)$ cut the axes at A and B, find the length of AB.

3 For each of these functions, the domain is $x \in \mathbb{R}$.
Find the inverse function, $f^{-1}(x)$, and sketch the graphs of $f(x)$ and $f^{-1}(x)$ on the same axes, showing any intersection with the axes.
State the range of $f(x)$ and the domain and range of $f^{-1}(x)$, and find $f'(3)$.

a $f(x) = \ln x + 5,\ x > 0$ **b** $f(x) = e^x + 4$ **c** $f(x) = \frac{1}{2}e^x$

4 For each of these functions, find the inverse function, $f^{-1}(x)$, and sketch the graphs of $f(x)$ and $f^{-1}(x)$ on the same axes, showing any intersection with the axes. State the range of $f(x)$ and the domain and range of $f^{-1}(x)$.

a $f(x) = \ln(x - 2),\ x > 2$ **b** $f(x) = e^{x+1}$ **c** $f(x) = 3\ln(1 - x),\ x < 1$

5 Given that $f(x) = e^x$, find

a $f^{-1}(x)$ **b** $f'(x)$ **c** $[f(x)]^{-1}$

d $f^2(x)$ (i.e. $ff(x)$) **e** $f''(x)$ **f** $[f(x)]^2$

6 Given that $f(x) = \ln x$, find

a $f^{-1}(x)$ **b** $f'(x)$ **c** $[f(x)]^{-1}$

7 Solve for x exactly.

a $e^{3x} = e^{2x+1}$ **b** $e^{x^2+2} = e^{7-4x}$ **c** $e^{2x} = 7$

d $\ln(x + 1) = \ln(6 - 3x)$ **e** $\ln(x^2 - 3) = \ln(6 - x^2)$ **f** $\ln(2x - 1) = 5$

8 $y = e^{2x} - e^x$

a Find any stationary points on the curve.

b Sketch the curve.

9 Find the range of values of x for which $f(x) = x - 3\ln x$ is an increasing function.

10 For the curve $y = e^{3x}$, find

a the gradient when $x = 2$

b the coordinates of the points where the tangent to the curve at $x = 2$ meets the axes

c the area bounded by the curve, the tangent and the y-axis.

11 $y = e^x - x^3$

a Show that $\frac{dy}{dx} = 1$ and $\frac{d^2y}{dx^2} = 1$ when $x = 0$.

b Find the area enclosed by the curve, the axes and $x = 1$.

12 $y = 4x + \frac{1}{x}$

a Find the coordinates of any turning points on the curve and state the nature of the point(s).

b Write down the equation of an asymptote to the curve.

c Find the area enclosed by the curve, the x-axis, $x = \frac{1}{2}$ and $x = 1$.

Test yourself

1 The gradient of $y = 2e^x + 1$ at $x = 0$ is

A 3 **B** $2e + 1$ **C** $2e$ **D** 1 **E** 2

2 The area enclosed by the curve $y = e^x - 1$, the x-axis and the line $x = 2$ is

A $e^2 - 1$ **B** $e^2 - 2$ **C** $\dfrac{e^3}{3} - 2 - e$ **D** $e^2 - 3$ **E** $\dfrac{e^2}{2} - 2$

3 The graph of $y = 9x^2 - 2\ln x$ has a minimum when x is equal to

A $\dfrac{\sqrt{2}}{3}$ **B** $\left(\frac{2}{3}\right)^{\frac{1}{4}}$ **C** $\ln 9$ **D** $e^{-\frac{9}{2}}$ **E** $\frac{1}{3}$

4 The area enclosed between the curve $y = \dfrac{1}{x} + 1$, the x-axis and the lines $x = 2$ and $x = 6$ is

A $\frac{1}{3}$ **B** $4 + \ln 3$ **C** $\frac{2}{9}$ **D** $4 + \ln 4$ **E** $\ln 2$

5 $\displaystyle\int_e^{e^2} \frac{1}{x}\,dx$ is equal to

A 0 **B** $e^2 - e$ **C** 1 **D** 2 **E** $2e - 1$

➤➤➤ Key points

Differentiation of e^x and $\ln x$

$f(x) = e^x \Leftrightarrow f^{-1}(x) = \ln x$

$$\frac{d}{dx}(e^x) = e^x \Leftrightarrow \int e^x\,dx = e^x + c$$

$$\frac{d}{dx}(e^{kx}) = ke^{kx} \Leftrightarrow \int e^{kx}\,dx = \frac{1}{k}e^{kx} + c$$

$$\frac{d}{dx}(\ln x) = \frac{1}{x} \Leftrightarrow \int \frac{1}{x}\,dx = \ln x + c$$

The definite integral

$$\int_a^b \frac{1}{x}\,dx$$

can be evaluated if *both* limits have the same sign, i.e. the discontinuity ($x = 0$) does not lie between a and b. Then

$$\int_a^b \frac{1}{x}\,dx = \Big[\ln|x|\Big]_a^b$$

18 Limits

Before starting this chapter you will need to know

- how to work with algebraic expressions (Chapter 2)
- how to sketch a curve (Chapter 7)
- about function notation (Chapter 10).

18.1 The idea of a limit

In this section the idea of a limiting process, which is fundamental to the understanding of calculus, is introduced and asymptotes are discussed.

Consider the function $f(x) = \frac{1}{x}$ $\left(\text{or } y = \frac{1}{x}\right)$.

The function is not defined for $x = 0$; it is interesting, however, to investigate the function for values of x close to zero and for large values of x.

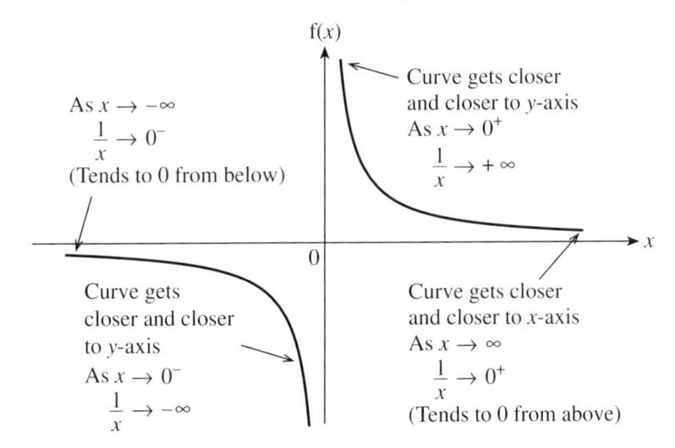

The larger the value of x, the smaller the value of $\frac{1}{x}$.

For example, when $x = 1000$, $\frac{1}{x} = \frac{1}{1000}$ and when $x = 10\,000$, $\frac{1}{x} = \frac{1}{10\,000}$.

$\frac{1}{x}$ gets closer and closer to zero the larger x gets.

$\frac{1}{x}$ tends to zero through positive values, i.e. $\frac{1}{x}$ tends to zero from above.

Expressed formally: as $x \to \infty$, $\frac{1}{x} \to 0^+$

Read 'as x tends to infinity, $\frac{1}{x}$ tends to zero from above'.

Similarly, as $x \to 0^+$, $\frac{1}{x} \to +\infty$.

As the values of x increase, the curve approaches closer and closer to the x-axis and so the x-axis is an **asymptote** to the curve.

✓ ***Remember*** The curve gets nearer and nearer to its asymptote but never reaches it.

As the values of x approach zero from above (i.e. from the positive side of the x-axis) the curve approaches closer and closer to the y-axis. The graph shoots off to $+\infty$. As the values of x approach zero from below (i.e. from the negative side of the x-axis) the curve also approaches closer and closer to the y-axis. The graph shoots off to $-\infty$. The y-axis is also an asymptote to the curve.

Limiting value or limit

The result 'as $x \to \infty$, $\frac{1}{x} \to 0$' could be expressed as 'the limit as $x \to \infty$ of $\frac{1}{x}$ is zero'.

Expressed more formally this is written as

$$\lim_{x \to \infty} \frac{1}{x} = 0$$

In this case, zero is the **limiting value** or **limit**.

✓ ***Note*** Just as an asymptote is never reached, neither is a limit ever reached. The important point is to be able to get as close as you want.

Consider again the function $f(x) = \frac{1}{x}$ as $x \to \infty$ and its limiting value, zero. Imagine this discussion:

B says to A: I want to be within $\frac{1}{1000}$ of the limit, 0. What value of x should I take?

A replies: To be within $\frac{1}{1000}$ of the limit, you could take any value of $x > 1000$.

C says to A: I want to be within $\frac{1}{10\,000}$ of the limit, 0. What value of x should I take?

A replies: To be within $\frac{1}{10\,000}$ of the limit, you could take any value of $x > 10\,000$.

If A can always answer such a question, enabling the questioner to get as close to the limit as is wanted, the function is said to tend to a limit.

Limits such as $\lim_{x \to 0} \frac{1}{x}$, where the function being considered is not fully defined, are interesting to investigate.

The idea of a limit can also be applied where functions are fully defined:

e.g. $\lim_{h \to 0} (2a + 2ah + h^2) = 2a$.

As h gets closer and closer to 0, $2a + 2ah + h^2$ gets closer and closer to $2a$. By choosing an appropriate value of h one can get as close to $2a$ as one wants.

The study of limits of functions is too complex to give more than an introduction at this stage. Examples 1 to 3 illustrate some of the possible situations, and while not comprehensive, provide tools for investigation.

18.2 Investigating limits

Limits of functions are investigated here by:

- using a calculator
- sketching a graph
- algebraic methods

Using a calculator and/or sketching a graph can indicate what the limit is likely to be. Algebraic methods can be used to prove that the limit has a particular value.

Example 1 Investigate limits, with a calculator, or preferably using a spreadsheet.

a $\lim_{n \to \infty} \left(1 + \frac{1}{n}\right)^n$

Since the limit is required as n tends to infinity the value of $\left(1 + \frac{1}{n}\right)^n$ must be evaluated for larger and larger values of n.

The values in the table are given correct to 3 decimal places.

n	10	50	100	1000	10 000	1000 000
$\left(1 + \frac{1}{n}\right)^n$	2.594	2.692	2.705	2.717	2.718	2.718

The sequence of values for $\left(1 + \frac{1}{n}\right)^n$ suggests a limit of 2.718 (correct to 3 decimal places).

This limit is one of the ways of defining the number e. This very special irrational number, given the symbol e by Euler, is useful in many area of mathematics and science. Many theories in higher mathematics, economics, statistics and probability depend on e and numerous natural phenomena in physics, chemistry and biology could not be exactly described without it.

b $\lim_{x \to 0} \frac{\sin x}{x}$

Note x is in radians so put the calculator into radian mode.

Since the limit is required as x tends to zero the value of $\frac{\sin x}{x}$ must be evaluated for smaller and smaller values of x.

The values in the table are given correct to 3 decimal places.

x	1	0.7	0.4	0.1	0.0001	0.000 01
$\frac{\sin x}{x}$	0.841	0.920	0.974	0.998	1.000	1.000

The sequence of values for $\frac{\sin x}{x}$ suggests a limit of 1.

Example 2 Investigate, by drawing a sketch, the function $f(x) = \dfrac{3}{x+1}$.

✓ ***Remember*** Graphs can be sketched using a graphics calculator, graphics package or by calculating a sufficient number of points to be able to draw a sketch or by curve sketching techniques (see Chapters 7 and 10).

The function $f(x) = \dfrac{3}{x+1}$ is not defined for $x = -1$.
The graph shows the behaviour of the function near $x = -1$, and the axes.

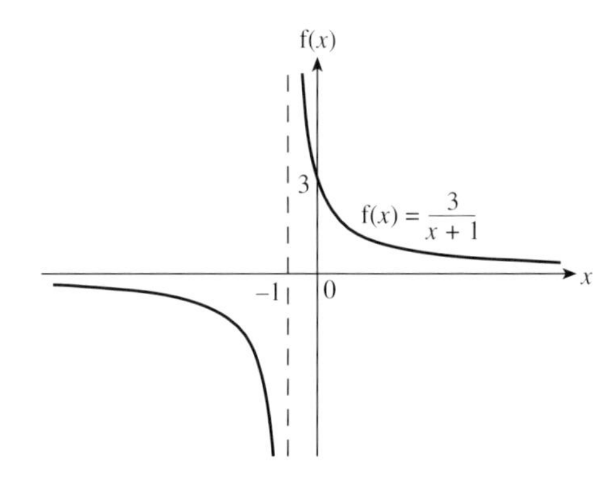

- As x tends to -1 from above ($x \to -1^+$), i.e. the right-hand branch of the curve, $f(x)$ tends to $+\infty$.
- As x tends to -1 from below ($x \to -1^-$), i.e. the left-hand branch of the curve, $f(x)$ tends to $-\infty$.
- As $x \to +\infty$, $f(x)$ tends to zero from above.
- As $x \to -\infty$, $f(x)$ tends to zero from below.

As $x \to \pm\infty$ the curve approaches closer and closer to the x-axis.
The x-axis ($y = 0$) is an asymptote.

As $x \to -1$ the curve approaches closer and closer to the line $x = -1$.
The line $x = -1$ is also an asymptote.

✓ ***Note*** Asymptotes are not usually shown on graphics calculators. On certain calculators what appears to be asymptotes are drawn. Be wary! The calculator may be incorrectly joining up two branches of the graph.

Example 3 Investigate limits algebraically.

a $\displaystyle\lim_{x\to\infty} \frac{3x+2}{x}$

$$\frac{3x+2}{x} = 3 + \frac{2}{x}$$

Rewriting the expression makes it easy to see that the limit is 3.

As $x \to \infty$, $\dfrac{2}{x} \to 0$

$$\therefore \quad \lim_{x\to\infty}\left(\frac{3x+2}{x}\right) = 3$$

b $\lim_{x \to \infty} \frac{3x}{3+x}$

$$\frac{3x}{3+x} = \frac{3}{\frac{3}{x}+1}$$

Rewriting the expression by dividing the numerator and denominator by x enables the limit to be found.

As $x \to \infty$, $\frac{3}{x} \to 0$

$$\therefore \quad \lim_{x \to \infty}\left(\frac{3x}{3+x}\right) = 3$$

c $\lim_{a \to 0}(3x^2 + 3ax + a^2) = 3x^2$

As a gets closer and closer to 0, the terms $3ax$ and a^2 get closer and closer to 0.

d $\lim_{x \to 2} \frac{x^2 - 4}{x - 2}$

Notice that $x - 2$ is a factor of $x^2 - 4$.

$$\frac{x^2-4}{x-2} = \frac{(x-2)(x+2)}{x-2}$$

$(x - 2)$ can be cancelled if it is not zero, i.e. $x \neq 2$.

$$= x + 2 \qquad x \neq 2$$

$\frac{x^2-4}{x-2}$ is not defined for $x = 2$.

As $x \to 2$, $x + 2 \to 4$

$$\therefore \quad \lim_{x \to 2}\left(\frac{x^2-4}{x-2}\right) = 4$$

EXERCISE 18a

1 Use a calculator or spreadsheet to investigate these limits.

a $\lim_{x \to \infty} \frac{2x-7}{x-4}$

b $\lim_{x \to 2} \frac{x^2+5x-14}{x-2}$

c $\lim_{x \to \infty} \left(1 + \frac{2}{x}\right)^x$

d $\lim_{x \to 0} \frac{1 - \cos x}{x^2}$

(Work in radian mode)

2 Use algebraic methods to find these limits, if they exist.

a $\lim_{x \to \infty} \frac{5x-1}{10+2x}$

b $\lim_{x \to \infty} \frac{x+1}{x^2}$

c $\lim_{x \to \infty} \frac{x^2+1}{x}$

d $\lim_{x \to \infty} \frac{5}{1+x}$

3 Find the limits of these expressions as $x \to 5$.

a $\frac{x^2-4x-5}{x-5}$

b $\frac{x^2-25}{x-5}$

c $\frac{x^3-125}{x-5}$

d $\frac{x^2-25}{(x-5)^2}$

➤➤➤ Key points

Limits

Understanding the idea of a limit and how to deal with infinitely large and infinitesimally small numbers will give a better understanding of calculus. It will also help in grasping the idea of asymptotes and of convergent sequences.

19 Proof

19.1 Mathematical proof

Mathematical proof is the process of starting with an assumption, or a statement which is given, and, by logical argument, arriving at a conclusion. There is no unique correct way of setting out a mathematical proof. It may be expressed using words or symbols or both.

✓ *Note* Any argument which will convince the reader is acceptable as a proof.

The techniques of proof in mathematics can take various forms. Throughout this book, problems are solved and results proved using logical deduction. Only 'deductive proof' is considered in this chapter. An example of one other method of proof, known as ***'reductio ad absurdum'****, is given on page 5. Other forms of proof are considered in Book 2.*

In **deductive proof** each statement must be *deduced* logically from the previous statement. A number of words and symbols are used in mathematics to express the relationship between statements.

Fermat was a French mathematician and lawyer. He is best remembered for his work on number theory, particularly what became known as Fermat's Last Theorem. His theorem stated that the equation $x^n + y^n = z^n$ has no solution in whole numbers for $n > 2$. Fermat, in claiming that he had proved this result, wrote in the margin that he had 'a truly marvellous demonstration ... which this margin is too narrow to contain'.
Mathematicians struggled to prove the theorem for nearly three hundred years. In 1995, Andrew Wiles, an English mathematician working in the USA, finally proved the theorem, after many years of work. He had dreamed of doing so from the age of ten when he first heard of it. Using numerous branches of mathematics, his proof took over one hundred pages, so it is unlikely that Fermat's claim was correct.

19.2 Relationships between statements

Earlier chapters have dealt with the relationship between two algebraic expressions (Chapter 3 with equations and Chapter 4 with inequalities and identities) and the relationship between two sets of numbers (Chapter 10: Functions).

This section looks at the relationship between two mathematical statements.

The relationship can be expressed in different ways. Three important ways are

- using implication signs
- in terms of **necessary conditions** and **sufficient conditions**
- using the terms 'if', 'only if' and **'if and only if'**.

$\Rightarrow$	implies
$\not\Rightarrow$	does not imply
$\Leftarrow$	is implied by
$\Leftrightarrow$	implies and is implied by

✓ *Note* The expression 'only if' is included here for completeness but is not much used.

Consider these three statements, p, q and r, about a triangle ABC,

- p: $\triangle$ABC is isosceles
- q: AB = AC
- r: $\angle B = \angle C$

The relationship between statements p and q can be expressed in the following ways:

- Since two equal sides imply an isosceles triangle, then $q \Rightarrow p$.
- It can also be seen that q is a sufficient condition for p and that p is a necessary condition for q.

'Sufficient' because knowing q is true is enough to ensure that p is true.'Necessary' because if p were not true q could not be true.

- Alternatively, it may be stated that $\triangle$ABC is isosceles *if* AB = AC.

Although $q \Rightarrow p$ the implication cannot be reversed.
$p \not\Rightarrow q$ because $\triangle$ABC may be isosceles with another pair of sides equal (not AB = AC).
So q is sufficient for p but not necessary. However, it is true that q *only if* p, i.e. q is true only if p is true.

Looking at the relationship between q and r:

- $q \Rightarrow r$ because two equal *sides* implies that the *angles* opposite the sides are equal. Also $r \Rightarrow q$ because two equal *angles* implies the *sides* opposite the angles are equal. So $q \Leftrightarrow r$ (or $r \Leftrightarrow q$).
- The relationship can also be expressed as 'q is a necessary and sufficient condition for r' and vice versa.
- An alternative form is 'q if and only if r' or 'q iff r' and vice versa.

Equivalence of implication signs, necessary and sufficient conditions and if and only if

Equivalent statements for any two statements p and q.

$p \Rightarrow q$	p is a sufficient condition for q q is a necessary condition for p	p only if q
$p \Leftarrow q$	q is a sufficient condition for p p is a necessary condition for q	p if q
$p \Leftrightarrow q$	q is a necessary and sufficient condition for p	p if and only if q

✓ ***Note*** $p \Rightarrow q$ and $q \Leftarrow p$ are identical.

It may not be immediately evident that '$p \Rightarrow q$' is equivalent to 'q is a necessary condition for p'. However, consider this argument (which uses *reductio ad absurdum*).

Assume q is *not* a necessary condition, i.e. q may be *not* true although p is true. But $p \Rightarrow q$ and since p is true, q must be true.

Therefore there is a contradiction: the assumption 'q is not true' leads to 'q is true'. Hence the original assumption must be false and so q is a necessary condition for p.

Example 1 Link pairs of statements using the signs $\Rightarrow$, $\Leftarrow$, $\Leftrightarrow$, $\not\Rightarrow$.

a p: $ab = 0$

q: $a = 0$

$q \Rightarrow p$ (or $p \Leftarrow q$)

$p \not\Rightarrow q$

a being zero will definitely make *ab* zero, so $q \Rightarrow p$. Put in another way: *ab* being zero is implied by *a* being zero, so $p \Leftarrow q$.

a does not *have* to be zero in order to make *ab* zero (*b* could be zero instead) so $p \not\Rightarrow q$.

b p: $x^3 > 0$ $x \in \mathbb{R}$

q: $x > 0$

$p \Leftrightarrow q$

The cube of a +ve number is +ve and the cube root of a +ve number is +ve, so $x^3 > 0$ implies $x > 0$ and vice versa. $\therefore$ $p \Rightarrow q$ and $q \Rightarrow p$. (x is a real number.) These can be combined as $p \Leftrightarrow q$ or $q \Leftrightarrow p$. $x^3 > 0$ implies and is implied by $x > 0$.

Example 2 Link pairs of statements in terms of necessary and sufficient conditions.

a p: $x = 4$

q: $x^2 = 16$

p is a sufficient condition for q.

$x = 4 \Rightarrow x^2 = 16$ but $x^2 = 16 \not\Rightarrow x = 4$ because x could be -4. So p is sufficient for q, but not necessary, as x could be -4.

Or, q is a necessary condition for p.

q is necessary for p, because if $x^2 \neq 16$ then x could not be 4, but not sufficient, as x could be -4.

b p: $x = 4$

q: $3x + 1 = 13$

If $x = 4$ then $3x + 1 = 13$ and vice versa.

$x = 4$ is a necessary and sufficient condition for $3x + 1 = 13$.

Example 3 Prove that $x^2 - 1 = 0$ if and only if $x = 1$ or $x = -1$.

Let statement p be $x^2 - 1 = 0$ and statement q be $x = 1$ or $x = -1$.

Proof

To prove p iff q, start with p and deduce q.

$$x^2 - 1 = 0$$
$$\Rightarrow \quad (x + 1)(x - 1) = 0$$
$$\Rightarrow \quad x = -1 \quad \text{or} \quad x = 1$$

Also $x = 1$ or $x = -1$

Then start with q and deduce p.

$$\Rightarrow \quad (x - 1) = 0 \quad \text{or} \quad (x + 1) = 0$$
$$\Rightarrow \quad (x + 1)(x - 1) = 0$$
$$\Rightarrow \quad x^2 - 1 = 0$$

So $p \Rightarrow q$ and $q \Rightarrow p$ and hence $p \Leftrightarrow q$, i.e. p iff q.

So $x^2 - 1 = 0$ if and only if $x = 1$ or $x = -1$.

State the conclusion.

✓ ***Note*** All the steps are reversible in Example 3 so the proof could have been expressed as

$$x^2 - 1 = 0$$
$$\Leftrightarrow \quad (x + 1)(x - 1) = 0$$
$$\Leftrightarrow \quad x = -1 \quad \text{or} \quad x = 1$$

So $x^2 - 1 = 0$ if and only if $x = 1$ or $x = -1$.

EXERCISE 19a

1 For these pairs of statements replace the ... with $\Rightarrow$, $\Leftarrow$ or $\Leftrightarrow$. Assume N is a positive integer.

a $x^2 = 36 \ \ldots \ x = -6$

b $x(x+1) = 0 \ \ldots \ x = 0$

c $x(x+1) = 0 \ \ldots \ x = 0$ or $x = -1$

d $b^2 - 4ac < 0 \ \ldots \ ax^2 + bx + c = 0$ has no real roots.

e The last digit of N is 1. ... The last digit of N^2 is 1.

f The triangle is equilateral. ... The three sides of the triangle are equal.

g $x^2 < x \ \ldots \ x < 1$

h N is a multiple of 5. ... Last digit of N is zero.

i $x = 0 \ \ldots \ \cos x = 1$

j $\mathrm{f}(x) = 3x + 1 \ \ldots \ \mathrm{f}^{-1}(x) = \dfrac{x-1}{3}$

k The nth term of a sequence is $3n + 2$. ... The terms of the sequence differ by 3.

l $\mathrm{f}(x) = 3x^2 + 4x + 1 \ \ldots \ \mathrm{f}'(x) = 6x + 4$

m In the triangle ABC $a^2 + b^2 = c^2$. ... The triangle ABC is right angled.

2 Complete these statements with 'necessary', 'sufficient', or 'necessary and sufficient'.

a $2x + 1 = 9$ is a ... condition for $x = 4$.

b A ... condition for $\sin x = \frac{1}{2}$ is $x = 30°$.

c $|r| < 1$ is a ... condition for $r < 1$.

d A ... condition for N to be a multiple of 4 is N even.

e $x - 2$ is a factor of $\mathrm{f}(x)$ is a ... condition for $\mathrm{f}(2) = 0$.

f A ... condition for y to have a minimum value at (h, k) is for $\dfrac{\mathrm{d}^2y}{\mathrm{d}x^2} > 0$ when $x = h$.

g $|r| < 1$ is a ... condition for a GP to have a sum to infinity.

h $x^3 < 0$ is a ... condition for $x < 0$.

i $\displaystyle\int_0^k x^3 \mathrm{d}x = 4$ is a ... condition for $k = 2$.

j A ... condition for xy to be rational is x and y rational.

k $x = \sqrt{3} - 1$ is a ... condition for $x = \dfrac{2}{\sqrt{3}+1}$.

l A ... condition for $\log_a b = c$ is $a^c = b$.

m x is a recurring decimal is a ... condition for x is a rational number.

3 Prove, in each of these cases, that p is a necessary and sufficient condition for q.

a p: $x^2 - 2x = 3$
q: $x = 3$ or $x = -1$

b p: $x^2 + 2x - 4 = 0$
q: $x = -1 \pm \sqrt{5}$

c p: $x^2 - 3x > 0$
q: $x < 0$ or $x > 3$

d p: $3(x+4) - 1 = 5$
q: $x = -2$

4 Prove, in each of these cases, that $p \Rightarrow q$ but $q \not\Rightarrow p$, that is, that p is a sufficient, but not necessary condition for q.

a p: $x = 9$
q: $x^2 = 81$

b p: $y = 0$
q: $xy = 0$

c p: $\theta = 60°$
q: $\tan\theta = \sqrt{3}$

d p: $m = 4$ and $n = 2$
q: $\dfrac{\log a^m}{\log a^n} = 2$

5 Prove that the sum of the first n even numbers is $n(n+1)$.

6 Prove that the sum of n terms of an AP, with first term a and common difference d, is $\frac{n}{2}\left(2a + (n-1)d\right)$.

7 Prove that the sum of n terms of a GP, with first term a and common ratio r, is $\dfrac{a(r^n - 1)}{r - 1}$

8 **a** By completing the square prove that the roots of $x^2 + px + q = 0$ are

$$x = \frac{-p \pm \sqrt{p^2 - 4q}}{2}$$

b Hence prove that $x^2 + px + q = 0$ has real roots if and only if $p^2 - 4q > 0$.

9 Prove that $x + \dfrac{1}{x} \geqslant 2$ for all $x > 0$.

10 Prove that the equation $\dfrac{4}{2-x} = x$ has no real roots.

11 Prove that the equation
$x^3 - 3x^2 + 2x - 6 = 0$
has only one real root.

12 Prove that the equation
$x^4 - 3x^3 - 3x^2 - 3x - 4 = 0$
has exactly two real roots.

13 Prove that $xy + x + y = 36$ has no positive integer solutions.

14 Prove that the arithmetic mean of two non-negative numbers is greater than or equal to their geometric mean.

15 Prove that $n^3 - n$ is always a multiple of 6 for $n \geqslant 2$.

16 Prove that if the sum of the digits of a positive integer is divisible by 9 then the number is divisible by 9.

17 Prove that, for any positive integer, if the difference between the sum of the digits in the odd positions and the sum of the digits in the even positions is a multiple of 11 (including zero) then the number is a multiple of 11.

18 Prove that, in base n arithmetic, if the sum of the digits of a number is divisible by $n - 1$ then the number is divisible by $n - 1$.

Extension material on minimum definitions

Consider the ways of testing whether a quadrilateral, ABCD, is a square.

- 'ABCD has four equal sides' is a necessary condition (but not sufficient, ABCD could be a rhombus).
- 'ABCD has four right angles' is a necessary condition (but not sufficient, ABCD could be a rectangle).
- 'ABCD has four equal sides and four right angles' is a sufficient condition for ABCD to be a square. It is, in fact, *more than* sufficient, more information is given than is needed.

When a condition, or set of information, is *just* sufficient, it can be thought of as a **minimum definition**. It is useful, when, for example, proving that a quadrilateral is a parallelogram, to be aware of possible minimum definitions.

Example 4 Which conditions are sufficient to ensure that ABCD is a parallelogram?

State if the condition is just sufficient, more than sufficient or not sufficient.

a Two pairs of sides parallel

This is just sufficient to ensure ABCD is a parallelogram.

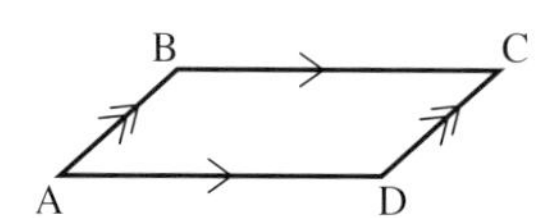

b Opposite angles equal

This is just sufficient to ensure ABCD is a parallelogram.

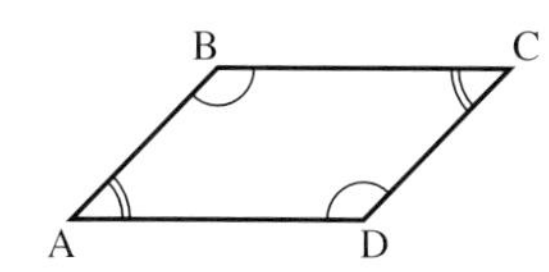

c One pair of sides parallel

This is not sufficient to ensure ABCD is a parallelogram. It would be sufficient, however, to ensure ABCD is a trapezium.

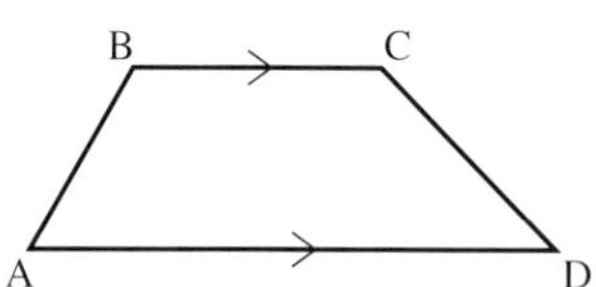

d Diagonals which bisect each other and one pair of sides parallel

This is more than sufficient to ensure ABCD is a parallelogram because 'diagonals which bisect each other' would be sufficient.

✓ ***Note*** There are many conditions which are *necessary* if ABCD is a parallelogram. For example: opposite sides parallel, opposite angles equal, opposite sides equal, diagonals which bisect each other. Some of these necessary conditions are sufficient on their own to ensure that ABCD is a parallelogram.

Example 5 Give two possible minimum definitions for a quadrilateral ABCD to be a rectangle.

Three angles are right angles.

> If three angles are 90° so must the fourth, since the sum of angles of a quadrilateral is 360°. So three angles of 90° is sufficient to ensure ABCD is a rectangle.

One pair of opposite sides equal and parallel, and one angle of 90°.

> One pair of opposite sides equal and parallel is sufficient to ensure ABCD is a parallelogram. One angle of 90° is sufficient to ensure the parallelogram is a rectangle.

EXERCISE 19b (Extension)

In this exercise, for each shape all conditions given are necessary. Some conditions are just sufficient to define the shape, some are more than sufficient, and others are not sufficient to define the shape.

1 State whether the given conditions are just sufficient, more than sufficient or not sufficient to define the shape.
For a triangle to be an equilateral triangle:

a Three angles of 60° **b** Two angles of 60°

2 Repeat Question 1, for a square with these conditions.

a Quadrilateral with equal length perpendicular diagonals

b Quadrilateral with two axes of symmetry

c Quadrilateral with three axes of symmetry

d Quadrilateral with four axes of symmetry

3 Repeat Question 1, for a parallelogram with these conditions.

a Quadrilateral with one pair of sides equal and parallel

b Quadrilateral with 180° rotational symmetry

c Quadrilateral with both pairs of opposite sides equal and parallel

4 Repeat Question 1, for a rectangle with these conditions.

a Quadrilateral with equal diagonals

b Quadrilateral with equal diagonals which bisect each other

5 Repeat Question 1, for a rhombus with these conditions.

a Quadrilateral with four equal sides

b Quadrilateral with perpendicular diagonals

6 Repeat Question 1, for a regular hexagon with these conditions.

a Hexagon with six equal sides

b Hexagon with six equal angles

c Hexagon with six equal sides and six equal angles

d Hexagon with six equal sides and five equal angles

e Hexagon with six equal sides and four equal angles

f Hexagon with six axes of symmetry

g Hexagon with three axes of symmetry

Key points

Relationships between statements

For any two mathematical statements, there are four possible cases.

- $p \Leftrightarrow q$ p is a necessary and sufficient condition for q.
- $p \Rightarrow q$ p is a sufficient condition for q but not necessary.
  $q \not\Rightarrow p$
- $q \Rightarrow p$ p is a necessary condition for q but not sufficient.
  $p \not\Rightarrow q$
- $p \not\Rightarrow q$ Neither p nor q are necessary or sufficient conditions for each other.
  $q \not\Rightarrow p$

A condition, or set of information, which is just sufficient can be used as a definition.

Equivalent statements for *any* two statements *p* and *q*		
$p \Rightarrow q$	p is a sufficient condition for q q is a necessary condition for p	p only if q
$p \Leftarrow q$	q is a sufficient condition for p p is a necessary condition for q	p if q
$p \Leftrightarrow q$	q is a necessary and sufficient condition for p	p if and only if q

Spot the Error

There are 20 questions in this exercise and all have incorrect solutions originally produced by students. You should work through each question carefully and see if you can spot the errors made in the working. When you find any errors, write out a completely correct solution to the question.

Question 1 Given that $f(x) = x^2 - 1$, $g(x) = x^2 + 4x + 3$ and that $h(x) = \dfrac{f(x)}{g(x)}$ sketch the graph of $y = h(x)$.

Solution h(x) can be simplified by cancellation.

$$h(x) = \frac{\cancel{x^2} - 1}{\cancel{x^2} + 4x + 3} = \frac{-1}{4x + 3}$$

There is a vertical asymptote when the denominator is zero: $x = -\frac{3}{4}$.

$x \to \pm\infty \Rightarrow y \to 0$, so the x-axis is a horizontal asymptote.

$x = 0 \Rightarrow y = -\frac{1}{3}$

$y = 0$ cannot be solved.

The only intercept is therefore $(0, -\frac{1}{3})$

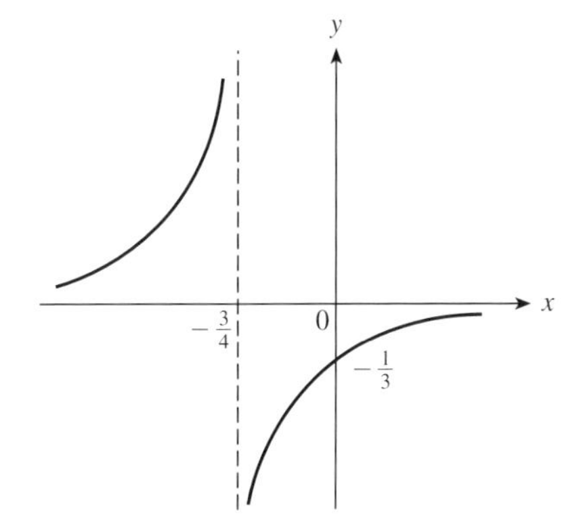

Question 2 A series has terms a, ad, ad^2, ad^3, ...

Find the possible values of d given that the sum of the first four terms of the series is twice the sum of the first two terms.

Solution Using $S_n = \dfrac{n}{2}\left(2a + (n-1)d\right)$, we obtain the equations

$S_4 = \frac{4}{2}(2a + 3d)$ and $S_2 = \frac{2}{2}(2a + d)$

which simplify to

$S_4 = 4a + 6d$ and $S_2 = 2a + d$

But $S_4 = 2S_2$, so $4a + 6d = 2(2a + d)$

$\Rightarrow \quad 6d = 2d$

$\Rightarrow \quad 4d = 0$

$\Rightarrow \quad d = 0$

Question 3

Find the range of values of m for which the straight line $y = mx - 1$ meets the curve $y = x^2 - x$ in two distinct points.

Solution

$x^2 - x = mx - 1 \Rightarrow x^2 - (m + 1)x + 1 = 0$

The discriminant of this quadratic equation is

$$\begin{aligned}(m + 1)^2 - 4 &= (m + 1 + 2)(m + 1 - 2)\\ &= (m + 3)(m - 1)\end{aligned}$$

For the line to meet the curve in two distinct points, the discriminant must be positive.

$(m + 3)(m - 1) > 0$

$\Rightarrow \quad m + 3 > 0 \text{ or } m - 1 > 0$

$\Rightarrow \quad m > -3 \text{ or } m > 1$

Question 4

$f(x) = 12x^4$ and $g(x) = 16x^2$.

Obtain the equation of the normal to the curve $y = \dfrac{f(x)}{g(x)}$ at the point whose x-coordinate is 2.
Find the coordinates of the point where this normal cuts the y-axis.

Solution

$$\frac{dy}{dx} = \frac{f'(x)}{g'(x)} = \frac{48x^3}{32x} = \frac{3}{2}x^2$$

$$x = 2 \Rightarrow \frac{dy}{dx} = \frac{3}{2} \times 2^2 = 6$$

The gradient of the required normal is therefore $-\frac{1}{6}$.

$$x = 2 \Rightarrow \quad y = \frac{12 \times 2^4}{16 \times 2^2} = 3$$

Using $y - y_1 = m(x - x_1)$, the equation of the normal is

$y - 3 = -\frac{1}{6}(x - 2)$

$\Rightarrow \quad 6(y - 3) = -(x - 2)$

$\Rightarrow \quad x + 6y = 20$

This normal cuts the y-axis when y is zero and then $x = 20$.
The coordinates of the required point are therefore $(20, 0)$.

Question 5

Describe how the graph of $y = x^2 + 6x + 7$ may be obtained from the graph of $y = x^2$.
The domain of the function f is all real values of x.
State the range of the function $f(x) = x^2 + 6x + 7$.

Solution

$x^2 + 6x + 7 = (x + 3)^2 - 2$

The graph of $y = x^2 + 6x + 7$ may therefore be obtained by translating the graph of $y = x^2$ by $\binom{3}{-2}$.

The range of f is $y \geqslant -2$.

Question 6 A geometric progression of positive terms, with first term 1, is such that $\frac{t_6}{t_4} = 25$. Find the product of the third and the fifth terms.

Solution Let the nth term be t_n, so that $t_n = ar^{n-1}$.

$$\frac{t_6}{t_4} = 25 \Rightarrow \frac{ar^5}{ar^3} = 25$$
$$\Rightarrow \quad r^2 = 25$$
$$\Rightarrow \quad r = \pm 5$$

However, all the terms of the progression are positive, so $r = 5$.

$$t_3 \times t_5 = 1 \times 5^2 \times 1 \times 5^4$$
$$= 5^2 \times 5^4$$
$$= 25^{2+4}$$
$$= 25^6$$
$$= 244\,140\,625$$

Question 7 Obtain the range of the function $f(x) = x^2 - 2x - 3$ which is only defined for the domain $0 \leqslant x \leqslant 4$.

Solution Consider the endpoints: $f(0) = -3$, $f(4) = 5$.

The range of the function is therefore $-3 \leqslant y \leqslant 5$.

Question 8 Find the values of x in the interval $-2\pi \leqslant x \leqslant 2\pi$ for which $2\sin^2 x + \cos x = 1$.

Solution Using the identity $\sin^2 A + \cos^2 A = 1$, the equation becomes

$$2(1 - \cos^2 x) + \cos x = 1$$
$$\Rightarrow \quad 0 = 2\cos^2 x - \cos x - 1$$
$$\Rightarrow (2\cos x + 1)(\cos x - 1) = 0$$
$$\Rightarrow \quad \cos x = -\tfrac{1}{2} \text{ or } \cos x = 1$$

From one of the special triangles,

$$\cos^{-1}\left(\tfrac{1}{2}\right) = \frac{\pi}{3}$$

so

$$\cos^{-1}\left(-\tfrac{1}{2}\right) = -\frac{\pi}{3}$$

If 2π is added, another solution is obtained:

$$-\frac{\pi}{3} + 2\pi = \frac{5\pi}{3}$$

$\cos^{-1}(1) = 0$.

Two more solutions can be obtained by adding and subtracting 2π.
There are five solutions altogether in the interval specified:

$$x = -2\pi, -\frac{\pi}{3}, 0, \frac{5\pi}{3}, 2\pi$$

Question 9 Find the local maximum and minimum values of the function $f(x) = 1 + x + \frac{1}{x}$.

Solution $f(x) = 1 + x + x^{-1} \Rightarrow f'(x) = 1 - x^{-2}$

$$= 1 - \frac{1}{x^2}$$

Maximum and minimum values occur when $f'(x) = 0$. Hence

$$1 - \frac{1}{x^2} = 0 \Rightarrow \quad 1 = \frac{1}{x^2}$$

$$\Rightarrow \quad x^2 = 1$$

$$\Rightarrow \quad x = \pm 1$$

$f(1) = 3$, $f(-1) = -1$

Clearly, the maximum point is $(1, 3)$ and the minimum point is $(-1, -1)$.

Question 10 In triangle PQR, the obtuse angle QPR is $\theta°$. Angle PRQ is 30°, and the lengths PQ and QR are 6 cm and 8 cm respectively. Find the value of $\cos\theta$.

R, 30°, θ, P, 8, 6, Q

Solution Using the sine rule.

$$\frac{8}{\sin\theta} = \frac{6}{\sin 30°}$$

$$\Rightarrow \sin\theta = \frac{8 \sin 30°}{6}$$

$$= \tfrac{4}{6}$$

$$= \tfrac{2}{3}$$

$\theta = \sin^{-1}(\tfrac{2}{3}) = 41.81°$(2 d.p.), so $\cos\theta = \cos(41.81) = 0.745$ (3 s.f.)

Question 11 Express $\left(1 - \frac{x}{3}\right)^3$ in ascending powers of x.

Solution By the binomial expansion:

$$\left(1 - \frac{x}{3}\right)^3 = 1 - 3\left(\frac{x}{3}\right) + 3\left(\frac{x}{3}\right)^2 - \left(\frac{x}{3}\right)^3$$

Simplifying $= 1 - x + \frac{x^2}{3} - \frac{x^3}{27}$

Multiply by 27 to tidy up $= 27 - 27x + 9x^2 - x^3$

Question 12

Show that there is a stationary point where $x = 1$ on the curve

$y = x^4 - 4x^3 + 6x^2 - 4x + 3.$

Determine the nature of this point.

Solution

$$\frac{dy}{dx} = 4x^3 - 12x^2 + 12x - 4$$
$$= 4(x^3 - 3x^2 + 3x - 1)$$
$$x = 1 \Rightarrow \quad \frac{dy}{dx} = 4(1 - 3 + 3 - 1)$$
$$= 0$$

There must therefore be a stationary point when $x = 1$.

$$\frac{d^2y}{dx^2} = 12x^2 - 24x + 12$$
$$x = 1 \Rightarrow \quad \frac{d^2y}{dx^2} = 12 - 24 + 12$$
$$= 0$$

The stationary point cannot be a maximum or minimum, and so must be a point of inflexion.

Question 13

S denotes the sum to infinity of the series $1 - 2x + 4x^2 - 8x^3 + \cdots$.
Find the value of x for which $S = \frac{2}{3}$.

Solution

The series is geometric, with first term $a = 1$ and common ratio $r = 2x$

$$S = \frac{a}{1 - r} = \frac{1}{1 - 2x}$$
$$S = \tfrac{2}{3} \Rightarrow \quad \frac{1}{1 - 2x} = \frac{2}{3}$$
$$\Rightarrow \quad 3 = 2(1 - 2x)$$
$$\Rightarrow \quad 4x = -1$$
$$\Rightarrow \quad x = -\tfrac{1}{4}$$

Question 14

Find the range of values of k for which $f(x) = 4x^2 - 4x + k$ is always positive.

Solution

The discriminant of the quadratic equation $4x^2 - 4x + k = 0$ is

$$(-4)^2 - 4 \times 4 \times k = 16 - 16k$$
$$= 16(1 - k)$$

The discriminant is always positive if $16(1 - k) > 0$

$$\Rightarrow \quad 1 - k > 0$$
$$\Rightarrow \quad k < 1$$

Question 15

Describe in words how the graph of $y = \ln(x - 1)$ may be obtained from the graph of $y = \ln x$.

If $f(x) = \ln(x - 1)$, state the largest possible domain of f and find the range of f.

Solution

The graph of $y = \ln(x - 1)$ can be obtained by translating the graph of $y = \ln x$ by $\binom{1}{0}$.

The range of f is $x > 1$ and the largest possible domain of f is all real numbers.

Question 16

Sketch the graph of $y = (1 - x)(2 - x)(3 - x)$.

Hence solve the inequality $(1 - x)(2 - x)(3 - x) < 0$.

Solution

Intercepts are (1, 0), (2, 0) and (3, 0).

The shape is the usual shape for cubics.

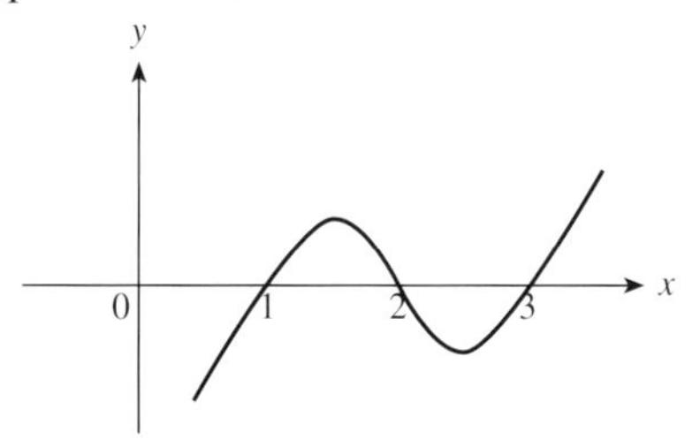

The solutions to the inequality are $x < 1$ or $2 < x < 3$.

Question 17

Obtain the coordinates of all the points where the curves $y = 2\sin x \cos x$ and $y = 2\cos x$ meet in the interval $0 \leqslant x \leqslant 2\pi$.

Solution

$$2\sin x \cos x = 2\cos x \Rightarrow \frac{2\sin x \cos x}{2\cos x} = 1$$

$$\Rightarrow \qquad \sin x = 1$$

The only solution in the interval $0 \leqslant x \leqslant 2\pi$ is $x = \dfrac{\pi}{2}$.

Question 18 $p(t) = t^3 - t^2 - t + 1$. Evaluate $p(1)$. Hence factorise $p(t)$.

Sketch the graph of $y = p(t)$.
State the range of values of t for which $p(t) > 0$.

Solution $p(1) = 1 - 1 - 1 + 1 = 0 \Rightarrow (t + 1)$ is a factor of $p(t)$.

$$\begin{aligned} p(t) &= t^3 - t^2 - t + 1 \\ &= (t + 1)(t^2 - 2t + 1) \\ &= (t + 1)(t - 1)^2 \end{aligned}$$

Intercepts are $(-1, 0)$, $(1, 0)$ and $(0, 1)$.
$p(t) > 0 \Rightarrow t > -1$

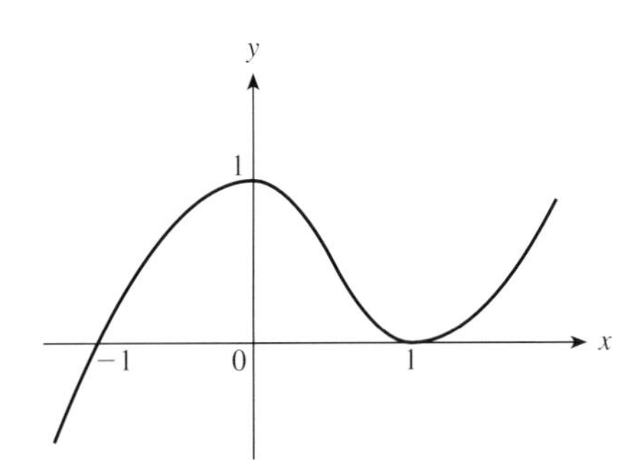

Question 19 In triangle ABC, angle BAC is 13 degrees, and the lengths AB and AC are 12 metres and 14 metres respectively. Find the length of BC and angle ACB, both correct to 1 decimal place.

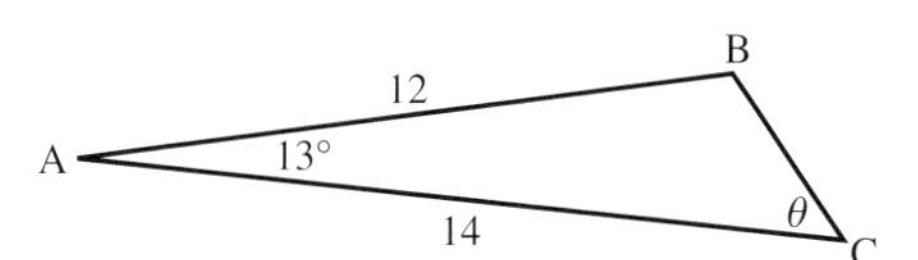

Solution Using the cosine rule:

$$BC^2 = 12^2 + 14^2 - 2 \times 12 \times 14 \times \cos 13^\circ$$

$$\Rightarrow \quad BC = 3.6 \text{ (1 d.p.)}$$

Let angle ACB be θ.
Using the sine rule:

$$\frac{12}{\sin\theta} = \frac{BC}{\sin 13^\circ}$$

$$\Rightarrow \quad \sin\theta = \frac{12\sin 13^\circ}{3.6} = 0.7498$$

$$\Rightarrow \quad \theta = 48.6 \text{ (1 d.p.)}$$

Question 20

A is the point where the curve with equation

$$y = x - \frac{1}{x^2}$$

meets the x-axis. B is the point (2, 0). The curve meets the line $x = 2$ at the point C.

Find the area of the finite region bounded by the straight lines AB and BC, and by that part of the curve between A and C.

Solution

The curve meets the x-axis when $y = 0$.

$$x - \frac{1}{x^2} = 0 \Rightarrow x = \frac{1}{x^2}$$

$$\Rightarrow \qquad x^3 = 1$$

$$\Rightarrow \qquad x = 1$$

So A is the point (1, 0).

The required area is

$$\int_1^2 \left(x - \frac{1}{x^2}\right) \mathrm{d}x = \int_1^2 (x - x^{-2})\, \mathrm{d}x$$

$$= \left[\frac{1}{2}x^2 - \frac{x^{-3}}{-3}\right]_1^2$$

$$= \left[\frac{1}{2}x^2 + \frac{1}{3x^3}\right]_1^2$$

$$= \left(2 + \frac{1}{24}\right) - \left(\frac{1}{2} + \frac{1}{3}\right)$$

$$= \frac{29}{24}$$

Revision Exercise 4

1 Find simplified forms of $\frac{dy}{dx}$ when

a $y = \ln(x^n)$ where n is an integer

b $y = \ln(kx)$ where k is any constant

2 $f(x) = 4e^{\frac{x}{2}} - 1$ for all real x; $g(x) = 2\ln(3x+1)$ for $x > -\frac{1}{3}$.
Find the inverse functions $f^{-1}(x)$ and $g^{-1}(x)$, stating the domain each case.

3 $f(x) = e^{2x}$, $g(x) = 1 - \ln x \quad (x > 0)$ and $h(x) = e^{-x}$.

a Simplify $e^{\ln x}$ and $\ln(e^x)$.

b Hence obtain a simpler expression for $e^{k \ln x}$.

c Show that the composite functions gf and hg are both linear functions, of the form $ax + b$, where a and b are constants to be determined.

4 Show that if

$$\int_1^x \left(t + \frac{1}{t}\right) dt = 2$$

then x satisfies the equation $x^2 + 2\ln x - 5 = 0$.

5 Decide which of the three symbols $\Rightarrow$, $\Leftarrow$ or $\Leftrightarrow$, if any, should replace ...

a $a - c = b - c \ \dots \ a = b$

b $\frac{a}{c} = \frac{b}{c} \ \dots \ a = b$

c $a = b \ \dots \ a^2 = b^2$

d $a = b \ \dots \ |a| = |b|$

e $ac = bc \ \dots \ a = b$

f $a^c = b^c \ \dots \ a = b$

g $c^a = c^b \ \dots \ a = b$

h $e^{a^2} = e^{b^2} \ \dots \ a = b$

i $\sin a = \sin b \ \dots \ a = b$

j $a = -b \ \dots \ \cos a = \cos b$

k $a^2 = 1 \ \dots \ a = 1$

l $a = 30° \ \dots \ \sin a = \frac{1}{2}$

m $a + b = 0 \ \dots \ a^2 + b^2 = 0$

n $a = 1 + \sqrt{2} \ \dots \ a^2 = 3 + \sqrt{8}$

o $a < b \ \dots \ -a > -b$

p $a < b \ \dots \ \frac{1}{a} > \frac{1}{b}$

q $a > b > 0 \ \dots \ a^2 > b^2 > 0$

r $(a-1)^2 > 0 \ \dots \ a > 1$

s $y = x^2 + 3x \ \dots \ \frac{dy}{dx} = 2x + 3$

t $f(a) = f(b) \ \dots \ a = b$

u $\ln a = \ln b \ \dots \ a = b$

v $\int_0^a f(x)\,dx = \int_0^b f(x)\,dx \ \dots \ a = b$

w $f'(a) = f'(b) \ \dots \ a = b$

x $a - b = b - a \ \dots \ a = b$

y $x(x-1)(x+2) = 0 \ \dots \ x = 1$ or $x = -2$

z $f(x) < g(x)$ for $a \leqslant x \leqslant b \ \dots \ \int_a^b f(x)\,dx < \int_a^b g(x)\,dx$

6 Prove that, with the usual notation, the area of a triangle is $\frac{1}{2}ab\sin C$.
(Prove for an acute-angled triangle and for an obtuse-angled triangle.)

7 Prove that the distance between the points A(a_1, a_2) and B(b_1, b_2) is

$$\sqrt{(b_1 - a_1)^2 + (b_1 - a_2)^2}$$

8 Prove that, for a geometric series with first term a and common ratio r, where $|r| < 1$, the sum to infinity, S_∞, is given by

$$S_\infty = \frac{a}{1 - r}$$

Examination Questions 4

Functions e^x and $\ln x$

1 **a** Factorise $2y^3 + y^2 - 13y + 6$.

b Use the substitution $y = e^x$ to solve the equation

$$2e^{3x} + e^{2x} - 13e^x + 6 = 0,$$

giving your answers correct to three decimal places. *WJEC*

2 The curve with equation $y = \frac{1}{2}e^x$ meets the y-axis at the point A.

a Prove that the tangent at A to the curve has equation $2y = x + 1$.

The point B has x-coordinate $\ln 4$ and lies on the curve. The normal at B to the curve meets the tangent at A to the curve at the point C.

b Prove that the x-coordinate of C is $\frac{3}{2} + \ln 2$ and find the y-coordinate of C.

c Find, in terms of e, the area of the finite region bounded by the curve with equation $y = \frac{1}{2}e^x$, the coordinate axes and the line with equation $x + 2 = 0$.

EDEXCEL

3 The figure shows part of the curve with equation $y = 3e^{2x} - 1$. Find, giving your answer in terms of e, the area of the finite region bounded by the curve with equation $y = 3e^{2x} - 1$, the x-axis and the lines with equations $x = 0$ and $x = 2$.

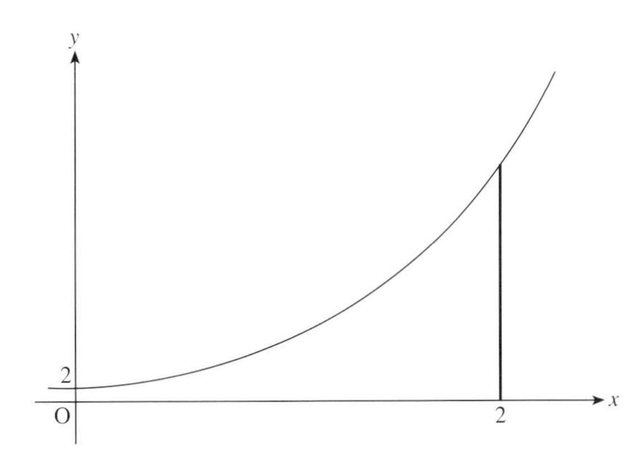

LONDON

4 The points P and Q lie on the curve with equation $y = e^{\frac{1}{2}x}$. The x-coordinates of P and Q are $\ln 4$ and $\ln 16$ respectively.

a Find an equation of the line PQ.

b Show that this line passes through the origin O.

c Calculate the length, to 3 significant figures, of the line segment PQ.

The finite region R is bounded by the arc of the curve with equation $y = e^{\frac{1}{2}x}$ between P and Q, the lines $x = \ln 4$, $x = \ln 16$ and the x-axis.

d Using integration, determine the area of R. *LONDON*

5 The functions f and g are defined over the set of real numbers by

f: $x \mapsto 3x - 5$,

g: $x \mapsto e^{-2x}$.

a State the range of g.

b Sketch the graphs of the inverse functions f^{-1} and g^{-1} and write on your sketches the coordinates of any points at which a graph meets the coordinate axes.

c State, giving a reason, the number of roots of the equation

$f^{-1}(x) = g^{-1}(x)$.

d Evaluate $fg(-\frac{1}{3})$, giving your answer to 2 decimal places. *LONDON*

Proof

1 The diagram below shows sketches of the line with equation $x + y = 4$ and the curve with equation $y = x^2 - 2x + 2$ intersecting at points P and Q. The minimum point of the curve is M. The shaded region R is bounded by the line and the curve.

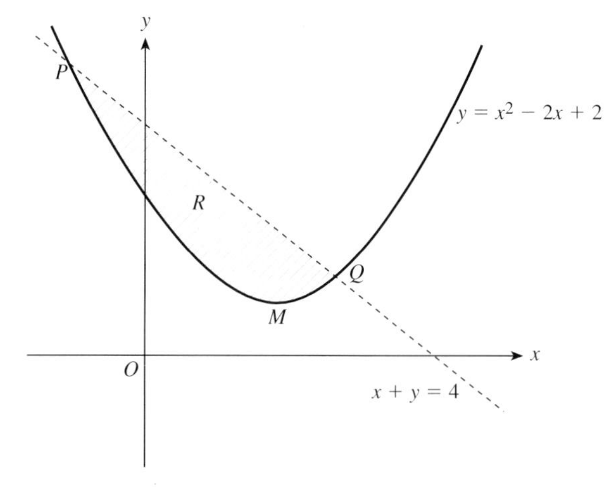

a Show that the coordinates of M are (1, 1).

b Find the coordinates of the points P and Q.

c Prove that the triangle PMQ is right-angled and hence show that the area of the triangle PMQ is 3 square units.

d Show that the area of the region R is $1\frac{1}{2}$ times that of the triangle PMQ.

AQA

2 A curve has equation $y = x^2 + kx + 9$

a Given that the curve does not cross or touch the x-axis, find the set of values that k can take.

b In the case when $k = 8$, express the equation of the curve in the form $y = (x + a)^2 + b$, finding the values of a and b.

c In the case when $k = -7$, prove that the curve crosses the x-axis at a point $(\alpha, 0)$ where $1.6 < \alpha < 1.7$. *AQA*

3 **a** An arithmetic series has first term a and common difference d. Prove that the sum of the first n terms of this series is

$$\frac{1}{2}n[2a + (n - 1)d]$$

The first three terms of an arithmetic series are k, 7.5 and $k + 7$ respectively.

b Find the value of k.

c Find the sum of the first 31 terms of this series. *EDEXCEL*

Answers

1 Sets of Numbers, Surds and Indices

Exercise 1a (p. 4)

1 a $\frac{2}{3}$ b $\frac{4}{9}$ c $\frac{4}{33}$ d $\frac{11}{36}$
e $\frac{11}{90}$ f $3\frac{403}{990}$ g $\frac{16}{33}$ h $4\frac{2}{9}$

2 a 0.14 b 0.016
c $0.\dot{5}$ d $0.\dot{3}\dot{6}$
e $6.\dot{2}8571\dot{4}$ f $0.1\dot{6}$
g 0.375 h $0.\dot{7}1428\dot{5}$

4 b must not contain factors other than 2 and/or 5

Exercise 1b (p. 10)

1 a 5 b $\frac{1}{2}$ c 48 d $\frac{1}{2}$
e $\dfrac{a}{b}$ f 15 g 21 h $\dfrac{p}{q}$
i $\dfrac{1}{4p}$ j $\dfrac{9a}{2b}$

2 a $2\sqrt{2}$ b $2\sqrt{3}$ c $3\sqrt{3}$
d $5\sqrt{2}$ e $3\sqrt{5}$ f $11\sqrt{10}$
g $5\sqrt{3}$ h $4\sqrt{2}$ i $6\sqrt{2}$
j $7\sqrt{2}$

3 a $\sqrt{18}$ b $\sqrt{12}$ c $\sqrt{80}$ d $\sqrt{24}$
e $\sqrt{72}$ f $\sqrt{216}$ g $\sqrt{128}$ h $\sqrt{1000}$
i $\sqrt{175}$ j $\sqrt{392}$

4 a $\frac{1}{5}\sqrt{5}$ b $\frac{1}{7}\sqrt{7}$ c $-\frac{1}{2}\sqrt{2}$
d $\frac{2}{3}\sqrt{3}$ e $\frac{1}{2}\sqrt{6}$ f $\frac{1}{4}\sqrt{2}$
g $-\frac{1}{2}\sqrt{3}$ h $\frac{3}{8}\sqrt{6}$ i $\sqrt{2}-1$
j $2+\sqrt{3}$

Exercise 1c (p. 11)

1 a $3\sqrt{2}$ b $6\sqrt{3}$ c $4\sqrt{7}$
d $5\sqrt{10}$ e $28\sqrt{2}$ f 0

2 a $\frac{6}{7}+\frac{2}{7}\sqrt{2}$ b $9+4\sqrt{5}$
c $-1+\sqrt{2}$ d $4-2\sqrt{3}$
e $-1-\sqrt{2}$ f $\frac{1}{2}+\frac{3}{4}\sqrt{2}$

3 a $5+2\sqrt{6}$
b $\frac{1}{2}(5+\sqrt{3}+\sqrt{5}+\sqrt{15})$
c $-7+3\sqrt{6}$
d $4+\sqrt{10}$
e $3+2\sqrt{2}$
f $\sqrt{2}$

4 a 12 b $3\sqrt{3}$ c 6 d 2
e $3\sqrt{3}$ f $\sqrt{3}$ g $4\sqrt{3}$ h $\frac{1}{6}\sqrt{3}$
i 30 j 4 k $3\sqrt{3}$ l $11\sqrt{3}$

5 a $6\sqrt{10}$ b 24 c $6\sqrt{6}$
d $\frac{19}{25}\sqrt{5}$ e $4\sqrt{2}$ f 1

Exercise 1d (p. 11)

1 a $8\sqrt{3}$ b $22\sqrt{3}$ c $72\sqrt{15}$

2 a $\frac{7}{36}\sqrt{6}$ b $\frac{3}{7}+\frac{5}{14}\sqrt{2}$ c 0

3 a $\dfrac{4\sqrt{5}+21}{19}$
b $3\sqrt{3}-3\sqrt{2}+\sqrt{6}-2$
c $-\dfrac{\sqrt{6}}{4}+\dfrac{\sqrt{2}}{4}+\dfrac{1}{2}$
d $\dfrac{x+y+2\sqrt{xy}}{x-y}$
e $\dfrac{a\sqrt{b}-\sqrt{c}}{a^2b-c}$
f $x-\sqrt{x^2-1}$

5 $a=2$, $b=3$ or $a=12$, $b=\frac{1}{2}$

6 a $3\sqrt[3]{2}$ b $2\sqrt[6]{3}$ c $4\sqrt[4]{5}$

7 a $2-\sqrt{2}$ b $4(2+\sqrt{3})$
c $-2-\sqrt{3}$ d $2+\sqrt{3}$
e $3+2\sqrt{2}$ f $6+4\sqrt{2}$

8 a 2.2% b 1%

Exercise 1e (p. 15)

1 a 5 b 3 c 2 d 7
e $\frac{1}{2}$ f 1 g -2 h -1
i 16 j 9 k 125 l 343
m $\frac{1}{8}$ n $\frac{2}{3}$ o $\frac{3}{2}$ p $\frac{2}{3}$

2 a 1 b $\frac{1}{3}$ c 1 d $\frac{1}{4}$
e $\frac{1}{8}$ f 2 g 9 h 1
i $\frac{1}{27}$ j $-\frac{1}{6}$ k 1 l $2\frac{1}{4}$
m 4 n 3 o $4\frac{1}{2}$ p $\frac{5}{9}$

3 a $\frac{1}{2}$ b $\frac{1}{4}$ c $\frac{1}{2}$ d $\frac{1}{8}$
e $\frac{1}{9}$ f 2 g 2 h 9
i $1\frac{1}{2}$ j $1\frac{1}{2}$ k $1\frac{1}{2}$ l $\frac{16}{81}$

4 a 0.4 b $\frac{8}{27}$ c $3\frac{3}{8}$ d $\frac{2}{3}$

Exercise 1f (p. 16)

1 a x^{-1} b x^{-2} c $x^{\frac{1}{2}}$ d $x^{\frac{1}{3}}$
e x^{-4} f x^4 g $x^{-\frac{1}{2}}$ h x^7
i $x^{-\frac{1}{3}}$ j $x^{\frac{2}{3}}$ k $x^{-\frac{3}{4}}$ l $x^{-\frac{5}{2}}$

2 a $3x^{-1}$ b $\frac{4}{3}x^{-1}$ c $6x^{\frac{1}{2}}$ d $5x^{-3}$
e $\frac{1}{4}x^{-4}$ f $\frac{1}{3}x^{\frac{1}{2}}$ g $\frac{1}{5}x^{-\frac{1}{2}}$ h $6x^7$
i $\frac{4}{5}x^{-\frac{1}{3}}$ j $7x^{\frac{2}{3}}$ k $2x^{-\frac{3}{4}}$ l $\frac{8}{3}x^{-\frac{1}{2}}$

Exercise 1g (p. 17)

1 a a^3 b $4b^2$ c x^8
d y^{11} e $6b^5$ f $24a^6$
g $15x^5y^3$ h a^2 i x^2
j y^4 k $64a^6$ l $4a^6$
m a^{m^2+m} n a^{2m+2} o $2x^{-1}y$
p u^6 q v^{2x} r v^{3x}
s v^{6x} t v^{2x^2} u 1
v $x^{\frac{1}{6}}$ w a^{x-y+z} x $3y^8$
y p^{-5} z 1

2 a s^{-2}; $\dfrac{1}{s^2}$ b y^{-5}; $\dfrac{1}{y^5}$
c t^{-b}; $\dfrac{1}{t^b}$ d x^{p-q}; $\dfrac{1}{x^{q-p}}$

3 a $16\pi^2r^2$ b $4a^6$ c b^4c^6
d $\dfrac{4a^2}{b^2}$ e $9y^6$ f $\dfrac{10^4a^6}{b^4}$
g $4a$ h $\frac{9}{16}a^{\frac{1}{2}}$

4 a x^4 b $2y$ c $5ab^2$
d $6x^3$ e $a^{-2}b^3$ f $-2a$
g $3xy^3$ h $\dfrac{10}{9x^5y^4}$

5 a $\dfrac{4}{x^2}$ b $\dfrac{1}{3a}$ c $\dfrac{4t^2}{3s}$
d 1 e $\frac{1}{2}a$ f $9b$
g $12x$ h $60x^4y^3$ i $4a^4$
j $\frac{1}{2}b^4$ k $4x^6y^{10}$ l 1
m $-2b^2c^5$ n $-4l^2m$ o $-2xy^2$
p $d^{10}e^{15}$ q $60a^3b^3$ r $\dfrac{n}{m}$
s $-m^5$ t n^6 u $2h^5$
v $64p^{-6}$ w $\frac{27}{2}a^{-5}$

6 a 25 b 4 c 1000 d 16
e 4 f 512 g 4 h 9

Extension Exercise 1h (p. 18)

1 a 250 b 4 c 375 d $\frac{1}{2}$
e 0.008 f 62.5 g 5 h 36

2 a 99 b 14 c 6 d 12
e 88 f 75

3 a $x^{\frac{1}{8}}$ b x^{-4}

5 a $\frac{1}{2}$ b 1 c 2 d $\frac{1}{8}$

6 a 2^{-n} b 3^{n+1} c $x^{-\frac{7}{12}}$ d $x^{\frac{n+3}{2}}$

8 $\sqrt{2}^{\left(\left(\sqrt{2}^{\sqrt{2}}\right)^{\sqrt{2}}\right)}=\left(\sqrt{2}^{\sqrt{2}}\right)^{\sqrt{2}}$

Miscellaneous Exercise 1i (p. 19)

1 **a** 5 **b** 20 **c** $3\sqrt{5}$ **d** $-4\sqrt{5}$ **e** 2 **f** $5\sqrt{5}$ **g** $\sqrt{10}$

2 **a** $4\sqrt{5}$ **b** $4\sqrt{2}$ **c** $6\sqrt{2}$ **d** $11\sqrt{5}$

3 **a** $\frac{1}{3}\sqrt{3}$ **b** $\frac{1}{2}\sqrt{2}$ **c** $\frac{4}{7}\sqrt{7}$ **d** $\dfrac{4+\sqrt{10}}{6}$ **e** $\sqrt{6}-2$ **f** $\frac{1}{4}\sqrt{6}$ **g** $3(\sqrt{6}+\sqrt{5})$

4 $4\sqrt{6}$ cm

5 $(14+2\sqrt{7})$ cm; $(5\sqrt{7}-2)$ cm^2

6 $(15-8\sqrt{3})$ cm

7 $20\sqrt{13}$ cm

8 $12\sqrt[3]{10}$ cm; $(6\times 10^{\frac{2}{3}})$ cm^2

9 $x=3,\ y=2$

10 **a** 3 **b** 64 **c** 7 **d** 1 **e** 1000 **f** 1

11 **a** 7^9 **b** 3^{11} **c** 80 **d** 5^7 **e** 992 **f** 2^5 **g** 8^2 **h** 222 **i** 7^3 **j** 7^4 **k** 5^9

12 **a** a^8 **c** $5c^3$ **d** d^9 **f** $6f^5$ **g** $20g^5$ **h** h^{12} **i** i^{12} **j** $9j^2$ **k** $4k^6$ **l** $49l^{12}$ **m** m^6n^3 **n** p^6q^{12} **o** $9r^2s^2$ **p** v^3w^3 **q** x **r** y^4 **s** z^5

13 **d** d^4 **e** $5e$ **f** $7f^2$ **g** g^3 **h** h^4 **i** $5i^2$ **j** j^5 **l** l^2m^5 **m** $2np$ **n** q^2 **o** $2r^7$ **p** $7s^4$ **q** 0

Test Yourself (p. 21)

1 A **2** B **3** B **4** D **5** B **6** A **7** D **8** D **9** B **10** D

2 Algebraic Expressions

Exercise 2a (p. 24)

1 **a** 63 **b** 24 **c** $-\frac{3}{4}$ **d** n^2-2n **e** $9k^2-6k$ **f** a^2-1

2 **a** 1 **b** 126 **c** $\frac{91}{64}$ **d** -7 **e** 2 **f** 0 **g** a^3+1 **h** $27k^3+1$

3 **a** $25+10h+h^2$ **b** $10+h$ **c** $2a+h$

Exercise 2b (p. 26)

1 **a** $x^4+2x^3-x-5;\ 4$ **b** $-x^5+3x^3+1;\ 5$ **c** $6x^4-x^3-2x^2;\ 4$ **d** $-10;\ 0$

2 **a** $2;\ -5$ **b** $3;\ 1$ **c** $-1;\ 0$ **d** $0;\ -10$

3 **a** $-3y^3+2x$ **b** $-6x^2-2xy-3y^2$ **c** $3x^3-7x^2-4x$ **d** $2ab+8a^2b-7ab^2$

4 **a** x^2+2x+1 **b** x^2+4x+4 **c** $4x^2+4x+1$ **d** $x^2-10x+25$ **e** x^2+3x+2 **f** $x^2+7x+12$ **g** x^2-x-12 **h** x^2-x-2 **i** $2x^2+3x+1$ **j** $3x^2-14x+8$ **k** $16x^2-9$ **l** x^2-4

5 **a** $2a^2-5a-3$ **b** $4d^2+11de+6e^2$ **c** $6-11x+4x^2$ **d** $-56w^2+113w-56$ **e** $9l^2-25$ **f** $9x^2+24x+16$ **g** $4h^2-4h-35$ **h** $10x^2-x-21$ **i** $6x^2+11x+4$ **j** $4-49x^2$ **k** $4y^2-12y+9$ **l** $16-b^4$ **m** x^3-3x^2+3x-1 **n** $a-b$

6 **a** $4k^2+16k+20$ **b** $2m^2+6m+10$ **c** $7s^2+6s-7$ **d** $2v^2+18$ **e** $-2y^2-24y-15$

7 **a** x^3-x^2+3x+4 **b** $-x^3+3x^2+3x-6$ **c** $x^5+x^4-7x^3+7x^2+15x-5$ **d** x^3+4x^2+2x-1 **e** $x^4+6x^3+7x^2-6x+1$ **f** $x^3+13x^2-3x-10$

8 **a** 8 **b** 14 **c** 15

9 **a** 9 **b** 9 **c** 2 **d** -7

10 **a** $7x^4-2x^3+4x^2-x+3$ **b** $-14x^4+4x^3+x^2-x$ **c** $21x^6-13x^5+19x^4-5x^3+5x^2-x+2$ **d** $10x^5-3x^4+3x^3+x$

11 **a** 8 **b** 24

12 **a** $42x^5+9x^4-7x^3+41x^2+18x-4$ **b** $x^4-2x^2y^2+y^4$ **c** $4y^7+12y^6-8y^5-10y^4+y^3+25y^2-10y-14$ **d** $u^6+2u^3v^2-4u^3w+v^4-4v^2w+4w^2$ **e** $6x^3y+2x^2-9xy^2-3y$ **f** $12x^3+44x^2+5x-7$

Exercise 2c (p. 30)

1 **a** $3,\ 60$ **b** $1,\ 56$ **c** $2,\ 360$ **d** $2,\ 420$ **e** $1,\ 210$ **f** $1,\ 3150$

2 **a** $(a+b),\ ab(a+b)$ **b** $xy,\ x^3y^2$ **c** $2x^2,\ 4x^3y$ **d** $ab,\ 6a^2b^3$ **e** $cd,\ 4c^3d^5$ **f** $2c,\ 12abc^2d$ **g** $4ab,\ 24a^3b^4c^2$ **h** $17p^2r^3,\ 102p^4q^2r^5$ **i** $(3x+1),\ x^2(2x-1)(3x+1)$ **j** $x(x-1),\ 2x^2(x+1)(x-1)$ **k** $ab(b+c),\ a^2b^2(b+c)^2$ **l** $4(c+d),\ 12(a+b)(c+d)$

Exercise 2d (p. 31)

1 **a** $\frac{1}{3}$ **b** $\frac{1}{3}$ **c** $\frac{10}{27}$ **d** $\frac{2}{13}$ **e** $\frac{5}{7}$ **f** $\frac{3}{8}$ **g** $\frac{23}{27}$ **h** $\frac{7}{48}$

2 **a** $2x$ **b** $\frac{1}{2}b$ **c** a **d** $\dfrac{2x}{y}$ **e** $\dfrac{c}{a}$ **f** $\frac{2}{3}p^4$ **g** $\frac{3}{2}abc$ **h** $\dfrac{z^2}{xy}$ **i** $\dfrac{3x+1}{x+1}$ **j** -1 **k** $\dfrac{2x^2}{x-y}$ **l** $\dfrac{2}{3x}$

3 **a** $b^2(1-b)$ **b** $a(a+b)$ **c** $5a(a-2)$ **d** $y^4(y-1)$ **e** $9c(2c^2-d^2)$ **f** $4a^2(1-4b)$ **g** $27(3x-2)$ **h** $3x(x^2-2x+3)$ **i** $x(4x^2+x-1)$ **j** $2a(a^2-2a-1)$ **k** $7a(a-ab+2b^3)$ **l** $3x^2y(x^2-2xy+3y^2)$

4 **a** $\frac{1}{2}gh(g+j)$ **b** $\frac{1}{2}h(a+b)$ **c** $\frac{1}{3}lm(l-2m)$ **d** $\frac{1}{6}\pi r^2(8r+3h)$

5 **a** 3400 **b** 122 **c** 2900 **d** 161.4 **e** 10.5 **f** 1580 **g** 30 **h** $27\,000$

Exercise 2e (p. 36)

1 **a** $x(x-36)$ **b** $6x(x-6)$ **c** $2x(x-2)$ **d** $x(5x-2)$ **e** $x(x+3)$ **f** $4x(x+1)$

2 a $(x+1)(x+2)$
b $(x+7)(x+1)$
c $(x+2)(x+4)$
d $(x+8)(x+1)$
e $(x-1)(x-3)$
f $(x-3)(x-5)$
g $(x-10)(x-2)$
h $(x-4)(x+1)$
j $(x-1)(x+8)$
k $(x+4)(x-1)$
l $(x+9)(x-10)$
m $(x+12)(x-15)$
o $(x-10)(x+1)$

3 a $(3x+11)(x+1)$
b $(x+7)(3x+1)$
d $(x+2)(2x+1)$
e $2(x+1)(2x+1)$
f $3(x+1)^2$
i $(x+2y)(5x+y)$
j $(2p-q)(4p-5q)$
k $(x-4)(6x-1)$
l $2(q-6)(3q-4)$
m $(2y-3)(5y-3)$
n $(2a-3)(3a-2)$
o $5(c-1)(c-2)$
q $(3z-2)^2$
s $3(x-4)(x+3)$
t $(5x-1)(5x-2)$

4 a $(a-7)(a+2)$
b $(b-3)(b+7)$
c $(c-2)(c+4)$
d $(d-1)(d+6)$
e $(e-6)(e+1)$
f $(2f+1)(f-1)$
g $(2g-1)(g+1)$
i $(x-3y)(x+7y)$
j $(3j-1)(j-1)$
k $(k-3)(2k+1)$
l $(3-l)(5+l)$
m $(1+2m)(1-4m)$
n $(n-2p)(n+4p)$

5 a $(a+2)(a-2)$
b $(b+12)(b-12)$
c $(c+3d)(c-3d)$
d $(5e+4f)(5e-4f)$
e $(6g+1)(6g-1)$
f $(7h+8j)(7h-8j)$
g $4(2k-5)(2k+5)$
h $25(l+3)(l-3)$
i $3(l+2)(l-2)$
j $2(m+5n)(m-5n)$
k $(3z^2+a)(3z^2-a)$
l $(ef^2g^3+11)(ef^2g^3-11)$
m $(9h^2+4)(3h+2)(3h-2)$
n $(l^4+16)(l^2+4)(l+2)(l-2)$
o $(13+m)(13-m)$

6 a $(2-z)(1+5z)$
b $(1-y)(2-5y)$
c $(2+w)(1-3w)$
d $(3-y)(1+2y)$
e $(1-t)(3+5t)$
f $(1-2j)(1+j)$
g $(x-6)(x-1)$
h $(1-x)(2+x)$
i $(6-x)(3+x)$

7 a $(f-2)^2$
b $(x+1)(x+2)$
c $2(k+4)(k-4)$
d $(1-4v)(1+5v)$
e $7(x-2)(x+1)$
f $7(1+2c)(1-2c)$
i $(1-5u)(1-4u)$
j $a(x-4)(x+1)$
k $(s-1)(19s-8)$
l $2l(l-6)$
m $(2g+1)(5g+4)$
n $(a-1)(6a+25)$

8 a $(m+n)(y+z)$
b $(x-y)(c+d)$
c $(5-n)(x-y)$
d $(a+b)(a-c)$
e $(a+b)(5+b)$
f $(1-2c)(y-3a)$
g $(x+1)(x^3+2)$
h $(y-1)(y^2+1)$
i $(a+1)(b-1)$

9 a 140 **b** 800 **c** -1500
d 0.4 **e** -400 **f** 14 049

10 a $(t-3)(t+2)$
b $(2t+5)(3t-2)$
c $(7-2t)(1+6t)$
d $(2t-r)(3t-2r)$
e $(3t-4)(4t-3)$
g $(2t-3u)(3t+5u)$
h $12(t+1)(t-2)$
i $(4t+3)(6t-5)$
j $(3t+4)(8t-3)$
k $(1-x)(1+6x)$
l $(2t-3)(3t-4)$
m $(4-3t)(5t+2)$
n $7(1+2c)(1-2c)$
o $4(3t^2-13t-2)$
p $(3t+1)(4t-9)$
q $(t-6)(4t+1)$
r $(2t-3)^2$
s $(t-3)(4t-5)$
t $(t-15)(4t+1)$
u $4(5t+1)(5t-1)$

11 a $n^2(n+3)(n-3)$
b $\pi(R+r)(R-r)$
c $(a+b)(x^2+2)$
d $(e^2+1)(e^2+3)$
e $(2-d)(3+d)$
f $(x^3+2)(2x-1)$
g $(c+2d)(c-2d)$
i $(a+b)(2x+y)$
j $3(4t^2-6t-3)$
k $4(t-1)^2$
m $l(1-3l)(1+l)$
n $(x+7)(x-8)$
o $6(2+x)(1-x)$

12 a a, $6a$
b c, abc
c xy, $10x^2y^2$
d $a+3$, $6(a+3)$
e $b-1$, $12(b-1)$
f $2(a-2d)$, $12(a-2d)$
g $a-b$, $ab(a-b)$
h $2b$, $30a^2bc^2$
i 1, $30abcd$
j $x-5$, $(x-5)(x+2)(x-1)$
k $x-3$, $(x-3)(x-2)(x+2)$
l $a-3b$, $2(a-3b)(a+3b)$
m $2pq^2$, $8p^4q^3$
n $2x^2$, $4x^3y$
o $2c$, $12abc^2d$

13 a $c-1$, $c(c-1)^2(c^2+c+1)$
b $d+2$, $(d+2)(d-2)(d^2-2d+4)$
c $3a+1$, $(3a+1)(5a+1)(4a-1)$
d $a+b$, $(a+b)(a+2b)(a-2b)$
e $x(x-3)$, $x^2(x-3)(x+5)(x^2+3x+9)$
f $x(x-1)$, $x^2(x+1)(x-1)(2x-1)$

14 a $-3(x+2)$
b $-(x+3)$
c $4x$
d $(x+1)(x+2)(2x+9)$
e $(N+1)^2(N+2)^2$
f $(a+b)(a^2-ab+b^2)$
g $x(x+7)(3x^2+19x-7)$
h $12(x+2)$
i $(x+2)(5x+12)$
j $x(5x+14)$

Exercise 2f (p. 42)

1 a 4 **b** 35 **c** 180
d 12 **e** 16

2 a $1\frac{1}{14}$ **b** $\frac{1}{20}$ **c** $5\frac{25}{36}$
d $\frac{29}{36}$ **e** $1\frac{9}{10}$ **f** $14\frac{9}{10}$
g $1\frac{31}{35}$ **h** $65\frac{7}{12}$ **i** $1099\frac{7}{12}$

3 a 9 **b** $\frac{3}{4}$ **c** $\frac{2}{3}$
d $9\frac{4}{5}$ **e** 17 **f** $25\frac{1}{2}$
g 72

4 a $3\frac{1}{2}$ **b** 5

5 a $1\frac{4}{5}$ **b** $\frac{1}{8}$ **c** $1\frac{4}{5}$
d $\frac{5}{6}$ **e** $\frac{3}{8}$ **f** $1\frac{1}{3}$

Exercise 2g (p. 42)

1 a $3abc$ **b** $8n^2t$ **c** $12ac$
d $3e$ **e** $2a(a-b)$
f $9y$ **g** $91x$

2 a $\frac{5}{a}$ b $\frac{7a}{12}$
c $\frac{1}{x}$ d $\frac{5y}{12}$
e $\frac{2b-3a}{ab}$ f $\frac{8}{15x}$
g $\frac{1-36a}{12a}$ h $\frac{5b+4}{8}$
i $\frac{x}{3}$ j $\frac{x^2+z^2}{xyz}$
k $\frac{m^2+n^2}{mn}$ l $\frac{2a^3-3b^2}{3a^2}$
m $\frac{15y+31}{3y}$ n $\frac{5-x}{x^2-1}$
o $\frac{x^2+10x+7}{x(x+1)}$ p $\frac{2b^2+a^2-ab}{ab}$
q $\frac{2a}{a^2-b^2}$ r $\frac{x+10}{x^2-4}$
s $\frac{ax-ay}{(a-x)(a-y)}$ t $\frac{u-7v}{24}$
u $\frac{48-7x}{7-x}$

3 a $\frac{56b-33c}{24}$
b $\frac{68-9x}{20}$
c $\frac{13x+9}{15}$
d $\frac{x}{x^2-9}$
e $\frac{27x-89y+17}{18}$
f $\frac{7x+14}{(x-4)(x+2)(x+3)}$
g $\frac{x+4}{(x-3)(x+4)(x-2)}$
h 1
i $\frac{(5a-1)(2a-1)}{a(a-1)(3a-1)}$

4 a $\frac{b}{a}$ b $\frac{9x^3}{5z}$ c $3a^2b^2$
d $\frac{2x^2}{3}$ e $\frac{6x^2}{y}$ f $\frac{3x^2}{2y}$
g $\frac{b}{2c}$ h $\frac{a}{d}$ i 1
j $\frac{c}{a}$ k -1 l $3(a-b)$

5 a $\frac{n}{3}$ b -2 c $\frac{d(d-2)}{2}$
d $\frac{c-d}{d^3}$ e $\frac{a^2cd}{5b^2}$ f $\frac{a+b}{x-y}$

6 a $\frac{a^2}{b^2}$ b $c(1-d)$ c $\frac{18y^3}{5}$
d $\frac{a+2}{a}$ e $\frac{b}{2}$ f $\frac{u-2}{3u}$

7 a $\frac{y}{x}$ b $\frac{2b}{a}$
c $\frac{c}{ac+b}$ d $\frac{y}{x-yz}$
e $\frac{x^4+x^3}{x^3-1}$ f $\frac{1}{a-b}$
g $\frac{a-1}{a}$ h $\frac{1}{a+1}$
i $\frac{2+3x}{5-x^2y}$ j $\frac{2(x-3)}{x-4}$
k $\frac{5(x+2)}{3(x+1)}$ l $-(1+a)$

8 a $\frac{8}{x^2}$ b $\frac{1}{6(2-x)}$
c $\frac{x+2}{2}$ d $\frac{8(x+5)}{x+2}$
e $\frac{x-1}{x+1}$ f $\frac{x}{x-1}$
g $\frac{1}{4}$ h $\frac{(x+2)^2}{(x+3)^2}$
i $\frac{(x+2)^2}{(x-3)^2}$ j xy

Extension Exercise 2h (p. 44)

2 $(x+1)(y+1)$

3 $13x^n$

4 a $\frac{x^2}{x+1}$ b $(2N+1)(2N+3)$
c $3x^2+3hx+h^2$ d $\frac{ad+bc}{ac+bd}$

5 a $\frac{x^2}{\sqrt{x^2+1}}$ b $\frac{1}{(x+1)^{\frac{2}{3}}}$

Miscellaneous Exercise 2i (p. 45)

1 a 4 b $\frac{13}{20}$ c 32 d $\frac{6}{7}$
e $\frac{105}{16}$ f $\frac{7}{8}$ g -1 h $\frac{30}{7}$
i $\frac{1}{8}$ j $\frac{15}{4}$ k 4 l $\frac{5}{8}$
m 147 n -1 o $\frac{7}{24}$ p $\frac{3}{2}$

2 a $3x$ b $x(4x-1)$
c $(4x-1)^2$ d $4x+\frac{1}{x}$
e $4+\frac{2}{x}$ f $\frac{3}{4x-1}$
g 6 h 9
i $x+1$ j $\frac{x(4x-1)}{9}$
k $\frac{3x}{x+2}$ l $1-x$

3 a 200 b $\frac{1}{58}$ c 40 000

4 a $a+b$ b $\frac{2}{T+t}$
c $-\frac{1}{t}$ d $-tT$

5 a $\frac{4hx}{(x+h)^2(x-h)^2}$
b $-\frac{2N+5}{(N+2)(N+3)}$
c $-\frac{1}{(n+1)^2}$
d $\frac{3a+4}{(a+1)(a-1)}$

Test Yourself (p. 46)

1 C **2** C **3** D **4** D **5** B
6 B **7** C **8** E **9** D **10** B

3 Equations

Exercise 3a (p. 52)

1 a $x=-\frac{5}{7}$ b $x=\frac{2}{3}$ c $x=3$
d $x=\frac{1}{2}$ e $x=\frac{1}{3}$ f $x=1$
g $x=2$ h $y=-\frac{1}{2}$ i $a=5$
j $b=0$ k $c=7\frac{2}{3}$ l $d=5\frac{1}{2}$
m $e=0$ n $m=3$ o $v=-2$
p $x=2\frac{3}{5}$ q $k=\frac{1}{4}$

2 a $a=48$ b $x=1\frac{11}{16}$
c $a=24$ d $x=2$
e $x=-1\frac{4}{5}$ f $x=5$
g $y=-16\frac{2}{3}$ h $x=3$
i $y=\frac{1}{2}$ j $x=1\frac{2}{3}$
k $x=1\frac{1}{2}$ l $x=2$
m $x=15$ n $x=\frac{1}{7}$
o $x=5$ p $x=4$
q $x=0.5$ r $x=2$
s $x=-4$ t $a=5$
u $x=-12$ v $x=4$
w $x=\frac{2}{3}$ x $x=7$
y $x=17$ z $x=\frac{7}{11}$

3 8.5 m

4 $-2\,\mathrm{m\,s^{-2}}$

5 23 sweets

6 $x=32$

7 144 plants

Exercise 3b (p. 55)

1 a $x=\frac{b+c}{a}$ b $x=a-b$

c $x = \frac{d}{c}$ d $x = \frac{e}{f}$

e $x = \frac{g - j}{h}$ f $x = \frac{k}{m - l}$

g $x = \frac{3 + a}{b}$ h $x = ab - n$

i $x = \frac{3(d - b)}{2}$ j $x = \frac{k}{h + j}$

k $x = \frac{n}{p - m}$ l $x = \frac{2t}{s}$

m $x = \frac{c}{a} - b$ n $x = \frac{pq}{r - p}$

o $x = \frac{2d - 3b}{3a - 2c}$ p $x = \frac{bc - a}{c}$

q $x = \frac{t - s}{p}$ r $x = \frac{cr - aq}{ap + cs}$

s $x = \frac{(3a - 2)b}{2a + 3}$ t $x = \frac{b(1 + a)}{1 - a}$

u $x = \frac{4my - 2y - 1}{2 + 2m}$

2 a $x = a^2$ b $x = \frac{1}{3}a^2$

c $x = \frac{1}{9}a^2$ d $x = (b - a)^2$

e $x = b^2 - a$ f $x = \pm\sqrt{c}$

g $x = \pm\sqrt{d - c}$ h $x = \frac{c^2}{a^2} + b$

i $x = \left(\frac{b + 1}{a}\right)^2$ j $x = \pm\sqrt{k}$

k $x = \frac{d^2}{e^2}$ l $x = ab^2$

m $x = c$ n $x = y^3$

o $x = y^{\frac{3}{2}}$ p $x = p^{\frac{n}{m}}$

q $x = \pm\frac{1}{\sqrt{q}}$ r $x = \frac{1}{s^4}$

3 a $r = \frac{C}{2\pi}$

b $p = \frac{c}{v}$, $v = \frac{c}{p}$

c $u = v - at$, $a = \frac{v - u}{t}$, $t = \frac{v - u}{a}$

d $b = \frac{A}{l}$

e $t = \frac{pv}{k}$, $p = \frac{kt}{v}$

f $v_2 = \frac{p_1 v_1 t_2}{p_2 t_1}$, $t_1 = \frac{p_1 v_1 t_2}{p_2 v_2}$

g $P = \frac{100I}{RT}$

h $r = \pm\sqrt{\frac{A}{\pi}}$

i $t = \pm\sqrt{\frac{2S}{g}}$

j $r = \pm\sqrt{\frac{S}{4\pi}}$

k $y = d^2$

l $z = \pm\sqrt{d}$

m $h = \frac{3a^2}{4}$

n $y = \frac{t^2}{4\pi^2}$

o $l = \frac{t^2 g}{4\pi^2}$, $g = \frac{4\pi^2 l}{t^2}$

p $a = \pm\sqrt{c^2 - b^2}$

q $h = \frac{3V}{\pi r^2}$, $r = \pm\sqrt{\frac{3V}{\pi h}}$

r $R = \pm\sqrt{\frac{A}{\pi} + r^2}$, $r = \pm\sqrt{R^2 - \frac{A}{\pi}}$

s $u = \frac{fv}{v - f}$, $v = \frac{fu}{u - f}$, $f = \frac{uv}{u + v}$

t $P = \frac{100A}{100 + RT}$, $T = \frac{100(A - P)}{PR}$

u $n = \frac{2s}{a + l}$, $a = \frac{2s}{n} - l$

v $h = \pm\sqrt{\frac{A^2}{\pi^2 r^2} - r^2}$

w $R = \frac{2aE}{L} + r$

x $b = \frac{ak}{k + rt}$

y $s = \sqrt[3]{72\pi V^2}$

z $u = \pm\sqrt{v^2 - \frac{2A}{m}}$

Exercise 3c (p. 64)

1 a $x = 2, x = -\frac{1}{2}$ b $x = 3, x = 4$

c $y = 2, y = 3$ d $y = \pm 4$

e $x = 0, x = 9$ f $x = 0, x = 1\frac{2}{3}$

g $x = -3, x = 7$ h $x = -4, x = 3$

i $x = 3$ j $x = -3, x = -2$

k $x = 1\frac{1}{2}, x = 2$ l $e = -2, e = \frac{2}{3}$

m $d = -1, d = 2\frac{2}{3}$ n $e = 2, e = -\frac{2}{3}$

o $f = -\frac{2}{3}, f = \frac{3}{4}$ p $g = -6, g = \frac{1}{5}$

q $y = \pm 7$ r $x = \pm\frac{3}{5}$

s $x = 0, x = 6$ t $x = \pm\frac{2}{3}$

u $y = \pm 5$

2 a $a = \frac{2}{3}, a = 1$ b $b = 1, b = 1\frac{1}{2}$

c $c = \frac{1}{2}, c = 3$ d $d = 1, d = 2\frac{1}{2}$

e $e = -2, e = -\frac{1}{3}$ f $f = -\frac{1}{2}, f = 2$

g $g = -2, g = 1\frac{1}{2}$ h $h = 0, h = 1$

i $k = -2\frac{1}{3}, k = 2\frac{1}{2}$

j $l = -2, l = 0$ k $m = 0, m = 4$

l $t = 0, t = \pm 10$ m $u = 0, u = 7$

n $w = \pm 1$ o $x = 1, x = 2$

p $y = 1$ q $k = -\frac{3}{2}, k = \frac{1}{9}$

r $x = -4, x = \frac{2}{5}$

3 a $x = -1 \pm \sqrt{6}$ b $x = 2 \pm \sqrt{11}$

c $t = 5 \pm 3\sqrt{3}$ d $s = -3 \pm 2\sqrt{3}$

e $r = -\frac{5}{2} \pm \frac{\sqrt{29}}{2}$ f $t = \frac{3}{2} \pm \frac{\sqrt{37}}{2}$

g $a = \frac{1}{2} \pm \frac{\sqrt{5}}{2}$ h $b = -\frac{7}{2} \pm \frac{\sqrt{37}}{2}$

i $x = -\frac{1}{2}, x = 1$ j $x = 1 \pm \frac{\sqrt{21}}{3}$

4 a $x = \frac{1}{2} \pm \frac{\sqrt{5}}{2}$; $x = -0.618, x = 1.62$

b $x = -3, x = -\frac{1}{2}$

c $x = \frac{1}{2}, x = 3$

d $x = -\frac{7}{4} \pm \frac{\sqrt{73}}{4}$; $x = -3.89$, $x = 0.386$

e $x = \frac{7}{4} \pm \frac{\sqrt{73}}{4}$; $x = -0.386$, $x = 3.89$

f $x = \frac{7}{4} \pm \frac{\sqrt{73}}{4}$; $x = -0.386$, $x = 3.89$

g $x = \pm\sqrt{5}$; $x = \pm 2.24$

h $x = \frac{1}{12} \pm \frac{\sqrt{97}}{12}$; $x = -0.737$, $x = 0.904$

i $x = \frac{2}{3} \pm \frac{\sqrt{10}}{3}$; $x = -0.387$, $x = 1.72$

j $x = -\frac{19}{12} \pm \frac{\sqrt{553}}{12}$; $x = -3.54$, $x = 0.376$

5 a $x = 0, x = 1$

b $x = 0, x = 1$

c $x = \frac{1}{3}, x = \frac{1}{2}, x = 1$

d $x = 0, x = \pm 1$

e $x = \pm 2$

f $x = -k, x = \pm l$

6 a $x = \pm\sqrt{3}$ b $y = -1, y = 27$

c $z = \frac{1}{4}$ d $x = \sqrt[3]{3}, x = \sqrt[3]{4}$

e $x = -5, x = 4$ f $a = \pm 2\sqrt{3}$

7 10 years old

8 $l = 2.11$

9 $r = 5$

10 a $t = \frac{3}{5}$ or $t = 1$

11 25 jars, 8 cartons

Exercise 3d (p. 71)

1 a Min 2, at $x = 1$
b Min -16, at $x = -3$
c Max 17, at $x = 3$
d Max 5, at $x = -1$
e Min $-3\frac{1}{4}$, at $x = -1\frac{1}{2}$
f Min $-13\frac{1}{4}$, at $x = 2\frac{1}{2}$
g Max $3\frac{1}{4}$, at $x = -\frac{1}{2}$
h Max $11\frac{1}{4}$, at $x = 1\frac{1}{2}$
i Min -7, at $x = -2$
j Min $3\frac{11}{12}$, at $x = \frac{1}{6}$
k Max $6\frac{1}{8}$, at $x = -\frac{1}{4}$
l Max 7, at $x = 1$

2 a Min -2; vertex $(1, -2)$, y-intercept $(0, -1)$
b Min 5; vertex $(-2, 5)$, y-intercept $(0, 9)$
c Max 12; vertex $(3, 12)$, y-intercept $(0, 3)$

3 $a = \frac{1}{4}b^2$

4 a $k = 1$
b $k = \pm 12$
c $k = -2$

6 a $(x-2)(x-3) = 0$
b $(x-3)(x+5) = 0$
c $x(x+6) = 0$
d $(x-p)(x-q) = 0$

8 b $x = 0.14$

12 $k = -2, k = -\frac{2}{3}$

Extension Exercise 3e (p. 72)

1 a $x = -1\frac{1}{3}, x = \frac{1}{3}$ b $x = -1, x = \frac{1}{3}$
c $x = -4, x = 3$ d $x = -4, x = 15$
e $x = 3\frac{1}{2}, x = 14$ f $x = -2, x = 4$

2 a $x = a, x = a + b, x = a - b$
b $x = 0$
c $x = \pm a$
d $x = p + q$
e $x = 0$
f $x = -k, x = 2k$

3 a $y = \dfrac{(K-k)x - hK + Hk}{H - h}$
b $m = \dfrac{2x - 3y + 4}{3x - 2y + 2}$
c $x = 2ct$
d $c = 3m + 4$
e $x = \dfrac{c}{t}(1 - t^2)$
f $R = \dfrac{r(a + b + 2r)}{b - a}$

4 $x = b, x = \dfrac{1}{b+1}$

Miscellaneous Exercise 3f (p. 73)

1 a $x = \frac{1}{5}$
b Any value
c $x = \pm 2$
d $x = 0, x = 4$
e $x = 0, x = \pm 2$
f $x = 0, x = 7$
g $x = -4, x = 0, x = 5$
h $x = \pm 3$
i $x = \pm 1, x = \pm 4$
j $x = \pm\frac{2}{3}$
k $x = 0, x = \pm 1$
l $x = \pm 1$

2 a $x = \dfrac{b}{a-2}$ b $x = \pm\sqrt{r^2 - y^2}$
c $x = \dfrac{dk - b}{a - ck}$ d $x = \dfrac{1}{2l^2}$

3 a $x = 0, x = -k$ b $x = \pm a$
c $x = 0, x = -k$ d $x = a \pm b$

4 $x - 3x^{\frac{1}{3}} - 2$

7 $p = 5, q = \frac{1}{5}, r = \frac{4}{5}$, min $\frac{4}{5}$ when $x = \frac{1}{5}$

8 $k = \frac{1}{6}$

9 a E.g. $y = x(x-4)$
b E.g. $y = (x-1)(x-3)$
c $y = -(x-2)^2$
d $y = 3(x-2)^2$
e $y = (x-2)^2 + 3$

Test Yourself (p. 74)

1 B 2 E 3 D 4 A 5 C
6 B 7 D

4 Inequalities, Identities and the Modulus Function

Exercise 4a (p. 76)

1 True for a, b, c, e, g
False for d, f

2 True for a, b, c, f, g
False for d, e

Exercise 4b (p. 77)

1 a $x < -\frac{2}{3}$ b $x \geqslant -\frac{1}{2}$ c $x \leqslant 1$
d $x < -3$ e $a > \frac{11}{4}$ f $b < -\frac{1}{3}$
g $c \geqslant -\frac{2}{3}$ h $d \leqslant \frac{11}{3}$ i $e \geqslant -2$
j $f > 1$ k $h < 0$ l $x \leqslant 2$
m $x > -2$ n $x < \frac{17}{12}$

2 a $g > 5$ b $x > -1$
c $x > \frac{5}{3}$ d $x \leqslant \frac{18}{13}$

3 a $-1 < x < 5$ b $1 \leqslant x \leqslant 2$
c $-3 < x < -2$ d $-\frac{4}{5} < x \leqslant \frac{4}{5}$
e $-\frac{1}{2} < x \leqslant \frac{8}{3}$ f $-1 < x < \frac{3}{2}$

Exercise 4c (p. 81)

1 a $2 < x < 3$
b $x < -4$ or $x > 5$
c $x \leqslant -\frac{1}{2}$ or $x \geqslant 1$
d $x \leqslant \frac{3}{2}$ or $x \geqslant \frac{5}{2}$
e $x < 0$ or $x > 1$
f $x < -2$ or $x > 3$
g $1 < x < 2$
h $x < -2$ or $x > 9$
i $x \leqslant -2$ or $x \geqslant 3$
j $x < 0$ or $x > \frac{4}{3}$
k $y < 3$ or $y > 4$
l $y \leqslant -1$ or $y \geqslant 5$
m $\frac{1}{2} \leqslant y \leqslant \frac{2}{3}$
n $-1 < y < \frac{3}{8}$
o $-3 \leqslant u \leqslant -\frac{1}{2}$
p $-4 < v < \frac{1}{2}$
q $x = -\frac{1}{2}$
r No solution

2 a $-\frac{1}{3} < x < 2$
b $x < -\frac{5}{9}$ or $x > 1$
c $1 < x < 4$
d $x = 2$
e $x \leqslant 0$ or $x \geqslant \frac{1}{5}$
f $-8 < x < 2$

3 a $x \leqslant -3, 1 \leqslant x \leqslant 2$
b $x < \frac{1}{2}, 1 < x < 4$
c $x < \frac{1}{5}$
d $-2 \leqslant x \leqslant -1, 1 \leqslant x \leqslant 2$

Exercise 4d (p. 82)

1 a $A = 2, B = 3$
b $A = 1, B = 1$
c $A = 2, B = 3$
d $A = 6, B = 1$
e $A = 1, B = -1$
f $A = 1, B = 2$
g $A = 2, B = 1$

2 a $A = 1, B = 2, C = 3$
b $A = 2, B = -1, C = 3$
c $A = 2, B = -1, C = 3$
d $A = 3, B = -\frac{1}{2}, C = -\frac{1}{2}$
e $A = -2, B = 1, C = 1$
f $A = 2, B = 1, C = -1$

Exercise 4e (p. 84)

1 a $-2 < x < 2$
b $x \leqslant -3$ or $x \geqslant 3$
c $-4 < x < 6$

xercise 4f (p. 86)

a $x=-5, x=3$ b $x=-2, x=3$
c $x=3$ d $x=-1, x=2$
e $x=-\frac{1}{3}, x=2$ f $x=-1$
g $x=-\frac{1}{2}, x=2$ h $x=0, x=1$
i $x=-\frac{1}{3}, x=5$ j $x=\frac{4}{3}, x=4$
k $x=-2, x=0$ l $x=0, x=2$

a $-5<x<3$
b $x \leqslant -2$ or $x \geqslant 3$
c $x \in \mathbb{R}, x \neq 3$
d $-1 \leqslant x \leqslant 2$
e $-\frac{1}{3}<x<2$
f $x \leqslant -1$
g $-\frac{1}{2} \leqslant x \leqslant 2$
h $x \leqslant 0$ or $x \geqslant 1$
i $-\frac{1}{3}<x<5$
j $\frac{4}{3}<x<4$
k $x \leqslant -2$ or $x \geqslant 0$
l $0 \leqslant x \leqslant 2$

xtension Exercise 4g (p. 87)

a $x<-2, 1<x<\frac{3}{2}$
b $x<1$

a $A=1, B=-1, C=2$
b $A=1, B=-2, C=3$
c $A=1, B=-3, C=4$
d $A=3, B=-7$
e $A=5, B=-3, C=7$
f $A=1, B=4, C=5$

a $x=1$ b $x=-\frac{5}{3}, x=5$

a $x<1$ b $-\frac{5}{3}<x<5$

Miscellaneous Exercise 4h (p. 87)

True for all values of x: a, c, and j
True for some values of x: b, d, f, g and i
True for no value of x: e, h and k

a $y>9$
b $x \leqslant -3$ or $x \geqslant 9$
c $x<-2$ or $x>2$
d $-10 \leqslant x \leqslant 10$
e $x<-2$ or $x>1$
f $-2<x<5$
g $x<5-\sqrt{3}$ or $x>5+\sqrt{3}$
h $x \leqslant -4$ or $x \geqslant \frac{1}{2}$

$A=12, B=-7$

$A=2, B=1, C=-3$

a $k<\frac{9}{4}$
b $k<-2\sqrt{6}$ or $k>2\sqrt{6}$
c $-\frac{1}{4}\sqrt{2}<k<\frac{1}{4}\sqrt{2}$

7 a $k>9$
b $-2\sqrt{2}<k<2\sqrt{2}$
c $-\frac{3}{4}<k<3$

Test Yourself (p. 88)

1 A 2 D 3 B 4 D

5 Simultaneous Equations

Exercise 5a (p. 92)

1 a $x=4, y=2$ b $c=8, d=7$
c $x=7, y=4$ d $g=3, h=3$
e $x=5, y=1$ f $r=4, s=3$
g $t=3, u=2$ h $x=-4, y=7$
i $x=4, y=-1$ j $x=1, y=2$
k $n=4, p=\frac{1}{2}$ l $x=2, y=\frac{1}{2}$

2 a $s=2, t=3$ b $a=\frac{7}{4}, y=\frac{1}{4}$
c $b=-1, x=2$ d $y=-1, z=1$
e $x=2, y=-1$ f $q=-1, r=2$
g $p=3, q=2$ h $r=-1, s=-1$
i $x=3, y=0$ j $x=3, y=1$

Exercise 5b (p. 95)

1 a $x=\frac{1}{4}, y=\frac{3}{2}$
b $x=7, y=4$
c $x=-1, y=3$
d $x=10, y=-1$
e $x=9, y=1$
f $s=8, x=5$
g $x=\frac{11}{19}, y=-\frac{18}{19}$
h $x=\frac{10}{29}, y=\frac{7}{29}$

2 a $x=-1, y=-2$
b $x=\frac{23}{13}, y=-\frac{11}{13}$
c $x=0, y=\frac{7}{2}$
d $x=3, y=-2,$
e $x=\dfrac{dm-bn}{ad-bc}, y=\dfrac{an-cm}{ad-bc}$

3 a $(\frac{1}{2}, \frac{5}{2})$ b $(1, 9)$
c $(-1, 1)$ d $(\frac{11}{2}, \frac{9}{2})$

4 Apples £1.40/kg; pears £1.60/kg

5 a 0.6 g b 0.9 g

6 Mariko 32 sweets; Brian 22 sweets

7 $55\,\text{km h}^{-1}$ and $110\,\text{km h}^{-1}$

8 Siobhan is 16 and her brother 11 years old

9 Mass 1.5 kg; speed $2\,\text{m s}^{-1}$

10 $AB=9$ cm; $AC=15$ cm

11 Exton Park: won 7, drawn 4; Wyeville United: won 8, drawn 4

12 $a=6, b=1$

13 6 maths questions, 5 biology questions

14 a $2.5\,\text{km h}^{-1}$ b $1.5\,\text{km h}^{-1}$

Exercise 5c (p. 101)

1 a $x=3, y=9; x=-2, y=4$
b $x=1, y=1; x=-3, y=9$
c $x=0, y=0; x=6, y=12$
d $x=6, y=5; x=1, y=0$
e $x=3, y=3; x=-3, y=-3$
f $x=4, y=2; x=-4, y=-2$

2 a $x=1, y=8; x=-8, y=-1$
b $x=1, y=4; x=-2, y=-2$
c $x=3, y=4; x=-4, y=-3$
d $x=2, y=0; x=0, y=1$
e $x=1, y=2; x=4, y=-4$
f $x=-1, y=-1; x=0, y=-\frac{1}{2}$

3 a $x=2, y=-3; x=-1, y=3$
b $x=-2, y=10$
c $x=5, y=-9; x=-2, y=5$
d $x=0, y=-10; x=5, y=-5$

Exercise 5d (p. 104)

1 $k=\frac{1}{10}$

2 $k<13.5$

4 $k=2$

6 30 cm by 20 cm

7 a 6 years old b 36 years old

8 8 cm and 15 cm

9 $a=3; b=4$

Extension Exercise 5e (p. 106)

1 a $x=6, y=4, z=2$
b $x=-\frac{34}{3}, y=-\frac{11}{3}, z=\frac{103}{3}$
c $x=1, y=3, z=5$
d $x=12, y=18, z=6$

2 a One b ∞ c None

3 a $x=10c, y=7c$
b $x=tT, y=t+T$
c $x=t, y=\dfrac{1}{t}; x=-\dfrac{1}{t^3}, y=-t^3$
d $x=4a, y=0; x=5a, y=3a$

4 a $x=2, y=5; x=-2, y=5$
b $x=2, y=\frac{1}{2}; x=-2, y=\frac{1}{2}$
c $x=\pm 3, y=\pm 10; x=\pm 1, y=\pm 2\sqrt{5}$

5 $x=\frac{13}{2}, y=2; x=3, y=-5$

6 a $x=4, y=7; x=-4, y=-7; x=7, y=4; x=-7, y=-4$
b $x=7, y=5; x=5, y=7$
c $x=4, y=3; x=-4, y=-3$
$x=6, y=2; x=-6, y=-2$

7 6 ohms and 3 ohms

8 $a = \frac{1}{2}, b = 6$ or $a = 3, b = \frac{1}{6}$

10 **a** $x = 3, y = 4; x = -1, y = -2$
b $x = \frac{1}{2}, y = 2; x = 2, y = 1$
c $x = 5, y = 2; x = 3\frac{1}{2}, y = 1$
d $x = -\frac{5}{2}, y = -\frac{11}{4}; x = 2, y = 4$

Miscellaneous Exercise 5f (p. 108)

1 **a** $x = 1, y = -1$
b $x = 2, y = 3$
c $x = 3, y = 4; x = 4, y = 3$
d $x = \frac{52}{11}, y = \frac{101}{11}; x = -2; y = -11$
e $x = \frac{21}{11}, y = \frac{13}{11}$
f $x = 2; y = -2$

2 $(\frac{1}{4}, 0)$

3 $(1, 3), (-\frac{16}{31}, -3\frac{2}{31})$

5 $(2\frac{1}{3}, \frac{1}{3}), (3, 1)$

6 **a** $k > -11$ **b** $k = -11$

7 $k < -\frac{2}{5}\sqrt{5}$ or $k > \frac{2}{5}\sqrt{5}$

8 $k = -2$ or $k = -14$

9 $k < -2\sqrt{5}$ or $k > 2\sqrt{5}$

10 2 and 5

11 **a** 42 climbers **b** 21 staff

12 17°C and 12°C

13 $a = 3, b = 5; a = 2\frac{1}{2}, b = 4$

14 **a** 2 cm **b** 0.95 cm

15 $\frac{3}{8}$

Test Yourself (p. 109)

1 D **2** B **3** A **4** A **5** E
6 C **7** C **8** E **9** E **10** D

6 Further Work on Polynomials

Exercise 6a (p. 112)

1 **a** $1 + 4x + 6x^2 + 4x^3 + x^4$
b $1 - 5x + 10x^2 - 10x^3 + 5x^4 - x^5$
c $1 + 6x + 15x^2 + 20x^3 + 15x^4 + 6x^5 + x^6$
d $1 - 6x + 15x^2 - 20x^3 + 15x^4 - 6x^5 + x^6$

2 **a** $1 + 8x + 24x^2 + 32x^3 + 16x^4$
b $1 - 15y + 90y^2 - 270y^3 + 405y^4 - 243y^5$
c $1 + 12z + 48z^2 + 64z^3$
d $1 - \frac{3x}{2} + \frac{3x^2}{4} - \frac{x^3}{8}$
e $a^7 + 7a^6b + 21a^5b^2 + 35a^4b^3 + 35a^3b^4 + 21a^2b^5 + 7ab^6 + b^7$
f $a^{10} - 5a^8b^2 + 10a^6b^4 - 10a^4b^6 + 5a^2b^8 - b^{10}$
g $a^6 - 3a^4b^2 + 3a^2b^4 - b^6$

3 **a** $x^4 + 4x^3y + 6x^2y^2 + 4xy^3 + y^4$
b $x^5 + 5x^4y + 10x^3y^2 + 10x^2y^3 + 5xy^4 + y^5$
c $81 + 108x + 54x^2 + 12x^3 + x^4$
d $x^3 - 6x^2 + 12x - 8$
e $8 - 6x + \frac{3x^2}{2} - \frac{x^3}{8}$
f $\frac{1}{x^3} + 3 + 3x^3 + x^6$
g $16 - 32x^3 + 24x^6 - 8x^9 + x^{12}$

4 **a** **i** $a^3 + 3a^2b + 3ab^2 + b^3$
ii $a^3 - 3a^2b + 3ab^2 - b^3$
b **i** 14 **ii** $10\sqrt{2}$ **iii** $40\sqrt{2}$

5 **a** 194 **b** $160\sqrt{6}$ **c** 98

Exercise 6b (p. 117)

1 **a** $x^2 + 5x + 6$ **b** $x^2 + x - 12$
c $x^2 + x + 1$ **d** $x^2 + x - 6$
e $2x^2 + 5x - 3$ **f** $x^2 + 2x + 1$
g $x^2 + x + 2$ **h** $2x^2 + 2x + 1$
i $x^2 - 3x + 4$ **j** $x^2 + 4x - 1$
k $2x^2 + 4x - 7$ **l** $x^2 + 9$

2 **a** $4x^2 + 6x - 3$
b $2x^3 - 3x^2 + 4x - 3$
c $x^3 - 2x^2 + 4x - 3$
d $x^3 + 4x^2 - 2x - 2$
e $6x^3 - 3x^2 - 2x + 1$

3 **a** $x^2 + 2x + 4, -3$
b $x^2 + 4x - 10, 8$
c $x^2 - 5x + 6, 0$
d $x^2 - 5x + 9, -19$
e $2x^2 - 6x + 17, 0$
f $2x^2 - 5x + 6, 0$
g $x^2 + 3x - 1, 11$
h $2x^2 - 3x + 5, -16$

4 **a** $1 + \frac{4}{x+5}$ **b** $1 - \frac{10}{x+8}$
c $2 + \frac{7}{x-3}$ **d** $1 - \frac{8}{x^2+3}$
e $1 - \frac{3x+5}{x^2+3x}$ **f** $1 - \frac{8x}{x^2+3x}$
g $\frac{7}{x+5} - 1$ **h** $-3 - \frac{2}{x-1}$

5 **a** $x^2 - 3x + 1$ **b** $x^2 + 3x - 1$
c $3x^2 - 2x + 1$ **d** $2a - 1$

6 **a** $x + 3$ **b** $x - 2$
c $x^2 - 2x + 3$ **d** $x^2 + 3x - 4$
e $2x^2 - 3x - 1$ **f** $x^2 + 4x - 5$
g $4x^2 + 2x - 5$ **h** $2x^2 + 3x - 4$
i $x^2 - x + 3$

7 **a** $x^2 + 3$, remainder -4
b $x^2 + 4x + 4$, remainder -8
c $x^2 - 5x + 3$, remainder -15
d $2x^2 + 5x - 3$, remainder $20x - 12$
e $4x^2 + 8$, remainder $-4x + 16$
f $x^2 - 4x - 2$, remainder 6
g $x^2 - 3x + 4$, remainder 12
h $4x^2 + 2x - 7$, remainder -2
i $x^2 + 2x + 3$, remainder $-9x + 3$

Exercise 6c (p. 121)

1 **a** $-12, -12, -6, 0, 0; x + 2$ and $x - 2$
b $-1, 0, -2, 19, -21; x - 1$
c $0, 6, -2, 88, -24; x$
d $3, 0, 0, 3, 3; x - 1$ and $x + 1$

3 **a** $a = -10$ **b** $a = 4$ **c** $a = 5$

4 $x - 2, x + 3; x = -3, x = 1$ or $x = 2$

5 **a** $(x - 1)(x - 2)(x + 2)$
b $(x + 1)(x - 2)(x + 3)$
c $(x - 1)(x + 2)(x - 3)$
d $(x + 2)(x - 2)(2x + 1)$

6 **a** $x = -2, x = 1$ or $x = 2$
b $x = -3, x = -1$ or $x = 2$
c $x = -2, x = 1$ or $x = 3$
d $x = -2, x = -\frac{1}{2}$ or $x = 2$

7 $x + 3, 2x - 1; x = 2, x = -3$ or $x = \frac{1}{2}$

8 $a = 4, b = 1; (x - 1)(x + 2)(x + 3)$

9 $a = 0, b = 0; x(x + 1)^2(2x - 1)$

10 **a** $(x - 4)(x + 1)$
c $x = 4, x = -1$ or $x = \pm 2\sqrt{2}$

Exercise 6d (p. 122)

1 **a** 2 **b** 18 **c** -11
d -1 **e** 2 **f** $-\frac{5}{2}$

2 **a** $a = -3$ **b** $a = 2$
c $a = 4$ **d** $a = 2$

3 $a = 4, b = -5$

4 $a = 3, b = -1, c = -2$

5 $a = 2, b = -1, c = -2$

6 $a = -3$

7 $a = 2$

8 $a = -5$

10 **a** -2 **b** 2

12 n odd

xtension Exercise 6e (p. 123)

2 $p = 3, q = 7, r = -2$

3 a $8 + 12x + 18x^2 + 13x^3 + 9x^4 + 3x^5 + x^6$
  b $27 + 27x - 45x^2 - 35x^3 + 30x^4 + 12x^5 - 8x^6$
  c $1 - 4x + 10x^2 - 16x^3 + 19x^4 - 16x^5 + 10x^6 - 4x^7 + x^8$

4 a $1 - 4x + 2x^2$
  b $1 + 10x + 55x^2$
  c $64 + 192x + 48x^2$

5 a $178\sqrt{3}$ b $144\sqrt{2}$

8 $2x - 1, 2x + 3, 3x + 1$

9 a $(x + 2)(x + 3)(2x + 1)$
  b $(2x - 1)(x^2 + 1)$

0 $a = 3$

1 $a = 3, b = 2$

2 $a = 1$, b can take any value

Aiscellaneous Exercise 6f p. 124)

1 $x^2 + 3x + 6$

2 $x^2 + 2x - 5$
  a $x = 2$
  b $x = 2$
  c $x = 2$ or $x = -1 \pm \sqrt{6}$

3 $a = 1, b = 4$

4 a $1 + 4x + 6x^2$ b $1 - 6x + 12x^2$
  c $1 + \frac{5x}{3} + \frac{10x^2}{9}$ d $16 - 32x + 24x^2$
  e $\frac{1}{x^6} + \frac{6}{x^4} + \frac{15}{x^2}$

5 $a = -5$

6 a $1 - 4x + 6x^2$
  b $1 + 15x + 90x^2$
  c 36

7 $a = -9, b = 9$

8 $x(x + 1)(x - 2)(2x + 1)$; $x = 0$, $x = -1$, $x = 2$ or $x = -\frac{1}{2}$

9 b $x = 2, x = -1 \pm \sqrt{7}$

10 $a = -1$

11 a $a = 3$

12 a $1 + 4x + 6x^2 + 4x^3 + x^4$
  c $x = 0$

13 $a = -3, b = 6, c = 5$

Test Yourself (p. 125)

1 D 2 C 3 E 4 B 5 B
6 A 7 A 8 D

7 Graphs

Exercise 7a (p. 136)

9 a $y = x^2 - 1$
  b $y = (x + 1)^2$
  c $y = 4x^2$
  d $y = x^2 + 6x + 11$

10 a $y = \sqrt{x} - 1, x \geqslant 0$
  b $y = \sqrt{x + 1}, x \geqslant -1$
  c $y = -\sqrt{x}, x \geqslant 0$
  d $y = 2 + \sqrt{x + 3}, x \geqslant -3$

14 A: (2, −3), (−2, 3), (−2, −3)
  B: (3, 0), (−3, 0), (−3, 0)

15 O: (0, 0), (3, 0), (0, 0), (3, 0)
  A: (3, −2), (6, 2), (−3, 2), (0, 2)
  B: (5, 0), (8, 0), (−5, 0),(−2, 0)

16 b A: (−4, 0), (−4, 0)
  B: (−3, −4), (−3, 2)
  C: (2, 4), (2, −2)
  D: (4, 2), (4, −1)
  O: (0, 0), (0, 0)
  c Stretch parallel to y-axis, sf 2; reflection in x-axis

17 b A: (−3, 0), (−4, 3)
  B: (−2, −2), (−3, 1)
  C: (3, 2), (2, 5)
  D: (5, 1), (4, 4)
  O: (1, 0), (0, 3)
  c Translation $\binom{1}{0}$; translation $\binom{0}{3}$

18 $(x + 1)^2 + 7$;
  vertex (−1, 7), intercept (0, 8)

19 a $(x - 1)^2 + 3$;
  vertex (1, 3), intercept (0, 4)
  b $(x + 2)^2 - 9$;
  vertex (−2, −9), intercept (0, −5)
  c $(x - 3)^2 - 6$;
  vertex (3, −6), intercept (0, 3)
  d $\left(x + \frac{1}{2}\right)^2 + \frac{3}{4}$;
  vertex $\left(-\frac{1}{2}, \frac{3}{4}\right)$, intercept (0, 1)
  e $8 - (x + 1)^2$;
  vertex (−1, 8), intercept (0, 7)

20 (−1, 1), (0, 0), (1, 1)

21 (−1, −1), (0, 0), (1, 1)

22 $f(x) = \frac{1}{x^2}$

23 b $y = |f(x)|$: (−3, 0), (−1, 0), (3, 0), (0, 2)
  $y = f(|x|)$: (−3, 0), (3, 0), (0, −2)

Test Yourself (p. 140)

1 D 2 C 3 B 4 C 5 B
6 D 7 E

8 Coordinate Geometry and the Straight Line

Exercise 8a (p. 148)

1 a 13 b $\sqrt{41}$
  c $2\sqrt{37}$ d $\sqrt{(p - r)^2 + (q - s)^2}$
  e $3\sqrt{10}$ f 4
  g 4 h $\sqrt{74}$
  i 13

2 a $(5\frac{1}{2}, 8)$ b $(1\frac{1}{2}, 5)$
  c (5, −4) d $\left(\frac{p + r}{2}, \frac{q + s}{2}\right)$
  e $(-1\frac{1}{2}, -2\frac{1}{2})$ f (6, 11)
  g (3, 2) k $(-\frac{1}{2}, -4\frac{1}{2})$
  l $(0, 3\frac{1}{2})$

3 17

4 PQ = PR; $(-\frac{5}{2}, \frac{9}{2})$

5 LM = LN; $(-\frac{3}{2}, -\frac{3}{2})$

6 a AC; 25; $\frac{1}{2}$
  b AB; $25\frac{1}{2}$; 3

7 $h = 9\frac{1}{4}$

8 P, R and S

9 A, B and D; $5\sqrt{2}$

10 13; $6\frac{1}{2}$

11 $a = 2, b = -3$

12 $k = -3$ or $k = 5$

13 $3(\sqrt{2} + \sqrt{10})$

15 a BCED
  b ACFD
  c ACED, BCFD

Exercise 8b (p. 157)

1 a $\frac{9}{4}$ b $\frac{3}{2}$ c $-\frac{4}{5}$
  d $-\frac{10}{11}$ e 0 f $\frac{s - q}{r - p}$
  g −1 h $\frac{b}{a}$ i $-\frac{1}{14}$
  j $-\frac{1}{6}$

2 a $-\frac{1}{3}$ **b** -4 **c** $\frac{1}{6}$
d $\frac{3}{2}$ **e** $-\frac{1}{2m}$ **f** $\frac{a}{b}$
g $\frac{2}{m}$

3 Parallel **a**, **f**
Perpendicular **b**, **d**, **g**
Neither **c**, **e**

4 Yes **a**, **e**, **f**
No **b**, **c**, **d**

5 a (2, 5) **b** (−3, 20) **c** (0, −1)

6 a $x = 2$ **b** $x = 0$ **c** $x = -2\frac{1}{2}$

7 a (2, 0); (0, −6) **b** $(1\frac{3}{5}, 0)$; (0, 4)
c (3, 0); (0, −4) **d** (0, 0); (0, 0)

9 a (−3, 0), (0, 2) **b** (−2, 0), $(0, \frac{1}{2})$
c (−2, 0), (0,−6) **d** $(\frac{5}{7}, 0)$, $(0, -\frac{5}{3})$

10 a $y = \frac{1}{3}x$ **b** $y = -2x$ **c** $y = mx$

11 a $y = \frac{1}{4}x$; gradient $\frac{1}{4}$
b $y = -\frac{5}{4}x$; gradient $-\frac{5}{4}$
c $y = \frac{3}{2}x$; gradient $\frac{3}{2}$
d $y = \frac{7}{4}x$; gradient $\frac{7}{4}$
e $y = \frac{q}{p}x$; gradient $\frac{q}{p}$

12 a $y = 3x + 2$ **b** $y = 3x - 1$
c $y = \frac{1}{5}x + 2$ **d** $y = \frac{1}{5}x + 4$

13 a $y = \frac{2}{3}x + 2$; gradient $\frac{2}{3}$; intercept 2
b $y = \frac{1}{4}x + \frac{1}{2}$; gradient $\frac{1}{4}$; intercept $\frac{1}{2}$
c $y = -3x - 6$; gradient −3; intercept −6
d $y = \frac{7}{3}x - \frac{5}{3}$; gradient $\frac{7}{3}$; intercept $-\frac{5}{3}$
e $y = -4$; gradient 0; intercept −4
f $y = -\frac{l}{m}x - \frac{n}{m}$; gradient $-\frac{l}{m}$; intercept $-\frac{n}{m}$

14 a $y = 4x - 1$
b $y = 3x + 11$
c $x - 3y - 17 = 0$
d $3x + 4y - 41 = 0$
e $3x - 6y - 4 = 0$
f $y = ax - a$

15 a $3x - 4y + 21 = 0$
b $5x + 4y - 23 = 0$
c $3x + 11y - 35 = 0$
d $x - 5y - 19 = 0$
e $2x + 3y - 7 = 0$
f $hx + ky - 4hk = 0$

16 a $3x - 4y + 1 = 0$
b $5x - 2y + 16 = 0$
c $7x - y - 28 = 0$
d $3x - 4y - 6 = 0$

17 $\frac{8}{21}$

18 $a = 8$

19 $a{:}b = 3{:}2$

21 $5\sqrt{2}$; $(3\frac{1}{2}, 4\frac{1}{2})$

22 $\frac{1}{2}\sqrt{34}$; $(\frac{3}{4}, -1\frac{3}{4})$

Exercise 8c (p. 160)

1 a (7, −7) **b** $(-1\frac{1}{2}, -5\frac{1}{2})$
c $(1\frac{4}{7}, -1\frac{6}{7})$ **d** (4, −7)

2 $y = \frac{1}{8}x$

3 a (5, 6); $\frac{1}{2}$; −2; $y = -2x + 16$
b (−3, 6); −2; $\frac{1}{2}$; $y = \frac{1}{2}x + 7\frac{1}{2}$
c $(-1\frac{1}{2}, -1)$; 8; $-\frac{1}{8}$; $y = -\frac{1}{8}x - 1\frac{3}{16}$
d $(4p, 2q)$; $\frac{q}{3p}$; $-\frac{3p}{q}$;
$3px + qy - 12p^2 - 2q^2 = 0$

4 $2x - 5y + 19 = 0$

5 $26x + 4y - 21 = 0$

6 a $4x - 3y - 13 = 0$ **b** (4, 1)
c 5

7 $2\sqrt{5}$

8 a $2x + 7y - 14 = 0$
b $2x - 7y - 14 = 0$

9 $\sqrt{85}$, $6x + 7y - 85 = 0$

10 (1, 8); 52

12 b 12; 78

13 $2x + y - 17 = 0$; $72\frac{1}{4}$

14 $x - y = 0$, $2x + 2y - 9 = 0$;
$(\frac{3}{2}, 3)$, $(3, \frac{3}{2})$; $\frac{3}{2}\sqrt{5}$

16 **a**, **c**

17 $a = -2, b = 9$ or $a = \frac{5}{2}, b = -9$

18 $a = -2, b = 4$

Extension Exercise 8d (p. 162)

2 $3x + 4y + 1 = 0$; $4x - 3y - 7 = 0$

4 $13x - 8y = 0$, $4x + y - 30 = 0$,
$x - 2y + 12 = 0$; $(\frac{16}{3}, \frac{26}{3})$

5 $x + 2y + 4 = 0$; $8x - y + 15 = 0$;
$10x + 3y - 45 = 0$

6 $\left(\frac{1}{3}\sqrt{3}, \frac{1}{3}\sqrt{3}\right)$

7 (−11, 3); 174

8 $3x + 2y - 2 = 0$, $4x + y + 1 = 0$;
$(-\frac{4}{5}, 2\frac{1}{5})$

10 (1, 6)

13 $13x + y - 22 = 0$

14 9; $\frac{2}{13}\sqrt{13}$; $2\frac{1}{12}$

Miscellaneous Exercise 8e (p. 163)

1 a $3x - 5y + 14 = 0$
b $3x + 5y = 14$
c $2x + 5y + 14 = 0$

2 a $2x - 3y + 12 = 0$
b (3, 6)

3 a $x + 2y = 0$ **b** (2, −1)
c $\sqrt{5}$

4 b PQR = 26.6°

6 a $y = x$ **b** $(3\frac{1}{2}, 3\frac{1}{2})$

7 a (8, 4) **b** 40

8 a $(2h, -2k)$ **b** $-\frac{3k}{h}$
c $hx - 3ky - 2h^2 - 6k^2 = 0$

9 $x + 3y - 17s = 0$

10 a P_1 (0, 7), P_2 (1, 10), P_3 (2, 13)
b $y = 3x + 7$

11 a (0, 3), (4, 0)
b $-4y + 3x = 12$
$4y - 3x = 12$
$3y + 4x = 12$
c 6

12 b $8\frac{1}{3}$; $26\frac{2}{3}$

13 b (0, 6), (12, 30)
c 60

14 a (0, −12); (4, 0), (−3, 0)
b (0, 2); $(\frac{2}{3}, 0)$, $(\frac{1}{2}, 0)$
c (0, 9); touches x-axis at (3, 0)
d (0, 0); (9, 0); touches x-axis at (0, 0)
e (0, 25); (−1, 0); touches x-axis at (5,0)
f (0, 9); (1, 0), (−1, 0), (3, 0), (−3, 0)

15 a (6, 40), (−1, 5) **b** $7\sqrt{26}$

16 $PQ = 11\sqrt{10}$

17 64.4°

18 a $3\sqrt{10} + 5\sqrt{2}$

Test Yourself (p. 165)

1 D **2** D **3** C **4** E **5** D
6 C **7** C **8** B **9** B **10** C

Revision Exercise 1 (p. 167)

1 a $2-\sqrt{2}$ b $2\sqrt{2}-2$

2 a $-5-3\sqrt{2}$ b $-6-5\sqrt{2}$

3 a $24\sqrt{2}$ b $17-12\sqrt{2}$ c $3\sqrt{2}-4$

4 $7-4\sqrt{3}$, $2+\sqrt{3}$

5 a x^9 b $x^{\frac{1}{2}}$ c $x^{\frac{7}{12}}$

6 a $x=\frac{1}{4}$ b $x=2\pm\sqrt{2}$ c $x=-1$

7 a $(x+1)(x-1)$
 b $2(x+1)(x-1)$
 c $3x(x+2)(x-2)$
 d $(x+1)(x-1)(x^2+1)$
 e $a(b+c)(b-c)$
 f $p(q+1)(q-1)$
 g $y(x+y)^2$

8 $x(x+1)(2-x)$

9 a $2\sqrt{2}-1$ b $2-\sqrt{2}$ c $2+\frac{3}{2}\sqrt{2}$

0 a $(x+4)(x-3)$
 b $(x^2+4)(x+\sqrt{3})(x-\sqrt{3})$
 c $(\sqrt{x}+4)(\sqrt{x}-3)$
 d $\left(\frac{1}{x}+4\right)\left(\frac{1}{x}-3\right)$
 e $(x+5)(x-2)$
 f $3x(x+4)(x-3)$

1 a $(x-2)(x+1)$
 b $\frac{1}{2}(x-2)(x+1)$
 c $x^{\frac{1}{2}}(x-2)(x+1)$

2 a equation, $x=0$
 b equation, $x=2$
 c identity
 d equation, no solution
 e identity

3 $x=\dfrac{2y-1}{y+1}$

4 b $\phi=\frac{1}{2}(1+\sqrt{5})$

5 a $x=2$
 b $x=\frac{7}{3}$ or $x=5$
 c $x=-\frac{1}{6}$ or $x=\frac{7}{6}$

6 a $\left(x+\dfrac{p}{2}\right)^2+q-\dfrac{p^2}{4}$

7 a 0 b 2 c 0
 d 0 e 2 f 1

8 a $\mathbb{R}$ b None c $\mathbb{N}, \mathbb{Z}, \mathbb{Q}, \mathbb{R}$
 d $\mathbb{Z}, \mathbb{Q}, \mathbb{R}$ e $\mathbb{Q}, \mathbb{R}$

9 a $x=\dfrac{5\pm\sqrt{41}}{2}$ b $x=1$ and $x=4$

20 $-\frac{1}{6}\leqslant x\leqslant 2$

21 $a=3$, $x=2$

22 $x=-6.68$ or $x=-2993.32$

23 $a=4$, $b=1$

24 (3, 2)

25 a 4 b 4 c 4 d 2

26 a $x=\pm\sqrt{5}$
 b $-\sqrt{5}\leqslant x\leqslant\sqrt{5}$
 c 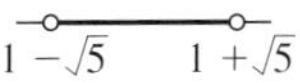

27 Radius = 5 cm, height = 2 cm

28 $n=60$, $p=\frac{1}{12}$

29 a Translation $\binom{-2}{-3}$
 b Translation $\binom{1}{0}$, stretch s.f. 3 parallel to y-axis (or vice-versa)
 c Stretch s.f. 3 parallel to x-axis and stretch s.f. $\frac{1}{2}$ parallel to y-axis (or vice-versa)
 d Stretch s.f. $\frac{1}{2}$ parallel to x-axis, reflection in x-axis, translation $\binom{0}{1}$. (Translation must be last.)

30 a 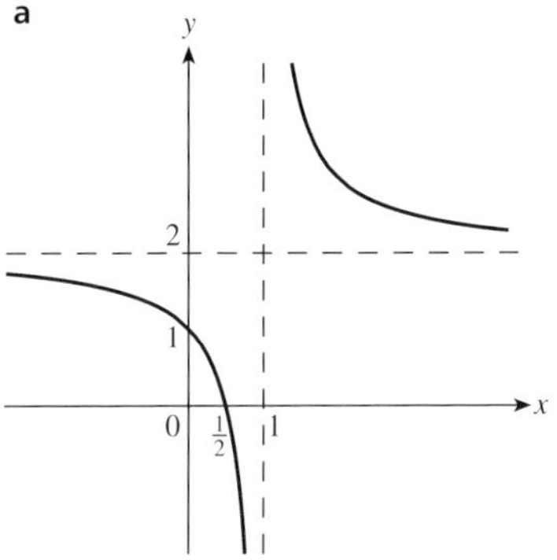

 b 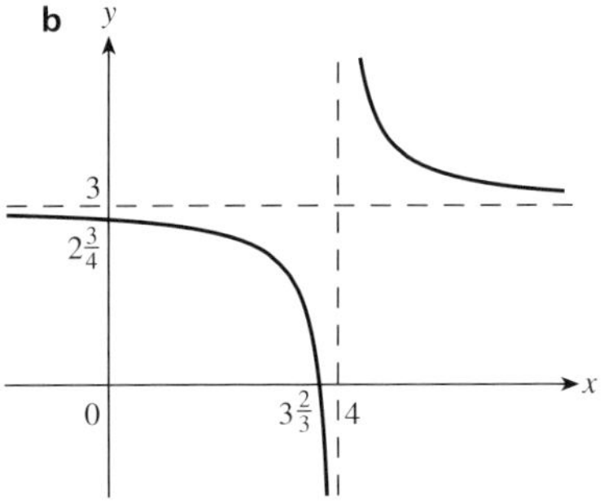

31 a 3; $x=1$, $x=3$
 b $(x-2)^2-1$
 c 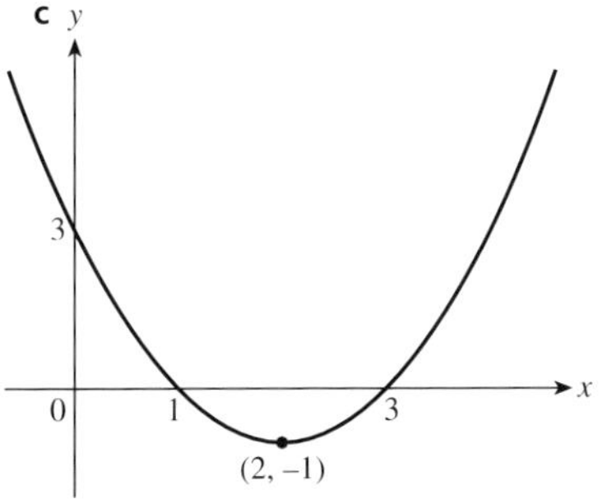

 d $1<x<3$

32 a 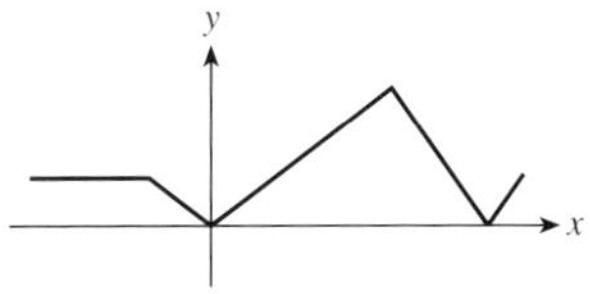

 b 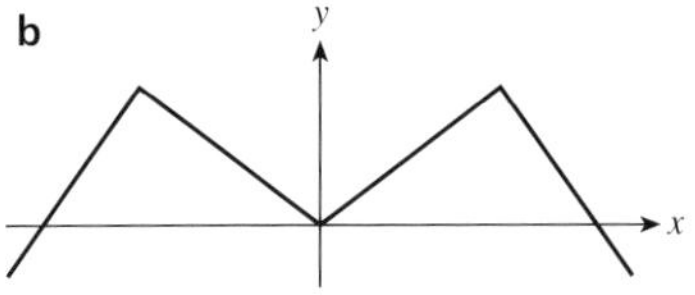

 c 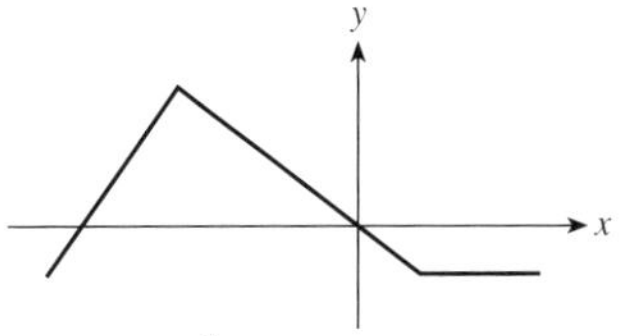

 d 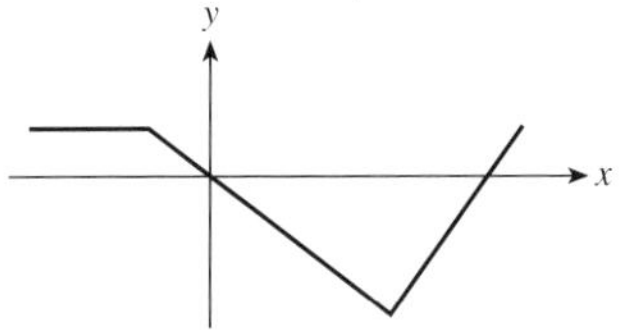

33 (−2, −32), (0, 0), (2, 32)

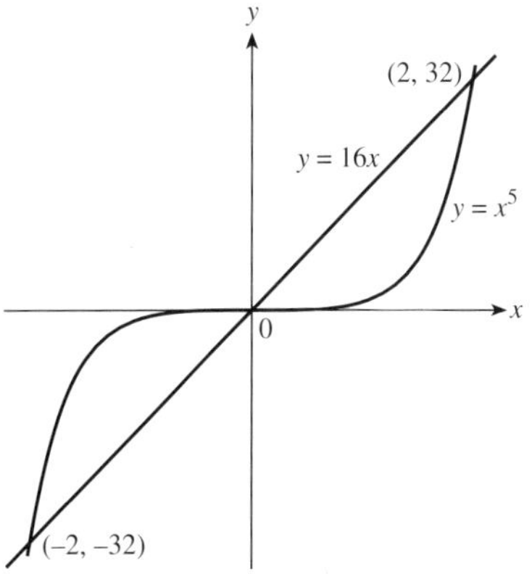

34 Intercept (0, 0) for $y=-x^2$
Intercepts (2, 0), (0, −8) for $y=(x-2)^3$
Intersect at (1, −1)

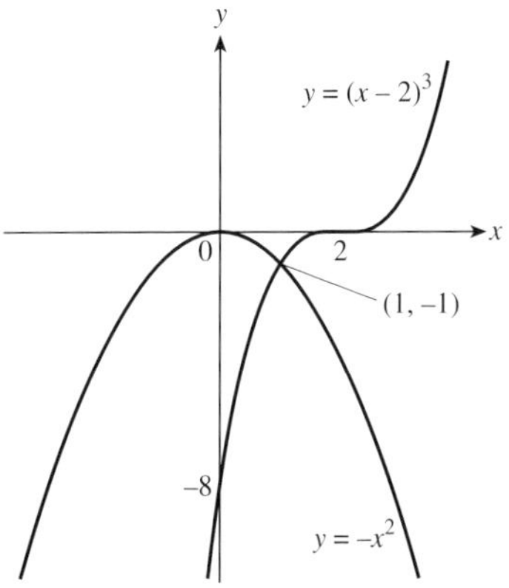

35 $x=2$

Examination Questions 1

Algebra (p. 170)

1 **i** $\frac{1}{49}$ **ii** $\frac{\sqrt{x}}{2}$

2 **i** $x = 3, y = 2$
ii $y = 3x - 7$ touches $y = x^2 - 3x + 2$ at $(3, 2)$

3 **a** $-32 + 11\sqrt{7}$ **b** $11 + 4\sqrt{7}$

4 $(x - 4)^2 = 7, 4 \pm \sqrt{7}$

5 **a** $x \leqslant -\frac{1}{2}, x \geqslant \frac{7}{3}$
b $(\frac{3}{2}, 6)$ min

6 $(3, 1), \left(-\frac{11}{5}, -\frac{8}{5}\right)$

7 **a** $1 + x^2 + x^3 + x^5$
b 1.000 001 001 000 001

8 **a** $4x - 10 > 32$ **b** $x(x - 5) < 104$
c $10.5 < x < 13$

9 **b** $x = 0, x = -4$

10 $x = \frac{1}{16}, x = 64$

11 **a** $1 \pm \sqrt{13}$
b $x < 1 - \sqrt{13}, x > 1 + \sqrt{13}$

12 **a** $x = -5, x = 4$ **b** $x < -5, x > 4$

13 $x = -\frac{7}{2}$

14 $k < -6, k > 6$ (or $|k| > 6$)
i $a = -2\sqrt{3}, b = -3; -3$
ii $\sqrt{3}, 3\sqrt{3}$

15 $\frac{1}{3a^2}$

16 $\frac{a}{4} < x < \frac{a}{2}$

17 $k < -12, k > 12$ or $|k| > 12$

18 £33.30

19 **a** **i** e.g. 4.5 **ii** e.g. $\sqrt{17}$
b Statement is false; 1

20 $x = 2, y = 3; x = 15, y = -10$

21 Sketch touches at $x = 2a$; $\frac{3a}{2}, \frac{5a}{2}$

22 **i** $x = 2\frac{1}{2}$ **ii** $y = -\frac{ax + c}{b}$

23 $\frac{13}{3} < x < \frac{29}{3}$

24 $x < 1$

25 $-3 < a < 3$ or $|a| < 3$

26 $(x - 1)(x + 7)$

27 $x = -1, y = 2; x = 2, y = -1$

28 $x = -\frac{3}{2}$

Factor Theorem (p. 172)

1 $(x + 1)(3x + 2)(x - 4)$

2 **a** $a = 4, b = -5$ **b** $3x + 1$

3 **a** $a = 0$ **b** $(x + 1)^2(x - 2)$

4 **b** $(2x + 1)(x - 2)(x + 2)$
c $-2, -\frac{1}{2}, 2$

5 $k = -12; \frac{1}{2}(-1 \pm 3\sqrt{5})$

6 **b** $(x + 3)(2x^2 - x - 5)$
c $-1.35, 1.85$

Remainder Theorem (p. 173)

1 **a** $c = 9, d = -14$
b $x - 2, x = \frac{1}{2}(-7 \pm \sqrt{77})$

2 **a** -16
b $a = 4$
c **ii** $b = -2$, or $b = 3$, or $b = 6$

3 **a** $A = 3, B = 5, C = 2$
b $a = \pm\frac{5}{2}$

4 **a** **i** 12 **ii** $x = -3, x = 1$, or $x = 2$
b $a = 3, b = -3; (2x + 1)$
c $p = -3, p = 1$

5 **a** $a = -3$
b $x = -\frac{1}{2}, x = -1$, or $x = 2$
c $b = \frac{7}{2}, c = \frac{3}{2}$

Coordinate Geometry (p. 173)

1 $\left(\frac{2}{13}, \frac{5}{13}\right)$

2 $2y - x = 4$

3 **b** 70

4 **b** $y = 11 - 2x, y = \frac{1}{2}(x - 13); (7, -3)$
c 15

5 **a** $2\sqrt{221}$ **b** $11x - 10y + 19 = 0$

6 **b** 4.8

7 **a** $3x + 4y - 10 = 0$

8 **a** $(-3, 5)$ **b** $5x - 2y = 29$

9 **a** $(2, 6)$ **b** $y + 3x = 12$

10 **a** $7x + 5y - 18 = 0$ **b** $\frac{162}{35}$

11 **a** $2y - 3x = -3$ **b** $(3, 3)$

12 $(-4, 3), (6, 8)$

13 $(5, -3), \left(-6, \frac{13}{3}\right)$

14 **i** $x + 3y - 3 = 0$ **iv** $3\sqrt{10}$

16 $16\sqrt{2}$

17 $(2, 3), y + 5x = 13; 2y - 3x + 13 = 0$
i $(3, -2)$ **ii** $(1, 8)$ **iii** 26

18 $2y + 3x = 22$; B(0, 11), D(8, −1); $\frac{4\sqrt{65}}{5}$

9 Calculus–Differentiation

Exercise 9a (p. 181)

1 **a** $4x^3$ **b** 1 **c** $4x$
d $2x$ **e** 0 **f** $-\frac{2}{x^3}$
g 5

Exercise 9b (p. 185)

1 **a** $12x^{11}$ **b** $21x^6$ **c** 5
d 5 **e** $10x - 3$ **f** 0
g $-5x^{-6}$ **h** $-12x^{-4}$ **i** $-\frac{2}{x^3}$
j $-\frac{2}{x^2}$ **k** $\frac{6}{x^3}$ **l** $-\frac{1}{x^4}$
m $\frac{4}{x^5}$ **n** $-\frac{15}{4x^6}$ **o** $\frac{1}{3}x^{-\frac{2}{3}}$
p $-\frac{3}{2}x^{-\frac{5}{2}}$ **q** $\frac{1}{2}x^{-\frac{1}{2}}$ **r** $\frac{1}{4}x^{-\frac{3}{4}}$
s $-\frac{1}{2}x^{-\frac{3}{2}}$ **t** $x^{-\frac{4}{3}}$ **u** $6\sqrt{x}$
v $-\frac{3}{4}x^{-\frac{3}{2}}$

2 **a** $12x^3 - 6x^2 + 2x - 1$
b $8x^3 + x^2 - \frac{1}{2}x$
c $6x^5 - x^{-2} + \frac{3}{2}x^{-\frac{3}{2}}$
d $3ax^2 + 2bx + c$
e $18x^2 - 8$
f $15x^2 + 3x$
g $-6x^{-2} - 6x^{-3} - \frac{3}{2}x^{-\frac{5}{2}}$
h $1 - x^{-2}$

3 **a** -1
b 0
c $12x^2 - 3$
d $ax - 2b$
e $4x + 2$
f $-6x^{-3} - 9x^{-4}$
g $\frac{1}{2}x^{-\frac{1}{2}} + \frac{1}{3}x^{-\frac{2}{3}} + \frac{1}{4}x^{-\frac{3}{4}}$
h $\frac{3}{2}x^{-\frac{1}{2}} - 2x^{-\frac{3}{2}} - 5x^{-2}$
i $x^2 - 1$
j $2x + 3$

4 **a** $36x + 6$ **b** $-\frac{10}{9}x^{-\frac{5}{3}}$
c 0 **d** $-x^{-\frac{3}{2}} - \frac{9}{4}x^{-\frac{5}{2}}$

5 **a** $5 - 20t, -20$
b $9t^2 - 8t + 7, 18t - 8$
c $3 + 10t^{-3}, -30t^{-4}$
d $u + at, a$

6 **a** 1, 2 **b** 1, 1 **c** 3, −4
d −5, 4 **e** 4, 4 **f** 9, −24
g 2, 0 **h** 18, $8\frac{1}{4}$

7 **a** (4, 16) **b** (−2, −8), (2, 8)
c (0, 0) **d** $\left(\frac{3}{2}, -\frac{5}{4}\right)$

e $(-1, 8), (1, 6)$
f $(8, 2)$
g $(-\frac{1}{3}, \frac{4}{27}), (1, 0)$
h $(1, 4), (3, 0)$
i $(\frac{1}{2}, -\frac{3}{2}), (-\frac{1}{2}, \frac{3}{2})$
j $(4, \frac{2}{3})$

8 $a = 3, b = -4$

9 $c = 4, d = -\frac{1}{2}$

10 a 4 b 14 c $\frac{1}{2}$

12 $y' = 68; y'' = 31\frac{1}{2}$

13 9.2 cm/yr; 2 cm/yr

14 a $-2.13°C\ cm^{-1}$ b $6.04°C\ cm^{-2}$

15 a $5.76\ g\ l^{-1}\ s^{-1}$

Exercise 9c (p. 189)

1 a $y = 4x - 4$
b $y = 24x - 46$
c $y = -\frac{1}{2}x + \frac{3}{2}$
d $y = 1 - x$
e $x - 16y + 52 = 0$
f $y = 4 - 2x$

2 a $x + 4y = 18$
b $x + 24y = 1204$
c $y = 2x - \frac{7}{2}$
d $y = x + 1$
e $32x + 2y = 135$
f $2x - 4y + 11 = 0$

3 $y = 2x - 10$

4 $a = -1; b = 7$

5 a $x = 1, x = -2$ b $y = -4, y = 23$

6 a 6 b $y = 6x + 2$ c $(-\frac{2}{5}, -\frac{2}{5})$

7 a $(0, 0), (1, 0), (2, 0)$
b $y = 2x, y = 1 - x, y = 2x - 4$

8 a $(1, 3), (-4, -12)$
b $y = -2x + 5, y = 8x + 20$
c $(-\frac{3}{2}, 8)$

9 a $(-\frac{1}{3}, -\frac{11}{9})$ b $y = -\frac{11}{9}; x = -\frac{1}{3}$

10 $h = \frac{8}{3}, k = \frac{16}{5}$

11 a $2\frac{1}{2}$ b $2\frac{1}{2}$

12 $(7\frac{1}{2}, -12)$

13 $a = -1; b = 3$

14 $a = -4; b = 1$

15 a $(-2, 0), (2, 0)$
b $y = \frac{1}{2}x + 1, y = -\frac{1}{2}x + 1$

16 a $y = x + 3, y = \frac{1}{2}x + 6$

Exercise 9d (p. 194)

1 a $(2, -6)$
b $(-3, -2)$
c $(\frac{1}{3}, -\frac{1}{3})$
d $(2, 7), (-2, -1)$
e $(-2\frac{1}{2}, -30\frac{1}{4})$
f $(0, 5), (1, 4), (-1, 4)$
g $(2, 41), (-2, -23)$
h $(1, 2)$

2 c $(\frac{3}{2}, \frac{3}{4})$

3 a $(0, 0)$ min
b $(2, 8)$ max, $(3, 7)$ min
c $(-2, 0)$ min
d $(1, 1)$ min, $(3, 5)$ max
e $(0, 0)$ min
f $(\frac{2}{5}, 20)$ min, $(-\frac{2}{5}, -20)$ max
g $(2, 4\sqrt{2})$ min

4 a $x = 3$ or $x = -7$
b $x = \pm 1$
c $x = \frac{1}{2}$
d $x = -1$
e $x = \sqrt[3]{\frac{10}{\pi}}$

5 a $(0, 0)$ inflexion
b $(0, 0)$ inflexion, $(3, -162)$ min, $(-3, 162)$ max
c $(0, 0)$ inflexion, $(-2\frac{1}{4}, -8\frac{139}{256})$ min
d $(3, 47)$ max, $(-5, -38\frac{1}{3})$ min
e $(\frac{1}{3}, -54)$ min, $(-\frac{1}{3}, 54)$ max
f $(-2, -12)$ inflexion

6 a $f'(x) = 6x(1 - x)$
b $f(0) = 0, f(1) = 1$
d $0 < x < 1$
e $x < 0, x > 1$
g 2 roots

7 a $f'(x) = 2x - 1$
b $x = \frac{1}{2}, f(x) = -2\frac{1}{4}$, min
c increasing: $x > \frac{1}{2}$; decreasing: $x < \frac{1}{2}$
e 2 roots

8 i $f'(x) = 3x^2 - 12$;
$x = -2, f(x) = 16$, max;
$x = 2, f(x) = -16$, min;
incr: $x < -2, x > 2$;
decr: $-2 < x < 2$; 3 roots
ii $f'(x) = -2 - 2x$;
$x = -1, f(x) = 4$, max;
incr: $x < -1$;
decr: $x > -1$; 2 roots
iii $f'(x) = 3x(2 - x)$;
$x = 0, f(x) = 0$, min;
$x = 2, f(x) = 4$, max;
incr: $0 < x < 2$;
decr: $x < 0, x > 2$; 2 roots
iv $f'(x) = -3x^2$;
$x = 0, f(x) = 3$, inflexion;
incr: none;
decr: $x < 0, x > 0$; 1root
v $f'(x) = 3x^2 - 10x + 3$;
$x = \frac{1}{3}, f(x) = 2\frac{13}{27}$, max;
$x = 3, f(x) = -7$, min;
incr: $x < \frac{1}{3}, x > 3$;
decr: $\frac{1}{3} < x < 3$; 3 roots

9 a $(1, 2)$ min, $(-1, -2)$ max
b $(\frac{1}{4}, \frac{1}{4})$ max
c $(\frac{1}{2}, 3)$ min
d $(2, 12)$ min

10 $a = -22, b = \frac{11}{5}$

11 a $a = 3, b = -5$

12 a 2 s b 0.9 s, 6.05 m

Exercise 9e (p. 199)

1 a $100 - x$
b $A = 100x - x^2$
c $\frac{dA}{dx} = 100 - 2x; x = 50$
d 50 m by 50 m, $2500\ m^2$

2 $125\,000\ m^2$, 250 m by 500 m

3 a 50 m b $0 < t < 5$

4 a Height $= \frac{500}{x^2}$
External surface area $= x^2 + \frac{2000}{x}$
b $x = 10$ c $300\ m^2$

5 a $S = \pi r^2 + \frac{54\pi}{r}$ b $r = 3$
c $27\pi\ cm^2$

6 a $5x$ d $V = \frac{15}{16}x(1620 - 15x^2)$
e $x = 6$ f $6075\ cm^3$

7 2 cm, 3 cm

8 $18\ cm^3, x = 1$

9 $7\frac{11}{27}\ cm^3, x = \frac{2}{3}$

10 a $h = \frac{10}{\pi r^2}$ d 1.2 m, 2.3 m, $26\ m^2$

12 a $A = 2\pi r^2 + 2\pi rh, V = \pi r^2 h$
b $h = \frac{12 - r^2}{r}, V = \pi r(12 - r^2)$
c $r = 2$

13 a £6 b £np

15 $\frac{125}{27\pi} \approx 1.47\ m^3$

16 a $\frac{1}{144}(17x^2 - 16lx + 8l^2)$
b min

Extension Exercise 9f (p. 202)

1 a $(-2, 19)$ inflexion, $(0, 3)$ min
b $x > 0$
c $x < -2$, $-2 < x < 0$

2 $\left(-p^2, -\frac{1}{p}\right)$

3 $a = 2$, $b = -4$, $c = -1$

4 $x + t^2y - 4t = 0$

5 $\left(\frac{1}{5}, \frac{16}{5\sqrt[4]{5}}\right)$

6 a $y = x + 3$ **b** $\left(-\frac{5}{4}, \frac{7}{4}\right)$, $(1, 4)$

7 70 g; 30 g; 15 kg

8 a $-0.1\left(\frac{3}{2}a^{\frac{1}{2}} - 2a^{-\frac{1}{2}} - 2a^{-\frac{3}{2}}\right)$
b $a = 2$

9 a $1.2x^{-\frac{2}{5}} - 0.48x^{-\frac{1}{5}}$
b 7.8 km; 97.7 km

10 $a = 2\frac{4}{5}$; $x + 3y = 7$

11 a $4\frac{1}{2}$ cm^2
b 4 cm^2

13 Area $= \dfrac{9x^2}{2} + \dfrac{400}{3x}$

14 $x = 20$

15 $AP^2 = x^4 - x^2 + 1$; $\left(\frac{1}{2}\sqrt{2}, \frac{1}{2}\right)$, $\left(-\frac{1}{2}\sqrt{2}, \frac{1}{2}\right)$

16 a At $x = 1$: $y = 2$, $x = 1$
At $x = -1$: $y = -2$, $x = -1$
b At $x = 1$: $y = 2$, $x = 1$
At $x = -1$: $y = 2$, $x = -1$
c n odd, answer as for **a**
n even, answer as for **b**

Miscellaneous Exercise 9g (p. 204)

1 a $-\dfrac{6}{x^3}$ **b** $-\dfrac{1}{4x^{\frac{3}{2}}}$ **c** $-\dfrac{1}{x^{\frac{5}{3}}}$

2 a $9x^2 + \dfrac{4}{x^2}$ **b** 13

3 a $(2, 8)$, $(-2, -8)$
b $(1, -10)$, $(-1, 10)$
c $(4, 96)$
d $(2, 8)$, $(-1, -1)$

4 a $(-1, 2)$ max, $(1, -2)$ min
b $(-2, -16)$ min, $(0, 0)$ max, $(2, -16)$ min
c $(1, 3)$ max
d $(1, 4)$ min

5 $a \geqslant 0$

6 a $y = 4 - x$; $y = x$ **c** $(-2, -2)$

7 a Sometimes increasing, sometimes decreasing
b Always increasing
c Always decreasing

9 a 6, min **b** 7, max
c $\frac{7}{8}$, min **d** $\frac{17}{2}$, max

10 b $\frac{7}{2}\pi$; 3π

11 $a = 3$, $b = 8$ or $a = -7$, $b = -32$

12 -3 cm s^{-1}, dec; 7 cm s^{-1}, inc

13 a $x < 2$, $x > 3$ **b** $2 < x < 3$

14 $y = 1$, $y = 1$, $y = 0$

15 $y = 3x \pm 8$

16 256 cm^3

17 32 m

18 a $a = 12$, 288 cm^3 **b** 10 cm^3/day

19 a 3 mm/h; 0 **b** 6 mm/h^2

20 a 13 min **b** 11 a.m.

21 a $n = 10$; 118 mg
b 15 mg/day; $4\frac{1}{2}$ days

22 a 1004 mb
b -0.25 mb/km
c $-0.000\,63$ mb/km^2

Test Yourself (p. 207)

1 B	**2** C	**3** B	**4** E	**5** C
6 A	**7** A	**8** D	**9** E	**10** C

10 Functions

Exercise 10a (p. 216)

1 a $\{0, 4, 8, 16\}$; one-to-one
b $y \in \mathbb{R}$, $y \geqslant 1$; many-to-one
c $y \in \mathbb{R}$, $-7 < y < 5$; one-to-one
d $y \in \mathbb{R}$, $y \neq 0$; one-to-one
e $y \in \mathbb{R}$, $-2 \leqslant y \leqslant 128$; one-to-one
f $y \in \mathbb{R}$, $-2 \leqslant y \leqslant 1$; many-to-one
g $y \in \mathbb{R}^+$; many-to-one

2 a $\left\{3, 5\frac{1}{2}, 8, 10\frac{1}{2}\right\}$; one-to-one
b $x \in \mathbb{R}$, $4 < x < 49$; one-to-one
c $x \in \mathbb{R}$, $x < -2$ and $x > 2$; many-to-one
d $x \in \mathbb{R}$, $7 \leqslant x \leqslant 12$; one-to-one
e $x \in \mathbb{R}$, $1 < x \leqslant 3$ and $-3 \leqslant x < -1$; many-to-one

3 a $f(x) = (x - 1)^2 + 8$
b $y \in \mathbb{R}$, $y \geqslant 8$

4 a $y \in \mathbb{R}$, $y \geqslant -6\frac{1}{4}$
b $x = 1$ or $x = -4$

5 a $p = 7$, $q = 1$
b $y \in \mathbb{R}$, $y \leqslant 7$

6 a $y \in \mathbb{R}$, $y \geqslant -11$
b $y \in \mathbb{R}$, $y \geqslant -\frac{7}{2}$
c $y \in \mathbb{R}$, $y \geqslant -\frac{5}{4}$
d $y \in \mathbb{R}$, $y \leqslant \frac{33}{4}$

7 a $(2, 5)$
c $x = 4$

8 b $y \in \mathbb{R}$, $y > 4$
c $x = 5$

9 b $y \in \mathbb{R}$, $0 \leqslant y \leqslant 9$
c Horizontal line cuts twice
d $x = \frac{1}{2}$ or $x = \frac{9}{2}$

10 a $f(x) = 2 + \dfrac{5}{x - 1}$
b $A\left(-\frac{3}{2}, 0\right)$; $B(0, -3)$; $C(1, 2)$; $x = 1$, $y = 2$
c $y \in \mathbb{R}$, $y \neq 2$
d $x = 1 \pm \sqrt{5}$

Exercise 10b (p. 221)

1 a 4 **b** 16
c $3x^2 + 4$ **d** 16

2 a $x + 3$; $x + 3$ **b** $6x + 3$; $6x - 1$
c x; x **d** $9 - 6x$; $1 - 6x$
e $x^2 + 1$; $(x + 1)^2$
f $\dfrac{1}{2x}$; $\dfrac{2}{x}$ **g** $\dfrac{1}{1 + x}$; $\dfrac{1}{x} + 1$
h $2(2x + 1)(x - 1)$; $2(x + 1)(x - 2)$

3 a $\dfrac{1}{x^2}$ **b** $\dfrac{1}{x^2}$
c $\dfrac{1}{3x - 1}$ **d** x^4
e x **f** $9x - 4$
g $\dfrac{3}{x^2} - 1$ **h** $\dfrac{1}{(3x - 1)^2}$
i $\left(\dfrac{3}{x} - 1\right)^2$ **j** $\dfrac{3}{x^2} - 1$
k $\dfrac{1}{3x^2 - 1}$ **l** $\dfrac{1}{(3x - 1)^2}$

4 a $k = 2$

5 a $x = -2$ or $x = \frac{2}{3}$
b $x = -\frac{1}{2}$
c $x = \frac{1}{3}$ or $x = -1$
d $x = \frac{1}{9}$ or $x = -1$

6 a $2x^2 + 7$, $y \in \mathbb{R}$, $y \geqslant 7$
b $2x^3 + 7$, $y \in \mathbb{R}$
c $(2x + 7)^2$, $y \in \mathbb{R}$, $y \geqslant 0$
d $(2x + 7)^3$, $y \in \mathbb{R}$

7 a fg:$x \to (x+4)^2 - 3$, gf:$x \to x^2 + 1$
b $y \geqslant -3$, $y \geqslant 1$
c $k = -\frac{3}{2}$
d $l = \frac{1}{2} \pm \frac{1}{2}\sqrt{7}$

8 a $x + 10$; $x + 15$; $x + 5n$
b $g(x) = 2x$
c $h(x) = \dfrac{x}{a}$

9 a $gf(x) = 12x^2 - 12x + 5$
b $a = 1$, $b = 1$
c $x = -4$ or $x = 2$

10 a $x + 4$
b $8x^4 + 24x^2 + 21$
c x
d $\dfrac{1}{2(x+2)^2 + 3}$
e $\dfrac{1}{2x^2 + 5}$
f $\dfrac{2}{x^2} + 5$
g $\dfrac{1}{2x^2 + 3} + 2$
h $\dfrac{x^2}{2 + 3x^2}$

11 a $y \geqslant 1$, $y \geqslant 4$
b $ff(x) = |x| + 2$, $y \geqslant 2$;
$gg(x) = (x^2 + 4)^2 + 4$, $y \geqslant 20$;
$fg(x) = x^2 + 5$, $y \geqslant 5$

12 a $x \geqslant -2$ **b** $x \leqslant 4$
c $-2 \leqslant x \leqslant 2$ **d** $0 < x \leqslant \frac{2}{3}$

Exercise 10c (p. 227)

1 a $\dfrac{x}{3}$ **b** $x - 4$
c $x + 5$ **d** $6x$
e $\dfrac{1}{x}$, self-inverse **f** $\sqrt{x}$
g $\dfrac{x+4}{3}$ **h** $\dfrac{3-x}{2}$
i $4 - x$, self-inverse **j** $5x - 6$
k $\dfrac{5}{x}$, self-inverse **l** $\dfrac{x-1}{x}$

2 a $\dfrac{3x-5}{2}$, $\mathbb{R}$
b $\frac{3}{2}(x - 5)$, $\mathbb{R}$
c $3\left(\dfrac{x}{2} - 5\right)$, $\mathbb{R}$
d $\dfrac{x}{2} - \dfrac{5}{6}$, $\mathbb{R}$
e $\dfrac{3x}{2} - 5$, $\mathbb{R}$
f $x^2 - 4$, $x \geqslant 0$
g $\dfrac{x}{7} + 4$, $\mathbb{R}$
h $\dfrac{4-x}{7}$, $\mathbb{R}$
i $\sqrt{\dfrac{x-2}{3}}$, $x \geqslant 2$
j $\dfrac{4}{7x}$, $x \neq 0$, self-inverse
k $\dfrac{1}{x} - 1$, $x \neq 0$
l $\dfrac{1}{1 - \frac{1}{x}} = \dfrac{x}{x-1}$, $x \neq 0$, $x \neq 1$, self-inverse
m $\dfrac{1}{x-1}$, $x \neq 1$
n $\dfrac{3}{5x}$, $x \neq 0$, self-inverse
o $\dfrac{a}{bx}$, $x \neq 0$, self-inverse
p $4x^2$, $x \in \mathbb{R}^+$
q $2 - x^2$, $x \geqslant 0$
r $\sqrt[3]{x+1}$, $\mathbb{R}$
s $\dfrac{\sqrt{x+4} - 1}{3}$, $x \geqslant -4$
t $\dfrac{(x-5)^2 + 1}{2}$, $x \geqslant 5$

3 a $y > -9$; $\sqrt{x+9} - 3$; $x > -9$, $y > -3$
b $y > 3$; $\sqrt{x-3} + 2$; $x > 3$, $y > 2$
c $y \leqslant 3$; $\sqrt{3-x} - 1$; $x \leqslant 3$, $y \geqslant -1$

4 a i $\dfrac{x-1}{3}$, $\mathbb{R}$ **iv** $x = -\frac{1}{2}$, $\left(-\frac{1}{2}, -\frac{1}{2}\right)$
b i $\dfrac{2-x}{4}$, $\mathbb{R}$ **iv** $x = \frac{2}{5}$, $\left(\frac{2}{5}, \frac{2}{5}\right)$

5 a $f^{-1}(x) = \dfrac{x-2}{3}$; $g^{-1}(x) = \dfrac{1}{x}$;
$gf(x) = \dfrac{1}{3x+2}$

7 a $x \geqslant 0$, $y \geqslant 0$; $\sqrt{x}$
b $x \geqslant -2$, $y \geqslant 0$; $\sqrt[4]{x} - 2$
c $x \geqslant -1$, $y \leqslant 4$; $\sqrt{4-x} - 1$

8 b Symmetrical in $y = x$

9 b $f^{-1}(x)$:$(-1, 0)$, $(0, 2)$
$f(x-2)$:$(4, 0)$, $(0, -2)$

10 a $f^{-1}(x) = \dfrac{4}{x} + 1$, $\mathbb{R}^+$
c $x = 2.56$

11 b and **c**

12 a $f(6) = \frac{1}{2}$
b $f^{-1}(2) = 2$
c $k = 2$ or $k = -5$

13 a $g^{-1}(x) = \dfrac{2x-1}{2-x}$, $x \in \mathbb{R}$, $x \neq 2$
b $x = \pm 1$

14 a $h^{-1}(x) = -\dfrac{1}{x} - 1$, $x \in \mathbb{R}$, $x \neq 0$

15 a $f^{-1}(x) = \dfrac{ax-1}{x+2}$, $x \neq -2$
b $a = 7$
c $a = -\frac{1}{2}$

Exercise 10d (p. 236)

1 a $(3, 0)$; touches x-axis at $(0, 0)$; $y \to \mp\infty$; min $(0, 0)$, max $(2, 4)$
b $(6, 0)$; touches x-axis at $(0, 0)$; $y \to \pm\infty$; max $(0, 0)$, min $(4, -32)$
c $(0, 9)$, $(\pm 1, 0)$, $(\pm 3, 0)$; about y-axis; $y \to +\infty$; max $(0, 9)$, min $(\pm\sqrt{5}, -16)$
d $(0, 0)$, $\left(\pm\sqrt{\frac{5}{3}}, 0\right)$; 180° rotational symmetry about $(0, 0)$; $y \to \pm\infty$; inflexion $(0, 0)$, max $(-1, 2)$, min $(1, -2)$

2 a $(0, -18)$, $(3, 0)$; max $(-1, -16)$, min $(1, -20)$; $y \to \pm\infty$
b $(0, 0)$, $(\pm 2\sqrt{3}, 0)$; min $(-2, -16)$, max $(2, 16)$; $y \to \mp\infty$
c $(0, 8)$, $(2, 0)$; inflexion $(2, 0)$; $y \to \mp\infty$
d $(1, 0)$, $(0, -4)$; none; $y \to \pm\infty$

3 b $-\frac{1}{16} < k < 0$; $k = 0$; $k = -\frac{1}{16}$ or $k > 0$; none; $k < -\frac{1}{16}$

4 b None; $c < 432$; $c = 432$; $c > 432$

5 a $y = 1 - \dfrac{4}{x+1}$ **b** $y \to 1$
c -1, $x = -1$ **d** $(0, -3)$, $(3, 0)$

8 Even: **a** and **c**
Odd: **b** and **d**
Neither: **e**

Extension Exercise 10e (p. 237)

1 a $fg(x) = \dfrac{x-4}{4x-10}$
$gf(x) = \dfrac{2x+7}{-4x-11} = -\dfrac{2x+7}{4x+11}$
$g^{-1}(x) = \dfrac{4x+2}{x-1}$
b $x = -2$

2 b $2 \leqslant y \leqslant 9$

3 a $\text{gf}(x) = \dfrac{x}{(x-3)(x+5)}$

$\text{fg}(x) = \dfrac{(1+5x)(1-3x)}{x}$

b No solution; $x = \frac{1}{3}$ or $x = -\frac{1}{5}$

4 b $0 \leqslant y \leqslant 2$

6 $2^n x - (2^n - 1)$

7 c $\dfrac{x^2+6}{x^2-4} + \dfrac{5x}{x^2-4}$

8 Integers

×	E	O
E	E	E
O	E	O

+	E	O
E	E	O
O	O	E

Functions

×	E	O
E	E	O
O	O	E

+	E	O
E	E	N
O	N	O

11 a $x = 2n + 1, n \in \mathbb{Z}$
b 9 solutions
c $x = \dfrac{16n}{9}$

Miscellaneous Exercise 10f (p. 239)

1 a 7 **b** $x^3 - 1$
c $(x-3)^3 + 2$ **d** 1

2 a 77 **b** 30
c 1 **d** $\frac{1}{77}$

3 a $5x$; $7 - x$; $\dfrac{7-x}{5}$; $7 - 5x$
b $x = \frac{7}{6}$

4 a $\dfrac{6-x}{5}$ **b** $x = 1$

5 a hgf **b** ghf **c** gfh
d fgh **e** fhg **f** hfg

6 a cuts at (0, 0), touches at (1, 0); $y \to \pm\infty$; min (1, 0), max $\left(\frac{1}{3}, \frac{4}{27}\right)$
b touches at (0, 0), (2, 0); $y \to +\infty$; min (0, 0) and (2, 0), max (1, 1)
c touches at (−1, 0), cuts at (2, 0), (0, 2); $y \to \mp\infty$; min (−1, 0), max (1, 4)
d cuts at (0, 0), $\left(-\sqrt[3]{4}, 0\right)$; $y \to +\infty$; min (−1, −3)

8 a f and g: one-to-one; h: many-to-one
b $\text{fgh}: x \to \dfrac{2x^2+20}{x^2+5}$
c Yes
d $2 < y \leqslant 4$
e $x = \pm\sqrt{5}$

9 a $a = 5, b = 2$
b $\left(\frac{3}{2}\right)$, $\left(0, \frac{1}{3}\right)$, $\left(\frac{1}{2}, 0\right)$
c $x = -2$ or $x = 4$

10 b $\text{f}(x) = \pm 1$

11 b $c < -1$ or $c > 0$

12 b $\text{f}^{-1}(x) = \sqrt{\dfrac{x+4}{3}}, x \geqslant -4$

13 b $\text{f}'(x) = \begin{cases} 1 & 0 \leqslant x \leqslant 1 \\ 3 - 2x & 1 \leqslant x \leqslant 2 \\ -1 & 2 \leqslant x \leqslant -3 \end{cases}$

Test Yourself (p. 240)

1 C **2** D **3** C **4** A **5** A
6 C **7** D **8** E **9** D **10** D
11 D **12** B

11 Exponential and Logarithmic Functions

Exercise 11a (p. 244)

1 Bases:
a 10 **b** 10 **c** 3
d 4 **e** 2 **f** $\frac{1}{2}$
g a
Logarithms:
a 2 **b** 1.6021 **c** 2
d 3 **e** 0 **f** −3
g b

2 a $\log_2 16 = 4$ **b** $\log_3 27 = 3$
c $\log_5 125 = 3$
d $\log_{10} 1\,000\,000 = 6$
e $\log_{12} 1728 = 3$ **f** $\log_{16} 64 = \frac{3}{2}$
g $\log_{10} 10\,000 = 4$ **h** $\log_4 1 = 0$
i $\log_{10} 0.01 = -2$ **j** $\log_2\left(\frac{1}{2}\right) = -1$
k $\log_9 27 = \frac{3}{2}$ **l** $\log_8\left(\frac{1}{4}\right) = -\frac{2}{3}$
m $\log_{\frac{1}{3}} 81 = -4$ **n** $\log_e 1 = 0$
o $\log_{16}\left(\frac{1}{2}\right) = -\frac{1}{4}$ **p** $\log_{\frac{1}{8}} 1 = 0$
q $\log_{81} 27 = \frac{3}{4}$ **r** $\log_{\frac{1}{16}} 4 = -\frac{1}{2}$
s $\log_a c = 5$ **t** $\log_a b = 3$
u $\log_p r = q$

3 a $2^5 = 32$ **b** $3^2 = 9$
c $5^2 = 25$ **d** $10^5 = 100\,000$
e $2^7 = 128$ **f** $9^0 = 1$
g $3^{-2} = \frac{1}{9}$ **h** $4^{\frac{1}{2}} = 2$
i $e^0 = 1$ **j** $27^{\frac{1}{3}} = 3$
k $a^2 = x$ **l** $3^b = a$
m $a^c = 8$ **n** $x^y = z$
o $q^p = r$

4 a 6 **b** 2 **c** 7
d 2 **e** $\frac{1}{3}$ **f** 0
g $\frac{1}{3}$ **h** 3 **i** 3
j −1 **k** $\frac{1}{2}$ **l** 2

Exercise 11b (p. 246)

1 a $\log a + \log b$ **b** $\log a - \log c$
c $-\log b$ **d** $2\log a + \frac{3}{2}\log b$
e $-4\log b$
f $\frac{1}{3}\log a + 4\log b - 3\log c$
g $\frac{1}{2}\log a$ **h** $\frac{1}{3}\log b$
i $\frac{1}{2}\log a + \frac{1}{2}\log b$ **j** $1 + \log a$
k $-2 - 2\log b$ **l** $\frac{1}{2}\log a - \frac{1}{2}\log b$

2 a $\log 6$ **b** $\log 2$
c $\log 6$ **d** $\log 2$
e $\log(ac)$ **f** $\log\left(\dfrac{xy}{z}\right)$
g $\log\left(\dfrac{a^2}{b}\right)$ **h** $\log\left(\dfrac{a^2b^3}{c}\right)$
i $\log\sqrt{\dfrac{x}{y}}$ **j** $\log\left(\dfrac{p}{\sqrt[3]{q}}\right)$
k $\lg(100a^3)$ **l** $\lg\left(\dfrac{10a}{\sqrt{b}}\right)$
m $\lg\left(\dfrac{a^2}{2000c}\right)$ **n** $\lg\left(\dfrac{10x^3}{\sqrt{y}}\right)$
o $\log\left(\dfrac{b^a}{a^b}\right)$

3 a 3 **b** 2 **c** 2
d 1 **e** $\log 2$ **f** $\log 7$
g $-\log 2$ **h** 0 **i** 0
j 3 **k** 2 **l** $\frac{2}{3}$

Exercise 11c (p. 249)

1 a 2 **b** y **c** 5 **d** n
e 7 **f** n **g** 5 **h** 5
i x **j** 0 **k** $2x + 1$ **l** e
m 1 **n** 1

2 a 1.086 **b** −0.631
c −3.170 **d** 1.585
e −1.292 **f** 2.059
g 0.861 **h** 6.456

Exercise 11d (p. 251)

1 a $x = 6$ **b** $x = -5$
c $x = 3.79$ **d** $x = -3$
e $x = 0.158$ **f** $x = 5$
g $x = 5.03$ **h** $x = 0.403$
i $x = 0$

2 a $x = 0.756$ **b** $x = -7.06$
c $x = 1.16$ **d** $x = -2.58$
e $x = 6.84$ **f** $x = 0$

3 a $x = 1.58$
b $x = 1$ or $x = 2$
c $x = 0$ or $x = 2$
d $x = 2$
e $x = -1$ or $x = 1$
f $x = -1$ or $x = 0$

g $x = 1.21$
h $x = 0.792$
i $x = 0.631$ or $x = 1.26$
j $x = 0$ or $x = 2.32$

4 $t = \dfrac{s \log a}{\log b}$

Extension Exercise 11e (p. 251)

1 **a** $x = 3$ **b** $x = 125$ or $x = \frac{1}{125}$
c $x = 2$ **d** $x = 4.56$
e $x = 4$ **f** $x = 1$

2 **a** $x = 1, y = 1$ **b** $x = 2, y = 4$
c $x = a^5, y = a^3$ **d** $x = 1, y = 3$

3 **a** $\frac{3}{2}$ **b** 3

4 **a** $xy = 1000$ **b** $5^x = 6$
c $x^3 = 10y^2$ **d** $x = 5y^3$

5 $a = 4$

6 **a** 40 digits **b** 131 digits

Miscellaneous Exercise 11f (p. 252)

1 **a** $\log_2 32 = 5$ **b** $\log_{10} 100 = 2$
c $\log_a c = b$ **d** $\log_p q = 3$
e $\log_{27} 3 = \frac{1}{3}$ **f** $\log_3 \frac{1}{3} = -1$

2 **a** $2^3 = 8$ **b** $6^2 = 36$
c $a^c = b$ **d** $d^e = c^4$
e $p^4 = 8$ **f** $c^q = 3$

3 **a** 7 **b** 3 **c** 4
d 4 **e** $\frac{1}{4}$ **f** -2

4 **a** $\log a + 2\log b - \log c$
b $\frac{1}{2}\log a + \frac{1}{2}\log b$
c $4\log a - 2\log b - \log c$
d $2\log a + 3\log b + 4\log c$

5 **a** $\log\left(\dfrac{a}{b}\right)$ **b** $\log(\sqrt{x}y^3)$
c $\log 62.5$ **d** $\log x^{3a}$

6 **a** 2 **b** 6 **c** $\log 8$
d $\log 3$ **e** 4 **f** $\frac{1}{3}$

7 **a** $n = -10$ or $n = 100$
b $x = \frac{9}{8}$
c $x = 1.26$
d $x = \frac{1}{2}$
e $x = 0.146$
f $y = -8$ or $y = 1$
g $x = 0$ or $x = 1$
h $x = 0$ or $x = -0.208$
i $x = 2.81$
j $x = -2$ or $x = 1$

8 **a** 4.6%

Test Yourself (p. 253)

1 D **2** B **3** D **4** C **5** C
6 B **7** E **8** D **9** A **10** B

Revision Exercise 2 (p. 254)

1 **a** $12x^3 - 32x + 16$
b $4 - 3x^{-2} - x^{-3}$
c $3x^{\frac{1}{2}} - x^{-\frac{1}{2}}$

2 $y = 4x - 4$, $y = -4x - 12$; $(-1, -8)$

3 **a** $(x - 3)(x^2 + x + 3)$
b Tangent $y = 15x - 40$;
normal $x + 15y = 78$

4 $x + y = \frac{5}{2}$, $x + 3y = 10$

5 **a** 1 **b** 0 **c** 2

6 **a** (0, 0) infl; (1, −1) min
b $(0, 0)$, $\left(\frac{10}{9}, 0\right)$
d $y \geqslant -1$
e $0 < x < \frac{10}{9}$

7 $x = 10\,\text{m}$, $y = 5\,\text{m}$

8 $x = \dfrac{100}{\pi + 4}$ cm; area $= 700\,\text{cm}^2$

9 **a** **i** hf **ii** gf **iii** gh
iv fg **v** hg **vi** fh
b **i** fhg **ii** gfh **iii** hgf
iv ghf **v** hfg **vi** fgh

10 **a** hg **b** fhg **c** fh
d hfg **e** hf **f** gh

11 **a** $(x - 2)^2 - 1$ **b** (3, 0)
c

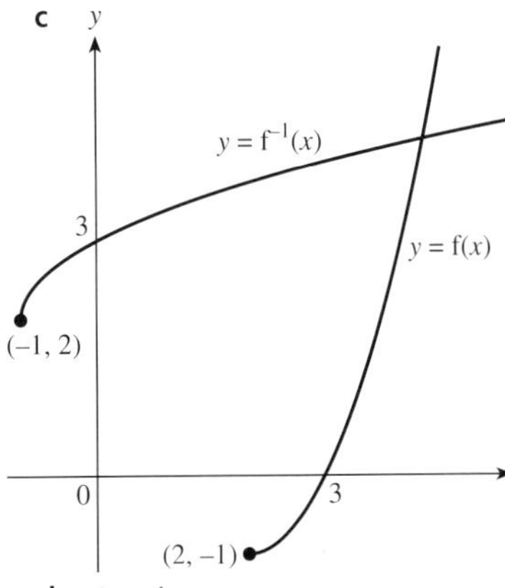

d $y \geqslant -1$
e $f^{-1}(x) = 2 + \sqrt{x + 1}$, $x \geqslant -1, y \geqslant 2$
g $\left(\dfrac{5 + \sqrt{13}}{2}, \dfrac{5 + \sqrt{13}}{2}\right)$

12 **a** $(-3, 4)$
b $(0, -5)$, $(-1, 0)$
c

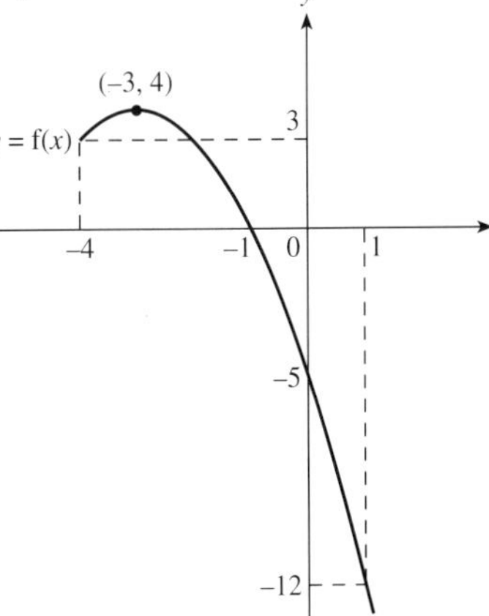

d $-12 \leqslant y \leqslant 4$

13 **a** $f^{-1}(x) = \dfrac{3x + 1}{2 - x}$

14 Even: **c** Odd: **d** and **e**
Neither: **a**, **b** and **f**

15

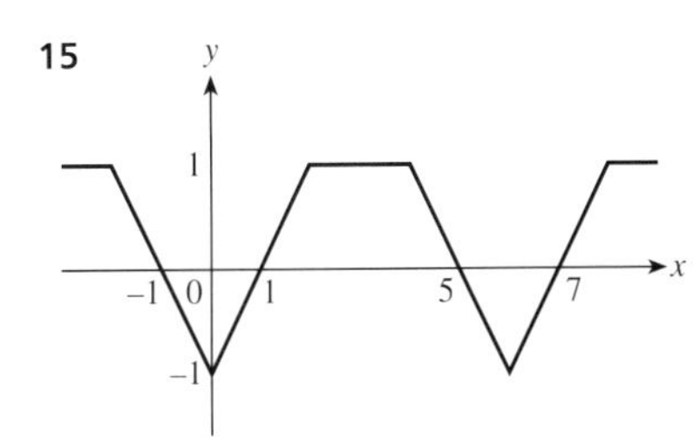

16 **a** $\log 20$ **b** $-\log 2$

17 **a** $x = 8$ **b** $x = 1.26$
c $x = 32$ **d** $x = 1.74$

18 $x = 8$

19 $x = 1.58$

20 **a** $x = 33$ **b** $x = \sqrt[3]{10}$

21 $f^{-1}(x) = 10^{\frac{x+1}{2}}$; $x \in \mathbb{R}, y > 0$

22 $x = -1.869$

23 **a** $\left(-1, \frac{1}{4}\right)$ **b** $y = 0$
c $\left(0, \frac{1}{2}\right)$, $(0, 1)$
d

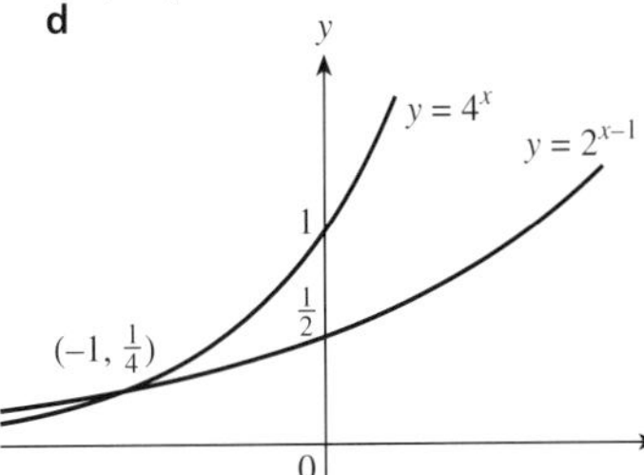

24 a $(t-3)(t-5)(t-7)$
b $x = 1.58, x = 2.32, x = 2.81$

25 $f^{-1}(x) = \log_3(2x) - 1$; domain $x \in \mathbb{R}^+$, range $y \in \mathbb{R}$

Examination Questions 2

Differentiation (p. 257)

1 (0, 0) min, (4, 32) max; $x < 0, x > 4$; $y = 12x - 8$

3 a $(-2, -16)$ min, (1, 11) max

4 ii 2304

5 $(4, -159)$ min, $(-2, 57)$ max

6 i a $x = -2, x = 1$, or $x = 3$
b $x = -1, x = 2$
iii $x < -1, x > 2$

7 b $0, \pm 2\sqrt{2}$ **c** 3

8 $2y + x = 7$; $(\frac{1}{2}, \frac{13}{4})$

9 (3, 0) min, $(-3, -12)$ max

10 a $2x + 4y + \pi x$ **b** $4xy + \frac{1}{2}\pi x^2$
d 14, 7.0 **e** 700

11 $V = \frac{x}{2}(75 - x^2)$, $125\,\text{cm}^3$

12 b 5, 25

13 c 1200

Functions (p. 259)

1 a $x \geqslant 1$ **b** $f^{-1}(x) = (x-1)^2$
c $fg(x) = 1 + x$ **e** $y = 1 + |x|$

2 a $h(x) = 2\sqrt{x-3} - 5$
b $x \geqslant 3, y \geqslant -5$

3 b $y > 1$ or $f(x) \in (1, \infty)$
c $f^{-1}(x) = \sqrt{x-1} - 1$
d Range: $(-1, \infty)$; domain: $(1, \infty)$

4 a $y \geqslant 0$
b $x = 0$ or $x = 8$
c $x = 2$ and $x = 6$

5 ii $a + b = -3$
iii $a = 0, b = -3$; $a = 2, b = -5$

6 i $f(x^{-1}) = 2x$
ii $f^{-1}(x) = \frac{2}{x}$

7 b $x = \frac{1}{2}$ and $x = \frac{3}{2}$

8 a $f^{-1}(x) = \frac{x+1}{4}$
b $gf(x) = \frac{3}{8x-3}, x \in \mathbb{R}, x \neq \frac{3}{8}$
c $x = -0.076$ and $x = 0.826$

9 a $gf(x) = \frac{1}{x-5} - 4$
b $x > 5, y > -4$

10 a i $ff(x) = 9x - 8$
ii $fg(x) = \frac{36}{x} - 14$
iii $g^{-1}(x) = \frac{12}{x+4}, x \neq -4$
b $a = -18$; $b = 30$

11 $a = 2, b = -4$
b $x \geqslant -4$
c $f^{-1}(x) = \sqrt{x+4} - 2$

12 a $f^4(x) = 16x - 45$
b $a = 2$; $b = -3$
c $f^{-1}(7) = 5$

13 $fg(x) = \frac{3}{x+4}, x \in \mathbb{R}, x \geqslant 0$;
$(gf)^{-1}(x) = \frac{3(x-2)}{1-x}$

14 a $y > 0$
b $f^{-1}(x) = \frac{2}{x}\sqrt{1+x^2}$
c $x > 0$

15 a $a = 5$; $b = -2$
b i $f^{-1}(x) = \frac{x+3}{2}$
ii $ff(x) = 4x - 9$
iii $gg(x) = x$
iv $fg(x) = \frac{16}{x} - 3$

Exponential and Logarithmic Functions (p. 262)

1 $x = 1.58$

2 a $x = 0.113$ **b** $x = \frac{1}{2}$
c $\frac{1}{2}(3 + 3a - b)$

3 a i $x = \frac{1}{2}$ **ii** $y = -4$ or $y = 20$
b $n = 0.845\ (= \log_{10}^{7})$, $a = 0.2$

4 a $\frac{6}{y}$ **b** $t = 1$ or $t = -216$

5 c $10y^2 - 10001y + 1000 = 0$
d $x = -1$ or $x = 3$

6 a $y = \frac{9}{2}x + \frac{3}{2}$ **b** $x = -\frac{1}{9}$

7 a 2^{10x} **b** 2^{3x-3}; $x = \frac{1}{7}$

8 $x = -1.11$

9 $x = 1.77$

10 $x = 0.774$

11 $90 < x < 110$; 453 to 472 inclusive

12 Sequences and Series

Exercise 12a (p. 268)

1 a 3, 6, 9, 12; 101st
b 3, 9, 27, 81; 6th
c 1, 5, 9, 13; 62nd
d 6, 4, 2, 0; 20th
e 1, 16, 81, 256; 11th
f 0, 3, 8, 15; 29th

2 a 31, 36, 41; $u_n = 5n + 6$; divergent
b $\frac{1}{256}, \frac{1}{1024}, \frac{1}{4096}$; $u_n = \frac{1}{4^{n-1}}$; convergent to 0
c 8, 5, 2; $u_n = 23 - 3n$; divergent
d 10, 12, 14; $u_n = 2n$; divergent
e 32, 64, 128; $u_n = 2^n$; divergent
f $\frac{5}{6}, \frac{6}{7}, \frac{7}{8}$; $u_n = \frac{n}{n+1}$; convergent to 1
g 25, 36, 49; $u_n = n^2$; divergent
h 125, 216, 343; $u_n = n^3$; divergent
i 250, 432, 686; $u_n = 2n^3$; divergent
j 6, 9, 3; $u_n = 3n, 1 \leqslant n \leqslant 3$; $u_{n+3} = u_n, n \geqslant 1$; periodic, period 3
k $-11, 13, -15$; $u_n = (-1)^n(2n+1)$; oscillating, non-periodic
l 16, 8, 4; $u_n = \frac{512}{2^n} = 2^{9-n}$; convergent to 0
m 28, 39, 52; $u_n = n^2 + 3$; divergent
n $-1, 1, -1$; $u_n = (-1)^{n+1}$; oscillating, periodic, period 2
o $\frac{1}{1000}, \frac{1}{10\,000}, \frac{1}{100\,000}$; $u_n = \frac{100}{10^n} = 10^{2-n}$; convergent to 0

3 a 3, 7, 11, 15, 19, 23; divergent
b 64, 32, 16, 8, 4, 2; convergent to 0
c 1, 4, 9, 16, 25, 36; divergent
d 6, 3.5, 2.25, 1.625, 1.3125, 1.156 25; convergent to 1
e 1, 2, 2, 1, $\frac{1}{2}$, $\frac{1}{2}$; periodic, period 6
f $-4, -6, -2, -10, 6, -26$; oscillating, non-periodic
g 4, 2, $\frac{1}{2}$, $\frac{1}{32}$, $\frac{1}{8192}$, 1.86×10^{-9}; convergent to 0
h 3, 4, 9, 64, 3969, 15 745 024; divergent
i 1, 2, 5, -2, 1, 2; periodic, period 4
j 3, $\frac{2}{3}$, $-\frac{1}{2}$, 3, $\frac{2}{3}$, $-\frac{1}{2}$; periodic, period 3
k 7, 19, $-\frac{1}{2}$, 7, 19, $-\frac{1}{2}$; periodic, period 3
l $\frac{1}{2}$, 2, 1, 2, 2, 4; divergent non-periodic
m 3, 2, $-2, -8, -12, -8$; oscillating,

4 a 1, 1, 2, 3, 5, 8, 13, 21, 34, 55
b 1, 2, 1.5, $1.\dot{6}$, 1.6, 1.625, 1.615 3846, 1.619 0476, 1.617 6471

Exercise 12b (p. 272)

1 **a** $1^3 + 2^3 + 3^3 + 4^3$
b $2^2 + 3^2 + \cdots + n^2$
c $1^2 + 1 + 2^2 + 2 + \cdots + n^2 + n$
d $\dfrac{1}{1 \times 2} + \dfrac{1}{2 \times 3} + \dfrac{1}{3 \times 4}$
e $2^2 + 2^3 + 2^4 + 2^5$
f $-1^2 + 2^2 - 3^2 + 4^2$
g $1^1 + 2^2 + 3^3 + \cdots + n^n$
h $-\frac{1}{3} + \frac{1}{4} - \frac{1}{5} + \frac{1}{6}$
i $n(n-1) + (n+1)n + (n+2)(n+1)$
j $\dfrac{n-2}{n-1} + \dfrac{n-1}{n} + \dfrac{n}{n+1}$

2 **a** $\displaystyle\sum_1^n r$ **b** $\displaystyle\sum_1^{n+1} r^4$
c $\displaystyle\sum_1^5 \frac{1}{r}$ **d** $\displaystyle\sum_2^5 3^r$
e $\displaystyle\sum_1^5 \frac{r}{3^{r-1}}$ **f** $\displaystyle\sum_1^5 \frac{r(2r+1)}{2(r+1)}$
g $\displaystyle\sum_1^6 (-1)^r r$ **h** $\displaystyle\sum_1^6 (-1)^{r+1} 2^{r-1}$
i $\displaystyle\sum_2^6 r(r+5)$ **j** $\displaystyle\sum_1^5 (-1)^{r+1} r(2r+1)$

3 **a** 21 **b** 45 **c** 44
d $3\frac{11}{20}$ **e** $-4\frac{9}{10}$ **f** 150
g -80 **h** $\frac{37}{180}$ **i** 63
j 0 **k** 24 **l** 40

4 **a** $15k^2$ **b** $55n$ **c** $56a$
d $-k$ **e** $\dfrac{25a}{12}$ **f** $\dfrac{4a}{m}$

5 **a** 385 **b** 8281
c 805 **d** $\dfrac{n^2 + n - 30}{2}$
e 29 141 **f** 1 353 400
g 30 040 **h** $\frac{1}{6}n(n-1)(2n-1)$
i $n^2(2n+1)^2$ **j** $\frac{1}{3}n(n+1)(n+2)$

6 204 squares

Exercise 12c (p. 274)

1 **a** $1\frac{1}{2}$ **b** -3 **c** 0.1
e $\frac{1}{3}$ **g** n **i** $1\frac{1}{8}$
j -7 **l** -0.2

2 **a** 75; 147 **b** -34; -82
c $7\frac{1}{8}$; $\dfrac{5n-3}{8}$ **d** -148; $52 - 2n$
e $-13\frac{1}{2}$; $\dfrac{15-n}{2}$ **f** 799; $3 + 4n$

3 **a** 23 **b** 13 **c** 31
d 21 **e** 91 **f** 13

4 **a** 2601 **b** 420
c 250.5 **d** $121x$
e $\frac{1}{2}n((2a + (n-1)d)$

5 **a** 444 **b** -80
c 20 100 **d** -520
e $2n(n+2)$ **f** $\frac{1}{8}n(11-n)$

Exercise 12d (p. 280)

1 **a** 36 **b** 17 **c** 22 **d** 10
e 18 **f** $2n$ **g** n **h** n

2 **a** 90 **b** 123 **c** 163 **d** -187
e 53 **f** 82 **g** $41x$ **h** $a + 40d$

3 **a** 632 **b** 288
c $60\frac{1}{2}$ **d** -55
e $\dfrac{n}{2}(2a + n - 1)$ **f** $\dfrac{n}{2}(2a - (n-1)d)$

4 **a** 165 **b** 0 **c** 49
d $2n^2$ **e** 9 **f** pr^2

5 **a** 75 **b** 75
c 16 **d** 22
e $n(n+2)$ **f** $\frac{1}{4}(n-5)(10-n)$

6 1; 2

7 9; 268

8 14; 4

10 60

11 **a** 5, 7, 9 **b** 60

12 1; 64

13 -13; 42

14 $n = 6$

15 5; 3

16 7500

17 7650

18 $3\frac{1}{2}$; $\frac{1}{10}$; $148\frac{1}{2}$

19 **a** 12; 0.2 **b** 22

20 $x = 4$

21 14, 18

22 $z = -2$; 15

23 13 rows; 9 tins

24 **a** 22 rows
b **i** 52 trees **ii** 31 trees
c 9.8%

25 **a** 228 seats **b** 34.2%

26 **a** 5 pieces **b** 48 cm

Exercise 12e (p. 287)

1 **a** 3 **b** $\frac{1}{4}$ **c** -2 **d** -1
f a **g** 1.1 **j** 6

2 **a** 5×2^{10}; 5×2^{19}
b $10 \times \left(\frac{5}{2}\right)^6$; $10 \times \left(\frac{5}{2}\right)^{18}$
c $\frac{2}{3} \times \left(\frac{9}{8}\right)^{11}$; $\frac{2}{3} \times \left(\frac{9}{8}\right)^{n-1}$
d $3 \times \left(-\frac{2}{3}\right)^7$; $3 \times \left(-\frac{2}{3}\right)^{n-1}$
e $\frac{2}{7} \times \left(-\frac{3}{2}\right)^8$; $\frac{2}{7} \times \left(-\frac{3}{2}\right)^{n-1}$
f $3 \times \left(\frac{1}{2}\right)^{18}$; $3 \times \left(\frac{1}{2}\right)^{2n-1}$

3 **a** $\frac{242}{81}$ **b** $\frac{43}{16}$ **c** $-\frac{266}{243}$ **d** 683

4 **a** 9 **b** 8 **c** 7
d 8 **e** $n + 1$ **f** n

5 **a** $2^{10} - 2$ **b** $\frac{1}{2}\left(3^5 - \frac{1}{27}\right)$
c $0.03(2^7 - 1)$ **d** $-\frac{16}{405}\left[\left(\frac{3}{2}\right)^8 - 1\right]$
e $5(2^{n+1} - 1)$ **f** $a\left(\dfrac{1 - r^n}{1 - r}\right)$

6 **a** 1092 **b** 5193.98 **c** $\frac{31}{32}$

7 2; $2\frac{1}{2}$; $157\frac{1}{2}$

8 3, $\frac{2}{3}$; -3, $-\frac{2}{3}$

9 $n = 6$; $13\frac{1}{2}$

10 £10 700 000

11 $6\frac{3}{4}$

12 **a** 102 **b** 457
c 10.7 **d** 1590 or 75.9
e 1 110 000 **f** 362

13 8 terms

14 **a** k^8; k^{n-5} **b** 2; $2p^{5-n}$

15 $\frac{5}{2}$, $-\frac{1}{3}$

16 $\frac{5}{2}(3^n - 1)$; 16

17 **a** 1.4% **b** 134 000, 144 000
c 1 241 000

18 **a** 1.8% **b** 2.2%
c £8428 million

19 **a** $1500 \times 1.08 + 1500 \times 1.08^2 + \cdots + 1500 \times 1.08^{10}$
b £23 468.23

Exercise 12f (p. 290)

1 **a** **i** $\frac{3}{2}\left(1 - \left(\frac{1}{3}\right)^n\right)$ **ii** $\frac{3}{2}$
b **i** $24\left(1 - \left(\frac{1}{2}\right)^n\right)$ **ii** 24
c **i** $\frac{1}{3}\left(1 - \left(\frac{1}{10}\right)^n\right)$ **ii** $\frac{1}{3}$
d **i** $\frac{13}{99}\left(1 - \left(\frac{1}{100}\right)^n\right)$ **ii** $\frac{13}{99}$
e **i** $\frac{5}{9}(1 - (0.1)^n)$ **ii** $\frac{5}{9}$

f **i** $\frac{6}{11}(1-(0.01)^n)$ **ii** $\frac{6}{11}$
g **i** $\frac{2}{3}\left(1-\left(-\frac{1}{2}\right)^n\right)$ **ii** $\frac{2}{3}$
h **i** $\frac{81}{2}\left(1-\left(-\frac{1}{3}\right)^n\right)$ **ii** $\frac{81}{2}$

2 **a** 4 **b** $\frac{15}{2}$ **c** $\frac{81}{64}$ **d** $\dfrac{p}{1024}$

3 $\frac{2}{3}$

4 2; $\frac{1}{2}$; $\frac{1}{4}$

5 $\frac{3}{5}$, 40; $\frac{2}{5}$, 60

6 43.957

7 125

8 **a** 18.0
b $\frac{2}{3}$, 8

Extension Exercise 12g (p. 291)

1 **a** 6, 8, 10

2 1023

3 **a** $\sqrt{2}-1$ **b** $5\sqrt{2}-7$

4 **a** 1 metre **b** $15+7\sqrt{2}$ metres

5 **a** $x=3+\sqrt{5}$; $y=3-\sqrt{5}$
b $5(6+7\sqrt{5})$
c $5\sqrt{5}+11$

6 **a** 190 **b** 320.52

7 $27+29+\cdots+113$

8 3, 12, 48; $3\times 4^{n-1}$

10 **a** $30\,000\times 1.006^n - 250(1.006^{n-1} + 1.006^{n-2}+\cdots+1.006)$

14 **a** $\dfrac{n(n+1)}{2}$
b $\dfrac{nx^{n+1}-x^n(n+1)+1}{(x-1)^2}$

16 **a** 6 kg, 2 kg
b $8\left(1-\left(\frac{1}{4}\right)^7\right)$ kg, $8\left(1-\left(\frac{3}{4}\right)^7\right)$ kg

18 $24(2+\sqrt{2})$ cm

Miscellaneous Exercise 12h (p. 293)

1 2550

2 $\frac{3}{4}$, $-\frac{3}{2}$, 3

3 4234

4 $\frac{3}{4}$

5 18 terms

6 **a** Oscillating, non-periodic
b Convergent
c Divergent
d Oscillating; periodic, period 6
e Convergent
f Divergent
g Oscillating, periodic, period 4

7 **a** 30 **b** -15 **c** $\frac{3}{5}k$
d 10 **e** -73 **f** 0

8 432

9 $x=5$; $y=-1$

10 **a** $\frac{8}{9}$ **b** $\frac{4}{33}$ **c** $3\frac{2}{9}$
d $2\frac{23}{33}$ **e** $1\frac{1}{225}$ **f** $2\frac{317}{330}$

11 **a** $u_1=2$, $u_{n+1}=2u_n$, $n\geqslant 1$; 32
b $u_1=2$, $u_{n+1}=u_n+2n$, $n\geqslant 1$; 22

12 -9; 5

13 2, 4, 6, 8, 10

15 $n=35$

17 4, $15\frac{7}{8}$; -12, $57\frac{7}{8}$

18 $\dfrac{ar+b}{r+1}$; $\dfrac{br+a}{r+1}$

19 **a** 74 **b** -990

20 **a** £5674 **b** 12 years
c £254; £340

Test Yourself (p. 295)

1 B **2** E **3** A **4** A **5** A
6 D **7** B **8** B **9** D **10** D

13 Integration

Exercise 13a (p. 302)

1 **a** x^3+c **b** $\frac{3}{2}x^2+c$
c $\frac{3}{5}x^5+c$ **d** $3x+x^2+c$
e $\frac{1}{2}x^2-\frac{1}{3}x^3+c$ **f** $2x+c$
g $\frac{1}{2}ax^2+bx+c$ **h** $mx+c$
i $\frac{1}{2}x^2+c$

2 **a** $-\frac{1}{2}x^{-2}+c$ **b** $-x^{-1}+c$
c $-\frac{2}{3}x^{-3}+c$ **d** $-3x^{-1}+c$
e $\frac{1}{8}x^{-2}+c$ **f** $-\frac{1}{2}x^{-3}+c$
g $\frac{2}{3}x^{\frac{3}{2}}+c$ **h** $\frac{3}{4}x^{\frac{4}{3}}+c$
i $\frac{3}{2}x^{\frac{2}{3}}+c$ **j** $-2x^{\frac{1}{2}}+c$
k $2x^{\frac{1}{3}}+c$ **l** $-x^{\frac{1}{4}}+c$

3 **a** x^4+c
b $6x+\frac{1}{2}x^2+c$
c $\frac{4}{3}x^3+6x^2+9x+c$
d $\frac{1}{3}x^3+2x-x^{-1}+c$
e $\frac{2}{5}x^{\frac{5}{2}}+2x^{\frac{3}{2}}+c$
f $\frac{1}{4}x^4+\frac{2}{3}x^3+\frac{1}{2}x^2+c$

4 **a** $3x+\frac{5}{2}x^2+c$
b $2x^3+c$
c $-x^{-1}+c$
d $\frac{1}{2}x^2+\frac{4}{3}x^{\frac{3}{2}}+x+c$
e $\frac{1}{2}x^2+\frac{1}{3}x^3+c$
f $\frac{20}{3}x^{\frac{3}{4}}+\frac{4}{7}x^{\frac{7}{4}}+c$
g $\frac{3}{2}x^{\frac{1}{2}}+c$
h $\frac{1}{5}x^5+\frac{4}{3}x^3+4x+c$

5 **a** $\frac{2}{3}x^6+c$ **b** $-\frac{1}{16}x^{-4}+c$
c $4x+c$ **d** $12x^{\frac{1}{2}}+x+c$

6 **a** $\frac{1}{2}at^2+c$
b $\frac{1}{12}t^4+c$
c $\frac{1}{3}t^3+2t^2+3t+c$
d $-\dfrac{t^{-n}}{n}+c$
e $-t^{-1}-t^{-3}-\frac{1}{2}t^{-2}+c$
f $\frac{2}{5}t^{\frac{5}{2}}+\frac{2}{3}t^{\frac{3}{2}}+c$

7 **a** $\frac{1}{2}ax^2+c$
b $\frac{1}{3}ay^3+c$
c $-kx^{-1}+c$
d $\frac{1}{3}y^3-y+6y^{-1}+c$
e $\frac{2}{7}x^{\frac{7}{2}}+\frac{1}{3}x^3+c$
f $\frac{5}{6}y^{\frac{6}{5}}+c$
g $4x^{\frac{3}{4}}-3x^{\frac{2}{3}}+c$
h $\frac{6}{11}x^{\frac{11}{6}}+\frac{6}{5}x^{\frac{5}{6}}+c$
i $x^3+x-4\sqrt{x}+c$

8 $\mathrm{f}(x)=x^2+\dfrac{1}{x}-1$

9 $\mathrm{f}(x)=x^3-\frac{2}{3}x^{\frac{3}{2}}+4$

10 $y=x^3-\frac{1}{2}x^2-6x+6$

11 $s=ut+\frac{1}{2}at^2$

12 $y=x^2+5x-25$

13 $y=x^3+\dfrac{1}{x}-\dfrac{17}{2}$

14 **a** $y=x^3-4x^2+3x$
b (1, 0), (3, 0)

15 **a** $y=4x^2-x^3$ **b** (4, 0)
c $y=\frac{256}{27}$

16 **a** $y=2x^3+\dfrac{1}{2x^2}+\dfrac{1}{2}$
b $s=\dfrac{3t^2}{2}+\dfrac{8}{t}-8$

17 **a** $A=\frac{1}{2}x^4+\frac{1}{3}x^3-x^2-x+\frac{7}{6}$
b $\frac{4}{3}$

18 a $y = \frac{3x^2}{2} + c;\ y = \frac{3x^2}{2} + 3$

b $y = -\frac{4}{x} + 5x + c$

$y = -\frac{4}{x} + 5x + 9$

c $v = 3t^2 + t^3 + c;\ v = 3t^2 + t^3 - 8$

d $y = x + \frac{1}{x} + c;\ y = x + \frac{1}{x} + 2$

19 a $x^2 + 5$
b $ax^3 + bx^2 + cx + d$
c $f(x)$

Exercise 13b (p. 314)

1 a $3\frac{3}{4}$ **b** 2 **c** -2 **d** $36\frac{137}{144}$

2 a 9 **b** 81 **c** 0 **d** $\frac{1}{2}$

3 a $\frac{264}{5}$ **b** $\frac{15}{4}$ **c** $\frac{45}{32}$ **d** $\frac{45}{4}$
e 21 **f** $\frac{23}{36}$ **g** 1 **h** $\frac{1}{4}$

4 a $\frac{42}{5}$ **b** $\frac{4}{3}$ **c** $\frac{32}{3}$ **d** $\frac{28}{3}$

5 a 26 **b** $\frac{175}{3}$ **c** $\frac{53}{6}$ **d** $\frac{5}{2}$

6 $\frac{1}{6}$

7 50

8 a $\frac{7}{3}$ **b** 4 **c** $\frac{1}{2}$ **d** $\frac{1}{3}$

9 a $\frac{16}{3}$ **b** $\frac{64}{3}$ **c** 12 **d** $\frac{4}{3}$

11 a 9 **b** $\frac{45}{4}$
c 12 **d** $2(\sqrt{3} - \sqrt{2})$

12 a 18 **b** $\frac{16}{3}$ **c** 4 **d** $\frac{9}{2}$

13 a (1, 3), (3, 3); $\frac{4}{3}$
b (1, 5), (−2, 5); $\frac{9}{2}$
c (0, 0), (4, 8); $\frac{16}{3}$
d (−2, 12), (1, 3); $\frac{27}{2}$
e (−1, 0), (3, 4); $\frac{32}{3}$
f (0, 3), (4, 5); $\frac{4}{3}$

14 a A(1, 3), B(−1, 3) **b** $\frac{8}{3}$

15 a $\frac{32}{3}$ **b** $\frac{2}{15}$ **c** $\frac{32}{3}$ **d** 10 **e** $\frac{1}{3}$

16 a $1\frac{1}{2}$ **b** $\frac{11}{6}$ **e** $\frac{11}{6}$

17 b i $\frac{10}{3}$ **ii** $\frac{50}{3}$ **iii** $\frac{10}{3}n$

Extension Exercise 13c (p. 317)

1 b i 8 **ii** 24

3 a $\frac{2}{3}$ **b** 0 **c** $\frac{2}{3}$
d 6 **e** $\frac{2}{3}$ **f** 2
g $\frac{2}{3}k + 2m$ **h** $\frac{1}{3}$ **i** $-\frac{1}{6}$
j $\frac{22}{3}$ **k** 0

4 36

5 $y = x^3 - 3x^2 + 4x + 8;\ 10\frac{3}{4}$

6 $k = 3$

7 2 sq. ft

10 $\frac{27}{4}$

11 a $\frac{2}{3}$ **b** $\frac{n+1}{6}$

12 a $\frac{1}{3}x^3 + x^2$ **b** $9t^3 + 3t^2$
c 0 **d** 2

Miscellaneous Exercise 13d (p. 319)

1 a 0 **b i** $\frac{1}{4}$ **ii** $\frac{1}{4}$

2 a $y = \frac{1}{3}x^3 + 2x - 9$ **b** $y = -6\frac{2}{3}$

3 a $\frac{2}{7}x^{\frac{7}{2}} + \frac{2}{3}x^{\frac{3}{2}} + c$ **b** $\frac{11}{2}$
c $\frac{37}{24}$ **d** $\frac{2}{7}x^{3.5} + c$

4 $f(x) = x^3 - \frac{5}{2}x^2 - 2x + 2$

5 a $a = 6;\ b = -1$ **b** $y = 3x^2 - x$

6 a A$(1, \frac{3}{2})$, B(4, 3) **b** $AB = \frac{3\sqrt{5}}{2}$

7 Area A:Area B = 5:1

8 $\frac{64}{3}$

9 a $74\frac{2}{3}$ **b** $6\frac{2}{3}$

Test Yourself (p. 321)

1 D **2** A **3** A **4** C **5** B
6 D **7** D **8** E **9** A

14 Revision of Trigonometry, Geometry and Proportion

Exercise 14a (p. 331)

1 a 126 cm^3 **b** 2910 cm^3
c $1.08 \times 10^{12}\text{ km}^3$ **d** $12\sqrt{3}\text{ cm}^3$
e $50\pi\text{ cm}^3$

2 a 5.6 cm **b** 108 cm^3

3 a 22.7 cm **b** 3.61 cm
c 127 cm^3

4 b 0.24 m^3

5 a A, 10 **b** B, 65 **c** A, 150
d B, 20 **e** B, 1 **f** A, 1.2

6 a 2.592×10^3 kg **b** 8.2944×10^3 kg

7 1.92 m

8 a 7 in **b** 240 sq. in

9 29°

10 a $294\pi\text{ cm}^2$; 42π cm
b $2.45\pi\text{ cm}^2$; 5.6π cm

11 a 16.8 in, 12.6 in; 22.4 in, 16.8 in
b 36.6 in, 20.6 in; 43.6 in, 24.5 in
c $\frac{1}{4}$
d $\frac{1}{4}$

13 $m = \frac{5}{7}$

14 a 36 sides **b** 9 sides
c 77.3 cm^2 **d** 45.3 cm^2

15 a 60 **c** $9\frac{3}{13}$

16 a $r - 2$ or $\sqrt{r^2 - 10^2}$
b Radius = 26 cm
c ∠DOB = 22.6°
d 267 cm^2
e 26.9 cm^2

17 b 1:64 **c** $\frac{9\pi}{4};\ \frac{567\pi}{4}$

Exercise 14b (p. 335)

1 a $3\pi x^3$ **b** $\frac{1}{6}\pi y^3$ **c** $\frac{\sqrt{2}}{3}\pi r^3$

2 a $2\pi x(x + y)$ **b** $\frac{2V}{l} + 4\sqrt{lV}$

3 a $\frac{\pi h}{3}(l^2 - h^2)$ **b** $h = 6$

4 $\sqrt{3}x^2$

5 $\frac{\sqrt{2}}{2}y$

6 a $x + y = 30$ **b** $A = x(30 - x)$

7 $V = \frac{1}{2}x^2(45 - 4x)$

10 $\frac{d}{\sqrt[3]{2}}$ cm

11 a $r = \frac{10}{\sqrt{h}}$ **b** $h = \frac{100}{r^2}$

12 $x = 7, y = 3;\ x = 5, y = 9$

13 7 cylinders

15 $x = 3;\ y = 9$

Extension Exercise 14c (p. 336)

1 a 23.5 cm **b** $R = h\tan x° + \frac{r}{100}$

2 a 31:19 **b** Y MAX 2.13

4 91 m^2

6 b $5 \times \frac{12}{13};\ 5 \times \left(\frac{12}{13}\right)^2;\ 5 \times \left(\frac{12}{13}\right)^3$
d 65

Test Yourself (p. 339)

1 B 2 D 3 E 4 D 5 A
6 D 7 E

15 Trigonometry

Exercise 15a (p. 343)

1 $60°, 90°; \frac{\pi}{6}, \frac{\pi}{4}, \frac{2\pi}{3}, 2\pi$

2 a $90°$ b $45°$ c $60°$ d $120°$
e $30°$ f $270°$ g $450°$ h $720°$
i $900°$ j $240°$ k $630°$ l $135°$

3 a 2π b $\frac{\pi}{2}$ c $\frac{\pi}{4}$
d $\frac{\pi}{12}$ e $\frac{\pi}{3}$ f $\frac{2\pi}{3}$
g $\frac{5\pi}{3}$ h $\frac{3\pi}{2}$ i 3π
j $\frac{\pi}{6}$ k $\frac{5\pi}{6}$ l $\frac{5\pi}{2}$

4 a 2 b 1 c 1 d 3
e 3 f 3 g 3 h 2
i 4 j 4 k 4 l 3

Exercise 15b (p. 354)

1 a $\sin 10°$ b $-\tan 60°$
c $-\cos 20°$ d $-\sin 50°$
e $\cos 20°$ f $-\sin 35°$
g $\tan 40°$ h $-\cos 16°$
i $-\tan 37°$ j $-\cos 50°$
k $-\sin 70°$ l $-\tan 50°$
m $\cos 67°$ n $\sin 50°$
o $-\sin 80°$ p $\tan 4°$

2 a $-\operatorname{cosec} 50°$ b $\cot 20°$
c $-\sec 38°$ d $-\cot 24°$
e $-\operatorname{cosec} 53°$ f $-\sec 8°$
g $\operatorname{cosec} 69°$ h $\sec 1°$

3 a $\frac{1}{2}$ b $\frac{\sqrt{3}}{2}$ c $\frac{\sqrt{2}}{2}$ d $\frac{\sqrt{3}}{3}$
e 1 f $-\frac{\sqrt{2}}{2}$ g $-\frac{1}{2}$ h $-\sqrt{3}$
i $-\frac{\sqrt{2}}{2}$ j $\frac{1}{2}$ k $\frac{\sqrt{3}}{3}$ l $\frac{\sqrt{3}}{2}$
m $\frac{\sqrt{2}}{2}$ n $-\frac{\sqrt{2}}{2}$ o $\frac{\sqrt{3}}{3}$ p $-\frac{\sqrt{3}}{2}$

4 a $\frac{2\sqrt{3}}{3}$ b $\frac{2\sqrt{3}}{3}$ c $-\sqrt{3}$ d $\sqrt{2}$
e -2 f $-\sqrt{2}$ g $-\sqrt{3}$ h $-\frac{2\sqrt{3}}{3}$

5 a -1 b 1 c 0 d 0
e 0 f 0 g 0 h -1

6 a $\frac{\sqrt{2}}{2}$ b $\frac{1}{2}$ c $\frac{\sqrt{3}}{2}$
d 0 e $\frac{\sqrt{2}}{2}$ f $\sqrt{3}$
g $-\frac{\sqrt{3}}{2}$ h $\frac{1}{2}$ i 1
j $\frac{\sqrt{3}}{2}$ k $-\frac{\sqrt{3}}{3}$ l $-\frac{\sqrt{3}}{2}$

7 a $30°, 150°, 390°, 510°$
b $140°, 220°, 500°, 580°$
c $-200°, -20°, 160°, 340°$
d $\frac{5\pi}{4}, \frac{7\pi}{4}, \frac{13\pi}{4}, \frac{15\pi}{4}$
e $-\pi, \pi$
f $\frac{\pi}{3}, \frac{4\pi}{3}, \frac{7\pi}{3}, \frac{10\pi}{3}$

9 a Translation $\binom{0}{1}$, $360°$
b Translation $\binom{-60°}{0}$, $360°$
c Stretch s.f. $\frac{1}{2}$ parallel to x-axis, $180°$
d Stretch s.f. 2 parallel to x-axis, $720°$
e Reflection in x-axis, $360°$
f Reflection in y-axis, $360°$

10 a Translation $\binom{30°}{0}$ followed by stretch parallel to y-axis, s.f. 3, followed by translation $\binom{0}{-1}$
b i $y = \tan(\frac{1}{3}x - 10°) - 2$
ii $y = 2(\tan(x - 60°) + 4)$

11 a $-1 \leqslant y \leqslant 1$; 2π
b $-1 \leqslant y \leqslant 1$; π
c $y \in \mathbb{R}$; π
d $y \in \mathbb{R}$; $\frac{\pi}{3}$
e $-4 \leqslant y \leqslant 4$; 2π
f $-1 \leqslant y \leqslant 1$; 4π
g $-1 \leqslant y \leqslant 1$; $\frac{2\pi}{k}$
h $y \in \mathbb{R}$; $\frac{\pi}{k}$

12 a $0 \leqslant y \leqslant 2$; neither
b $-1 \leqslant y \leqslant 5$; even
c $5 \leqslant y \leqslant 15$; neither
d $0 \leqslant y \leqslant 2$; even
e $-1 \leqslant y \leqslant 1$; odd
f $-2 \leqslant y \leqslant 2$; even

Exercise 15c (p. 363)

1 a $\cos\theta$ b $\sin\theta$ c $\tan\theta$ d $\sin\theta$
e $\tan\theta$ f 1 g 1

2 a $\frac{\pi}{6}$ b $\frac{\pi}{3}$ c $\frac{\pi}{4}$
d 0.46 e 0.62 f 0.96
g $\frac{\pi}{6}$ h 0.62

3 a $\sin\theta = \frac{3}{5}$, $\tan\theta = \frac{3}{4}$
b $\cos\theta = -\frac{12}{13}$, $\tan\theta = -\frac{5}{12}$
c $\sin\theta = -\frac{7}{25}$, $\cos\theta = \frac{24}{25}$

4 a $60°, 300°$ b $45°, 225°$
c $90°$ d $150°, 210°$
e $120°, 300°$ f $36.9°, 143.1°$
g $0°, 240°, 360°$ h $4.3°, 184.3°$

5 a $\frac{\pi}{6}, \frac{7\pi}{6}$ b 0.78, 2.37
c $0, \frac{4\pi}{3}, 2\pi$ d $\frac{2\pi}{3}$
e 2.19, 4.10 f 0.20, 3.34

6 a $\frac{\pi}{6}, \frac{5\pi}{6}, \frac{7\pi}{6}, \frac{11\pi}{6}$
b $\frac{\pi}{6}, \frac{5\pi}{6}, \frac{7\pi}{6}, \frac{11\pi}{6}$
c $\frac{\pi}{12}, \frac{5\pi}{12}, \frac{13\pi}{12}, \frac{17\pi}{12}$
d $\frac{3\pi}{8}, \frac{7\pi}{8}, \frac{11\pi}{8}, \frac{15\pi}{8}$
e $\frac{\pi}{18}, \frac{11\pi}{18}, \frac{13\pi}{18}, \frac{23\pi}{18}, \frac{25\pi}{18}, \frac{35\pi}{18}$
f $\frac{\pi}{2}, \frac{7\pi}{6}, \frac{11\pi}{6}$

7 a $\pm 45°, \pm 135°$
b $-108.4°, 71.6°$
c $\pm 15°, \pm 45°, \pm 75°, \pm 105°, \pm 135°, \pm 165°$
d $\pm 37.8°, \pm 142.2°$
e $-168.4°, -131.6°, 11.6°, 48.4°$
f $-156.1°, -96.1°, -36.1°, 23.9°, 83.9°, 143.9°$

8 a $0°, 30°, 150°, 180°, 360°$
b $60°, 180°, 300°$
c $45°, 225°$
d $0°, 135°, 180°, 315°, 360°$
e $60°, 90°, 270°, 300°$
f $0°, 180°, 199.5°, 340.5°, 360°$
g $90°, 210°, 330°$
h $120°, 180°, 240°$
i $60°, 90°, 120°, 240°, 270°, 300°$
j $0°, 180°, 360°$
k $40.9°, 139.1°, 220.9°, 319.1°$
l $63.4°, 116.6°, 243.4°, 296.6°$

9 a $0, \pm\frac{\pi}{3}$
b $-\frac{\pi}{2}$
c $-\frac{\pi}{4}, \frac{3\pi}{4}, -2.21, 0.93$
d $-\frac{3\pi}{4}, \frac{\pi}{4}, 0.73, 2.41$
e $\frac{\pi}{6}, \frac{5\pi}{6}, \pm 1.91$
f $-\frac{7\pi}{8}, -\frac{3\pi}{8}, \frac{\pi}{8}, \frac{5\pi}{8}$

10 a $\dfrac{x^2}{a^2}+\dfrac{y^2}{b^2}=1$
b $(x-1)^2+(y-1)^2=1$
c $(x-4)^2+(y-2)^2=1$

12 a $1\frac{1}{2}$ b 2 c $\frac{1}{2}$ d $\frac{1}{2}$
e $\frac{2}{9}$ f 2 g 2 h $\frac{2}{3}$

15 $x=0.8$

16 $x=123°$

17 a $-2\frac{1}{2}\leqslant y\leqslant -1\frac{1}{2}$; 2π
b $y\in\mathbb{R}$; 2π
c $-1\leqslant y\leqslant 1$; π
d $y\in\mathbb{R}$; $\dfrac{\pi}{3}$

18 a 1, 90°; −1, 270° b 3, 0°; −3, 180°
c 2, 0°; −2, 360° d $\frac{1}{2}$, 135°; $-\frac{1}{2}$, 45°
e 3, 270°; −1, 90° f 5, 0°; 1, 60°
g 1, 270°; $\frac{1}{3}$, 90° h 1, 0°; $\frac{1}{7}$, 180°

19 No real roots: a and c

20 a $\cos\theta\cot\theta$ b $\operatorname{cosec}\theta\cot\theta$
c $\sec\theta$ d $\cot^2\theta$
e $\sec\theta$ f $-\operatorname{cosec}\theta$
g $\sin\theta$ h $\sec\theta\operatorname{cosec}\theta$

21 a $a\cot\theta$ b $b^2\operatorname{cosec}^2\theta$
c $b^2\cot\theta\operatorname{cosec}\theta$ d $c^2\tan^2\theta$
e $\dfrac{1}{c}\cot\theta$ f $\dfrac{1}{a}\tan\theta\sec\theta$
g $\dfrac{1}{b}\sin\theta\cos\theta$ h $\sin\theta$

22 a $-\frac{8}{15}$ b $\frac{17}{15}$

23 a $-\frac{25}{7}$ b $-\frac{25}{24}$

24 a $\dfrac{y^2}{b^2}-\dfrac{x^2}{a^2}=1$ b $\dfrac{x^2}{a^2}-\dfrac{y^2}{b^2}=1$
c $\dfrac{b^2}{y^2}-\dfrac{x^2}{a^2}=1$ d $\dfrac{b^2}{y^2}-\dfrac{x^2}{a^2}=1$

25 a 30°, 150°
b ± 35.3°, ±144.7°
c ± 109.5°
d −90°, 11.5°, 90°, 168.5°
e −90°, 41.8°, 90°, 138.2°
f −104.0°, −45°, 76.0°, 135°

Miscellaneous Exercise 15d (p. 365)

1 $-2\leqslant y\leqslant 2$ (or $|y|\leqslant 2$)
a 3 b 2 c 0

2 a $-1\leqslant y\leqslant 1$; reflect in x-axis; 360°
b $-1\leqslant y\leqslant 1$; stretch s.f. $\frac{1}{2}$ parallel to x-axis; 180°
c $-3\leqslant y\leqslant 3$; stretch s.f. 3 parallel to y-axis; 360°
d $-1\leqslant y\leqslant 1$; translation $\binom{-40°}{0}$; 360°
e $1\leqslant y\leqslant 3$; translation $\binom{0}{2}$; 360°
f $-1\leqslant y\leqslant 1$; reflect in y-axis and translate $\binom{20°}{0}$ or reflect in $x=10°$; 360°
g $0\leqslant y\leqslant 2$; stretch s.f. 2 parallel to x-axis, then translation $\binom{1}{0}$; 720°

3 a $f\left(\dfrac{\pi}{6}\right)=1$; $g\left(\dfrac{\pi}{5}\right)=\dfrac{9\pi}{20}$
b $|f(x)|\leqslant 2$; $g(x)\in\mathbb{R}$
c $fg(x)=2\sin\left(x+\dfrac{\pi}{4}\right)$; $gf(x)=2\sin x+\dfrac{\pi}{4}$
d $x=\dfrac{11\pi}{12}$ or $x=\dfrac{19\pi}{12}$

4 $x=\pm 120°$

5 E.g. $\left(\dfrac{2\pi}{15},\sqrt{3}\right)$

6 a $(x-1)(x-2)(2x-1)$
b $x=\frac{1}{2}$, $x=1$ or $x=2$
c i $x=\dfrac{\pi}{4},\dfrac{5\pi}{4}$; 1.1, 4.2; 0.5, 3.6
ii $x=\dfrac{\pi}{2}$; $\dfrac{\pi}{6},\dfrac{5\pi}{6}$
iii $x=0, 2\pi$; $\dfrac{\pi}{3},\dfrac{5\pi}{3}$

7 a $\dfrac{3+2\sqrt{3}}{6}$ b $\dfrac{4\sqrt{3}}{3}$
c $\dfrac{\sqrt{2}+1}{2}$ d $6+3\sqrt{3}$
e $\sqrt{3}$ f 0

8 a $-2\leqslant f(x)\leqslant 0$; $x=\pm\dfrac{\pi}{6}$
b $h_1(x)=x-\dfrac{\pi}{2}$, $h_2(x)=2x$

9 a $d_0=19$; 13 m
b 12 hours 35 minutes
c 14 m

10 a $a=2$
b 4

11 a 40; 6 seconds

12 a $\sqrt{1-k^2}$ b k
c $-k$ d k
e $-\sqrt{1-k^2}$

13 a $|y|\leqslant 1$; 2π
b $0\leqslant y\leqslant 1$; π
c $|y|\leqslant 1$; not periodic
d $y\geqslant 0$; π

14 $x=\dfrac{\pi}{3}$, $y=\dfrac{\pi}{4}$

15 $a=1$, $b=-2$, $c=3$; stretch s.f. $\frac{1}{2}$ parallel to O_x, stretch s.f. 2 parallel to O_y, reflect in x-axis, translate $\binom{0}{1}$.

16 a A; s.f. 6; $x=6\sqrt{2}$
b B; s.f. 4; $x=4\sqrt{3}$, $y=8$
c B; s.f. 2; $x=2$, $y=2\sqrt{3}$
d B; s.f. 3; $x=3\sqrt{3}$
e B; s.f. $\sqrt{3}$; $x=\sqrt{3}$, $y=3$
f A; s.f. $2\sqrt{2}$; $x=2\sqrt{2}$, $y=4$
g B; s.f. $\dfrac{3}{2}$; $x=\dfrac{3}{2}$, $y=\dfrac{3\sqrt{3}}{2}$

17 a $1+\sqrt{5}$

20 ff(1) = 0.540 302; fff(1) = 0.857 532; 0.739 085

Test Yourself (p. 368)

1 E 2 D 3 D 4 D 5 C
6 B 7 D 8 B 9 A 10 C

16 Further Applications of Trigonometry

Exercise 16a (p. 373)

1 $\dfrac{10\pi}{9}$ radians; 200°

2 a 7, 35 b 1.04, 2.704
c 10π, 30π

3 8 cm

4 6 cm

5 $\frac{4}{5}$ rad

6 3 cm²

7 4 rad

8 $\left(20+\dfrac{10\pi}{3}\right)$ cm; $\dfrac{50\pi}{3}$ cm²

9 15 s

11 $\dfrac{\pi}{8}$ m²

12 12 cm

13 3:π

14 6.44 cm

15 1.6:1

16 a $\dfrac{3l^2}{8}$ b $\dfrac{14l}{15}$

Exercise 16b (p. 378)

1 a 6.50 b 72.4 c 32.2
d 70.9 e 9

2 a 45.5 b 55.5 c 23.7 d 24.6

3 a 4 cm² b 1.82 cm² c 2.18 cm²

4 a $\dfrac{32\pi}{3}$; $16\sqrt{3}$; $\frac{16}{3}(2\pi-3\sqrt{3})$
b 92.7; 48; 44.7

5 a $151\,\text{cm}^2$ **b** $62.4\,\text{cm}^2$ **c** $364\,\text{cm}^2$

6 b $\frac{1}{2}r^2(2\pi - \theta + \sin\theta)$

7 a $\sqrt{3}r$ **b** $\sqrt{3}\pi r$

8 a $\dfrac{2\pi}{3}$ **b** area $= \dfrac{\pi r^3}{3}$

9 $\frac{25}{2}(2\sqrt{3} - \pi)$

10 a $6r,\ 4\sqrt{3}r$

Exercise 16c (p. 380)

No triangle possible: 1b, 2d, 2f, 2g

Just one triangle possible: 1a, 2b, 2c, 2e, 2i, 2j

More than one triangle possible: 2a, 2h

Exercise 16d (p. 388)

1 a $A = 48°, b = 13.8, c = 15.4$
b $E = 95°, d = 1.40, f = 1.80$
c $a = 19.7, A = 73.3°, B = 58.7°$ or $a = 3.84, A = 10.7°, B = 121.3°$
d $B = 56.1°, a = 6.53, c = 5.04$
e $X = 19.7°, x = 4.63, z = 8.29$
f $A = 24.3°, C = 26.7°, a = 4.18$

2 a $a = 13, B = 32.2°, C = 87.8°$
b $A = 38.2°, B = 81.8°, C = 60°$
c $D = 38.0°, E = 112.4°, F = 29.5°$
d $q = 68.0, P = 14.2°, R = 65.8°$
e $m = 2.65, L = 40.9°, N = 19.1°$

3 a $C = 45.1°, a = 231, b = 213$
b $A = 54.6°, B = 78.1°, C = 47.2°$
c $A = 35°, b = 232, c = 162$
d $A = 31.3°, B = 44.7°, c = 57.9$
e $B = 54.8°, C = 97.2°, c = 18.0$ or $B = 125.2°, C = 26.8°, c = 8.17$
f $A = 17.9°, B = 120°, C = 42.1°$

4 a $6\sqrt{2}$ **b** $120°$ **c** 1, 1 **d** $5\sqrt{2}$

5 1.43 km

6 25.8 m

7 1.04°

8 347.3°, 3.64 nautical miles

9 200 m

10 a 22.0° **b** 0.21 m

11 63 m

12 312 m

13 a 12.7 m **b** 39.2 m **c** 62.9 m

14 313 m

Extension Exercise 16e (p. 390)

2 $\dfrac{4a^2}{9}(\pi + 3\sqrt{3}) - \pi b^2$

3 a $8(8\sqrt{3} - \pi)\,\text{mm}^3$

6 a $\dfrac{\pi}{2}$
b $\dfrac{\pi}{2}$
c $\dfrac{3\pi}{4};\ \dfrac{3\pi}{4}$
d $\dfrac{5\pi}{6};\ \dfrac{5\pi}{6}$
e $\dfrac{7\pi}{8},\ \dfrac{9\pi}{10},\ \dfrac{(2n-3)\pi}{2(n-1)}$
f $\pi - \dfrac{\pi}{2n}$
g π

7 a $\sqrt{3} - \dfrac{\pi}{2}$
b $4 - \pi$
c i $\dfrac{3\pi}{5}$ **ii** $\cot\dfrac{\pi}{5}$ **iii** $5\cot\dfrac{\pi}{5} - \dfrac{3\pi}{2}$

8 a $6 + 2\pi$
b $8 + 2\pi$
c i $10 + 2\pi$ **ii** $12 + 2\pi$

Miscellaneous Exercise 16f (p. 393)

1 a $D = 104.5°, E = 46.6°, F = 29.0°$; 2.90
b $p = 5.24, Q = 34.7°, R = 49.3°$; 5.97
c $B = 38.2°, C = 110.8°, c = 9.07$; 14.0 or $B = 141.8°, C = 7.2°, c = 1.21$; 1.87

2 a $\frac{15}{2}$ **b** 3

3 2π radians

4 $x = 16$

5 a 210 **b** 14.5

6 10.5 cm

7 $45.1\,\text{m}^2$

9 a $A > 90°$ **b** $A = 90°$ **c** $A < 90°$
d $A = 60°$ **e** $A = 120°$

12 a $\frac{4}{5}r^2$ **b** $\frac{1}{4}\pi r^2$ **c** r^2 **d** $\frac{1}{4}\pi r^2$

Test Yourself (p. 395)

1 B	**2** D	**3** D	**4** D	**5** A
6 D	**7** C	**8** B	**9** E	**10** D

Revision Exercise 3 (p. 397)

1 a $n = 35$ **b** $n \geqslant 19$

2 $n^2 + \dfrac{3n}{2} + 2 - 2^{n+1}$

3 a $y - x$ **b** $55(x + y)$
c $x = 3, y = 2$

4 a $n = 24$ **b** $n = 20$

5 a 4; −0.5 **b** p; q^2

6 b 2409.5

7 a $u_n = 2^{n-2}, n \geqslant 2$ **b** 2^{n-1}

8 a 7260 **b** 6000 **c** 2400

9 4 m; 3.8 m

10 $\dfrac{2}{3}x^3 + 2x^2 - x + c$;
$\dfrac{4x^3}{3} - 4x^2 + 4x + c$

11 a $\dfrac{2(x+1)}{x}$ **b** $-2x^{-1} - x^{-2} + c$

12 a (3, 4) max; (0, −5), (1, 0), (5, 0)

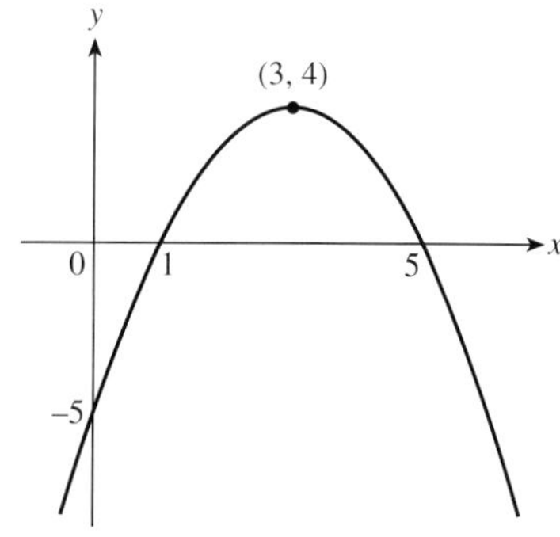

b $\frac{32}{3}$ **c** (2, 3), (4, 3) **d** $\frac{4}{3}$

13 a $x = -3, x = 1$, and $x = 2$
b

$y = 2x + 6$
(2, 10)
(1, 8)
6
−3
0
3
$y = 9x - x^3$

c $\frac{3}{4}$

16 a 1 **b** 2 **c** 4 **d** 1

17 $x = \frac{3\pi}{2}$; $x = \frac{7\pi}{6}$ and $x = \frac{11\pi}{6}$

18 a $x = 18.4°$
b $x = -80.8°$ or $x = 9.2°$
c $x = -160.5°$ or $x = -19.5°$
d $x = -130.5°$ or $x = 10.5°$
e $x = 70.5°$ or $x = 289.5°$
f $x = 30.3°$, $x = 139.7°$, $x = 210.3°$ or $x = 319.7°$

19 a $x = \pm\frac{\pi}{6}$, $x = \pm\frac{5\pi}{6}$
b $x = \pm\frac{\pi}{6}$, $x = \pm\frac{5\pi}{6}$

20 a Identity
b Equation: $x = 0, \pi, 2\pi$; $\frac{\pi}{2}$
c Equation: $x = 0, \pi, 2\pi$; $\frac{\pi}{2}, \frac{3\pi}{2}$
d Identity
e Identity

21 $\frac{(2y-1)^2}{9} + 4(x+4)^2 = 1$

22 $x = \frac{\pi}{4}$ or $x = \frac{5\pi}{4}$

24 a $r = 5, \theta = \frac{2}{5}$
b Perimeter = 12 cm

25 a $\frac{1}{2}r^2 \sin\theta$ b $\frac{1}{2}r^2\theta$
c 39% d 69%

Examination Questions 3

Sequences and series (p. 400)

1 $\frac{1}{2}$

2 −3, 2

3 $n = 41$

4 −3; $\frac{5}{2}$

5 a $\frac{2}{5}$; 200 b $\frac{1000}{3}$
c 8.9×10^{-4}

6 a 5; $\frac{1}{4}$ b 5975

7 a 26 733 b 53 467

8 71 240 toys

9 $u_5 = 676$; divergent

10 4380

11 a i 45 150 ii 40 500
b $x = 52$
i $\frac{2}{3}$ ii 216

12 a $u_1 = 76$, $u_2 = 60.8$
b $u_{21} = 0.876$
c 366
d 380

13 a 4 b 8 c 920

14 a 4; 9

Integration (p. 401)

1 a $\frac{32}{3}$
b ii 3.175

2 a $2x - \frac{2}{x^3}$
b $y = \frac{x^4}{2} + \frac{x^3}{3} - \frac{11}{6}$

3 a $-\frac{x^4}{4} + \frac{27x^2}{2} - 34x + c$
b 34
c 12

4 a $x + y = 4$ b $\frac{5}{6}$

5 a $\frac{3}{2}x^{-\frac{1}{2}} + 2x^{-\frac{3}{2}}$
b $2x^{\frac{3}{2}} - 8x^{\frac{1}{2}} + c$
c $A = 6, B = -2$

6 a $y + 8kx = 4k^2 + 16$; $k = -\frac{1}{4}$

7 a $2y + x = 3$ b $2\frac{29}{48}$

8 a A(1, 1), B(2, 4) e $\frac{1}{3}$

9 a (0, 0) max; (2, −4) min
c $6\frac{3}{4}$

10 a (2, 3)
b $y + 7x = 12$
c $\frac{20}{3}$

Trigonometry (p. 404)

1 $15\sin^2\theta + \sin\theta - 2 = 0$
$\theta = 19.5°, 160.5°, 203.6°, 336.4°$

2 $x = 30$, $x = 210$; intersection of graphs; 20 values

3 $\theta = 210°$ and $\theta = 330°$ (exact); $\theta = 48.6°$ and $\theta = 131.4°$ (1 d.p.)

4 $x = -72.6°, -17.4°, 107.4°, 162.6°$

5 a 120 cm^2 b 2.16 rad c 161.07 cm^2

6 b $r = 25$ c 2 rad d 625 cm^2

7 b 80.9 m c 26.7 m d 847 m^2

8 a (0, 1)
b $x = \frac{17\pi}{24}, \frac{23\pi}{24}, \frac{41\pi}{24}, \frac{47\pi}{24}$

9 a i $2 - \sqrt{3}$ ii $-(2 + \sqrt{3})$
b $x = \frac{3\pi}{2} = 4.71$ (2 d.p.); $x = 0.73$, $x = 2.41$

10 41.8°, 138.2°, 210°, 330°

11 $x = 150°$; $y = 250.5°$

12 19.3 cm

13 a $\frac{2\pi}{3}$ rad b $r = 0.788$

14 $\theta = 26°$, $\theta = 66°$ or $\theta = 146°$

15 a $\tan\theta = -\frac{1}{2}$ or $\tan\theta = -\frac{1}{3}$;
$\theta = 153.4°$ or $\theta = 333.4°$;
$\theta = 161.6°$ or $\theta = 341.6°$

16 $x = 6$

19 a $\frac{1}{2}r^2(\theta - \sin\theta)$

17 The Functions e^x and $\ln x$

Exercise 17a (p. 414)

1 a 20.1 b 1.39
c 0.0672 d −1.39

2 a $2e^x$ b $\frac{1}{x}$
c $6x - 5e^x$ d $\frac{1}{2}x^{-\frac{1}{2}} + \frac{2}{x}$
e $e^x - \frac{1}{x}$ f $-\frac{4}{x^2}$

3 a $e - \frac{1}{e}$ b $\ln 3$
c $3e^4 + 1$ d $-\ln 3$
e $e^3 - e^2 + \ln\left(\frac{3}{2}\right)$
f $2e^{-5} - 2e^{-1} - 3\ln 5$

4 a 4 b x
c 3 d $2x + 1$
e $3 - x$ f x
g 4 h $\frac{1}{64}$

5 a $y \geqslant 1$ b $y \in \mathbb{R}$
c $y > 0$ d $y \in \mathbb{R}$

6 a i e ii e
b i 0 ii 1
c i e + 4 ii e
d i 4 ii 1
e i e + 1 ii e + 3
f i e − 6 ii e − 3

7 a $2e^6 - 2$ b $\ln 3$ c 1

8 a $\left(-\ln 2, \frac{1}{2}\right)$; $(\ln 2, 2)$
b $(2, \ln 2)$; $\left(\frac{1}{2}, -\ln 2\right)$

9 $e^3 - 1$

10 $\ln 2$

11 $e - \dfrac{1}{e}$

12 $\ln 6$

13 a $\left(\frac{1}{2}, 3\right)$
b $2\ln 2 + \frac{21}{2}$

14 a $(1, 1), \left(\frac{1}{2}, \frac{1}{4} - \ln 2\right)$
b $y = 3x - 2$; $y = 3x - \frac{5}{4} - \ln 2$

17 a $y = 2x - 1 - \ln 2$
b $\left(\frac{1}{2} + \frac{1}{2}\ln 2, 0\right)$; $(0, -1 - \ln 2)$

18 a $(1, 2), (2, 1)$
b $\frac{3}{2} - 2\ln 2$

19 $2\ln 2$

20 a $y = (e - 1)x + 2$

21 a $ey = 1 + e^2 - x$
b $(1 + e^2, 0)$
c $\dfrac{e^3}{2} + e - 1$

Exercise 17b (p. 417)

1 a e^x **b** $4e^{4x}$ **c** $-e^{-x}$
d $-2e^{-2x}$ **e** $15e^{-5x}$ **f** $\frac{3}{2}e^{\frac{3x}{2}}$

2 a e^x **b** $2e^{4x}$ **c** e^{-x}
d $-\frac{1}{12}e^{-4x}$ **e** $-e^{-5x}$ **f** $-2e^{\frac{3x}{2}}$

3 a $\dfrac{1}{x}$ **b** $\dfrac{1}{x}$ **c** $\dfrac{3}{x}$
d $\dfrac{2}{x}$ **e** $-\dfrac{7}{x}$ **f** $\dfrac{2}{x}$

4 a $\ln x$ **b** $4\ln x$ **c** $\frac{1}{2}\ln x$
d $\frac{1}{3}\ln x$ **e** $-\frac{2}{3}\ln x$ **f** $-5\ln x$

5 $\frac{1}{3}e^3 - \frac{1}{3}e^{\frac{3}{2}} - \ln 2$

6 $\dfrac{1}{2} - \dfrac{1}{2e^4}$

7 a $(0, 0)$ **b** $e^{-4} + 3$

9 a -3 **b** $(1, -1)$

10 a $(0, 2)$
b Min $\left(-\frac{1}{3}\ln 2, 3 \times 2^{-\frac{2}{3}}\right)$
c $\dfrac{e^2}{2} - e^{-1} + \dfrac{1}{2}$

Extension Exercise 17c (p. 418)

2 a £2.25, £2.37, £2.44, £2.49, £2.52
b e

3 e

4 a $\ln 2$
b $\ln 3$
c e

5 a i $15 \times 15 = 225$
ii $10^3 = 1000$
iii $7^2 \times 8^2 = 3136$
b i $7.5^4 = 3164$
ii $6^5 = 7776$
iii $\left(\frac{30}{6}\right)^6 = 15\,625$
iv $\left(\frac{30}{7}\right)^7 = 26\,556$
v $\left(\frac{30}{10}\right)^{10} = 59\,049$
vi $\left(\frac{30}{15}\right)^{15} = 32\,768$
c Max of $\left(\dfrac{30}{x}\right)^x = 62092.67\ldots$ when $x = \dfrac{30}{e}$

Miscellaneous Exercise 17d (p. 418)

1 b $\frac{1}{3}(e^3 - 1)$

2 a $y \in \mathbb{R}^+$ **b** 1
c $f^{-1}(x) = \ln\left(\dfrac{x}{k}\right), x \in \mathbb{R}^+$ **e** $\sqrt{2}k$

3 a $f^{-1}(x) = e^{x-5}$; $y \in \mathbb{R}$; $x \in \mathbb{R}$, $y \in \mathbb{R}^+$; $f'(3) = \frac{1}{3}$
b $f^{-1}(x) = \ln(x - 4)$; $y > 4$; $x > 4$, $y \in \mathbb{R}$; $f'(3) = e^3$
c $f^{-1}(x) = \ln(2x)$; $y \in \mathbb{R}^+$; $x \in \mathbb{R}^+$, $y \in \mathbb{R}$; $f'(3) = \frac{1}{2}e^3$

4 a $f^{-1}(x) = e^x + 2$; $y \in \mathbb{R}$; $x \in \mathbb{R}$, $y > 2$
b $f^{-1}(x) = \ln x - 1$; $y \in \mathbb{R}^+$; $x \in \mathbb{R}^+$, $y \in \mathbb{R}$
c $f^{-1}(x) = 1 - e^{\frac{x}{3}}$; $y \in \mathbb{R}$; $x \in \mathbb{R}$, $y < 1$

5 a $\ln x$ **b** e^x **c** e^{-x}
d e^{e^x} **e** e^x **f** e^{2x}

6 a e^x **b** $\dfrac{1}{x}$ **c** $\dfrac{1}{\ln x}$

7 a $x = 1$ **b** $x = -5$ or $x = 1$
c $x = \frac{1}{2}\ln 7$ **d** $x = \frac{5}{4}$
e $x = \pm\dfrac{3\sqrt{2}}{2}$ **f** $x = \frac{1}{2}(e^5 + 1)$

8 a $\left(-\ln 2, -\frac{1}{4}\right)$

9 $x > 3$

10 a $3e^6$
b $(0, -5e^6), \left(\frac{5}{3}, 0\right)$
c $\frac{1}{3}(13e^6 - 1)$

11 b $e - \frac{5}{4}$

12 a min $\left(\frac{1}{2}, 4\right)$, max $\left(-\frac{1}{2}, -4\right)$
b $x = 0$
c $\frac{3}{2} + \ln 2$

Test Yourself (p. 420)

1 E **2** D **3** E **4** B **5** C

18 Limits

Exercise 18a (p. 425)

1 a 2 **b** 9
c 7.39 (e^2) **d** 0.5

2 a 2.5 **b** 0
c Not defined **d** 0

3 a 6 **b** 10
c 75 **d** Not defined

19 Proof

Exercise 19a (p. 430)

1 a $\Leftarrow$ **c** $\Leftrightarrow$ **e** $\Rightarrow$ **g** $\Rightarrow$
i $\Rightarrow$ **k** $\Rightarrow$ **m** $\Rightarrow$

2 a ns **c** s **e** ns **g** ns
i n **k** ns **m** s

Extension Exercise 19b (p. 433)

1 a M **b** J
2 a N **b** N **c** J **d** M
3 a J **b** J **c** M
4 a N **b** J
5 a J **b** N
6 a N **b** N **c** M **d** J
e N **f** M **g** J

Spot the Error (p. 435)

1

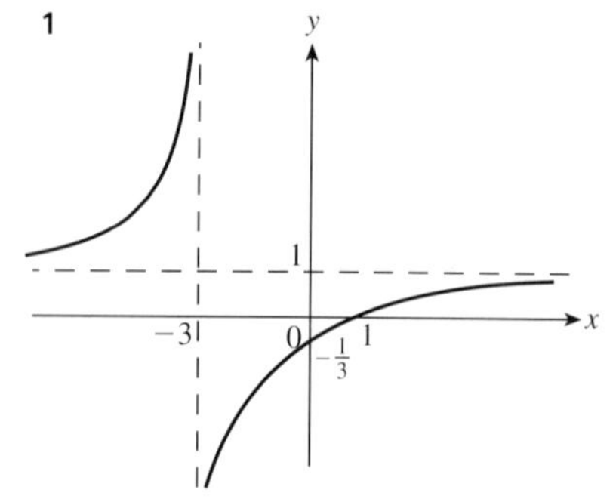

2 $d = \pm 1$

3 $m < -3, m > 1$

4 $3y + x = 11$; $\left(0, \frac{11}{3}\right)$

5 Translation $\binom{-3}{-2}$; $y \geqslant -2$

6 15625

7 $-4 \leqslant y \leqslant 5$

8 $0, \pm\dfrac{2\pi}{3}, \pm\dfrac{4\pi}{3}, \pm 2\pi$

9 (1, 3) min; (−1, −1) max

10 −0.745

11 $1 - x + \dfrac{x^2}{3} - \dfrac{x^3}{27}$

12 Minimum

13 $x = \frac{1}{4}$

14 $k > 1$

15 Translation $\binom{1}{0}$, $x > 1$, $y \in \mathbb{R}$, $f^{-1}(x) = e^x + 1$

16 $1 < x < 2$, $x > 3$

17 $\dfrac{\pi}{2}, \dfrac{3\pi}{2}$

18 $-1 < t < 1$, $t > 1$ (Two errors make factorisation correct).

19 $\theta = 49.5°$

20 1

Revision Exercise 4 (p. 443)

1 a $\dfrac{n}{x}$ b $\dfrac{1}{x}$

2 $f^{-1}(x) = 2\ln\left(\dfrac{x+1}{4}\right)$; $x > -1$;
$g^{-1}(x) = \dfrac{1}{3}(e^{\frac{x}{2}} - 1)$, $x \in \mathbb{R}$

3 a x; x b x^k
c $a = -2, b = 1$; $a = \dfrac{1}{e}, b = 0$

5 $\Leftrightarrow$ a, b, g, o, u, x
$\Rightarrow$ c, d, j, l, n, q, s, z
$\Leftarrow$ e, f, h, i, k, r, t, v, w, y
None m, p

Examination Questions 4

Functions e^x and $\ln x$ (p. 445)

1 a $(y-2)(y+3)(2y-1)$
b $x = \pm 0.693$

2 b $\frac{5}{4} + \frac{1}{4}\ln 4$
c $\frac{1}{2} - \frac{1}{2}e^{-2}$

3 $\frac{1}{2}(3e^4 - 7)$

4 a $x = y\ln 2$ c 2.43 d 4

5 a $g(x) > 0$ c 1 root d 0.84

Proof (p. 446)

1 b P(−1, 5), Q(2, 2)

2 a $|k| < 6$
b $y = (x+4)^2 - 7$; $a = 4$, $b = -7$

3 b $k = 4$ c 1751.5

Notation

Equality and inequality signs

$=$	equals *or* is equal to
$\equiv$	is identically equal to
$>$	is greater than
$\geqslant$	is greater than or equal to
$<$	is less than
$\leqslant$	is less than or equal to

Symbols linking statements

$\therefore$	therefore
$\Rightarrow$	implies; if ... then ...
$\Leftarrow$	is implied by
$\Leftrightarrow$	implies and is implied by; if, and only if, (also written as iff)

Other symbols

$\sqrt{a}$	the positive square root of a
$\in$	belongs to
$\notin$	does not belong to
∞	infinity
$\mathbb{N}$	the set of natural numbers
$\mathbb{Z}$	the set of integers
$\mathbb{Q}$	the set of rational numbers
$\mathbb{R}$	the set of real numbers

Ranges on a number line

(a, b)	the open interval $\{x \in \mathbb{R}: a < x < b\}$
$[a, b]$	the closed interval $\{x \in \mathbb{R}: a \leqslant x \leqslant b\}$
$(a, b]$	the interval $\{x \in \mathbb{R}: a < x \leqslant b\}$

Ranges can be illustrated graphically

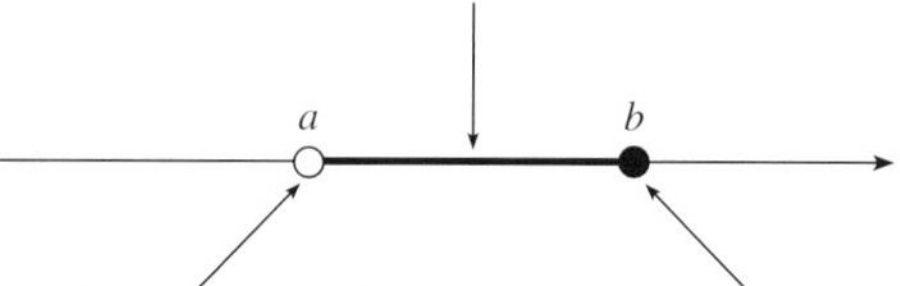

Function notation

$\sum_{i=1}^{n} a_i$	$a_1 + a_2 + \cdots + a_n$
$\mathrm{f}(x)$	the value of the function f at x
f^{-1}	the inverse function of the function f
δx	an increment of x
$\lim_{x \to a} \mathrm{f}(x)$	the limit of $\mathrm{f}(x)$ as x tends to a
$\frac{\mathrm{d}y}{\mathrm{d}x}$	the derivative of y with respect to x

Glossary

abscissa
The x-coordinate

algorithm
A systematic procedure for solving a problem

altitude of a triangle
The perpendicular distance from a vertex to the base

angle of elevation or depression
The angle between the line of sight and the horizontal

arithmetic progression
A series whose consecutive terms have a common difference

ascending powers of x
In order, smallest power of x first, e.g. $a_0 + a_1x + a_2x^2 + \cdots$

asymptote
A line to which a curve approaches

base of a log
b as in $\log_b x$

base of a power
b as in b^x; *see also* exponent, index

bearing
A direction measured from the North clockwise

binomial
An expression consisting of two terms, e.g. $x + y$

bisect
Cut into two equal parts

Cartesian equation
Equation of a curve involving x and y

chord
A straight line joining two points on a curve

circumcentre of a triangle
The centre of the circle which passes through all three vertices of the triangle

coefficient
The numerical factor in a term containing variables, e.g. -5 in $-5x^2y$

collinear
Lying on the same straight line

complex number
A number of the form $a + ib$ where $i = \sqrt{-1}$

composite function
A function which results from combining two functions so that the output of the first becomes the input of the second

congruent
Identical in shape and size

constant
A quantity whose value is fixed

constant term
The term in an expression which has no variable component , e.g. -3 in $x^2 - 5x - 3$

continuous curve or function
One whose graph has no break in it

convergent
Approaching closer and closer to a limit

coordinate
A magnitude used to specify a position

corollary
A result which follows directly from one proved

cubic equation
An equation of the form $ax^3 + bx^2 + cx + d = 0$, the highest power of x being 3

definite integral
An integral with limits

degree of a polynomial
The highest power of the variable, e.g. 2 in $x^2 - 5x - 3$

denominator
'Bottom' of a fraction – the divisor – remember D for Down

descending powers of x
In order, largest power of x first, e.g. $a_4x^4 + a_3x^3 + a_2x^2 + \cdots$

difference of squares
$x^2 - y^2 = (x + y)(x - y)$

discontinuous curve or function
One whose graph has a break in it

discriminant of a quadratic equation
The value of $b^2 - 4ac$ for the equation $ax^2 + bx + c = 0$

divergent
Tending to $+\infty$ or $-\infty$

dividend
A number (or expression) which is divided by a divisor to produce a quotient and possibly a remainder

divisibility tests
A number is divisible by
2 if the last digit is even
3 if the digit sum is divisible by 3
4 if the number formed by the last two digits is divisible by 4
5 if the last digit is 0 or 5

8 if the number formed by the last three digits is divisible by 8
9 if the digit sum is divisible by 9
11 if the sum of the digits in the odd positions differs from the sum of the digits in the even positions by 0 or any multiple of 11

divisor
cA number (or expression) by which another is divided to produce a quotient and possibly a remainder

domain
The set of 'inputs' to a function

even function
A function where $f(x) = f(-x)$; the function is symmetrical about the y-axis

exponent
In the power 3^4, 4 is the exponent; also called index

exponential function
A function of the form $a^{f(x)}$ where a is constant, e.g. 2^x; and e^x, *the* exponential function

foot of a perpendicular
The point where the perpendicular meets a specified line

frustum of a cone or pyramid
The part remaining when the top is cut off by a plane parallel to the base

function
A one-to-one or many-to-one relationship between the elements of two sets; for any value in the domain, the value in the range is uniquely determined

general solution
A solution, given in terms of a variable, which generates all required solutions

geometric progression (GP)
A series whose consecutive terms have a common ratio

HCF
Highest common factor

heptagon
A seven-sided 2D figure

hypotenuse
The side of a right-angled triangle opposite the right angle

identity
An equation which is true for all values of the variable(s)

improper fraction (algebraic)
Fraction where the degree of the numerator is greater than or equal to the degree of the denominator

improper fraction (numerical)
$\frac{p}{q}$ where $p > q$; p, q are +ve integers; *see also* proper fractions

incentre of a triangle
The centre of the circle which touches all three sides of the triangle

included angle
The angle between two given sides

increment
A small change in the value of a quantity

indefinite integral
An integral without limits

index (pl. indices)
In 3^4, 4 is the index; also called exponent

infinity (∞)
The concept of 'without end'

integer
A whole number, +ve or −ve or zero

inverse function
The function $f^{-1}(x)$ which 'undoes' the function $f(x)$

irrational number
A real number which is not rational, e.g $\sqrt{2}$, π, e

isosceles trapezium
A trapezium with an axis of symmetry through the mid-points of the parallel sides

kite
A quadrilateral with one diagonal an axis of symmetry

LCM
Lowest (or least) common multiple

LHS
Left-hand side, for example, of an equation

limit
The value to which a sequence converges

line segment
A finite part of an infinite line

ln
Napierian or natural log, to base e

logarithm (log) of a number
The power to which a base must be raised to obtain the number

lowest terms
In its lowest terms, a fraction which cannot be cancelled, the numerator and denominator having no common factor

major
The larger arc, sector or segment

mapping
A relationship between two sets

median of a triangle
A line joining a vertex to the mid-point of the opposite side

minor
The smaller arc, sector or segment

monomial
An expression consisting of one term

Napierian or natural log
log to the base e, ln

normal at a point
A line which passes through the point and is perpenducular to the curve at that point

numerator
'Top' of a fraction; the dividend

odd function
A function where $f(x) = -f(-x)$; the function has 180° rotational symmetry about the origin

ordinate
The y-coordinate

oscillating sequence
A sequence which neither converges to a limit, nor diverges to $+\infty$ or $-\infty$

parallelogram
A quadrilateral with both pairs of opposite sides parallel

period
The smallest interval (or number of terms) after which a function (or sequence) regularly repeats

periodic function or sequence
One which repeats at regular intervals

perpendicular bisector of AB
The line which bisects AB at right angles; the set of points equidistant from A and B

point of contact
The point at which a tangent touches a curve

polygon
A plane figure with many sides

polynomial (of degree n)
A sum of terms of the form
$a_0 + a_1 x + a_2 x^2 + \cdots + a_n x^n$.

power
For example, $81 = 3^4$ is the fourth power of 3; *see also* base, exponent, index

prime number
A positive integer which is divisible only by itself and 1
NB: 1 is not included in the set of prime numbers

prism
A solid with uniform cross-section

produce
Extend, as of a line

proper fraction (algebraic)
Fraction where the degree of the numerator is less than the degree of the denominator

proper fraction (numerical)
$\frac{p}{q}$ where , $p < q$; p, q are +ve integers; *see also* improper fraction

quadrant
One of the four parts into which the plane is divided by the coordinate axes

quadratic equation
An equation of the form $ax^2 + bx + c = 0$, the highest power of x being 2

quartic equation
An equation of the form
$ax^4 + bx^3 + cx^2 + dx + e = 0$,
the highest power of x being 4

quotient
The result of dividing one number or expression (dividend) by another (divisor) – there may be a remainder

radian
Measure of an angle; 1 radian = angle subtended at the centre of a circle radius r by an arc of length r; 1 radian $\approx 57^\circ$

range
The set of 'outputs' of a function

rational number
A number which can be expressed as $\frac{p}{q}$ where p and q are integers, $q \neq 0$

real number
A number corresponding to some point on the number line.

reciprocal of $\frac{a}{b}$
$\frac{b}{a}$; and vice versa, reciprocal of $\frac{b}{a}$ is $\frac{a}{b}$

reductio ad absurdum
Proof by assuming the result is not true and arriving at a contradiction

regular polygon
A polygon with all sides and all angles equal

respectively
In the order mentioned

rhombus
A parallelogram with four equal sides; the diagonals bisect each other at 90°

RHS
Right-hand side, for example, of an equation

right cone or pyramid
The vertex being vertically above the centre of the base

root of a number
$\sqrt[n]{a}$ (nth root of a); if nth root of a is b, then $b^n = a$

root of an equation
A solution of the equation

scale factor
The number by which corresponding lengths are multiplied in similar figures or in a transformation

scalene
A triangle with three unequal length sides

sector of a circle
Part of a circle bounded by an arc of the circle and two radii

segment of a circle
Part of a circle bounded by an arc of the circle and a chord

sequence
An ordered list of numbers or terms, e.g. 1, 2, 4, 8, ...

series
The sum of a sequence, e.g., $1 + 2 + 4 + 8 + \cdots$

sigma (Σ)
Symbol indicating summation, e.g.
$\sum_1^n r = 1 + 2 + \cdots + n$

similar
Having the same shape (all corresponding lengths being multiplied by the same scale factor)

slant height of a cone
The distance from the vertex to a point on the circumference of the base

solution
A value (or values) which satisfies the given problem

standard form
A number in the form $a \times 10^n$ where $1 \leqslant a < 10$ and n is an integer

subtended angle
Angle subtended by the line segment AB at C; the angle ACB

surd
An irrational root, e.g. $\sqrt{2}$, $\sqrt{7}$, $\sqrt[3]{11}$

tangent at a point
A line which passes through the point and touches the curve at that point

term (of a sequence)
One of a sequence, e.g. 4 in 1, 2, 4, 8, ...

term (of an expression)
Part of an expression. e.g. x^2, $-5x$ or -3 in $x^2 - 5x - 3$

trapezium
A quadrilateral with one pair of sides parallel

trinomial
An expression consisting of three terms

unknown
A letter which represents a specific value or values

variable
A letter which represents various values

vertex (pl. vertices) of a parabola
The turning point of a parabola

vertex (pl. vertices) of a polygon
The point where two sides meet

vertex (pl. vertices) of a solid
The point of a cone or the point where faces of the solid meet

Index